Teacher's Annotated Edition

HARRY LEWIS

Mathematics for Daily Living

McCormick-Mathers Publishing Company, Inc.
Cincinnati, Ohio 45202

ABOUT THE AUTHOR

Dr. Lewis has relied heavily on his many years of experience as a mathematics educator in urban secondary schools in writing this textbook. As both a teacher and a department chairman, he has taught mathematics on all grade levels and all ability levels to students in junior and senior high schools. He has also taught methods courses in mathematics at New York University and prepared graduate students for the actuarial examinations given by the Actuarial Society of America. Dr. Lewis is also the author of a textbook on demonstrative geometry and three textbooks on business mathematics. He has authored many articles on the teaching of mathematics and has been a contributor to one of the yearbooks of the National Council of Teachers of Mathematics. Dr. Lewis, formerly chairman of the mathematics department of East Side High School, Newark, N.J., is now principal of Arts High School in that city.

ACKNOWLEDGMENTS

The error-free text and its counterpart, the error-free key, are the dream—never the reality—of every author and every publisher. If even a modest degree of success has been achieved in attaining this, it is largely through the painstaking efforts and endless hours of reading and rereading on the part of my wife Beatrice.

ILLUSTRATIONS BY RUTH RILEY

PHOTO CREDITS:

Page 1—*Bijur from Monkmeyer;* Page 54—*Jim Cron from Monkmeyer;* Page 93—*Rogers from Monkmeyer;* Page 143—*Heron from Monkmeyer;* Page 182—*Internal Revenue Service;* Page 215—*Sybil Shelton from Monkmeyer;* Page 264—*Hays from Monkmeyer;* Page 298—*Hays from Monkmeyer;* Page 335—*Wide World Photos;* Page 387—*A. Patzig from Monkmeyer;* Page 430—*Monkmeyer Press Photo Service;* Page 460—*Merrim from Monkmeyer;* Page 507—*U.S. Department of Commerce;* Page 546—*Equitable Life Assurance Society of the United States.*

PREFACE

Why Consumer Mathematics?

"One of the most important of emerging subjects for the high-school curriculum is financial and consumer economics . . ." This recent quotation from a publication of the National Educational Association would perhaps be somewhat more accurate if the word "emerging" were replaced by "reemerging." During the 1930's and 1940's, there was some very lively activity in the field of consumer education on the secondary-school level. The 1950's, however, saw the coming of the age of Sputnik, and, with it, the heavy emphasis on hard-core college preparatory subjects. The School Mathematics Study Group and similar agencies concentrated their activities on a rethinking, and a revitalization, of the traditional approach to the teaching of mathematics. And, unfortunately, their design left no room for the bread-and-butter subject of consumer mathematics. It has been only within the last year or so that mathematics teachers have begun to realize that, although the need for the new thinking in mathematics was long overdue, it should not have been done to the exclusion of the utilitarian aspects of this field. For far too many students, exposure to the eleven field properties as a basis for understanding mathematics will lead to little more effective learning than the rote memorization of irrelevant principles that took place in the past. These students will profit more—and also enjoy more—in knowing why their salary checks are not so large as they thought they might be, or how much it will cost to buy and operate their cars than in exploring the distributive property of multiplication over addition.

The realization of the need for a reintroduction of the teaching of the consumer aspects of mathematics has, though, created a problem for the mathematics teacher. In his effort to find the text that would be best for the needs of his students, he has discovered that the long years of drought in this area have left him with either the necessity of adopting a book that dates back to the early 1950's, or else of developing material of his own. It was in an effort to fill this void that this text was written.

Suggestions for Using the Text

Although certain chapters are tied together—such as Chapters 1 and 2, Chapters 6 and 7, and Chapters 8, 9, and 10—with a minimum of caution the topics in this text can be taught in almost any order that the teacher prefers. It is suggested, however, that the teacher develop entire chapters rather than skip from units in one chapter to units in another. An effort has been made to try to explore each and every topic presented as fully as possible—keeping in mind the age and grade level of these students—rather than to give token exposure to a multitude of unrelated ideas. Teaching a few topics in depth will tend to have greater meaning for the student than a fleeting glimpse of far more topics than he can possibly assimilate.

TABLE OF CONTENTS

CHAPTER 1

AUTOMOBILE OWNERSHIP

As a child, you went through a series of waiting periods. One of these may have centered about the arrival of a wagon that Dad could use to pull you around the neighborhood. Dad provided the muscle power and you enjoyed the ride.

From the wagon you took a giant step to the tricycle. The energy needed for propelling the tricycle was yours. But with your over-abundance of energy, you probably hardly noticed the change.

The next biggest day of your life loomed when the "learner" wheels were removed from your brand-new bicycle, and you were free to ride your two-wheeler on your own.

The pleasure and excitement of riding your own bicycle wore off in time, though, and right now, if you don't already own one, you are probably looking forward impatiently to the day when you can become a car-owner.

Should you prefer to expose the students to an extensive review of the fundamental operations at the outset of the course, turn to Chapter 14. There you will find an ample number of exercises on these operations related to whole numbers, decimals, and fractions, plus a review of the concept of percent.

Unit 1:   Owning a Car

Before buying a car, there are a few facts you should know. First you should know how much it will cost; and second, how much it will cost to operate. In this chapter, you will learn how to determine these very important facts. You will also have called to your attention several other points that are connected with the operation of an automobile.

The first thing to consider is the money needed to buy a car. Most of you, if you are working only summers, or part time, probably do not have enough money to pay cash for a car.

If you are at all lucky, your Dad may give you his old car for a down payment. If not, you will have to save some money of your own before you can even approach an automobile dealer. No dealer will discuss a sale, except of a very, very inexpensive car, unless he is sure of a down payment.

The down payment can be made in cash, or in the form of another car that is being traded in for the purchase of a newer model. This simply means that the dealer is willing to give you a certain amount of money for your old car. You, in turn, then return the money to him in order to reduce the total amount you owe him. Take a specific example. Suppose you decide to buy a new car which costs $2,846.58. The trade-in value you are being granted on your old car is $326.58. The amount that remains to be paid is:

$$\$2,846.58 - \$326.58 = \$2,520$$

Incidentally, a dealer will almost always make the trade-in value an amount that will eliminate the pennies in the cost of the car. He will also round off the dollars to a number ending in 0 or 5. This helps make the arithmetic computation easier for everyone concerned.

Once the decision is made as to how much is still due after the down payment, you have two choices open. Either you can borrow the money directly from the automobile agency, or, if you prefer, you can go to your own bank and borrow the money there. Even when you elect to borrow the money from the dealer, you will learn that he is actually getting this money from a bank—possibly your own. (For this effort on his part, by the way, he receives a fee.) In any event, whichever choice you make, the method for computing the cost is the same. In both cases, reference is made to one of two tables similar to those on pages 3 and 5. The first of these tables is used when the loan involves the purchase of a new car, while the second pertains to a loan on a used car. You will see in the exercises that follow that the cost of bor-

This book was designed to be read and understood by the student. It is urged that part of the period be devoted to having either you, or the students, read the material aloud and discuss it. This course will be sterile if it is devoted entirely to computational aspects without class discussion.

NEW–CAR MONTHLY PAYMENT TABLE

	18 Months		24 Months		30 Months		36 Months	
Unpaid Balance	Amount Per Month	Total Life-Insurance Premium	Amount Per Month	Total Life-Insurance Premium	Amount Per Month	Total Life-Insurance Premium	Amount Per Month	Total Life-Insurance Premium
$ 20	$ 1.23	$ .14	$ .96	$ .19	$ .79	$ .24	$ .68	$ .30
40	2.46	.28	1.91	.38	1.58	.48	1.35	.59
60	3.69	.42	2.86	.57	2.36	.72	2.02	.88
80	4.92	.56	3.81	.76	3.14	.96	2.69	1.17
1,000	61.40	7.08	47.53	9.47	39.22	12.00	33.69	14.68
1,100	67.55	7.78	52.29	10.42	43.14	13.20	37.05	16.14
1,200	73.69	8.49	57.04	11.36	47.06	14.40	40.42	17.61
1,300	79.83	9.20	61.79	12.31	50.98	15.60	43.79	19.07
1,400	85.97	9.90	66.55	13.26	54.91	16.80	47.16	20.54
1,500	92.11	10.61	71.30	14.20	58.83	18.00	50.53	22.01
1,600	98.25	11.32	76.05	15.15	62.75	19.20	53.90	23.48
1,700	104.39	12.03	80.80	16.10	66.67	20.40	57.26	24.94
1,800	110.53	12.73	85.56	17.04	70.59	21.60	60.63	26.41
1,900	116.67	13.44	90.31	17.99	74.51	22.80	64.00	27.88
2,000	122.81	14.15	95.06	18.94	78.43	24.00	67.37	29.35
2,100	128.95	14.86	99.82	19.88	82.36	25.20	70.74	30.81
2,200	135.09	15.56	104.57	20.83	86.28	26.40	74.10	32.28
2,300	141.23	16.27	109.32	21.78	90.20	27.60	77.47	33.75
2,400	147.37	16.98	114.07	22.72	94.12	28.80	80.84	35.21
2,500	153.51	17.68	118.83	23.67	98.04	30.00	84.21	36.68
2,600	159.65	18.39	123.58	24.62	101.96	31.20	87.58	38.15
2,700	165.79	19.10	128.33	25.56	105.89	32.40	90.94	39.61
2,800	171.93	19.81	133.09	26.51	109.81	33.60	94.31	41.08
2,900	178.07	20.51	137.84	27.46	113.73	34.80	97.68	42.55
3,000	184.22	21.22	142.59	28.40	117.65	36.00	101.05	44.02

rowing money to buy a used car is a good deal greater than the cost of a loan for a new car. Can you explain why this should be so?

■ ILLUSTRATION 1: George Newsome borrowed $2,100 to purchase a new car. He agreed to pay this debt back monthly over a 2-year period. How much did this loan cost him?

▼ EXPLANATION: Since the loan was on a new car, you refer to the New-Car Monthly Payment Table on this page. To find the monthly payment, run your finger down the Unpaid-Balance column until you reach the numeral 2,100. Then place the edge of a piece of paper on the row containing 2,100. Follow this across until you come to the two columns that pertain to the 24-month payment plan. Why do you

Call attention to the fact that the numerals in the column labeled "Total Life-Insurance Premium" represent the entire premium and not the monthly installments. Thus, in Illustration 1, a little less than $1 is paid off monthly on the insurance, and this amount is included in the $99.82 payment.

stop there? The two numerals you are looking at are $99.82 and $19.88. The first of these, as indicated by the heading, represents the amount of each monthly payment, while the second is the total cost of the life insurance that you are urged (and sometimes required) to buy. By multiplying 24 by $99.82, you determine the total amount paid back over the 2-year period. This amount includes not only the charge for borrowing the money, but also the cost of the life insurance. In this illustration, the product turns out to be $2,395.68. Subtracting $19.88 from this leaves a difference of $2,375.80, which is actually the total amount paid on the $2,100 loan. Hence, after you subtract $2,100 from $2,375.80, the remainder of $275.80 is the cost of the loan, or what Mr. Newsome paid the bank above what he borrowed.

●SOLUTION:

$$\text{Monthly payment} = \$99.82$$
$$\text{Total of monthly payments} = 24 \times \$99.82$$
$$= \$2,395.68$$
$$\text{Total returned on debt alone} = \$2,395.68 - \$19.88$$
$$= \$2,375.80$$
$$\text{Cost of loan} = \$2,375.80 - \$2,100$$
$$= \$275.80$$

In the explanation, reference is made to the fact that you are urged to take out life insurance when borrowing money for the purchase of a car. Actually, many lending agencies refuse to lend money these days unless you insure yourself against the possibility of death. This is protection for them because, in the event of your death before the debt is completely paid back, the lending agency can recover the unpaid balance of the debt from the insurance company. In addition, of course, it also provides you with some peace of mind, for you know that your wife or, perhaps, your parents, will not be burdened with a car debt should something happen to you. Look at the table again and examine the figures for a $1,000 loan. Can you explain why the monthly payment is less on the 24-month plan than on the 18-month plan, while the life insurance cost is more?

■ILLUSTRATION 2: On reaching 19, Eric Sanford bought a used car as a birthday present for himself. He made a down payment of $460 on the total cost of $1,200, and the rest he agreed to pay off over a period of 30 months.

    a. What was the total amount that he paid back over the 30 months?

    b. What was the total life-insurance premium he had to pay?

As a class project, have the students visit an automobile agency to ask a salesman if he will permit them to copy a section of the payment table he used. Compare the monthly payments for his loans with those on pages 3 and 5.

USED–CAR MONTHLY PAYMENT TABLE

Unpaid Balance	12 Months Amount Per Month	12 Months Total Life-Insurance Premium	18 Months Amount Per Month	18 Months Total Life-Insurance Premium	24 Months Amount Per Month	24 Months Total Life-Insurance Premium	30 Months Amount Per Month	30 Months Total Life-Insurance Premium
$ 20	$ 1.89	$ .10	$ 1.33	$ .15	$ 1.06	$ .21	$ .89	$ .27
40	3.78	.20	2.66	.30	2.12	.42	1.78	.54
60	5.67	.30	3.98	.45	3.18	.63	2.67	.81
80	7.56	.40	5.30	.61	4.24	.84	3.57	1.09
500	47.30	2.50	33.43	3.85	26.50	5.28	22.35	6.84
600	56.76	3.00	40.11	4.62	31.80	6.33	26.82	8.21
700	66.22	3.50	46.80	5.39	37.10	7.39	31.29	9.57
800	75.69	4.00	53.48	6.16	42.40	8.45	35.76	10.94
900	85.15	4.50	60.17	6.93	47.70	9.50	40.23	12.31
1,000	94.61	5.00	66.86	7.70	53.00	10.56	44.70	13.68
1,100	104.07	5.49	73.54	8.47	58.30	11.61	49.17	15.05
1,200	113.53	5.99	80.23	9.24	63.60	12.67	53.64	16.41
1,300	122.99	6.49	86.92	10.01	68.90	13.72	58.11	17.78
1,400	132.45	6.99	93.60	10.78	74.20	14.78	62.58	19.15
1,500	141.91	7.49	100.29	11.55	79.50	15.84	67.05	20.52

● SOLUTION:

Since a used car is involved, you must use the Used-Car Monthly Payment Table on this page.

(a) Amount of loan = $1,200 − $460 = $740

$$\begin{array}{r} \text{Amount per month on } \$700 = \$31.29 \\ + \text{Amount per month on } \$\ 40 = \quad 1.78 \\ \hline \text{Amount per month on } \$740 = \$33.07 \end{array}$$

(b) Total paid over 30-month period = 30 × $33.07 = $992.10

$$\begin{array}{r} \text{Total life-insurance premium for } \$700 = \quad \$9.57 \\ + \text{Total life-insurance premium for } \$\ 40 = \quad .54 \\ \hline \text{Total life-insurance premium for } \$740 = \$10.11 \end{array}$$

▼ EXPLANATION: After making the down payment of $460, Eric still had $740 to repay. The numeral 740 does not appear in the Unpaid-Balance column. Hence, to determine the monthly payment on $740, you have to add the payment on $700 to the payment on $40. The first payment is $31.29, while the second is $1.78, making a total payment of $33.07. Similarly, in answer to Part (b), it is necessary to add the total life-insurance premium on $700 to that of the premium on $40. The total of these ($9.57 and $.54) is $10.11. Why was the Used-Car Monthly Payment Table used? How much would the monthly payment have been if the debt had been paid off over a 12-month period?

Ask the students to compare the monthly payments if the car purchased is new rather than used. Use the $1,000 loan for 24 months. Ask them if they can give a good reason why the payments on a new-car loan should be smaller than those on a used-car loan.

EXERCISES   A

Do you recall how to do the computation in the following exercises?
If not, you will probably want to refer to the pages indicated for additional help.

1. Arrange the following numerals in columns and add. (See page 551.)

a. $4.68 + 3.76$	$=$	8.44
b. $5.92 + 6.05 + 2.21$	$=$	14.18
c. $12.52 + 26.37 + 18.43 + 36.80$	$=$	94.12
d. $2.17 + 14.85 + 6.02 + 53.11$	$=$	76.15
e. $58.74 + 9.06 + .54 + 136.52$	$=$	204.86
f. $142 + 52.77 + 2 + .06 + 5.95$	$=$	202.78

2. Arrange the following numerals in columns and subtract. (See page 558.)

a. $58 - 23$	$=$	35	h. $2.95 - .42$	$=$	2.53
b. $164 - 31$	$=$	133	i. $26.47 - 2.13$	$=$	24.34
c. $89 - 86$	$=$	3	j. $5.39 - .06$	$=$	5.33
d. $154 - 72$	$=$	82	k. $4.29 - .57$	$=$	3.72
e. $281 - 16$	$=$	265	l. $8.73 - .27$	$=$	8.46
f. $307 - 54$	$=$	253	m. $7.08 - .12$	$=$	6.96
g. $300 - 96$	$=$	204	n. $200 - 5.82$	$=$	194.18

3. Arrange the following numerals in columns and multiply. (See page 566.)

a. 14×8	$=$	112	i. 12×24	$=$	288
b. 23×5	$=$	115	j. 51×13	$=$	663
c. 16×7	$=$	112	k. 73×30	$=$	2,190
d. 45×4	$=$	180	l. 46×25	$=$	1,150
e. 58×2	$=$	116	m. 60×19	$=$	1,140
f. 91×6	$=$	546	n. 87×46	$=$	4,002
g. 87×3	$=$	261	o. 38×54	$=$	2,052
h. 64×9	$=$	576	p. 29×82	$=$	2,378

4. Arrange the following numerals in columns and multiply. (See page 566.)

a. 2.21×3	$=$	6.63	i. 3.42×12	$=$	41.04
b. 3.45×4	$=$	13.80	j. 15.04×30	$=$	451.20
c. 4.07×5	$=$	20.35	k. 86.53×24	$=$	2,076.72
d. 6.38×6	$=$	38.28	l. 103.42×18	$=$	1,861.56
e. 17.26×7	$=$	120.82	m. 90.04×36	$=$	3,241.44
f. 23.85×8	$=$	190.80	n. 78.82×28	$=$	2,206.96
g. 31.06×9	$=$	279.54	o. 117.65×62	$=$	7,294.30
h. 40.02×2	$=$	80.04	p. 100.29×81	$=$	8,123.49

Throughout the book are sets of exercises such as these. Computational skills involved in the exercises pertaining to the unit topic are the same as in these exercises. If, after assigning exercises in B, you find students making far too many computational errors, then assign these exercises.

B

1. Find the monthly payment and the total life-insurance premium on each of the following loans. Use the New-Car Monthly Payment Table on page 3.

	Unpaid Balance	Period Of Debt	Monthly Payment	Total Life-Insurance Premium
a.	$1,500	18 months	$ 92.11	$ 10.61
b.	2,500	24 months	118.83	23.67
c.	1,400	36 months	47.16	20.54
d.	3,000	30 months	117.65	36.00
e.	1,200	24 months	57.04	11.36
f.	60	30 months	2.36	.72
g.	2,700	18 months	165.79	19.10
h.	1,600	36 months	53.90	23.48

2. Find the monthly payment and the total life-insurance premium on each of the following loans. Use the Used-Car Monthly Payment Table on page 5.

	Unpaid Balance	Period Of Debt	Monthly Payment -	Total Life-Insurance Premium
a.	$ 20	12 months	$ 1.89	$ .10
b.	500	24 months	26.50	5.28
c.	1,000	18 months	66.86	7.70
d.	80	30 months	3.57	1.09
e.	800	24 months	42.40	8.45
f.	1,300	12 months	122.99	6.49
g.	60	30 months	2.67	.81
h.	600	18 months	40.11	4.62

3. Determine the monthly payment on each of the following unpaid balances. Use the New-Car Monthly Payment Table on page 3.

	Unpaid Balance	Period Of Debt	Monthly Payment		Unpaid Balance	Period Of Debt	Monthly Payment
a.	$1,560	18 months	$ 95.80	d.	1,280	30 months	$ 50.20
b.	2,520	24 months	119.79	e.	1,760	18 months	108.08
c.	3,040	36 months	102.40	f.	2,920	24 months	138.80

4. Determine the total life-insurance premium on each of the following unpaid balances. Use the Used-Car Monthly Payment Table on page 5.

	Unpaid Balance	Period Of Debt	Total Life-Insurance Premium		Unpaid Balance	Period Of Debt	Total Life-Insurance Premium
a.	$ 540	12 months	$ 2.70	d.	760	24 months	$ 8.02
b.	960	30 months	13.12	e.	1,320	12 months	6.59
c.	1,560	18 months	12.00	f.	1,080	30 months	14.77

Caution the student not to write his answers in the textbook in the blank columns. They are there to give the student a guide to follow. There will be numerous exercises (See Exercise 8, page 8.) where he will have to obtain intermediate pieces of information before he can arrive at the answer he seeks.

5. Find the total repaid, including the life-insurance premium, on each of the following new-car loans.

Loan	Period Of Debt	Total Repaid
a. $1,000	30 months	$ 1,176.60
b. 1,500	30 months	1,764.90
c. 2,300	24 months	2,623.68
d. 2,700	36 months	3,273.84
e. 1,400	18 months	1,547.46
f. 2,560	30 months	3,012.00
g. 1,540	24 months	1,757.04
h. 3,020	24 months	3,445.20
i. 1,280	36 months	1,551.96
j. 2,640	18 months	2,917.98

6. Find the total repaid, including the life-insurance premium, on each of the following used-car loans.

Loan	Period Of Debt	Total Repaid
a. $ 500	30 months	$ 670.50
b. 800	12 months	908.28
c. 1,400	18 months	1,684.80
d. 580	30 months	777.60
e. 820	24 months	1,043.04
f. 1,540	12 months	1,748.28

7. How much more will be repaid than was originally borrowed on each of the following new-car loans?

Loan	Period Of Debt	Total Repaid	Total Life-Insurance Premium	Total Paid On Debt	Cost Of Loan
a. $1,000	24 months	$ 1,140.72	$ 9.47	$ 1,131.25	$ 131.25
b. 2,000	30 months	2,352.90	24.00	2,328.90	328.90
c. 3,000	36 months	3,637.80	44.02	3,593.78	593.78
d. 1,200	30 months	1,411.80	14.40	1,397.40	197.40
e. 2,100	18 months	2,321.10	14.86	2,306.24	206.24
f. 2,800	24 months	3,194.16	26.51	3,167.65	367.65
g. 2,220	30 months	2,612.10	26.64	2,585.46	365.46
h. 1,780	24 months	2,030.64	16.86	2,013.78	233.78

8. How much more will be repaid than was originally borrowed on each of the following used-car loans?

Loan	Period Of Debt	Total Repaid	Total Life-Insurance Premium	Total Paid On Debt	Cost Of Loan
a. $ 500	30 months	$ 670.50	$ 6.84	$ 663.66	$ 163.66
b. 1,400	12 months	1,589.40	6.99	1,582.41	182.41
c. 1,000	18 months	1,203.48	7.70	1,195.78	195.78
d. 640	30 months	858.00	8.75	849.25	209.25
e. 520	24 months	661.44	5.49	655.95	135.95

It might be well for the student to use two sheets of paper for his homework. One sheet will be a lined paper containing the outline of the exercises as shown above with the answers filled in. of course. The other will be an unlined paper showing the computations required to obtain each answer.

C

1. Steve Cleary purchased a new car valued at $2,746 by making a down payment of $546. He borrowed the remainder from the automobile dealer who used the New-Car Monthly Payment Table on page 3 for finding the terms of the loan.
   a. How much money did Steve have to borrow? $2,200
   b. If he agrees to repay the money over a 36-month period, including the life-insurance premium, what will be the total amount repaid? $2,667.60
   c. If he agrees to repay the money over an 18-month period, including the life-insurance premium, what will be the total amount repaid? $2,431.62
   d. How much more will it cost Steve if he repays the debt over a 36-month period rather than over an 18-month period? $ 235.98

2. When Mr. Gilbert purchased his car, he made a down payment of $758.46 on the $2,158.46 that was the cost of the car. Mr. Gilbert agreed to pay off the balance in monthly installments over a two-year period.
   a. How large was the unpaid balance? $1,400
   b. If the New-Car Monthly Payment Table on page 3 is used for computing the cost of the loan, how much will Mr. Gilbert have to repay? In computing the total repayment, include the cost of the life insurance. $1,597.20
   c. If the Used-Car Monthly Payment Table on page 5 is used for computing the cost of the loan, how much will Mr. Gilbert have to repay? In computing the total repayment, include the cost of the life insurance. $1,780.80
   d. How much more will it cost Mr. Gilbert to borrow the money he needs if the car he purchases is a used car rather than a new car? $ 183.60

3. Find the monthly payment and the total life-insurance premium on each of the following unpaid balances. Use the New-Car Monthly Payment Table on page 3.

	Unpaid Balance	Period Of Loan	Monthly Payment	Total Life-Insurance Premium
a.	$4,000	18 months	$ 245.62	$ 28.30
b.	3,600	24 months	171.12	34.08
c.	5,400	36 months	181.88	79.22

4. Find the total amount that will be repaid on a loan of $2,000 for a period of 12 months. The total payment is to include the life-insurance premium. Use the Used-Car Monthly Payment Table on page 5 to solve this problem. $2,270.64

You may find a difference of one penny in monthly payments between student answers to Problem 3. This is caused by combinations used to arrive at the unpaid balance. Thus, in Part B, a combination of $2,000 and $1,600 will give a monthly payment of $171.11; one of $1,800 and $1,800 will give $171.12.

Unit 2:   Automobile Insurance

Your money problems are not nearly over with the payment arranged for purchase of the car. All too frequently your dad will not permit you to drive the car unless you are well covered by insurance. He's afraid, of course, that if you get involved in an accident, he might be the one who has to pay for the damages. And if he doesn't want you to buy automobile insurance, then the state department of motor vehicles may very well want you to. At the present time, there are quite a number of states that require a car to be covered by insurance before it may be driven. Suppose, then, you spend a little time exploring how much this is going to cost you. Usually you are so anxious to get behind the wheel of a car that nothing seems to discourage you.

Section 1:   Bodily-Injury and Property-Damage Insurance

Of the four types of insurance that can be purchased for protection in driving a car, two cover you in the event you damage someone else's property, or inflict injury on some person other than a member of your own family. These are the two that the state department of motor vehicles wants you to have. In a way, it is not particularly interested in what harm you might do to yourself or your car by your poor driving. Its concern is whether you have enough insurance to pay for the damage you inflict on other people or their property. The two varieties of insurance that cover these situations are explained below.

Property-Damage Insurance: In this type of insurance, you protect yourself from suffering any financial loss in the event you damage someone's property. This property can include such things as a car, a house, a lawn, a bicycle, shrubbery, a storefront; in fact, just about anything. The amount of the damage for which the insurance company will pay depends on how much you insured yourself for. The amount can be as little as $5,000, or as much as $50,000. The most common policy, however, is for $10,000. This means that the insurance company will pay up to $10,000 for damage that you might have caused. Any amount over that, you, yourself, will have to pay. Thus, if the cost of the damage amounts to $14,000, the insurance company will pay $10,000, while you will have to pay the remaining $4,000. On the other hand, if you have purchased a $25,000 property-damage policy, then the insurance company will pay the entire $14,000, and you will pay nothing. How much will the insurance company have to pay, and how much will you have to pay in this case, if you have purchased a $5,000 property-damage policy?

Have the students check to determine whether their state requires automobile owners to purchase insurance before a car can be driven. If so, have them find out what type of insurance must be purchased and to what extent.

Bodily-Injury Insurance: By buying this type of insurance, you protect yourself from any financial loss in the event you injure anyone during an automobile accident in which you are at fault. These policies are so written that they cover two different possibilities. As an example, the basic bodily-injury policy is called the 10/20 policy. In this plan, your insurance company will pay any one person up to $10,000 for injuries that you may have caused that person during an accident. In addition, should more than one person be injured as a result of this same accident, then the company will pay no more than $20,000 to all of them, no matter how many people were involved. For instance, imagine that during an accident in which you are at fault, four people are injured. One of the injured persons sues you to collect money for the damages he suffered and is granted $14,500 by court action. The remaining three are granted amounts of $4,200, $2,500, and $2,000, respectively. In making payment, the insurance company will give only $10,000 to the person having the $14,500 injuries and you will have to pay the balance of $4,500. Since the total for the remaining three people, when added to the $10,000, comes to less than $20,000, the insurance company will pay the full amount to these three and you will have to pay them nothing. What do the numerals 20/40 mean in a 20/40 bodily-injury automobile insurance policy?

To determine the cost of either the bodily-injury, or property-damage, insurance requires reference to four different tables. The first of these is a Basic-Cost Table, part of which is shown here.

BASIC COST FOR BODILY–INJURY AND PROPERTY–DAMAGE INSURANCE

Territory

	01	02	05	06	25	26
B.I.	$80	$77	$66	$46	$37	$31
P.D.	$35	$33	$29	$26	$22	$19

Notice that the cost of the insurance depends on the territory in which you live. Each state is divided into a great many of these territories—only six of which appear here. The greater the history of accidents in a territory, the greater the cost of the insurance. Chances are that the 01 territory above is a busy city area, while the 26 territory is a sparsely settled country area. Why should you think this?

The next three tables are called factor tables. The term factor, as used here, is simply a number by which the basic premium is multiplied in order to find the actual cost of the insurance. For instance, in the following table, note that the cost of a 15/30 bodily-injury policy is found by multiplying the basic-cost premium by 1.09. Similarly, a

Most students enjoy telling about automobile accidents in which they, their parents, or their friends were involved. This, also, gives the student who is weak in arithmetic skills an opportunity to participate in the class discussion and, hopefully, an incentive to improve his work.

$25,000 property-damage policy will cost 1.08 times the premium shown in the Basic-Cost Table. What is the factor for a 25/50 bodily-injury policy? Notice that the greater the protection (coverage) you buy, the greater the factor will be that must be multiplied by the basic cost.

COVERAGE–LIMIT FACTOR TABLE
(Private Passenger Car)

Bodily Injury

10/20	15/30	20/40	25/50	50/100	100/300
1.00	1.09	1.15	1.19	1.30	1.41

Property Damage

5,000	10,000	25,000	50,000
1.00	1.05	1.08	1.13

The following table assigns a factor to you, depending on the number of points you have accumulated over the three-year period prior to purchasing the insurance. For each accident you have had during this time, you are assigned a point. And if you have had no accidents, then you are rewarded by having a factor (.85) that is less than 1. This means that the cost of the insurance for you may be less than the premiums shown in the Basic-Cost Table.

Points are assigned not only for accidents, but also for certain motor vehicle law violations. For example, three points are assigned to persons convicted of driving while intoxicated, or driving when their licenses have been suspended. Notice that a person who has accumulated at least 4 points in a three-year period will have to pay $2\frac{1}{2}$ times the basic cost. How much will a person have to pay if his poor driving has led to an accumulation of three points? Perhaps what should interest you most is that if you have just received your license, you will be considered to have no points.

DRIVING–RECORD FACTOR
(Three-Year Period)

Number of Points	0	1	2	3	4
Factor	.85	1.05	1.50	2.00	2.50

The last of the factor tables takes into consideration your age. At one time, insurance companies charged everyone the same amount of money and took into consideration only the area in which the person lived. So numerous were the complaints about this that studies were made to determine at what age levels the greatest number of accidents occurred. It was found that the unmarried young man under the age

Use the bodily injury factors to show that for less than half again as much cost a person can buy more than ten times as much protection; that is, compare the factor of 100/300 coverage with that of 10/20 coverage. Also, make a comparison of the $50,000 property damage factor with that of $5,000.

of 21 was the most reckless driver on the road. The factors are now set up whereby he will have to pay the most for his insurance. As the following table indicates, the older you become, the less will be the cost of your automobile insurance. In fact, once you reach the age of 30, as a male, you simply pay the basic premium. The crucial age for the female driver is 21.

There is another interesting and important point that shouldn't be overlooked. If the school you attend happens to have a behind-the-wheel driver-training course and you were lucky enough to have taken it, then you are granted a discount on the cost of the insurance. For instance, as an unmarried male under the age of 21 and the owner of a car, the youthful-driver factor will be only 3.15 rather than 3.50. In some territories, depending on the total coverage you are buying, this might mean a savings of anywhere from $50 to $100 a year. What are the factors for an unmarried male under the age of 21 who is not the owner of the car?

AGE–FACTOR TABLE

Female——Unmarried
(Under 21)

Driver Training	Factor
No	1.55
Yes	1.40

Male——Unmarried
(Under 21)

Driver Training	Not-Owner Factor	Owner Factor
No	2.50	3.50
Yes	2.25	3.15

Male——Unmarried

	21–24	25–30
Not-Owner Factor	1.60	1.50
Owner Factor	2.50	1.50

Male——Married
(Under 21)

Driver Training	Not-Owner Factor	Owner Factor
No	2.00	2.30
Yes	1.80	2.07

Male——Married
(21–24)

Not-Owner Factor	1.40
Owner Factor	1.40

The factor for any age not covered in this table is 1.00.

Use the age-factor table to have students answer such questions as, "Until what age will an unmarried male have to pay extra for his car insurance?" "Until what age will an unmarried female have to pay extra?" "Until what age will a married male have to pay extra?" "A married female?"

The following illustrations should help clear up any questions about the application of the four tables just presented. Three of the tables are needed for finding the factor, while the fourth is needed for the basic cost.

■ ILLUSTRATION 1: George Greenwood, who is unmarried at age 20, has just purchased a 50/100 bodily-injury insurance policy. He had had no driver-training course while in high school. In addition, last year he was involved in one accident. What total factor was used in computing the cost of this policy?

▼ EXPLANATION: The total factor consists of three parts:
                           1. The coverage-limit factor
                           2. The driver-record factor
                           3. The age factor
The table pertaining to each of these factors has to be examined to determine that individual factor. Thus, for the limits of 50/100, you find that the factor in the Coverage-Limit Table is 1.30. Similarly, the driving-record factor for one accident is 1.05, while the age factor for an unmarried male car owner under the age of 21, who has not had a driver-training course, is 3.50. The total factor is the sum of these three factors.

● SOLUTION:

$$\begin{array}{ll} \text{Coverage-limit factor} & = 1.30 \\ \text{Driving-record factor} & = 1.05 \\ \underline{+ \text{ Age factor}} & \underline{= 3.50} \\ \text{Total factor} & = 5.85 \end{array}$$

■ ILLUSTRATION 2: Mr. Edwin Murray is 23 years of age and lives in an area that is designated as a 25 territory by the automobile insurance companies. He had no record of accidents when he purchased a $25,000 property-damage policy. What did this policy cost him if he is married?

● SOLUTION:

$$\begin{array}{ll} \text{Coverage-limit factor} & = 1.08 \\ \text{Driving-record factor} & = .85 \\ \underline{+ \text{ Age factor}} & \underline{= 1.40} \\ \text{Total factor} & = 3.33 \\ \text{Basic cost for property-damage insurance} & = \$22 \\ \text{Total cost} \quad = 3.33 \times \$22 \\ \phantom{\text{Total cost} \quad} = \$73.26, \text{ or } \$73 \end{array}$$

Urge the students when doing their homework to follow an outline similar to that used in the solutions of the illustrations. Not only will this make for neater papers, but it will also make it a great deal easier for you to check their work.

▼EXPLANATION: The total factor is examined as in Illustration 1. By examining the table on page 11, you find that the basic cost of property-damage insurance in a 25 territory is $22. The actual cost, however, is the product of the basic cost and the total factor. This is $73.26. The cost of automobile insurance, though, is always rounded off to the nearest dollar. Hence, in this illustration, the premium will be $73. Had Mr. Murray purchased both property-damage and bodily-injury insurance, then the cost of each would have been rounded off to the nearest dollar before the total cost was determined.

EXERCISES   **A**

Do you recall how to determine the answer in each of the following exercises? If not, you will probably want to refer to the pages indicated for help.

1. Round off each of the following amounts to the nearest dollar (pages 593–596).
   a. $46.27 __$46.00__   c. $12.02 __$12.00__   e. $9.50 __$10.00__
   b. $54.75 __$55.00__   d. $46.51 __$47.00__   f. $.67 __$ 1.00__

2. Round off each of the following amounts to the nearest dime (pages 593–596).
   a. $12.61 __$12.60__   c. $85.35 __$85.40__   e. $7.96 __$ 8.00__
   b. $23.27 __$23.30__   d. $32.03 __$32.00__   f. $9.98 __$10.00__

B

1. What is the coverage factor on each of the following insurance policies?

Type Of Insurance	Coverage Limit	Factor
a. Bodily Injury	25/50	1.19
b. Bodily Injury	10/20	1.00
c. Bodily Injury	15/30	1.09
d. Property Damage	$25,000	1.08
e. Property Damage	$10,000	1.05
f. Property Damage	$50,000	1.13

2. What is the driving-record factor for persons who have the following number of points?
   a. Number of points: 2 __1.50__
   b. Number of points: 0 __.85__

Again caution the students not to write their answers in the empty columns. It would be well do do Exercise A orally, as well as those exercises on pages 593 and 594, plus any you design. This may very well be the first exposure students have had to rounding off an answer to the nearest dollar.

3. What is the age factor for each of the following drivers?

	Sex	Age	Married	Driver Training	Car Owner	Factor
a.	Female	26	—	—	—	1.00
b.	Male	34	—	—	—	1.00
c.	Male	26	Yes	—	—	1.00
d.	Male	22	No	—	No	1.60
e.	Female	20	Yes	—	—	1.00
f.	Female	19	No	Yes	—	1.40
g.	Male	24	Yes	—	Yes	1.40
h.	Male	21	No	—	No	1.60
i.	Male	17	No	No	Yes	3.50
j.	Female	18	No	No	—	1.55
k.	Male	29	No	—	Yes	1.50
l.	Male	45	—	—	—	1.00
m.	Male	19	No	No	No	2.50
n.	Male	24	Yes	—	No	1.40

4. Find the total factor in the purchase of each of the following bodily-injury insurance policies.

	Coverage Limits	Points	Sex	Age	Married	Driver Training	Car Owner	Total Factor
a.	10/20	0	M	32	—	—	—	2.85
b.	20/40	1	F	23	—	—	—	3.20
c.	50/100	2	M	21	No	—	No	4.40
d.	15/30	4	M	24	Yes	—	Yes	4.99
e.	25/50	3	F	19	No	Yes	—	4.59
f.	20/40	1	M	20	No	No	Yes	5.70

5. Find the total factor in the purchase of each of the following property-damage insurance policies.

	Coverage Limits	Points	Sex	Age	Married	Driver Training	Car Owner	Total Factor
a.	$ 5,000	1	M	28	Yes	—	—	3.05
b.	25,000	3	F	37	—	—	—	4.08
c.	10,000	0	M	22	Yes	—	Yes	3.30
d.	50,000	2	M	20	No	Yes	Yes	5.78

6. Find the cost of each of the following bodily-injury insurance policies.

	Coverage Limits	Territory	Points	Sex	Age	Married	Driver Training	Car Owner	Total Factor	Basic Cost	Total Cost
a.	10/20	01	0	M	46	—	—	—	2.85	$80	$228
b.	20/40	05	1	M	27	Yes	—	—	3.20	66	211
c.	50/100	26	3	F	20	Yes	—	—	4.30	31	133
d.	100/300	02	2	M	63	—	—	—	3.91	77	301
e.	15/30	25	4	M	21	No	—	Yes	6.09	37	225
f.	25/50	06	3	F	19	No	No	—	4.74	46	218

7. Find the cost of each of the following property-damage insurance policies.

Coverage Limits	Territory	Points	Sex	Age	Married	Driver Training	Car Owner	Total Factor	Basic Cost	Total Cost
								3.05	$33	$101
a. $ 5,000	02	1	M	28	Yes	—	—	2.98	19	57
b. 50,000	26	0	F	23	—	—	—	4.15	35	145
c. 10,000	01	2	M	22	No	—	No	6.73	29	195
d. 25,000	05	4	M	19	No	Yes	Yes			

C

1. Roger Baker was in an automobile accident in which his car damaged property to the extent of $11,500. Mr. Baker had $5,000 property-damage insurance coverage.
   a. How much of the damage was paid for by the insurance company?
   <u>$5,000</u>
   b. How much of the cost of the damage did Mr. Baker have to pay?
   <u>$6,500</u>
   c. If Mr. Baker had been covered by a $10,000 property-damage policy, how much of the cost of the damage would he, himself, have had to pay?
   <u>$1,500</u>
   d. If Mr. Baker had been covered by a $25,000 property-damage policy, how much of the cost of the damage would he, himself, have had to pay?
   <u>$0</u>

2. Mr. Lomb injured three people in an automobile accident in which he was at fault. His automobile-insurance coverage included a 20/40 bodily-injury liability policy.
   a. If only one of the injured persons claimed any damage and that claim was $14,000, how much of this amount would the insurance company pay? Assume that the courts upheld this claim.
   <u>$14,000</u>
   b. If the claim of the injured person in Part (a) had been $25,000, how much of this would the insurance company pay? <u>$20,000</u>
   c. If the three injured persons each claimed $10,000 and were granted this by court action, what is the total amount that the insurance company would have to pay?
   <u>$30,000</u>
   d. If the three injured persons in Part (c) had been granted $15,000 each, what is the total amount the insurance company would have to pay?
   <u>$40,000</u>
   e. If one of the three injured persons in Part (c) had been granted $24,000, while the remaining two were granted $5,000 each, what is the total amount that the insurance company would have to pay in settlement?
   <u>$30,000</u>

Stress Problems 1 and 2 of Group B. Although the student may never be called upon to determine the cost of insurance, it will certainly be necessary for him to know the extent to which he is insured should an accident occur.

    f. If one of the three injured persons in Part (c) had been granted $24,000, while the remaining two were granted $10,000 each, what is the total amount the insurance company would have to pay?   <u>$40,000</u>

3. Peter Ryan, who lives in an 06 territory, recently purchased a new car. He immediately covered himself with a 50/100 bodily-injury liability policy. During the past three years he has had no accidents. Peter is 20 years old and is not married.

    a. How much less would this policy have cost him if he had had a driver-training course than if he had not? $ <u>16</u>

    b. Assuming that Peter had had a driver-training course in school, how much less would this policy have cost him, since he had had no accidents, than if he had had three accidents during the preceding three years? $ <u>53</u>

    c. Assuming that Peter had had a driver-training course in school, how much less would this policy have cost him had he been able to convince his father to take over the ownership of the car and let Peter be the actual driver of the car? $ <u>42</u>

4. When Mr. Albert Channing purchased his car, he also purchased a $25,000 property-damage and a 100/300 bodily-injury insurance policy. He lives in an area designated as a 26 territory. Mr. Channing is 43 years old and has had but one accident during the past three years.

    a. How much will he have to pay for this coverage? $ <u>166</u>

    b. How much would Mr. Channing have had to pay if he had lived in an 01 territory? $ <u>387</u>

    c. How much does Mr. Channing save by being a resident of a 26 territory rather than of an 01 territory? $ <u>221</u>

Section 2: Collision and Comprehensive Insurance

It has been stated that there were four varieties of automobile insurance that you could purchase to protect yourself from any financial loss. The two that you have already examined—bodily-injury and property-damage insurance—afford you coverage against any damage or injury you might inflict upon someone else, or someone else's property. Now you are going to investigate the type of insurance you can buy that will cover you against the cost of damage to your own car.

Collision Insurance: Usually, the complete name for this coverage is given as collision, or upset, insurance, and its very name implies in exactly what way you are protected. Should your car be damaged in any

Recently, certain states have permitted insurance companies to add a rider to their policies, which covers the insured in the event of accidents caused by uninsured motorists. Have the students check to see if this can be done in their state, and what the extent of coverage would be.

way as a result of an accident with another car, or by having a blow-out and perhaps overturning, or by skidding into a tree, or by any one of a number of similar mishaps, then the insurance company will pay you for the cost of the damage to your car. The amount it will pay you, however, will depend on the type of policy you have purchased. To illustrate, if you have purchased a $25-deductible collision policy, then the insurance company will pay for that part of the damage to your car that exceeds $25. Thus, if the extent of the damage is $40, you will have to pay the first $25, while the remaining $15 will be paid by the company. Had the damage been $200, you will still pay only $25 for the repair, but now the insurance company will have to pay $175. How much would the insurance company have to pay if the damage were $500?

Collision insurance can be purchased for other deductible amounts, such as $50-deductible, $100-deductible, $200-deductible, and even larger amounts. Under the $50-deductible policy, if the extent of the damage to your car is $400, how much will you have to pay and how much will the insurance company have to pay? If the extent of the damage is only $40, how much will each of you have to pay? Of the various collision-insurance policies, the two most frequently purchased are the $50-deductible and the $100-deductible. Before you examine the table showing the premiums on these policies, which of these two do you believe would be the more expensive? Why?

Comprehensive Insurance: This variety of insurance protects you against practically any type of damage done to your car other than through collision or upset. In fact, you are even covered in the event your car is dented by objects falling from an airplane, or for any other equally unlikely event. However, most people purchase this policy for the fire and theft clauses that are contained in it. That is, if your car is either destroyed by fire, or stolen and never recovered, the insurance company will pay you the value of the car at that time. In the event that the fire does not completely destroy the car, then the company will pay the total cost for repairing it. Similarly, if the car is stolen and found some two weeks thereafter, the coverage will frequently be such that your transportation for these few weeks will be paid for, as well as any damage done to the car.

A comprehensive policy also contains a feature called the *malicious-damage clause*. Under this clause, you are protected from financial loss should some person throw a brick through the rear window of your car, slash the canvas top of your convertible, damage your radio antenna, or scratch his initials on the door, or any one of a number of similar pranks he can think up.

Although the coverage from falling objects was not treated in depth above, there are some states where the motorist has to pay an additional fee in order to be insured against hailstorm damage. Have the students determine if this is so in their state, and, if so, why the extra charge is made.

BASIC COST FOR COLLISION AND COMPREHENSIVE INSURANCE

Car Make: A		Territory					
		01	02	05	06	25	26
	Comprehensive	$ 24	$ 20	$ 15	$ 13	$ 12	$ 9
Age: 0–12 months	$50-Deductible	107	82	65	59	54	51
	$100-Deductible	59	49	36	33	32	30
	Comprehensive	21	17	13	11	10	8
Age: 13–36 months	$50-Deductible	93	71	57	52	48	43
	$100-Deductible	52	43	31	29	28	25
	Comprehensive	15	12	9	8	7	6
Age: 37 months and over	$50-Deductible	80	61	49	44	41	37
	$100-Deductible	45	37	27	25	24	21

Car Make: B							
	Comprehensive	33	29	22	18	17	13
Age: 0–12 months	$50-Deductible	148	114	91	82	76	71
	$100-Deductible	103	85	62	57	55	52
	Comprehensive	30	25	19	15	14	11
Age: 13–36 months	$50-Deductible	130	99	79	72	66	61
	$100-Deductible	90	74	54	50	48	45
	Comprehensive	21	17	13	11	10	8
Age: 37 months and over	$50-Deductible	111	85	68	62	57	51
	$100-Deductible	77	63	47	43	41	38

Car Make: C							
	Comprehensive	71	59	44	37	34	27
Age: 0–12 months	$50-Deductible	218	167	133	121	112	103
	$100-Deductible	159	130	96	88	84	81
	Comprehensive	60	50	37	31	29	23
Age: 13–36 months	$50-Deductible	191	146	117	106	98	91
	$100-Deductible	139	114	84	77	74	70
	Comprehensive	43	35	26	22	21	16
Age: 37 months and over	$50-Deductible	164	126	100	91	84	76
	$100-Deductible	119	98	72	66	63	61

The cost of the comprehensive and collision insurance is computed in much the same way as the property-damage and bodily-injury costs were found. However, as can be seen in the table above, in addition to considering the territory in which the car is garaged, both the make and the age of the car are taken into account in determining the premium on such a policy. Although the table here shows only three different makes of car, actual insurance tables have as many as fifty or sixty. Not only would a car such as a Buick be listed, but also each and every model of the Buick would have its own premium. Why should the premiums on a collision-insurance policy vary with the make of the car? Why should the premiums on a comprehensive-insurance policy

As a review of the earlier automobile insurance table, ask students why basic cost of collision and comprehensive insurance in territory 26 should be so much less than in territory 01. Also ask why it is that the greater the car cost, the greater the cost of collision and comprehensive insurance.

vary with the make of the car? Of the three makes of cars listed in the table, which of these is the most expensive to purchase?

■ILLUSTRATION: Joe Farnsworth has just purchased a new car of Make B, which he insured under a $50-deductible collision-insurance policy. During the previous three years Joe had one accident. He is 26 years old and unmarried. If he lives in a 25 territory, how much will this policy cost him?

●SOLUTION:

$$\begin{aligned} \text{Driving record factor} &= 1.05 \\ +\text{ Age factor} &= 1.50 \\ \hline \text{Total factor} &= 2.55 \\ \text{Basic cost for \$50-deductible} &= \$76 \\ \text{Total cost} = 2.55 \times \$76 & \\ = \$193.80, \text{ or } \$194 & \end{aligned}$$

▼EXPLANATION: The driving-record factor and the age factor are found as before. To determine the basic cost of the $50-deductible collision policy, examine that part of the table pertaining to the "B"-make cars. Since the car is new, it will fall into the age group of 0 to 12 months. By running your finger across the $50-deductible row in this group, you come to the column headed by the numeral "25," the territory in which Joe lives. The numeral $76 that your finger points to represents the basic cost for a $50-deductible collision-insurance policy on a new "B"-make car garaged in a 25 territory. The solution is completed by finding the product of the total factor of 2.55 and the basic cost of $76.

EXERCISES   A

1. In each of the following situations, the owner's car is covered by the collision insurance indicated. How much will the insurance company have to pay him for the damages incurred to his car?

	Type Of Collision-Insurance Policy	Extent Of Damage	
a.	$100-Deductible	$ 80	$ 0
b.	$100-Deductible	250	150
c.	$100-Deductible	940	840
d.	$100-Deductible	100	0
e.	$50-Deductible	75	25
f.	$200-Deductible	75	0
g.	$50-Deductible	850	800
h.	$250-Deductible	850	600

Call attention to the fact that the total cost of the collision insurance in the illustration was rounded off to the nearest dollar. In computing the cost of each of the various automobile insurance coverages, each is separately rounded off to the nearest dollar.

2. Find the basic cost of each of the following comprehensive-insurance policies.

	Age In Months	Car Make	Territory	Basic Cost
a.	5	A	02	$ 20
b.	14	A	05	13
c.	36	B	26	11
d.	25	B	01	30
e.	12	C	25	34
f.	42	C	06	22

3. Find the basic cost of each of the following $50-deductible collision-insurance policies.

	Age In Months	Car Make	Territory	Basic Cost
a.	17	A	01	$ 93
b.	39	B	25	57
c.	4	A	05	65
d.	0	C	26	103
e.	37	A	02	61
f.	24	B	06	72

4. Find the basic cost of each of the following $100-deductible collision-insurance policies.

	Age In Months	Car Make	Territory	Basic Cost
a.	42	C	26	$ 61
b.	0	B	05	62
c.	14	B	01	90
d.	36	A	25	28
e.	12	C	02	130
f.	37	A	05	27

5. Find the cost of each of the following comprehensive-insurance policies.

	Car Make	Age In Months	Territory	Points	Sex	Age	Married	Driver Training	Car Owner	Cost
a.	A	0	02	0	M	37	—	—	—	$ 37
b.	B	16	25	0	F	25	—	—	—	26
c.	A	21	06	1	M	22	Yes	—	Yes	27
d.	C	32	01	3	M	20	No	Yes	No	255
e.	A	38	26	0	M	17	No	No	No	20
f.	B	10	05	1	F	19	No	Yes	—	54

6. Find the cost of each of the following $50-deductible collision-insurance policies.

	Car Make	Age In Months	Territory	Points	Sex	Age	Married	Driver Training	Car Owner	Cost
a.	B	13	26	2	F	28	—	—	—	$ 153
b.	C	30	05	0	M	65	—	—	—	216
c.	A	0	01	0	F	20	Yes	—	—	198
d.	C	16	06	1	M	18	No	No	Yes	482

7. Find the cost of each of the following $100-deductible collision-insurance policies.

	Car Make	Age In Months	Territory	Points	Sex	Age	Married	Driver Training	Car Owner	Cost
a.	C	12	01	1	M	19	No	Yes	Yes	$ 668
b.	B	45	05	2	M	20	Yes	Yes	Yes	168
c.	A	1	26	3	M	25	Yes	—	—	90
d.	B	26	02	1	F	18	No	Yes	—	181

B

1. Bruce Williams, who is married, purchased a new "C"-make car on his 27th birthday. Bruce lives in an area designated as an 05 territory, and he had no accidents during the previous three years.
   a. How much will he have to pay for a $50-deductible collision-insurance policy? $246
   b. How much will he have to pay for a $100-deductible collision-insurance policy? $178
   c. How much more will a $50-deductible policy cost him than a $100-deductible policy? $ 68

2. On Edward's 18th birthday, his father gave him a used "B"-make car that was 27 months old. Edward had had a driver-education course in school and had never had an accident. He is not married and he lives at home with his parents in a 25 territory. The car was immediately insured under a comprehensive policy.
   a. If Edward's father had kept the ownership of the car in his own name, what would the insurance have cost? $ 43
   b. If Edward's father had had the ownership of the car turned over to Edward, what would the insurance have cost? $ 56
   c. How much would have been saved had the father kept the ownership of the car in his own name? $ 13

3. When Mr. Rothman, who is 48 years old, purchased his new "C"-make car, he immediately insured it for $100-deductible collision insurance, comprehensive insurance, 100/300 bodily-injury insurance, and $25,000 property-damage insurance. He had had two accidents during the preceding three years, and, during this time, he lived in an 02 territory.

The problems in Group B are interesting, for they show a comparison of the cost of insurance under different conditions. They should be assigned, however, only as extra-credit work for the more capable student.

a. What was the total cost of this coverage? $892

b. How much would the insurance have cost Mr. Rothman if he
   had had no accidents during the preceding three-year period?
                                                           $698

c. How much would Mr. Rothman have saved on his insurance if
   he had had no accidents? $194

Unit 3:   Operating Costs

The expenses you have been examining up to this point have nothing
at all to do with the actual driving of the car. These are the necessary
costs that you have to pay before you are even allowed to drive your
car.

The obvious expenses of operating a car are the cost of gasoline, of
oil, and of tires. The not-so-obvious ones that occur less frequently
are the cost of battery replacement, the changes in brake lining, the
alignment of the front wheels, and the need for new spark plugs, new
points, and so on as the car gets older and older. Also buried in the
costs are the federal and state taxes that have to be paid on many of
these purchases. Suppose you examine some of these costs now.

■ILLUSTRATION 1: Joe Evans uses his car to drive to and from
school and for pleasure driving on weekends. He finds that during an
average week he will use approximately 12 gallons of gasoline. How
much can Joe save each week by buying a grade of gasoline at 29.9¢
per gallon rather than one that would cost him 32.9¢?

●SOLUTION:

$$\text{Saving on each gallon} = 32.9¢ - 29.9¢$$
$$= 3¢$$
$$\text{Saving on 12 gallons} = 12 \times 3¢$$
$$= 36¢$$

▼EXPLANATION: The saving on each gallon is found by subtracting
the price per gallon of the cheaper gasoline from the price per gallon
of the more expensive gasoline. The difference turns out to be 3¢. Since
Joe purchases 12 gallons each week, his total saving is 12 times 3¢, or
36¢. Another and longer way of doing this problem is to determine the
cost of all 12 gallons of gasoline at the 29.9¢ price. How can this be
done? After that, the cost of the 12 gallons at the 32.9¢ price is determined. What would then have to be done with these two products to
find the saving?

■ILLUSTRATION 2: Pete Riker drove his car 15,000 miles last year.
He found that he averaged 20 miles to a gallon of gasoline. In addition, he had to add a quart of oil to the oil supply every 500 miles.

All too often adolescents will think only in terms of the cost of the car and the cost of the
insurance when purchasing a car. In addition to the operating costs shown here have them
compile a list of other expenses they can expect to incur.

a. If Pete paid 33.9¢ per gallon of gasoline, what was the total amount that he spent on gasoline during the year?

b. If the oil that Pete used in his car cost 65¢ per quart, what was the total amount he spent on oil during the year?

c. How much did Pete spend for both gasoline and oil during the year?

●SOLUTION:

(a) Number of gallons of gasoline purchased = 15,000 ÷ 20
$$= 750$$
Cost of each gallon of gasoline = 33.9¢, or $.339
Cost of 750 gallons of gasoline = 750 × $.339
$$= \$254.25$$

(b) Number of quarts of oil purchased = 15,000 ÷ 500
$$= 30$$
Cost of each quart of oil = 65¢, or $.65
Cost of 30 quarts of oil = 30 × $.65
$$= \$19.50$$

(c) Total cost of both gasoline and oil = $254.25 + $19.50
$$= \$273.75$$

▼EXPLANATION: For each 20 miles, the car used 1 gallon of gasoline. Hence, had the car been driven 40 miles, it would have used 2 gallons, and had it been driven 60 miles, it would have used 3 gallons of gasoline. Thus, you can see that the number of gallons of gasoline can be found by dividing the total distance traveled by the number of miles the car can travel on each gallon of gasoline. In this illustration, the number of gallons purchased was 750. Multiplying the 750 by the cost per gallon (33.9¢) gave you the total spent on gasoline ($254.25). Before finding the product of 750 and 33.9¢, it was necessary to rewrite the 33.9 cents in terms of dollars. How is this done? Why is this done? The cost of oil for the year was computed in exactly the same manner as for the cost of gasoline.

EXERCISES   A

Do you recall how to find the answer in each of the following exercises? If not, you will probably want to refer to the pages indicated for help.

1. Round off each of the following numbers to the nearest whole number (pages 593–594).

a. 46.2 _____46_____	e. 50.63 _____51_____	i. 9.9 _____10_____
b. 59.1 _____59_____	f. 58.47 _____58_____	j. 29.7 _____30_____
c. 93.7 _____94_____	g. 73.49 _____73_____	k. 99.6 _____100_____
d. 81.0 _____81_____	h. 85.51 _____86_____	l. 109.8 _____110_____

In the solution of Part A, above, it is necessary to rewrite 33.9¢ in terms of dollar units. Before doing this, have students express such numerals as 25¢, 34¢, 96¢, 7¢, and 3¢ as numerals with the dollar sign. Then ask them to state the general method of rewriting "cent" numerals as "dollar" numerals.

2. Round off each of the following amounts to the nearest cent (pages 593–596).

   a. $2.462 _$2.46_   d. $6.857 _$6.86_   g. $12.789 _$12.79_
   b. $5.501 _$5.50_   e. $7.496 _$7.50_   h. $36.583 _$36.58_
   c. $3.314 _$3.31_   f. $4.028 _$4.03_   i. $43.007 _$43.01_

3. Determine the quotient in each of the following exercises. Each answer will be a whole number (pages 576–577).

   a. 782 ÷ 34 = ___23___   j. 4,891 ÷ 67   = ___73___
   b. 675 ÷ 27 = ___25___   k. 3,034 ÷ 82   = ___37___
   c. 630 ÷ 45 = ___14___   l. 6,734 ÷ 91   = ___74___
   d. 992 ÷ 62 = ___16___   m. 20,150 ÷ 650 = ___31___
   e. 276 ÷ 12 = ___23___   n. 14,850 ÷ 450 = ___33___
   f. 495 ÷ 15 = ___33___   o. 20,250 ÷ 750 = ___27___
   g. 2,520 ÷ 56 = ___45___   p. 13,975 ÷ 325 = ___43___
   h. 1,908 ÷ 36 = ___53___   q. 17.500 ÷ 625 = ___28___
   i. 1,800 ÷ 75 = ___24___   r. 37,200 ÷ 775 = ___48___

4. Determine the quotient to the nearest whole number in each of the following exercises (pages 576–577).

   a. 83 ÷ 25 = ___3___   h. 224 ÷ 29 = ___8___
   b. 176 ÷ 34 = ___5___   i. 412 ÷ 74 = ___6___
   c. 182 ÷ 42 = ___4___   j. 566 ÷ 86 = ___7___
   d. 337 ÷ 64 = ___5___   k. 518 ÷ 43 = ___12___
   e. 325 ÷ 53 = ___6___   l. 573 ÷ 24 = ___24___
   f. 252 ÷ 37 = ___7___   m. 999 ÷ 51 = ___20___
   g. 305 ÷ 66 = ___5___   n. 3,462 ÷ 75 = ___46___
                     o. 3,995 ÷ 83 = ___48___

B

1. The federal tax on gasoline is 4¢ per gallon. How much tax is paid on each of the following purchases of gasoline?

	Number Of Gallons	Tax		Number Of Gallons	Tax		Number Of Gallons	Tax
a.	8	$ .32	e.	65	$ 2.60	i.	6.5	$ .26
b.	12	.48	f.	82	3.28	j.	8.5	.34
c.	15	.60	g.	154	6.16	k.	17.5	.70
d.	18	.72	h.	295	11.80	l.	49.5	1.98

2. The state tax per gallon of gasoline varies from state to state. The federal tax is 4¢ per gallon. In the following exercises, find the total tax paid on each of the purchases shown.

Have the students check, by examining the price listed at gasoline stations, to see if the federal tax is still 4¢ per gallon. At the same time, have them determine what their state gas tax is.

	Number Of Gallons	State Tax Per Gallon	State Tax	Federal Tax	Total Tax
a.	7	6¢	42 ¢	28 ¢	70 ¢
b.	9	7¢	63 ¢	36 ¢	99 ¢
c.	14	5¢	70 ¢	56 ¢	126 ¢
d.	25	9¢	225 ¢	100 ¢	325 ¢
e.	64	6¢	384 ¢	256 ¢	640 ¢
f.	58	6.5¢	377 ¢	232 ¢	609 ¢
g.	76	7.5¢	570 ¢	304 ¢	874 ¢
h.	124	6.5¢	806 ¢	496 ¢	1,302 ¢
i.	150	6.58¢	987 ¢	600 ¢	1,587 ¢

3. Find the cost, to the nearest cent, of each of the following purchases of gasoline.

	Number Of Gallons	Price Per Gallon	Exact Cost	Cost To the Nearest Cent
a.	5	28.9¢	$ 1.445	$ 1.45
b.	4	35.9¢	1.436	1.44
c.	8	31.9¢	2.552	2.55
d.	12	33.9¢	4.068	4.07
e.	18	39.9¢	7.182	7.18
f.	75	30.9¢	23.175	23.18
g.	86	37.9¢	32.594	32.59
h.	94	38.9¢	36.566	36.57
i.	4.3	36.9¢	1.5867	1.59
j.	6.7	36.9¢	2.4723	2.47
k.	8.2	34.9¢	2.8618	2.86
l.	12.4	32.9¢	4.0796	4.08

4. How many gallons of gasoline were used during each of the following trips?

	Distance Traveled	Miles Per Gallon	Number Of Gallons
a.	3,000 miles	15	200
b.	3,500 miles	14	250
c.	2,400 miles	8	300
d.	7,200 miles	25	288
e.	15,400 miles	22	700
f.	4,420 miles	26	170

5. How many quarts of oil were used during each of the following trips?

	Distance Traveled	Miles Per Quart	Number Of Quarts
a.	6,000 miles	500	12
b.	9,000 miles	600	15
c.	12,000 miles	750	16
d.	14,400 miles	450	32
e.	27,000 miles	1,500	18
f.	28,800 miles	1,800	16

Most people rarely think of the amount of tax they have to pay on each gallon of gasoline. xercise 2 is designed to point up this factor. It would be well to entertain a discussion of ʰhe federal and state taxes are spent.

6. Over the period of one year, a person purchased the number of gallons of gasoline shown in each of the following exercises. How much would he have saved had he been able to use the cheaper of the two grades of gasoline?

	Number Of Gallons	Cost Per Gallon Of Cheaper Grade	Cost Per Gallon Of More Expensive Grade	Saving Per Gallon	Total Saving
a.	600	28.9¢	32.9¢	$ .04	$ 24.00
b.	800	29.9¢	33.9¢	.04	32.00
c.	750	36.9¢	39.9¢	.03	22.50
d.	1,200	28.9¢	37.9¢	.09	108.00
e.	1,400	32.5¢	38.9¢	.064	89.60
f.	1,050	34.5¢	39.9¢	.054	56.70
g.	970	30.9¢	35.4¢	.045	43.65
h.	1,450	33.9¢	40.4¢	.065	94.25

7. What was the cost of the gasoline consumed on each of the following trips?

	Distance Traveled	Miles Per Gallon	Number Of Gallons Consumed	Cost Per Gallon	Total Cost
a.	6,000 miles	10	600	32.9¢	$ 197.40
b.	9,000 miles	15	600	33.9¢	203.40
c.	8,400 miles	12	700	35.9¢	251.30
d.	7,840 miles	14	560	31.5¢	176.40
e.	8,260 miles	28	295	39.5¢	116.53
f.	10,080 miles	16	630	34.9¢	219.87

C

1. The first summer after Bruce Wentz purchased his new car, he took a 12,000-mile trip around the country. He found that he was purchasing gasoline at an average price of 31.9¢ per gallon.
   a. How many gallons did he purchase if his car averaged 20 miles per gallon? _600_
   b. How much did he spend for gasoline? _$191.40_
   c. How many gallons of gasoline would he have purchased if his car had averaged 15 miles per gallon? _800_
   d. How much would he have spent for gasoline had his car averaged 15 miles per gallon of gasoline? _$255.20_
   e. How much was he able to save since his car averaged 20 miles per gallon of gasoline rather than 15 miles per gallon? _$ 63.80_
2. Gene Bradley is a salesman for Soft Tread Shoes, Inc. He drives his car approximately 45,000 miles each year on business. Mr. Bradley finds that his car averages 15 miles for each gallon of gasoline and 750 miles for each quart of oil.

Since the price of gasoline varies throughout the country, have the students check to determine whether those listed in these problems are reasonable for the area in which they live.

a. If the average price per gallon of gasoline that he purchases is 37.9¢, what is the total amount that he spends on gasoline during the year? $1,137

b. If the average price per quart of oil that he purchases is 65¢, what is the total amount that he spends on oil during the year? $ 39

c. What is the total amount that he spends on both gasoline and oil during the year? $1,176

3. In operating his car, Jim Butler finds that he uses 25 quarts of oil during the year.

a. If he purchased the oil at a gasoline station, he would have to pay 55¢ a quart. How much would he have to pay for the oil over the period of the year under these conditions?$ 13.75

b. If he purchased the oil in 4-quart containers at an auto-parts store, each can would cost him $1.60. How much would he have to pay for the oil under these conditions? $ 10.00

c. How much would he save each year if he purchased the oil in 4-quart cans at an auto-parts store? $ 3.75

Unit 4: Traveling by Road Map

Most people look forward to owning a car because they wish to travel. They want to see the national parks, or the Great Lakes, or the Gulf of Mexico, or New York City, or Las Vegas, or just about any place except where they happen to live. The nation is covered with excellent highways that enable you to get where you want to go quickly. In fact, you frequently travel so fast that you tend to overlook much of what you set out to see along the way.

The large gasoline companies have prepared road maps that they distribute at no charge to help you get about the country. No matter which company prepares the road maps, they are all read in much the same manner. The *legend* is usually in the lower right-hand corner. This is simply a description of what the different colored lines and the dotted lines represent, how to find the distance between towns, a scale of miles, and whatever else the mapmaker thinks is important to know in order to read the map.

In the section of the legend on page 31, notice that the distance between two relatively large stars on a road is indicated by a numeral between these stars. Similarly, the distance between two somewhat smaller stars is shown by a numeral between these stars. If you examine the section of map on page 30, you will notice that there is a star at Route 80 on Route 19 and another one at Route 322 on Route 19.

Emphasize Problem 1, for it was designed to show the student the difference in the cost of gasoline consumption if the cars varied by even so little as 5 miles per gallon. Repeat the same problem where one car averages 10 miles to the gallon, while the other averages 25 miles.

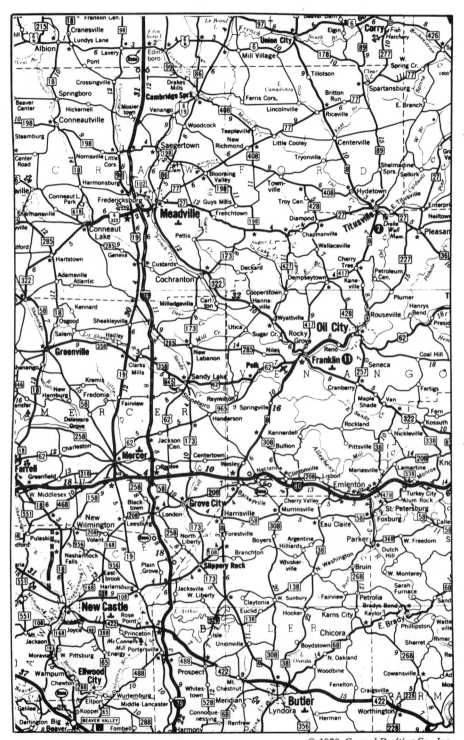

So large a map was deliberately included so that you could ask the students a great many questions pertaining to roads and distances between towns. As a word of caution, indicate to the students the neighborhood in which the road is located before asking the question.

About halfway between the two stars can be found the numeral 30. This indicates that the distance from Route 80 to Route 322 on Route 19 is approximately 30 miles. By looking closely at this same stretch of roadway, you can see a small star at Mercer and another one at Route 358. The small numeral 12 that appears midway between these two towns tells you that they are 12 miles apart. According to the legend, is Route 19 a state highway or a United States highway? How is it possible to tell the difference between the two? Why are some highways called state highways and others called United States highways?

Quite often, when you set out on a trip, you would like to have some idea of where you might stop each evening. Particularly during the summer months, if you haven't made room-reservations in the morning at the place where you expect to be that evening, you may well find yourself spending the night on the back seat of your car. Most hotel or motel chains are only too glad to call ahead for you each day to make reservations in one of their motels, and they'll do it free of charge. What is a chain of motels?

But knowing in the morning just where you are going to be that evening means knowing just how far you expect to travel that day. To determine this requires a little arithmetic. Consider a situation in which you are driving your car at approximately 40 miles per hour. In 2 hours you will have traveled 80 miles; in 3 hours, 120 miles. How far will you have traveled in 4 hours? Thus, you see that to determine the distance traveled, you need simply to multiply the speed at which the car is traveling by the number of hours it is driven. A car averaging 55 miles an hour for 6 hours will travel 330 miles during this period of

© 1970, General Drafting Co., Inc.

Ask each student to obtain a road map from a gasoline station. Compare the legends on the various maps. It might be interesting for them to know that in Europe they would have been charged the equivalent of anywhere from 25¢ to $1 for maps of poorer quality and of greater age.

time. In this situation, the 330 is simply the product of 55 and 6. You can generalize what you have just learned by expressing this by the following formula:

$$D = R \times T$$

where

D represents the distance traveled
R represents the average rate per hour
T represents the number of hours traveled

What is meant by the statement that a car is traveling at the rate of 40 miles per hour? Actually, no one can drive at the same speed for a full hour. You are either stopping for a red light, or slowing down for a detour, or speeding up to pass a truck, or, perhaps, just changing the position of your foot on the gas pedal because your leg is getting a bit tired. And so, if over the period of one hour your car has taken you on a route that is 40 miles long, then you say that the car has traveled at the rate of 40 miles per hour.

■ILLUSTRATION 1: On the first day of his trip to the West, Charles McCabe drove his car at an average rate of 60 miles per hour for a period of 7 hours. He stopped twice during the day to buy gas at 37.9¢ per gallon.
  a. How far did Charles travel that day?
  b. If his car averages 13 miles to the gallon of gasoline, determine, to the nearest gallon, how many gallons his car used that day.
  c. What was the approximate cost of the gasoline consumed that day?

●SOLUTION:
          (a) $D = R \times T$
                $= 60 \times 7$
                $= 420$ miles
          (b) Number of gallons consumed $= 420 \div 13$
                                        $= 32.3$, or 32 gallons
          (c) Cost of gasoline $= 32 \times 37.9$¢
                              $= 32 \times \$.379$
                              $= \$12.128$, or \$12.13

▼EXPLANATION: Determining the distance traveled in Part (a) is simply a matter of applying the distance formula. The product of the rate per hour and the number of hours equals the 420 miles, which is

To emphasize the meaning of an average speed of 40 miles per hour, ask the students to sit in the passenger's position in the front seat of a car and watch the speedometer. They will soon realize that the speed indicator is continuously varying, thus making a constant speed impossible.

the distance traveled. The more interesting feature is the solution to Part (b). Notice that the number of gallons is rounded off to the nearest gallon. This is usually done by most travelers, for when they say that their car averages 13 miles to the gallon of gasoline, they're not quite sure of this number. It may be 13.2 miles, or 13.3 miles, or 12.9, or 12.5, and they probably have rounded the number off to the nearest mile. Hence, to say that a car had used exactly 32.3 gallons of gas is inaccurate. Therefore, when the number of gallons is found, it seems that it would be wise to round the answer off to the nearest gallon. The answer is only approximate at best. Computing the answer to Part (c) needs no explanation, for you did quite a few of these problems in Unit 3.

EXERCISES   A

Use the map on page 30 when answering the questions in this set of problems.

1. Each of the following highways passes through Meadville. Which of them is a United States highway and which a state highway?
   a. 322 ___U. S.___   c. 86 ___State___   e. 27 ___State___
   b. 77 ___State___   d. 6 ___U. S.___   f. 19 ___U. S.___
2. When traveling along United States Highway 19 near Meadville, how far is it from United States Highway 322 to State Highway 285?   ___6___
3. When traveling along United States Highway 322 out of Franklin, how far is it to the point where United States Highway 322 meets United States Highway 19 just beyond Meadville?   ___32___
4. When traveling along State Highway 98, how far is it from United States Highway 322 to Lavery?   ___19___
5. When traveling along State Highway 8, how far is it from Titusville to Hydetown?   ___3___
6. When traveling along State Highway 108, how far is it from New Castle to Harlansburg?   ___9___
7. When traveling along United States Highway 322, how far is it from Meadville to Cochranton?   ___12___
8. When traveling along State Highway 8, how far is it from Oil City to Titusville?   ___15___
9. When traveling along State Highway 428, how far is it from Oil City to Diamond?   ___15___
10. When traveling along State Highway 77, how far is it from Meadville to Riceville?   ___21___

B

1. What is the distance traveled by an automobile under each of the following sets of conditions?

Rate	Number Of Hours	Distance In Miles		Rate	Number Of Hours	Distance In Miles
a. 40 mph*	5	200		f. 47 mph	6	282
b. 50 mph	3	150		g. 56 mph	9	504
c. 45 mph	2	90		h. 40 mph	2½	100
d. 65 mph	4	260		i. 60 mph	4½	270
e. 35 mph	7	245		j. 48 mph	5½	264

* Mph is the abbreviation for "miles per hour."

2. How many gallons of gasoline were used during each of the following trips? Find your answer to the nearest gallon.

	Distance Traveled	Miles Per Gallon	Number Of Gallons
a.	4,000 miles	9	444
b.	7,500 miles	11	682
c.	9,600 miles	16	600
d.	8,500 miles	18	472
e.	21,900 miles	17	1,288
f.	26,500 miles	24	1,104
g.	32,400 miles	19	1,705
h.	27,800 miles	28	993

3. How many gallons of gasoline were used during each of the following trips? Find your answer to the nearest gallon.

	Rate At Which Car Traveled	Number Of Hours	Distance In Miles	Miles Per Gallon	Number Of Gallons
a.	30 mph	5	150	8	19
b.	40 mph	4	160	15	11
c.	50 mph	7	350	12	29
d.	45 mph	9	405	25	16
e.	65 mph	6	390	14	28
f.	60 mph	2½	150	9	17
g.	56 mph	4½	252	16	16
h.	38 mph	5½	209	23	9

C

1. Last summer, Mr. and Mrs. Norris took a trip around the country. During a period of 8 weeks, they traveled 13,200 miles. They kept an accurate record of the gas they purchased and they found that their car averaged 14 miles to a gallon of gasoline.
   a. How many gallons of gasoline did they buy on the trip? Find your answer to the nearest gallon.   943
   b. If the average cost of the gasoline they purchased was 35.9¢ per gallon, what was the total cost of gasoline? $338.54

2. On the third day of his trip, Joe Green put in a full 9½ hours of driving on throughways. He averaged 62 miles per hour.
   a. How far did Joe travel that day?   <u>589 miles</u>
   b. If his car averages 18 miles to the gallon of gasoline, how many gallons did the car consume that day? Find your answer to the nearest gallon.   <u>33</u>
   c. If gas cost him 34.9¢ per gallon, what was the total cost of gasoline for that day?   <u>$11.52</u>

3. The Carters purchased a trailer which they towed around behind their car during their 6-week summer vacation. They found that they traveled about 5 hours each day at the average rate of 35 miles per hour.
   a. How far did they travel during the 6-week period?   <u>7,350 miles</u>
   b. With the trailer attached, the car averaged only 9 miles to the gallon of gasoline. How many gallons of gas did they purchase on the trip? Find your answer to the nearest gallon.   <u>817</u>
   c. If the trailer were not attached, the car would have averaged 14 miles to the gallon of gasoline. How many gallons of gas would the Carters have purchased if they did not have the trailer? Find your answer to the nearest gallon.   <u>525</u>
   d. The average cost of gasoline was 33.9¢ per gallon. How much would the Carters have saved on the cost of gasoline if they had not been towing a trailer?   <u>$98.99</u>

Unit 5: Determining Average Speed

In finding out at what speed you travel, you must refer back to the average speed per hour and the distance formula on page 32. It is this formula that involves the distance traveled during the day, the number of hours it took you to travel this distance, and the average hourly rate you were traveling.

In Unit 4, you knew the hourly speed and the number of hours the car was driven. By simply multiplying these two numbers, it was possible to find the distance traveled. Now, however, you know by looking at the mileage indicator on the car how far you have traveled during the day. By looking at your watch, you know how many hours it has taken you to travel that distance. What you would like to know, though, is how fast you were traveling, that is, your rate of speed. To show how the distance formula can be applied, first examine the following situation.

The product of 7 and 9 can be expressed by the following equality:

$$63 = 7 \times 9 \qquad (a)$$

Problem 3 provides the interesting feature of showing how the gasoline mileage drops drastically as soon as a trailer is attached to a car. Some of the students may be able to obtain similar information from the personal experiences of their parents.

You also know that if either 7 or 9 is divided into the 63, the quotient will be the other of the two numbers. Thus,

$$63 \div 7 = 9 \qquad \text{(b)}$$
$$\text{or: } 63 \div 9 = 7 \qquad \text{(c)}$$

Hence, you might say that in general the following is true:

> The Product of Two Numbers Principle: If the product of two numbers is divided by one of these numbers, the quotient will be the other of the numbers.

The principle is merely expressing in words what had been shown by the illustration above it. Which number represents the product in this illustration? Which number in (b) represents the quotient? Which number in (c) represents the quotient? If $912 = 24 \times 38$, then, without actually dividing, what is the quotient for $912 \div 24$? Also, what is the quotient for $912 \div 38$?

In what way, though, does all this apply to the distance formula? This formula is an expression showing the product of the two numbers:

$$D = R \times T$$

In the equality (a) above, 63 can be thought of as the replacement for D, while 7 is the replacement for R, and 9 is the replacement for T. With this in mind, if the number replacing D is divided by the number replacing T, then the quotient will have to be the replacement for R. Or, if the distance traveled is divided by the number of hours the car was driven, the quotient will be the average speed at which the car was moving. This can be expressed in terms of the following formula:

$$D \div T = R$$

or, as most people prefer to write it:

$$R = D \div T$$
$$\text{(Rate equals Distance divided by Time)}$$

■ILLUSTRATION 1: The Brombergs traveled 6½ hours last Sunday. When Mr. Bromberg checked the speedometer of his car, he found that he had covered 310 miles. To the nearest mile, at what average speed were they traveling?

●SOLUTION:

$$R = D \div T$$
$$= 310 \div 6\tfrac{1}{2}$$
$$= 310 \div 6.5$$
$$= 47.7 \text{ mph, or } 48 \text{ mph}$$

This is the first of several occasions on which the "Product of Two Numbers Principle" is used through the year. Emphasize it here through illustrations in addition to those shown, for you will want the students to recall it later in the work.

▼EXPLANATION: After replacing the Distance and Time in the formula by 310 and 6½, the problem becomes a simple division exercise. Notice, however, that the mixed number 6½ was changed to the decimal 6.5. Usually, it is a great deal easier to divide by a decimal than it is to divide by a mixed number.

While you are examining the speed at which you drive a car, it might be a good idea to spend a little time on this topic. The remark you hear about being able to "stop on a dime" is, of course, foolish. If you're traveling at 60 miles an hour, in the time it takes to get your foot off the gas pedal and onto the brake pedal, the car will have traveled 66 feet! This is before you even have a chance to apply the brakes! You will travel another 180 feet while you are doing this. Altogether, from the moment you start to react until the moment the car comes to a complete stop, you will have traveled at least 246 feet. This is longer than most city blocks, many of which are only a little more than 200 feet long.

The figures given above are based on ideal conditions. That is, they assume that the driver is alert and not drowsy from hours of driving; or has not turned his head to talk to someone in the back seat. Also, these figures are based on perfect road conditions—no ice, no snow, no oil slick, and no rain. Finally, they take for granted that the car's brakes are in good condition.

The time that it takes to react to the need for braking a car is called the *reaction time*. This is the time needed to remove your foot from the gas pedal and place it on the brake pedal. Studies have shown that it takes the normal person about ¾ of a second before he realizes that disaster is facing him. By using the distance formula, you could show that a car traveling at 10 miles per hour would travel 11 feet in this time. See if you can show that this is so. Another way of stating this is that for each mile per hour of speed that a car is traveling, it will travel just a little more than 1 foot during the reaction time of the driver.

■ILLUSTRATION 2: If a car is traveling at 55 miles per hour, approximately what distance will the car cover during the reaction time of the driver?

●SOLUTION:

Speed of car = 55 mph

Approximate distance traveled during reaction time = 55 feet

▼EXPLANATION: For each mile per hour of speed, the car will travel approximately 1 foot during the reaction time. Since the car is traveling at 55 miles per hour, the reaction distance of the car will amount to approximately 55 feet.

Material on this page and the next may be the most important topic discussed on this subject. Treat it seriously, for few drivers, particularly adolescents, give much thought to the distance a car travels, even under ideal conditions, from the moment the decision to stop is made until it actually stops.

The distance needed to bring a car to a complete stop once you have your foot on the brake pedal is a little more difficult to compute than the reaction distance. By making a careful check of a great many drivers in action, one study has shown that the braking distance can be found by using the following formula:

$$\text{Braking Distance} = (1/10 \times \text{Speed})^2 \times 5$$

Whenever a small 2 is placed above, and to the right of, a number, it means that this number should be multiplied by itself. Thus, 5^2 means 5×5; 8^2 means 8×8; 26^2 means 26×26, and so forth.

■ILLUSTRATION 3: A car is traveling at the rate of 60 miles per hour. What braking distance will the driver need in order to bring the car to a complete halt?

◾SOLUTION:

$$\begin{aligned}
\text{Braking Distance} &= (1/10 \times \text{Speed})^2 \times 5 \\
&= (1/10 \times 60)^2 \times 5 \\
&= (6)^2 \times 5 \\
&= 36 \times 5 \\
&= 180 \text{ feet}
\end{aligned}$$

◥EXPLANATION: After replacing the Speed with 60, the formula calls for finding 1/10 of 60, which is 6. Now you multiply 6 by itself and get a product of 36. The computation is then completed by multiplying 36 by 5, which equals 180. The 180 is the number of feet it will take a car traveling at 60 mph to stop, once the driver's foot is on the brake pedal.

Incidentally, the expression 6^2 is read as "6 square." Had it been 4^2, it would have been read as 4 square. How would you read 7^2? 9^2? 27^2? 3.5^2? What is the value of 7^2? 9^2?

■ILLUSTRATION 4: Mr. Kent is driving his car at 45 miles an hour. Approximately how far will the car travel from the moment he realizes that he must apply his brakes until the moment the car comes to rest?

◾SOLUTION:

$$\begin{aligned}
\text{Speed of car} &= 45 \text{ mph} \\
\text{Approximate reaction distance} &= 45 \text{ feet} \\
\text{Braking Distance} &= (1/10 \times 45)^2 \times 5 \\
&= (4.5)^2 \times 5 \\
&= 20.25 \times 5 \\
&= 101.25 \text{ feet, or } 101 \text{ feet} \\
\text{Total stopping distance} &= 45 \text{ feet} + 101 \text{ feet} \\
&= 146 \text{ feet}
\end{aligned}$$

To emphasize just how far the 146 feet is in Illustration 4, have two of the students measure off this distance on the road in front of the school and then report to the class what they have found. Then stress the fact that the car was traveling only 46 mph and weather conditions were good.

▼ EXPLANATION: The reaction distance was found as in Illustration 2, while the braking distance was found as in Illustration 3. The total stopping distance is merely the sum of these two distances.

EXERCISES   A

Do you recall how to find the answer in each of the following exercises? If not, you will probably want to refer to the pages indicated for help.

1. Change each of the following mixed numbers to a decimal (pages 575–576).
   a. 6½ _6.5_____   e. 9½ _9.5_____
   b. 7¼ _7.25_____   f. 7⅖ _7.4_____
   c. 8⅕ _8.2_____   g. 7³⁄₁₀ _7.3_____
   d. 5¾ _5.75_____   h. 4¼ _4.25_____

2. Find the quotient in each of the following exercises (pages 576–577).
   a. 217 ÷ 6.2 _35_____   e. 247 ÷ 9.5 ____26____
   b. 126 ÷ 8.4 _15_____   f. 693 ÷ 12.6 ____55____
   c. 162 ÷ 4.5 _36_____   g. 3,384 ÷ 14.4 _235_____
   d. 507 ÷ 7.8 _65_____   h. 5,969 ÷ 23.5 _254_____

3. Find the quotient in each of the following exercises. Before dividing, change each divisor to a decimal (pages 576–577).
   a. 297 ÷ 5½ _54_____   d. 957 ÷ 8¼ ____116____
   b. 540 ÷ 7½ _72_____   e. 1,700 ÷ 6¼ _272_____
   c. 798 ÷ 9½ _84_____   f. 1,786 ÷ 4¾ _376_____

4. Find the quotient to the nearest whole number in each of the following exercises. Before dividing, change each divisor to a decimal (pages 576–577).
   a. 247 ÷ 3½ _71_____   d. 526 ÷ 9¾ ____54____
   b. 325 ÷ 5½ _59_____   e. 475 ÷ 8¼ ____58____
   c. 481 ÷ 9½ _51_____   f. 583 ÷ 10½ ____56____

                              B

1. What is the approximate reaction distance needed to stop a car that is traveling at each of the following speeds?
   a. 60 mph ____60 ft.____   d. 85 mph ____85 ft.____
   b. 40 mph ____40 ft.____   e. 72 mph ____72 ft.____
   c. 35 mph ____35 ft.____   f. 63 mph ____63 ft.____

Another reminder about not writing in the empty columns might be in order here.

2. What is the average speed per hour at which each of the following cars is traveling? Find your answer to the nearest mile.

Distance Traveled	Time Spent In Traveling	Average Speed
a. 342 miles	7 hours	49 mph
b. 295 miles	6 hours	49 mph
c. 473 miles	8 hours	59 mph
d. 539 miles	10 hours	54 mph
e. 184 miles	2½ hours	74 mph
f. 197 miles	3½ hours	56 mph
g. 356 miles	6½ hours	55 mph
h. 471 miles	8½ hours	55 mph

3. What braking distance will a car travel if it is moving at each of the following speeds? Round off each answer to the nearest whole number.

Speed	Braking Distance	Speed	Braking Distance
a. 40 mph	80 ft.	f. 35 mph	61 ft.
b. 50 mph	125 ft.	g. 65 mph	211 ft.
c. 80 mph	320 ft.	h. 25 mph	31 ft.
d. 20 mph	20 ft.	i. 42 mph	88 ft.
e. 90 mph	405 ft.	j. 76 mph	289 ft.

4. Ten cars are traveling at the rates of speed indicated. What is the total distance each car will travel from the moment the driver realizes that he must apply the brakes until the moment the car stops? Round off each answer to the nearest whole number.

Speed	Reaction Distance	Braking Distance	Total Distance
a. 10 mph	10 ft.	5 ft.	15 ft.
b. 30 mph	30 ft.	45 ft.	75 ft.
c. 70 mph	70 ft.	245 ft.	315 ft.
d. 25 mph	25 ft.	31 ft.	56 ft.
e. 55 mph	55 ft.	151 ft.	206 ft.
f. 85 mph	85 ft.	361 ft.	446 ft.
g. 32 mph	32 ft.	51 ft.	83 ft.
h. 18 mph	18 ft.	16 ft.	34 ft.
i. 27 mph	27 ft.	36 ft.	63 ft.
j. 63 mph	63 ft.	198 ft.	261 ft.

C

1. On Wednesday of the first week of their trip, the Archers took 9 hours to travel 378 miles. The following day they drove for 5½ hours and covered 293 miles. At what average speed were they traveling during the two-day period?   46 mph

Use Problem 4 to compare the total distance needed for stopping a car that is traveling at different speeds. Point up the fact that a car traveling at 30 mph needs more than 3 times the distance to come to a stop than a car traveling at 10 mph.

2. On a wet road, the reaction time of the driver is the same as on a dry road. However, the braking distance is twice as great. A car is traveling on a wet road at the rate of 52 miles per hour.
   a. What is the reaction distance? <u> 52 ft. </u>
   b. What is the braking distance? <u> 270 ft. </u>
   c. What is the total distance a driver will need to stop a car that is traveling at 52 miles per hour on a wet road? <u> 322 ft. </u>

3. Mr. Straus is traveling at the rate of 41 miles per hour.
   a. What is the total distance he will need to stop the car if he is traveling on a dry road? <u> 125 ft. </u>
   b. What is the total distance he will need to stop the car if he is traveling on a wet road? <u> 209 ft. </u>
   c. How much more distance is needed if the road is wet than if it is dry? <u> 84 ft. </u>

4. How much more distance is needed to stop a car on a dry road if it is traveling at 60 miles per hour than if it is traveling at 30 miles per hour? <u> 165 ft. </u>

5. Mr. Trent is driving his car on a clear day at the rate of 60 miles per hour. He rounds a bend in the road and spots an accident pileup 200 feet ahead. Assuming he has good brakes, will he be able to stop in time if he does not swerve the car? <u> No. He needs 240 ft. </u> to stop and has only 200 ft.

Unit 6:   Paying for Traveling Costs

The cost of traveling by car over a period of several weeks usually comes to a fairly substantial sum. The amount needed for gasoline, lodging, and food begins to mount rapidly each day you are away from home. Hence, you can either take a large sum of money along with you hidden in a money belt at your waist, or locked in the car trunk. Neither place is really secure, for a thief knows all too well that these are the two places that you naturally use.

There are two principal ways in which people when traveling can solve their money worries. One of these is to obtain a credit card from a gasoline company. With one of these cards, it is possible to buy gas, oil, and even tires all over the country, at gasoline stations belonging to this company without using any money. In recent years, most gasoline companies have made arrangements with motel chains whereby the cost of lodging at any of the motels in that particular chain can be charged against the gasoline credit card. There is no charge to obtain the card, or to use the card. In this way, you can travel for a relatively long time with very little money. The only need for cash might be for meals or tourist trinkets.

Ask the students why the braking distance on a wet road should be at least twice the braking distance on a dry road. Some of the students may be able to relate experiences they have had when trying to stop their bicycles on a wet road.

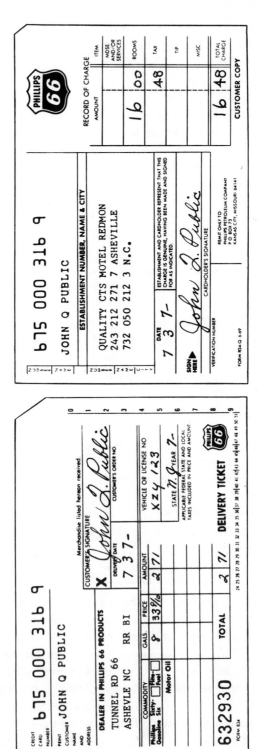

Have the students bring to class forms similar to those above. Compare the arrangement of information on the various forms.

Two credit card forms are shown at left. They are pretty much alike. The one on the left is the form used as a receipt after buying gas, while the one at the right is the receipt for motel lodging. Both of these forms are mailed to the credit office of the gasoline company. The company, in turn, pays both the owner of the gasoline station and the motel keeper. Then you are billed for these two items, as well as any others that you may have charged during the monthly period.

■ILLUSTRATION 1: The distance from Louisville, Kentucky, to Miami, Florida, is 1,126 miles. When William Sanford made the trip between the two cities, he drove only 6 hours each day at the average speed of 45 miles per hour. He charged the cost of lodging and gas against his credit card.

    a. How many hours did Mr. Sanford drive the car during the trip?
    b. If Mr. Sanford started early on the morning of the first day he traveled, how many nights of lodging did he have to pay for before arriving at Miami?
    c. If he paid $14 plus 5% tax for each night of lodging, what were the total motel costs while on the road?

● SOLUTION:

$$(a) \text{ Number of hours} = 1{,}126 \div 45$$
$$= 25.0 \text{ hours, or } 25 \text{ hours}$$
$$(b) \text{ Number of days on the road} = 25 \div 6$$
$$= 4.2$$
$$\text{Number of nights of lodging} = 4$$
$$(c) \text{ Cost of 4 nights lodging without tax} = 4 \times \$14$$
$$= \$56$$

$$\text{Tax on cost of lodging} = \$56 \times 5\%$$
$$= \$56 \times .05$$
$$= \$2.80$$
$$\text{Total motel costs} = \$56 + \$2.80$$
$$= \$58.80$$

▼EXPLANATION: To justify the use of division to find the answer to Part (a), consider the case of a person who was able to walk at the rate of 3 miles per hour. How long did it take him to walk 6 miles? How long did it take him to walk 21 miles? To find the answer of 2 hours in the first case, you had to divide the 6 by 3, while in the second case, you had to divide 21 by 3 to get the answer of 7 hours. In each situation, it was necessary to divide the distance the person traveled by the speed at which he traveled to determine the number of hours that it took him to cover the distance. In general, the formula can be stated as follows:

Inquire as to what a gasoline company would have to gain by issuing credit cards that can be used to pay for motel or hotel lodging.

$$T = D \div R$$
$$(\text{Time} = \text{Distance} \div \text{Rate})$$

This formula is just another form of the distance formula. When finding the answer to Part (a), you simply apply the same procedure as with the man walking at the rate of 3 miles per hour. Now, however, the numbers are somewhat larger.

In computing the answer to Part (b), you use the fact that Mr. Sanford's driving time is 25 hours. Since he drives only 6 hours each day, it will take him slightly more than 4 days to reach Miami. This means that he will have to seek lodging for 4 nights, and, on the 5th day, he will be on the road only a few hours before he reaches Miami.

For Part (c), you have to perform multiplication where one of the numbers is a percent number. Do you recall how to change a numeral in percent form to its equivalent decimal form? How was the numeral 5% changed to the decimal form .05 in the solution of this problem? It is not possible to multiply by a number that is expressed in its percent form. Change the percent form to the decimal form before multiplying.

■ ILLUSTRATION 2: Mr. Sanford's car in Illustration 1 averaged 14 miles to the gallon of gasoline.
  a. How many gallons of gasoline did he have to buy on the trip? Find your answer to the nearest gallon.
  b. If Mr. Sanford purchased gas at 34.9¢ per gallon, what was the total cost of gas that was charged against his credit card?
  c. What was the total bill sent to him by the gasoline company whose credit card he held? Consider both motel charges and gasoline charges.

● SOLUTION:
  (a) Number of gallons purchased $= 1126 \div 14$
                                  $= 80.4$ gallons, or 80 gallons
  (b) Cost of gasoline $= 80 \times \$.349$
                       $= \$27.92$
  (c) Total bill $= \$58.80 + \$27.92$
                 $= \$86.72$

▼ EXPLANATION: Parts (a) and (b) are done in exactly the same manner as the problems in the earlier units. The answer to Part (c) is found simply by adding the cost of the lodging found in Illustration 1 to the cost of the gasoline found in Part (b) of this problem.

The second method a traveler can use to protect his money is traveler's checks. They can be bought at almost any bank. American Express, First National City Bank of New York, and other companies sell them.

As stated above, the formula T = D ÷ R is but another form of the distance formula. Rather than use the explanation at the bottom of page 43 to obtain T = D ÷ R, you can resort to the "Product of two Numbers Principle" and obtain the same result.

For these two, the cost is exactly the same—10¢ for each $10 worth of checks. They can be purchased in amounts of $10, $20, $50, or $100.

All companies have designed checks that are pretty much the same. There are two places on the face of the check where you have to sign your name. At the time of purchase, you sign in one of these places in the presence of the bank teller. Then, when you have to cash a check, you again sign for the person to whom you are giving the check. In this way, the two signatures can be matched to check whether the same person signed them.

In the event that the checks are lost or stolen, you simply report the theft to the company from which you bought them. New checks will be issued immediately.

■ILLUSTRATION 3: Before the Johnson family set out on their trip, Mr. Johnson bought $850 worth of traveler's checks. How much did he have to pay for these checks?

●SOLUTION:

Cost of each $10 worth of traveler's checks = $.10
Number of $10 amounts in $850 = 850 ÷ 10
= 85
Cost of $850 worth of traveler's checks = 85 × $.10
= $8.50

▼EXPLANATION: Since the cost of traveler's checks is based on each $10 amount bought, it is necessary to find the number of $10 amounts in $850. To do this, divide 850 by 10 for a quotient of 85. Notice that the fastest way to divide a whole number ending in zeros by 10 is simply to cross off the end zero. To find the cost for 85 $10 amounts, at a cost of 10¢ for each $10 amount, simply multiply 85 by 10¢. Why was the 10¢ written in the form $.10?

■ILLUSTRATION 4: Mr. Johnson gave the waiter at the restaurant a $20 traveler's check in payment for the family's lunch. The total cost of the meal was $12.80. Mr. Johnson also tipped the waiter 15% of the bill. How much change from the $20 check did Mr. Johnson keep?

●SOLUTION:

Amount of tip = $12.80 × 15%
= $12.80 × .15
= $1.92
Total amount spent = $12.80 + $1.92
= $14.72
Change received from $20 check
= $20.00 − $14.72
= $5.28

Some travel agencies sell traveler's checks that are somewhat less expensive than those above. In addition, in recent years, during certain seasons, some banks sell traveler's checks at reduced prices. Have the students check to determine the cost.

▼ EXPLANATION: Before multiplying $12.80 by 15%, it is necessary to change the percent numeral to a decimal numeral. How is this done? After adding the cost of the meal to the amount of the tip, the total of $14.72 is subtracted from $20. Why was the $20 in the solution written in the form $20.00? Where does the decimal point belong in a numeral if none appears in that numeral?

EXERCISES   A

Do you recall how to find the answer in each of the following exercises? If not, you will probably want to refer to the pages indicated for help.

1. Change each of the following percent numerals to its equivalent decimal form (pages 583–584).

   a. 35% _____.35_____   e. 4% _____.04_____
   b. 45% _____.45_____   f. 7% _____.07_____
   c. 16.2% ___.162___   g. 3½% ___.035___
   d. 58.3% ___.583___   h. 5½% ___.055___

2. Find the product in each of the following exercises (pages 589–590).

   a. 20 × 15% ___3.00___   e. 137 × 5% __6.85__
   b. 65 × 24% __15.60__   f. 251 × 8% _20.08_
   c. 36 × 12% ___4.32___   g. 40 × 2½% _1.000_
   d. 125 × 36% _45.00_   h. 56 × 3½% _1.960_

3. Find the product in each of the following exercises. Round off each product to the nearest cent (pages 595–596).

   a. $6.84 × 13% __$ .89__   d. $29.67 × 5.6% __$1.66__
   b. $5.92 × 24% __$1.42__   e. $23.75 × 5½% __$1.31__
   c. $14.82 × 3.2% _$ .47_   f. $49.23 × 8½% __$4.18__

B

1. Find the state sales tax that had to be paid on each of the following motel bills.

Motel Bill	State Sales Tax Rate	Sales Tax		Motel Bill	State Sales Tax Rate	Sales Tax
a. $14.00	4%	$ .56		f. 12.50	3%	$ .38
b. 17.00	3%	.51		g. 9.50	4%	.38
c. 26.00	5%	1.30		h. 38.50	4.2%	1.62
d. 54.00	2%	1.08		i. 21.75	1½%	.33
e. 14.50	4%	.58		j. 53.25	3½%	1.86

When analyzing the solution of Illustration 3, page 45, with the students, have them divide several whole numbers ending in zero by 10. Ask them if the principle of crossing off the end zero will be true when the number is a decimal.

2. An average tip given to a waiter is 15% of the cost of the meal. How much will the waiter receive as his tip for serving meals where the costs are as follows?

	Cost of Meal	Waiter's Tip			Cost of Meal	Waiter's Tip
a.	$ 4.00	$ .60	e.		2.50	$ .38
b.	6.00	.90	f.		5.70	.86
c.	22.00	3.30	g.		12.30	1.85
d.	35.00	5.25	h.		26.85	4.03

3. How much will a person have to pay when purchasing traveler's checks for each of the following amounts?

	Total Value Of Traveler's Checks	Cost			Total Value Of Traveler's Checks	Cost
a.	$ 80	$ .80	e.		250	$ 2.50
b.	200	2.00	f.		780	7.80
c.	700	7.00	g.		4,500	45.00
d.	1,200	12.00	h.		1,450	14.50

4. How much change will a person receive after paying each of the following bills with traveler's checks?

	Amount Of Bill	Size Of Traveler's Check	Change
a.	$ 7.50	$ 10	$ 2.50
b.	6.95	10	3.05
c.	8.50	20	11.50
d.	12.45	20	7.55
e.	3.25	20	16.75
f.	16.50	50	33.50
g.	37.25	50	12.75
h.	29.30	100	70.70
i.	59.95	100	40.05
j.	64.19	100	35.81

5. How much change from each of the traveler's checks indicated will a person receive after having paid for the cost of the meal and tipped the waiter 15% of that cost?

	Cost Of Meal	Waiter's Tip	Total Cost	Size Of Traveler's Check	Change
a.	$ 3.00	$ .45	$ 3.45	$10	$ 6.55
b.	5.00	.75	5.75	10	4.25
c.	4.50	.68	5.18	10	4.82
d.	2.70	.41	3.11	10	6.89
e.	12.50	1.88	14.38	20	5.62
f.	17.50	2.63	20.13	50	29.87
g.	26.40	3.96	30.36	50	19.64
h.	37.60	5.64	43.24	50	6.76

The average tip a waiter receives varies from restaurant to restaurant and from area to area around the country. Discuss with the students what basic factors they would consider before giving the waiter a tip.

6. In each of the following exercises, a person spent the number of nights indicated at a motel. What will his total bill be for his stay at the motel? Include state tax.

	Cost Per Night	Number Of Nights	Total Motel Charge	State Tax Rate	State Tax	Total Charge, Including Tax
a.	$ 9.00	2	$ 18.00	2%	$ .36	$ 18.36
b.	12.00	4	48.00	3%	1.44	49.44
c.	16.00	5	80.00	4%	3.20	83.20
d.	10.50	2	21.00	5%	1.05	22.05
e.	12.50	6	75.00	3%	2.25	77.25
f.	16.50	10	165.00	4.2%	6.93	171.93
g.	18.50	8	148.00	1½%	2.22	150.22
h.	14.50	14	203.00	2½%	5.08	208.08

7. To the nearest hour, how many hours will it take to drive the distance shown in each of the following exercises?

	Total Distance Traveled	Average Rate	Number Of Hours
a.	240 miles	40 mph	6
b.	370 miles	50 mph	7
c.	420 miles	60 mph	7
d.	870 miles	50 mph	17
e.	625 miles	55 mph	11
f.	942 miles	55 mph	17
g.	673 miles	45 mph	15
h.	1,342 miles	65 mph	21
i.	1,075 miles	35 mph	31
j.	2,480 miles	62 mph	40

8. If a person travels the number of hours per day shown below, how many days will it take him to make the trip? Find your answer to the nearest day. Round off the number of hours needed to make the trip to the nearest hour.

	Total Trip Distance	Average Rate	Number Of Hours	Traveling Hours Each Day	Number Of Days
a.	940 miles	40 mph	24	4	6
b.	867 miles	30 mph	29	5	6
c.	1,250 miles	50 mph	25	5	5
d.	2,375 miles	60 mph	40	8	5
e.	3,295 miles	55 mph	60	7	9
f.	3,850 miles	65 mph	59	9	7

C

1. Janice Evans purchased 3 $100 traveler's checks, 8 $50 checks, 10 $20 checks, and 20 $10 checks. What was the total cost of these checks?

$11

2. Mr. Spellman and his family stayed 10 days at the shore in a motel at a cost of $21.50 per day. The state sales tax rate where they spent the vacation is 3%. In traveling to the motel and returning to their home, they had to purchase gas four times at a cost of $5.25, $4.90, $5.35, and $5.65. If both their motel and gasoline expenses were charged against their gasoline credit card, for what amount did the gasoline company bill them at the end of the month? $242.60

3. Bill Spivak used his car to travel from his home in Omaha, Nebraska, to the home of a friend in San Francisco, California—a distance of 1,725 miles. He planned to drive his car at an average rate of 60 miles per hour.

   a. How many hours should he plan on driving? Find your answer to the nearest hour.   29

   b. If he starts driving early in the morning and drives for eight hours each day, how many days will he be traveling? Find your answer to the nearest day.   4

   c. If he averages $9.50 per night as the cost for motel rooms and $7.75 per day for food, what will be the total cost for just these two expenses for the trip? In computing your answer, include the cost of food for the last day, but not the motel cost? Why?
   $ 59.50

Unit 7: Depreciation on a Car

Possibly the greatest expense connected with owning a car does not involve the use of the car at all. By merely buying a car and keeping it in a garage until the day you sell it costs quite a lot of money. Although you may never use the car, the value of the car decreases each year. Automobile manufacturers produce new models, and so the older ones are less in demand by buyers. Hence, the price of an older car decreases in spite of the fact that the car may be in excellent condition.

The decrease in the value of a car over a period of years is called the *depreciation* on the car. Thus, a car that had an original value of $4,000 and is worth only $1,000 at present is said to have *depreciated* $3,000 in value. To a small extent, the value of a car depends upon the condition the car is in, but its value is judged largely on how old the car is.

The greatest depreciation on a car occurs during the first year. In fact, if you buy a car from a dealer at 10:00 in the morning and sell it back to him at 11:00 that same morning, you would probably have to take a loss of several hundred dollars. A car for which you paid $5,400 one year will be worth only $3,200 the next—a loss of $2,200. However,

Automobile dealers usually subscribe to a monthly trade publication that gives them the wholesale value for that month of every standard car. Try to obtain a copy of this publication, for it will prove of interest to the students in this unit of the work.

the following year it can be sold for $1,300. During the second year it will have depreciated only $900 as against the $2,200 of the first year. By the time this car is six years old, it will be worth only $700. This is a drop in value of $4,700 over a six-year period, and yet, the car may have been driven very little. Within a year or two afterward, its value will be about $100. This is pretty much what its junk value will be. From that point on, it will retain that value until it is discarded.

Although depreciation varies from year to year, with the greatest depreciation occurring the first year, followed by smaller depreciation each succeeding year, car owners like to consider this depreciation as remaining the same. First they determine how much the car has decreased in value by subtracting the trade-in value from the amount they paid for the car. The total depreciation is then divided by the number of years they have owned the car. This technique of averaging is much the same as if you were finding your average weekly weight loss over a period of time. That is, if you lost 12 pounds in 4 weeks, you would say that, on the average, you had lost 3 pounds each week. Yet, usually, the greatest weight loss occurs the first week. After that first week, the amount lost is much less. In general you can state the following.

Average Annual Depreciation = Total Depreciation ÷ Number of Years

■ ILLUSTRATION: Mr. Elliott purchased a car for $3,600. Five years later, when purchasing a newer model, he received $600 as the trade-in value for the car. What was the average annual depreciation on the car?

● SOLUTION:

Total Depreciation = $3,600 — $600
$$= \$3,000$$

Average Annual Depreciation = Total Depreciation ÷ Number of Years
$$= \$3,000 \div 5$$
$$= \$600$$

▼ EXPLANATION: Finding the average annual depreciation depends upon knowing the total depreciation over the five-year period. To determine this total depreciation, subtract the trade-in value of the car from its original value. Then divide the total depreciation of $3,000 by the 5 years that Mr. Elliott owned the car. You then obtain an average annual depreciation of $600. Would you say that the car actually depreciated more than the $600 during the first year, or less than the $600? Was the depreciation during the fifth year actually more than the $600, or less than the $600?

The concept of "average annual depreciation" is of interest only to the car owner. It has no meaning to a dealer, for a car's value does not depreciate in this way. The owner, however, is often interested in knowing what the average annual cost of his car has been over the period he owned it.

EXERCISES   A

1. Find the average annual depreciation on each of the following cars. Find your answer to the nearest dollar.

	Total Depreciation	Number Of Years	Average Annual Depreciation
a.	$1,400	2	$ 700
b.	1,800	3	600
c.	2,300	4	575
d.	3,100	5	620
e.	1,750	3	583
f.	2,045	4	511
g.	2,726	5	545
h.	3,518	6	586

2. Find the average annual depreciation on each of the following cars. Find your answer to the nearest dollar.

	Value When New	Trade-in Value	Total Depreciation	Number Of Years	Average Annual Depreciation
a.	$3,400	$1,600	$ 1,800	4	$ 450
b.	1,800	400	1,400	5	280
c.	5,200	800	4,400	5	880
d.	4,700	2,375	2,325	3	775
e.	3,914	1,250	2,664	4	666
f.	2,827	425	2,402	6	400
g.	6,748	575	6,173	8	772
h.	2,436	50	2,386	9	265

B

1. George Bailey paid $3,128, plus a 3% state sales tax, when he purchased his new car. Three years later he sold the car for $1,465.
   a. How large was the sales tax that George had to pay? $93.84
   b. What was the total amount, including the tax, that he had to pay for the car? $3,221.84
   c. What was the total depreciation on the car? $1,756.84
   d. What was the average annual depreciation on the car? Find your answer to the nearest dollar. $586

2. Mr. Desmond purchased a new car for $3,650. If he trades in the car at the end of 3 years, he will receive $1,250 for it. However, if he keeps it for 5 years, its trade-in value will be $650.
   a. What is the average annual depreciation over the three-year period? $800
   b. What is the average annual depreciation over the five-year period? $600
   c. How much greater is the average annual depreciation over the three-year period than over the five-year period? $200

Unit 8:   Chapter Review and Test

In solving some of the following problems, you will have to refer to the tables in this chapter.

1. Find the total amount repaid, including the life-insurance premium, on each of the following new-car loans.

Loan	Period Of Debt	Total Repaid
a. $2,000	18 months	$ 2,210.58
b. 2,600	30 months	3,058.80
c. 1,560	24 months	1,779.84
d. 2,840	36 months	3,443.76

2. In the purchase of automobile insurance, what age factor will be used for the following driver?

Sex	Age	Married	Driver Training	Car Owner	Factor
Male	19	No	Yes	Yes	3.15

3. Find the cost of a 50/100 bodily-injury insurance policy to the purchaser. Use the following information.

Points	Sex	Age	Married	Territory	Cost
2	Male	26	Yes	05	$ 251

4. Tom Willard was at fault in an automobile accident. As a result of court action, the driver of the other car was granted $14,500 for the injuries he suffered. If Tom carried a 10/20 bodily-injury insurance policy, how much did the insurance company pay the injured party?
   $10,000

5. When Joe Fry applied his brakes on an icy road, his car slid into a tree. The extent of damage to the car came to $135. How much of the cost of repairing the car did the insurance company pay if Joe has purchased a $50-deductible collision-insurance policy?
   $85

6. What is the cost of 10.6 gallons of gasoline at 32.9¢ per gallon? Find your answer to the nearest penny.
   $3.49

7. How many gallons of gasoline were used on a trip of 12,500 miles if the car averaged 14 miles to the gallon of gasoline? Find your answer to the nearest gallon.
   893

   How much did the driver of this car have to pay for gasoline if the average price per gallon was 35.9¢? Find your answer to the nearest penny.
   $320.59

8. According to the road map on page 30, how far is it from Franklin to Interstate Highway 80 along State Highway 8?
   16 miles

The chapter review and test at the close of each chapter can be used for the purpose of either a review, a test, or, as in this case, for both. There are enough problems here so that some can be used for review purposes, while the remainder can be used for testing.

9. How far will a car travel in 8 hours if it is moving at an average speed of 55 miles per hour? <u>440 miles</u>

10. During a trip, Mr. Steinhoff's total driving time was 54 hours. He found that he had averaged 50 miles per hour.
   a. How many miles did Mr. Steinhoff travel? <u>2,700 miles</u>
   b. If the car averaged 18 miles to the gallon of gasoline, determine, to the nearest mile, how many gallons were consumed. <u>150</u>
   c. If the average price of gasoline was 33.9¢ per gallon, what was the total cost of the gasoline consumed? <u>$50.85</u>

11. At what average speed would a car be traveling if it covered a distance of 342 miles in 8 hours? Find your answer to the nearest mile. <u>43 mph</u>

12. A car is traveling at the rate of 70 miles per hour.
   a. What is the approximate reaction distance at this speed? <u>70 ft.</u>
   b. What is the approximate braking distance at this speed? <u>245 ft.</u>
   c. How far will the car travel before coming to a complete stop after the driver has seen the need to apply his brakes? <u>315 ft.</u>

13. What is the cost of $350 worth of traveler's checks? <u>$3.50</u>

14. Mr. Clemens and his wife stayed at a motel for a period of 5 nights at a cost of $17.50 per night.
   a. What was the cost of lodging for the 5 nights? <u>$87.50</u>
   b. If the state tax rate was 4%, how much tax did Mr. Clemens have to pay? <u>$3.50</u>
   c. What was the total bill for these 5 nights? <u>$91.00</u>

15. After keeping his car for three years, Walter Adkins sold it for $1,850. He had paid $3,475 for the car.
   a. What was the total depreciation on the car? <u>$1,625</u>
   b. What was the average annual depreciation on the car? Compute your answer to the nearest dollar. <u>$542</u>

Notice that the problems above are pretty much the same as those that appear in the chapter. When testing or reviewing with the consumer arithmetic student, it is not advisable to introduce ideas that differ from the topic under review.

CHAPTER 2

COMMERCIAL TRANSPORTATION

There are a great number of people who prefer not to own a car. If you happen to live in a large city, owning a car can be quite a problem. All too often there are no garages in your neighborhood. And if there are, the rents are very high. But if you do not have a garage, you have the problem of trying to find a parking place. You cruise the streets, looking for a spot that seldom exists, or that is too small for your car. Time is consumed and tempers are rubbed raw.

The daily battle for parking space, plus the high cost of automobile insurance in the city, inevitably forces more people to sell their cars and take to taxis, buses, or subways. On those occasions when you would like to have a car, you are obliged to rent one. In this chapter, you will take a look at the cost of traveling by commercial transportation means other than those of your own car.

To create interest, have the students make a survey of the cost of public parking in the business area of the community. Also, ask them to inquire as to the monthly rental of a garage or parking space in the immediate vicinity of where they live.

Unit 1:   Renting a Car

The cost of renting a car varies from city to city, depending on the demand for rented cars in a particular area. Some rental agencies claim they are less expensive than others. On the whole, though, the charges of all agencies in the same area usually are pretty much the same. When a difference in price exists, it's likely that you are either getting a cheaper car, or an older car, or that the service is not quite so good. Often you will find that the cheaper rates include a hidden cost that is overlooked. For instance, with the larger rental agencies which have outlets throughout the country, it is possible to rent a car in one city and drop it off in another. However, the smaller companies do not offer this service. It is necessary, therefore, to return the car to the place from which it was rented. Not giving this service, and having the agency send a man to pick up the car, runs up the charge.

The following two tables show the daily and weekly charges for two rental-car systems. The first of these agencies is probably the largest in

Company A Rental Rates

MAKE & TYPE OF CAR	DAILY (24 Hr.)	WEEKLY
INTERMEDIATE CARS		
(Ford Fairlane and similar makes)		
Sedan	$12. + 11¢ per mi.	$60. + 11¢ per mi.
STANDARD CARS		
(Ford Galaxie, Mustang and similar makes)		
Sedan	$12. + 12¢ per mi.	$60. + 12¢ per mi.
Convertible	$14. + 14¢ per mi.	$70. + 14¢ per mi.
Station Wagon	$14. + 14¢ per mi.	$70. + 14¢ per mi.
MEDIUM CARS		
(Mercury Cougar and similar makes)		
Sedan	$13. + 13¢ per mi.	$65. + 13¢ per mi.
Convertible	$15. + 15¢ per mi.	$75. + 15¢ per mi.

Company B Rental Rates

MAKE	DAILY	WEEKLY (7 Days)	HOURLY
Station Wagons Convertibles Sports Cars	$8.00 per 24-hour day plus 8¢ per mile	$50.00 plus 8¢ per mile	$1.50 plus 8¢ per mile
Full-Size Cars	$7.00 per 24-hour day plus 7¢ per mile	$45.00 plus 7¢ per mile	$1.50 plus 7¢ per mile
Compact Cars	$6.00 per 24-hour day plus 6¢ per mile	$40.00 plus 6¢ per mile	$1.50 plus 6¢ per mile

As pointed out above, not only does cost of car rental vary from company to company, but it also varies within a single company for different areas of the country. Have several students pick up "throw-aways" at a rental agency so that comparison can be made between the rates above with those of a local company.

the world, while the second advertises itself as a low-budget agency. At first glance, it would appear that the rates of Company B are a great deal lower than those of Company A. However, the lower rates do not include the cost of gas, while the higher ones do. Also, Company A provides an air-conditioner with the car at no extra charge, while Company B increases the charge by $2.00 per day and 2¢ per mile when this equipment is included.

There is still another point that shouldn't be overlooked. Although both companies provide you with automobile insurance protection at no extra cost, in the case of Company A, the coverage is clearly spelled out as $100,000–$300,000 public liability, $25,000 property damage, and $100-deductible collision insurance. In the case of Company B, examination of its information folder for this information is a waste of time, for it's nowhere to be found. It would seem that the coverage is a great deal less than with Company A. And yet, in spite of all this, there is no question but that Company B rates are much lower if you return the car to the agency from which it was rented. What is meant by public liability coverage of $100,000–$300,000? In what way are you covered by a $25,000 property-damage policy?

■ ILLUSTRATION 1: Mr. Morrell rented a station wagon from Company A for a single day. If he drove the car for 90 miles, what was the rental charge?

● SOLUTION:

$$\text{Base charge for the day} = \$14$$
$$\text{Cost per mile} = 14¢, \text{ or } \$.14$$
$$\text{Cost for 90 miles} = 90 \times \$.14$$
$$= \$12.60$$
$$\text{Total cost for the day} = \$14 + \$12.60$$
$$= \$26.60$$

▼ EXPLANATION: In addition to the $14 base charge on a station wagon, Mr. Morrell had to pay 14¢ for each mile he drove the car. Since he covered 90 miles during the day, his additional charge was 90 times 14¢, or $12.60. Why was the 14¢ in the solution written as $.14? By adding the base charge to the mileage cost, the total cost is found to be $26.60.

■ ILLUSTRATION 2: Rather than rent the station wagon from Company A, Mr. Morrell of the previous illustration rented it from Company B.

  a. What was the total cost in rental alone?
  b. If the station wagon averaged 10 miles to the gallon of gasoline, how many gallons of gasoline did Mr. Morrell use that day?

In computation for Illustration 1, make certain that students rewrite 14¢ in its equivalent form of $.14. Try to have students justify why it is necessary to convert the number from "cents" to its equivalent "dollar" form. They must realize that "base" and "mileage" charges must be in the same unit.

c. If the price of the gasoline purchased was 35.9¢, how much did Mr. Morrell have to pay for the gasoline he used?

d. What was the total cost of using the car that day?

e. How much would Mr. Morrell have saved by renting the car from Company B rather than Company A?

● SOLUTION:

(a) Base charge for the day = $8.00

Cost per mile = 8¢, or $.08

Cost for 90 miles = 90 × $.08

= $7.20

Total cost for rental = $8.00 + $7.20

= $15.20

(b) Number of gallons of gasoline used = 90 ÷ 10

= 9

(c) Cost of gasoline = 9 × $.359

= $3.231, or $3.23

(d) Cost for use of car = $15.20 + $3.23

= $18.43

(e) Saving on Company B car over Company A car = $26.60 − $18.43

= $8.17

▼ EXPLANATION: The rental rates charged by Company B do not include the cost of gasoline. Therefore, in Part (b), it is necessary to determine how many gallons had been used. By knowing the number of gallons of gasoline used, it is possible to find the cost of the gasoline. The combined rental of $15.20, plus the cost of the gasoline of $3.23, comes to $18.43, which is still $8.17 less than the charge of $26.60 made by Company A.

EXERCISES   A

1. Find the cost of renting each of the cars below for a day. Use the rate table for Company A. Copy the chart on your paper. **Do not write in this book.**

Type of Car	Base Rate	Number Of Miles	Cost Per Mile	Mileage Cost	Total Cost
a. Intermediate Sedan	$ 12	20	$ .11	$ 2.20	$ 14.20
b. Standard Convertible	14	40	.14	5.60	19.60
c. Standard Sedan	12	50	.12	6.00	18.00
d. Medium Sedan	13	30	.13	3.90	16.90
e. Medium Convertible	15	75	.15	11.25	26.25
f. Standard Convertible	14	93	.14	13.02	27.02

When examining the saving of $8.17, the students should realize that the driver of a Company B car may not have been covered by insurance. It is very possible that the cost of this coverage would consume some of the $8.17 saving.

2. Find the cost of renting each of the cars below for a week. Use the rate table for Company A.

Type of Car	Base Rate	Number Of Miles	Cost Per Mile	Mileage Cost	Total Cost
a. Standard Sedan	$ 60	200	$ .12	$ 24.00	$ 84.00
b. Intermediate Sedan	60	300	.11	33.00	93.00
c. Medium Convertible	75	500	.15	75.00	150.00
d. Standard Station Wagon	70	850	.14	119.00	189.00
e. Medium Sedan	65	743	.13	96.59	161.59

3. Find the cost of renting each of the cars below for a day. Do not include the cost of gasoline. Use the rate table for Company B.

Type of Car	Base Rate	Number Of Miles	Cost Per Mile	Mileage Cost	Total Cost
a. Station Wagon	$ 8.00	35	$ .08	$ 2.80	$ 10.80
b. Full-Size Car	7.00	67	.07	4.69	11.69
c. Compact Car	6.00	92	.06	5.52	11.52

4. Find the total cost of renting each of the cars below for a week. The cost of gasoline is to be included at the price shown. Round off the cost of gasoline to the nearest cent. Use the rate table for Company B.

Type of Car	Base Rate	Number Of Miles	Cost Per Mile	Mileage Cost	Number Of Gallons	Cost Per Gallon	Gasoline Cost	Total Cost
a. Sports Car	$ 50	300	$ .08	$ 24.00	25	34.9¢	$ 8.73	$ 82.73
b. Compact Car	40	500	.06	30.00	23	32.9¢	7.57	77.57
c. Full-Size Car	45	275	.07	19.25	28	35.9¢	10.05	74.30
d. Convertible	50	934	.08	74.72	86	37.9¢	32.59	157.31
e. Full-Size Car	45	1,258	.07	88.06	94	36.9¢	34.69	167.75

5. A person rented a sports car from Company B for the number of days shown below. Find the cost of this rental. Include gasoline.

	Number Of Days	Total Base Cost	Number Of Miles	Mileage Cost	Miles Per Gallon	Number Of Gallons	Cost Per Gallon	Gasoline Cost	Total Cost
a.	2	$ 16	150	$ 12.00	15	10	32¢	$ 3.20	$ 31.20
b.	3	24	70	5.60	14	5	36¢	1.80	31.40
c.	4	32	156	12.48	12	13	37¢	4.81	49.29
d.	5	40	338	27.04	13	26	35¢	9.10	76.14

B

1. Company A advertises a weekly vacation rental plan whereby, for $88, a person receives a Ford Galaxie sedan and a full tank of gasoline. There is no mileage charge for the first 500 miles.

   a. The tank of this car holds 20 gallons of gasoline. How far can a person travel on the full tank of gasoline if the car averages 15 miles to the gallon?   300 miles

Notice that each of the exercises above is carefully outlined so that, as the student supplies the fill-in for each column as he moves from left to right, he is inevitably led to the answer he is called upon to determine.

b. If a person drives the 500 miles during the week, to the nearest gallon, how many gallons of gasoline will he have to buy?
<u>13</u>

c. At 35.9¢ per gallon, what will the total cost be of the gasoline purchased?
<u>$4.67</u>

d. What will be the total cost for use of the car during the week? Include the cost of the gasoline.
<u>$92.67</u>

2. If the car in Problem 1 is driven for more than 500 miles, then the person must pay 7¢ per mile, in addition to buying his own gas. A person drove the car 1,000 miles.

a. How much will he have to pay the company for the last 500 miles that he drove the car?
<u>$35</u>

b. What was the total rental charge for the week? Do not include the cost of the gasoline.
<u>$123</u>

3. A large car-rental agency advertises a "7-Day Vacation Plan" for $99. Included with the car is a full tank of gasoline. No charge is made for mileage on the first 1,000 miles.

a. How much rental charge will a person have to pay if he uses the car for exactly 1,000 miles?
<u>$99</u>

b. Considering your answer to Part (b) of Problem 2, how much will a person save by renting a car from this company rather than from Company A if he drives the car for 1,000 miles? <u>$24</u>

4. A person rented a Ford Galaxie sedan from Company A for a period of one week under its normal weekly rate, shown in the table on page 55. He drove the car for 500 miles.

a. What base cost did he have to pay?   <u>$60</u>
b. What was his mileage charge?   <u>$60</u>
c. What was the total charge for the week?   <u>$120</u>
d. Considering your answer to Part (d) of Problem 1, how much could the person have saved if he had rented the car under the vacation plan rather than under the normal rates? (Remember that, under the normal rates, the company pays for the gasoline.)
<u>$27.33</u>

Unit 2: Traveling by Bus

PART 1

When you travel around the city by bus, you usually simply go out to the corner and, within a reasonable time, a bus comes along to pick you up. If you happen to live at the end of a bus line, the chances are that you have some idea that a bus leaves the bus station at certain

The problems above were designed to point up the saving of a long-term special rental over rentals covering shorter periods of time. Fundamentally, a primary objective of this course is to teach the student how to make comparisons between alternatives where consumer costs are at stake.

times during the day. If all goes well, it will pass your corner a few
moments afterward. Actually, all means of public transportation, including buses, must travel on certain approved time schedules. Sometimes, though, on subzero, snowy days you wonder if buses are running at all!

Most bus schedules look much like the one shown here. Notice that
the table is headed by the word WEEKDAYS. This implies that other
schedules are followed on Saturdays, Sundays, and holidays. Will the
buses run more frequently or less frequently on weekends than they
do on weekdays? How do you explain your answer?

The half of the table below gives the time schedule for buses starting
at such points as Butler, Pompton Lakes, and Mountain View and
traveling to Newark. The half of the table on page 61 shows the time

Route Number 114

WEEKDAYS

TO NEWARK

BUTLER Bus Station	POMPTON LAKES Bus Station	MOUNTAIN VIEW Center	SINGAC Four Corners	LITTLE FALLS Main & Center Sts.	CEDAR GROVE Bowden Road	MONTCLAIR D.L. & W. Station	BLOOMFIELD Bloomfield Center	NEWARK P.R.R. Station
—	5.32	5.39	5.44	5.47	5.54	6.05	6.10	6.29
—	—	6.05	6.10	6.13	6.20	6.31	6.36	6.55
—	6.10	6.30	6.35	—	—	6.48	6.53	7.13
—	—	—	6.35	6.38	6.47	7.01	7.07	7.34
—	—	6.52	6.57	7.00	7.09	7.23	7.29	7.51
6.20	6.40	7.00	7.05	—	—	7.23	7.29	7.49
—	—	—	7.12	7.15	7.24	7.38	7.44	8.04
—	—	7.20	7.25	7.28	7.37	7.51	7.57	8.17
—	7.03	7.25	7.30	—	—	7.48	7.54	8.14
—	—	7.35	7.40	7.43	7.52	8.06	8.12	8.32
—	—	—	8.00	8.03	8.12	8.26	8.32	8.59
7.30	7.50	8.12	8.17	8.20	8.29	8.43	8.49	9.09
8.10	8.25	8.47	8.52	8.55	9.04	9.17	9.22	9.42
—	9.00	9.22	9.27	9.30	9.39	9.52	9.57	10.17
—	10.00	10.22	10.27	10.30	10.39	10.52	10.57	11.17
—	11.00	11.22	11.27	11.30	11.39	11.52	11.57	12.17
11.40	12.00	12.22	12.27	12.30	12.39	12.52	12.57	1.17
—	1.00	1.22	1.27	1.30	1.39	1.52	1.57	2.17
—	1.55	2.17	2.22	2.25	2.34	2.47	2.52	3.12
—	—	—	—	2.54	3.03	3.16	3.22	3.49
2.50	3.10	3.32	3.37	3.40	3.49	4.02	4.08	4.35
—	—	—	—	4.10	4.19	4.32	4.38	5.05
—	4.20	4.42	4.47	4.50	4.59	5.12	5.18	5.45
—	—	—	—	5.00	5.09	5.22	—	—
4.30	5.15	5.35	5.40	5.43	5.49	6.00	6.04	6.23
—	6.45	7.05	7.10	7.13	7.19	7.30	7.34	7.53
8.13	8.25	8.45	8.50	8.53	8.59	9.10	9.14	9.33
—	—	—	—	12.00	12.06	12.17	—	—

It might be well to distribute 4" x 6" cards to the students and insist that they keep them in
their textbooks for use as a guide to reading this and other tables that appear in the text. To
make this course as realistic and practical as possible, the students will be called upon to work
with many long tables.

schedule for buses traveling in the opposite direction, that is, from Newark to Mountain View, Pompton Lakes, and Butler. Do all the buses that leave Newark on this route take passengers to Butler? If not, how many of the buses that leave Newark during the day take passengers to Butler? How many buses on Route Number 114 Leave Newark each week-day?

■ ILLUSTRATION 1: At what time does the bus that leaves Butler at 7:30 A.M. arrive in Newark?

● SOLUTION:

Time of leaving Butler = 7:30 A.M.

Time of arrival in Newark = 9:09 A.M.

▼ EXPLANATION: The numbers in lightface type in the table indicate the time between 12:00 midnight and 12:00 noon. Those numbers

Route Number 114

WEEKDAYS

				TO BUTLER				
NEWARK P.R.R. Station	BLOOMFIELD Bloomfield Center	MONTCLAIR D.L. & W. Station	CEDAR GROVE Bowden Road	LITTLE FALLS Main & Center Sts.	SINGAC Four Corners	MOUNTAIN VIEW Center	POMPTON LAKES Bus Station	BUTLER Bus Station
6.20	—	—	—	7.05	—	—	—	—
6.35	6.56	7.00	7.11	7.18	7.21	7.26	7.55	8.07
6.59	7.23	7.28	7.42	7.50	7.53	7.58	8.19	—
7.30	7.54	7.59	8.13	8.21	8.24	8.29	8.50	—
8.00	8.24	8.29	8.43	8.51	—	—	—	—
8.30	8.54	8.59	9.13	9.21	9.24	9.29	9.50	—
9.30	9.54	9.59	10.13	10.21	10.24	10.29	10.50	11.29
10.25	10.49	10.54	11.08	11.16	11.19	11.24	11.45	—
11.25	11.49	11.54	12.08	12.16	12.19	12.24	12.45	—
12.25	12.49	12.54	1.08	1.16	1.19	1.24	1.45	2.17
1.25	1.49	1.54	2.08	2.16	2.19	2.24	2.45	—
2.25	2.49	2.54	3.08	3.16	3.19	3.24	3.45	4.19
2.57	3.26	3.32	3.46	3.55	—	—	—	—
3.25	3.54	4.00	4.15	4.24	4.27	4.32	4.53	5.14
4.00	4.29	4.35	4.49	4.58	—	—	—	—
4.15	4.41	4.47	5.01	5.10	5.13	5.18	5.39	5.59
4.33	4.59	5.05	5.19	5.28	5.31	5.36	—	—
4.45	5.11	5.17	5.31	5.40	5.43	5.48	—	—
4.50	5.16	5.22	—	—	5.39	5.44	6.05	—
5.00	5.26	5.32	5.46	5.55	5.58	6.03	—	—
5.15	5.41	5.47	6.01	6.10	6.13	6.18	—	—
5.20	5.46	5.52	—	—	6.09	6.14	6.35	—
5.40	6.08	6.13	6.27	6.36	6.39	6.44	—	—
6.00	6.23	6.29	6.41	6.49	6.52	6.57	7.18	—
6.35	6.54	6.58	7.08	7.13	7.16	7.21	7.41	7.53
8.05	8.24	8.28	8.38	8.43	8.46	8.51	9.11	9.23
9.35	9.54	9.58	10.08	10.13	10.16	10.21	10.41	—
11.13	11.32	11.36	11.46	11.51	—	—	—	—
12.25	12.44	12.48	12.58	1.03	1.06	1.10	—	—

Students frequently have difficulty recalling what part of the day is represented by the different sets of type. Try having them associate the light type with the "light," or early hours, and the dark with the "dark," or evening hours. This seems to work for some students.

in the dark, or boldface, type indicate the time of day between 12:00 noon and 12:00 midnight. The former hours are usually abbreviated by the letters A.M. and the latter by the letters P.M. What words do these letters represent? In solving this problem, run your finger down the column headed by Butler until you come to the numeral 7.30. This numeral is but a short way of writing 7:30 A.M. All the numerals in this column represent the various hours at which buses leave Butler for Newark. There are only 7 numerals in this column. This implies that there are only 7 trips that buses on Route Number 114 make from Butler to Newark each day. After placing the edge of a piece of paper along the row containing the numeral 7.30, run your finger across the table until it comes to the column headed by Newark. The numeral 9.09, at which your finger comes to rest, represents the time at which the 7:30 A.M. Butler bus arrives in Newark.

■ILLUSTRATION 2: How long does it take the bus that leaves Butler at 7:30 A.M. to make the trip to Newark?

●SOLUTION:
      Time of leaving Butler = 7:30, or 7 hours and 30 minutes
      Time of arrival in Newark = 9:09, or 9 hours and 9 minutes
      Traveling time = 9 hours and 9 minutes − 7 hours and 30 minutes
                          = 8 hours and 69 minutes − 7 hours and 30 minutes
                          = 1 hour and 39 minutes

▼EXPLANATION: In finding the number of hours from 7:30 to 9:09, it is necessary to subtract the first number from the second. To do this, you must think of 7:30 in terms of its actual meaning of 7 hours and 30 minutes. Similarly, 9:09 means 9 hours and 9 minutes. At this point, it is best that this subtraction problem be written vertically, for then it is far easier to understand and far easier to complete.

9 hours and 9 minutes
− 7 hours and 30 minutes

Since it is impossible to subtract 30 minutes from 9 minutes, you have to rewrite the 9 hours as 8 hours and 1 hour. The purpose of doing this is to change the 1 hour into 60 minutes. Then, by combining this with the 9 minutes, you end up with a number from which 30 minutes can be subtracted. Thus:

      9 hours and 9 minutes = 8 hours and 1 hour and 9 minutes
                          = 8 hours and 60 minutes and 9 minutes
                          = 8 hours and 69 minutes

With this information, it is possible to complete the solution.

Before discussing Illustration 2 with the students, you may want to spend some time showing that a time such as 8:10 is the equivalent of 7:70. It may even be wise to do orally several points of Exercise 2, page 64, at this point.

$$8 \text{ hours and } 69 \text{ minutes}$$
$$- 7 \text{ hours and } 30 \text{ minutes}$$
$$1 \text{ hour and } 39 \text{ minutes}$$

■ ILLUSTRATION 3: How long does it take the 12:25 P.M. bus out of Newark to make the trip to Butler?

● SOLUTION:

Time of leaving Newark = 12:25
Time of arrival in Butler = 2:17 P.M., or 14:17
Traveling time = 14 hours 17 minutes — 12 hours 25 minutes
= 13 hours 77 minutes — 12 hours 25 minutes
= 1 hour 52 minutes

▼ EXPLANATION: In order to understand the computation in the solution above, it is necessary to realize that a time such as 1:00 P.M. is much later than a time of 8:00 A.M. of the same day. In fact, it is 5 hours later. The simplest way of finding the time lapse of 5 hours is to consider midnight as being the 0 hour of any day. Under this consideration, 8:00 would be 8 hours after the 0 hour of the day, and, in the same way, 1:00 P.M. would be 13 hours after the 0 hour. How was the 13 arrived at? Then, by subtracting the 8 hours from the 13 hours, you find that the time elapsed from 8:00 A.M. to 1:00 P.M. is 5 hours. Actually, by using this method of writing time, it is not necessary to write A.M. or P.M. after the hour. When a person said that the time was 8:20, everyone would know that this implied that it was 8 hours and 20 minutes after the 0 hour, which is midnight. Similarly, at 3:40 P.M., it would only be necessary to say that the time was 15:40 and omit mention of the P.M. Here, again, people would understand that 15 hours and 40 minutes had elapsed since the 0 hour. Hence, changing from P.M. time as you know it to be to time recorded by this method, can be done simply by adding 12 to the number of hours (unless the time happens to be between 12:00 noon and 1:00 P.M.) Why? How would you write 7:00 P.M. under this method of recording time? How would you write 4:15 P.M.? By this new method, would there be any change in the way you are presently writing A.M. time?

Now to return to the solution in Illustration 3. Notice that the time of 2:17 P.M. was rewritten as 14:17. How was the 14:17 arrived at? This change was made in order to be able to subtract the 12 hours and 25 minutes from the 14 hours and 17 minutes. Had the time been left as 2:17 P.M., it would have been much more difficult to find the time elapsed from 12:25 P.M. to 2:17 P.M.

If the bus had left Newark at 1:12 P.M. and had arrived at Butler at 3:09 P.M., would it be necessary to rewrite both of these hours under

Some of your students may be familiar with the 24-hour clock used in the armed services, which is basically the concept behind the explanation above. If no one is acquainted with the 24-hour clock, a report on it can be assigned for extra credit.

the new method of recording time in order to determine how long the trip was? Under what conditions only will it be necessary to rewrite the hours in order to determine the time lapse from one hour to another?

EXERCISES   **A**

1. When you consider midnight as the 0 hour of the day, how would you rewrite each of the following hours without using the letters A.M. or P.M.?

	Time Normal Recording	Time New Recording		Time Normal Recording	Time New Recording
a.	2:00 A.M.	2:00	i.	4:00 P.M.	16:00
b.	5:00 A.M.	5:00	j.	3:00 P.M.	15:00
c.	3:30 A.M.	3:30	k.	1:20 P.M.	13:20
d.	9:45 A.M.	9:45	l.	2:15 P.M.	14:15
e.	10:30 A.M.	10:30	m.	8:40 P.M.	20:40
f.	11:20 A.M.	11:20	n.	10:15 P.M.	22:15
g.	12:01 A.M.	0:01	o.	12:20 P.M.	12:20
h.	12:57 A.M.	0:57	p.	12:20 A.M.	0:20

2. Rewrite the following hours and minutes in terms of the number of hours and minutes indicated. The first exercise is completed for you.

	Write this		As this	
a.	5 hr. 20 min. =	4 hr.	80	min.
b.	7 hr. 20 min. =	6 hr.	80	min.
c.	6 hr. 0 min. =	5 hr.	60	min.
d.	10 hr. 15 min. =	9 hr.	75	min.
e.	4 hr. 5 min. =	3 hr.	65	min.
f.	11 hr. 23 min. =	10 hr.	83	min.
g.	17 hr. 0 min. =	16 hr.	60	min.
h.	15 hr. 36 min. =	14 hr.	96	min.
i.	14 hr. 12 min. =	13 hr.	72	min.
j.	22 hr. 3 min. =	21 hr.	63	min.
k.	21 hr. 9 min. =	20 hr.	69	min.
l.	17 hr. 1 min. =	16 hr.	61	min.

3. Find the difference in each of the following exercises.

a.   7 hr.   25 min.
     − 4 hr.   12 min.
     _____
       3 hr.   13 min.

b.   5 hr.   47 min.
     − 2 hr.   24 min.
     _____
       3 hr.   23 min.

c.   18 hr.   31 min.
     − 12 hr.   19 min.
     _____
        6 hr.   12 min.

d.   22 hr.   43 min.
     − 17 hr.   27 min.
     _____
        5 hr.   16 min.

You might want to discuss with the students why people consider midnight the 0 hour of the day rather than 12:00 noon as the 0 hour. Ask the brighter students to consider how the answers to Exercise 1 would be altered in the event 12:00 noon were considered as the 0 hour.

e.   21 hr. 55 min.   i.   17 hr. 10 min.
   —   9 hr. 38 min.   — 10 hr. 50 min.
   _____   _____
      12 hr. 17 min.   6 hr. 20 min.

f.   12 hr. 24 min.   j.   14 hr. 5 min.
   —   7 hr. 16 min.   — 12 hr. 20 min.
   _____   _____
       5 hr.   8 min.   1 hr. 45 min.

g.   8 hr.   k.   23 hr. 21 min.
   —   5 hr. 20 min.   — 20 hr. 25 min.
   _____   _____
       2 hr. 40 min.   2 hr. 56 min.

h.   15 hr.   l.   14 hr. 7 min.
   — 13 hr. 35 min.   — 12 hr. 53 min.
   _____   _____
       1 hr. 25 min.   1 hr. 14 min.

4. Find the elapsed time in each of the following exercises.

	From	To	Elapsed Time
a.	1:10 A.M.	1:50 A.M.	40 min.
b.	2:15 A.M.	2:40 A.M.	25 min.
c.	3:12 P.M.	4:20 P.M.	1 hr. 8 min.
d.	10:15 P.M.	11:48 P.M.	1 hr. 33 min.
e.	5:40 P.M.	6:10 P.M.	30 min.
f.	9:30 P.M.	11:20 P.M.	1 hr. 50 min.
g.	2:53 A.M.	9:05 A.M.	6 hr. 12 min.
h.	10:00 A.M.	2:00 P.M.	4 hr.
i.	11:00 A.M.	5:00 P.M.	6 hr.
j.	10:20 A.M.	1:30 P.M.	3 hr. 10 min.
k.	9:05 A.M.	3:20 P.M.	6 hr. 15 min.
l.	7:45 A.M.	2:30 P.M.	6 hr. 45 min.
m.	5:37 A.M.	7:10 P.M.	13 hr. 33 min.
n.	6:52 A.M.	9:07 P.M.	14 hr. 15 min.

B

When finding the answers to this set of exercises, use the bus schedule
on pages 60–61.

1. At what time will the buses that leave Butler at the hour indicated
   arrive at each of the locations indicated?

	Hour Of Leaving Butler	Location	Hour Of Arrival
a.	6:20 A.M.	Singac	7:05 A.M.
b.	7:30 A.M.	Montclair	8:43 A.M.
c.	8:10 A.M.	Bloomfield	9:22 A.M.
d.	11:40 A.M.	Newark	1:17 P.M.
e.	2:50 P.M.	Mountain View	3:32 P.M.
f.	4:30 P.M.	Little Falls	5:43 P.M.

Each of the exercises in the text was carefully designed so that they could be done with the 0
hour as midnight. You might want to ask your brighter students, however, to compare the time
lapse between 8:40 P.M. and 2:10 A.M.

2. At what time will the buses that leave Newark at the hour indicated arrive at each of the locations indicated?

	Hour Of Leaving Newark	Location	Hour Of Arrival
a.	7:30 A.M.	Bloomfield	7:54 A.M.
b.	10:25 A.M.	Little Falls	11:16 A.M.
c.	8:00 A.M.	Cedar Grove	8:43 A.M.
d.	5:20 P.M.	Singac	6:09 P.M.
e.	8:05 P.M.	Pompton Lakes	9:11 P.M.
f.	11:25 A.M.	Mountain View	12:24 P.M.

3. How long does it take the buses that leave Pompton Lakes for Newark at the hour indicated to reach each of the locations indicated?

	Hour Of Leaving	Location	Hour Of Arrival	Time Spent Traveling
a.	9:00 A.M.	Bloomfield	9:57 A.M.	57 min.
b.	10:00 A.M.	Newark	11:17 A.M.	1 hr. 17 min.
c.	7:03 A.M.	Montclair	7:48 A.M.	45 min.
d.	7:50 A.M.	Cedar Grove	8:29 A.M.	39 min.
e.	1:55 P.M.	Newark	3:12 P.M.	1 hr. 17 min.
f.	3:10 P.M.	Montclair	4:02 P.M.	52 min.
g.	12:00 P.M.	Newark	1:17 P.M.	1 hr. 17 min.

4. How long does it take the buses that leave Newark at the hour indicated to reach each of the locations indicated?

	Hour Of Leaving	Location	Hour Of Arrival	Time Spent Traveling
a.	8:00 A.M.	Little Falls	8:51 A.M.	51 min.
b.	9:30 A.M.	Pompton Lakes	10:50 A.M.	1 hr. 20 min.
c.	1:25 P.M.	Singac	2:19 P.M.	54 min.
d.	4:33 P.M.	Cedar Grove	5:19 P.M.	46 min.
e.	9:30 A.M.	Butler	11:29 A.M.	1 hr. 59 min.
f.	11:25 A.M.	Pompton Lakes	12:45 P.M.	1 hr. 20 min.
g.	12:25 P.M.	Singac	1:19 P.M.	54 min.

C

When answering the following questions, use the bus schedule on pages 60–61.

1. Consider the bus that leaves Butler at 6:20 A.M.
   a. How many stops will it make after leaving Butler? _6_
   b. At what places that Route Number 114 bus normally stops will it not stop on this trip? _Little Falls and Cedar Grove_
   c. Mr. Grant has to walk for approximately 10 minutes from the time he gets off the bus until the time he reaches the place where he works. He has to be at work at 9:00 A.M. in Montclair. Can he take the 7:30 bus out of Butler, or must he take the 6:20 bus?
   Yes

If he takes the 7:30 bus, he will arrive at work at 8:53.

2. George Peabody works in Newark but lives in Butler.

   a. If he misses the 4:15 bus out of Newark when going home in the afternoon, until what hour will he have to wait before the next bus leaves for Butler? <u>6:35 P.M.</u>

   b. How long is this waiting time? <u>2 hr. 20 min.</u>

3. Consider the schedule for the buses leaving Newark for Monclair.

   a. How long does it take the bus that leaves Newark at 6:35 in the morning to make this trip? <u>25 min.</u>

   b. How long does it take the bus that leaves Newark at 4:45 in the afternoon to make this trip? <u>32 min.</u>

   c. How much longer does it take the afternoon bus to make the trip than the morning bus? <u>7 min.</u>

   d. Why should the trip take more time in the afternoon than it takes in the morning? <u>More traffic at 4:45 P.M.</u>

PART 2

The time schedules for buses traveling long distances between states are somewhat more difficult to read than the one you have just examined. The following schedule is for Route Number 65A of an interstate bus company. The numbers that appear across the top line (7051, 9, 2029, 117, and so on) are the trip numbers on this route. For instance, Trip Number 7051 will leave the Port Authority terminal in New York City at 12:01 in the morning and arrive in Newark at 12:35. It will then continue until its next stop at State Road, Delaware. After making three more stops—at Perryville, Aberdeen, and Baltimore—it will arrive at Washington, D.C., at 5:15 in the morning. Notice that this table is read by going down the column, while the bus schedule on pages 60–61 is read by going across the row.

NON-STOP NEW YORK TO BALTIMORE ONLY 3 HRS. 30 MIN. **NEW YORK—BALTIMORE—(WASHINGTON)** **NON-STOP NEWARK TO BALTIMORE ONLY 3 HRS. 20 MIN.**

SOUTHBOUND—READ DOWN

Trip Numbers →	7051 NRN	9 NJS	2029 NAN	117	2033 NBN	7121 NwM	173	2057	2037 NRA	2053	115 NwM	2039	171	2041	2059	2045 NwM	165 NRc	127	7123 NBN	31 NRW	7125 NBN	2055
65A (ET)											Fri only						Sun only					FSu only
NEW YORK, NY																						
*Port Authority Term. ... Lv	1201	2 00	3 30	5 30	7 45	8 30	9 30	103C	1045	1230	1 30	1 45	2 30	3 45	4 30	5 30	6 30	7 30	8 30	8 30	9 30	10 30
*Jersey City, NJ. ... Lv	↓	▼	↓	↓	8 10	▼	↓	1110	↓	↓	↓	4 10	↓	↓	↓	↓	↓	↓	↓	↓	↓	↓
*Newark. ... Lv	1235	↓			8 30		10 05	1130			2 05	2 20	4 30		6 05		9 05		9 05			
*Bellmawr, NJ. ... Lv	↓				10 00																	
*Wilmington, DE. ... Lv	↓				10 50			1 45			4 35			8 20								
*State Road, DE (Clemente's Rest.) Ar	2 45	5#50			11#05			2#00			4#50		6 45	8 35								
*State Road, DE (Clemente's Rest.) Lv	2 45	6 05			11 15			2 10			5 00		6 45	8 35								
Elkton Jct., MD (Rts. 40-213-280)	↓	6 25			11 35			2 20			5 10											
Northeast Jct. (Ward Texaco)	↓	6 30			11 40			2 35			5 25											
*Perryville.	3 20	6 40			11 50		12 50	2 45			5 35		7 20		9 10		11 59					
*Aberdeen.	3 30	6 50			12 01		1 00	2 55			5 45		7 30		9 20							
*Edgewood Road.	↓	7 00			12 10			3 05			5 55											
Joppatowne.	↓	↓																				
*Baltimore. ... Ar	4 15	5 30 7 45	9 05	12 50	1159	1 45	2 00	3 55	4 00	5 30 6 40	6 05	8 15	8 05	1005	1000	11 00	12 40	12 25	1 00	2 00		
*Baltimore, MD. ... Lv	4 20	5 35 7 50	9 10	12 55		1 50		4 00			6 45	6 10	8 20		1010	1005	11 05					
*WASHINGTON, DC. ... Ar	5 15	6 30 8 45	10 05	1 50		2 45		5 00			7 40	7 05	9 15		1105	1100	11 59					

Whenever the time of day is shown in the bus table, it implies that the bus makes a stop at that place at that hour. Thus, Trip Number 31 leaves New York at 8:30 in the evening, stops in Newark at 9:05, and makes no other stops until it reaches Baltimore at 12:25. Incidentally, the numbers in dark type and the numbers in light type have exactly the same meaning as they had on the bus schedule on pages 60–61. In fact, all time schedules, whether they be bus, train, or plane, use the same notation to distinguish between P.M. and A.M. times.

■ ILLUSTRATION 1: Trip Number 117 makes only two stops between New York and Washington, while Trip Number 2033 stops at every point along the route. How much longer does Trip Number 2033 take in making the journey than Trip Number 117?

● SOLUTION:

Trip Number 117

Time of leaving New York = 5:30

Time of arrival at Washington = 10:05

Traveling time = 10 hr. 5 min. − 5 hr. 30 min.

$\qquad\qquad$ = 9 hr. 65 min. − 5 hr. 30 min.

$\qquad\qquad$ = 4 hr. 35 min.

Trip Number 2033

Time of leaving New York = 7:45

Time of arrival in Washington = 1:50 P.M., or 13:50

Traveling time = 13 hr. 50 min. − 7 hr. 45 min.

$\qquad\qquad$ = 6 hr. 5 min.

Extra time needed for Trip Number 2033 = 6 hr. 5 min. − 4 hr. 35 min.

$\qquad\qquad\qquad\qquad\qquad\qquad\qquad\quad$ = 5 hr. 65 min. − 4 hr. 35 min.

$\qquad\qquad\qquad\qquad\qquad\qquad\qquad\quad$ = 1 hr. 30 min.

▼ EXPLANATION: To find the traveling time for Trip Number 117, it is necessary to change 10 hours 5 minutes to 9 hours 65 minutes. How is this done? In writing the time of arrival at Washington for Trip Number 2033, you must rewrite 1:50 P.M. as 13:50. How does this help you find the traveling time?

It is impossible for an interstate bus company to publish a rate table showing the cost of transportation along all its routes. The airlines and trains can do this, as we shall soon see. However, buses stop at so many different places in traveling between cities that all the rates cannot be shown in a single table, for there are too many. Also, different trips between the same two cities will sometimes follow different routes. This, too, affects any rate table the company might want to publish.

It is interesting to note that the rates of all buses traveling between different states are determined by an agency of the federal government called the Interstate Commerce Commission. Hence, two different companies running buses over the same route between two cities must charge exactly the same rate. Since they cannot attract customers

It would seem as if a contradiction exists between the statement above in that a bus company cannot issue a rate table and the fact that one appears on page 69. This table is based on certain specific routes designated by the company. The cost would differ if the person selected an alternate route.

by lowering their rates, they try to attract them by offering better service. The fares in the following table are those charged between a few selected cities.

BUS FARES BETWEEN SELECTED CITIES

	Atlanta	Chicago	Denver	Los Angeles	San Francisco	Seattle	Washington
New York	$28.10	$31.25	$57.80	$84.15	$84.15	$77.85	$ 9.15
San Antonio	31.80	36.20	32.20	44.00	55.50	67.15	51.40
Seattle	66.60	49.50	38.30	33.20	25.05	—	73.00
Denver	45.60	28.50	—	36.10	36.10	38.30	50.75

To encourage travelers to use its buses both in going to their destinations and in returning, bus companies offer a discount rate on the purchase of round-trip tickets. A person who purchases one of these tickets pays 10% less than twice the one-way fare.

■ILLUSTRATION 2: How much will Mr. Burton pay for a round-trip bus ticket between Seattle and San Francisco?

●SOLUTION:

> One-way fare = $25.05
> Round-trip fare without the discount = 2 × $25.05
> $$= \$50.10$$
> Discount on round-trip fare = 10% × $50.10
> $$= .10 \times \$50.10$$
> $$= \$5.01$$
> Round-trip fare with discount = $50.10 − $5.01
> $$= \$45.09$$

▼EXPLANATION: If there were no discount on the round-trip fare, then Mr. Burton would have had to pay twice the one-way fare of $25.05, or $50.10. However, the bus company offers a 10% discount. The percent numeral, 10%, has to be changed to its equivalent decimal form, .10, before the product of 10% and $50.10 can be found. How do you change a percent numeral to its equivalent decimal form? Subtracting the discount from the two-way cost gives you the round-trip fare of $45.09.

EXERCISES   A

Do you recall how to find the answer in each of the following exercises? If not, you will probably want to refer to the pages indicated for help.

It might be well to point out that the person who purchases a round-trip ticket and then tries to obtain a rebate on the return part of the ticket will not receive half the price he paid. Use Illustration 2 as an example to determine how much the company will return to him.

1. Change each of the following percent numerals to its equivalent decimal numeral form (pages 583–584).

a. 20%   .20   d. 2%   .02   g. 4.5%   .045

b. 35%   .35   e. 5%   .05   h. 5.2%   .052

c. 42%   .42   f. 7%   .07   i. 6.7%   .067

2. Find the product to the nearest penny in each of the following exercises (pages 589–590).

a. $10\% \times \$62.00 =$ $ 6.20   f. $10\% \times \$75.15 =$ $ 7.52

b. $10\% \times \$45.50 =$ $ 4.55   g. $5\% \times \$123.25 =$ $ 6.16

c. $20\% \times \$56.30 =$ $11.26   h. $20\% \times \$156.45 =$ $31.29

d. $25\% \times \$87.40 =$ $21.85   i. $30\% \times \$187.75 =$ $56.33

e. $35\% \times \$93.20 =$ $32.62   j. $10\% \times \$193.95 =$ $19.40

B

1. At what time will each of the following trips arrive in Wilmington, Delaware?

a. Trip Number 2033 10:50 A.M. c. Trip Number 2039 4:35 P.M.

b. Trip Number 2037 1:45 P.M. d. Trip Number 2045 8:20 P.M.

2. Find the time spent on each of the following bus trips.

	Trip Number	From	To	Leaving Time	Arrival Time	Length Of Time
a.	7051	Baltimore	Washington	4:20 A.M.	5:15 A.M.	55 min.
b.	7123	New York	Baltimore	8:30 P.M.	12:40 A.M.	4 hr. 10 min.
c.	2037	Wilmington	Baltimore	1:45 P.M.	3:55 P.M.	2 hr. 10 min.
d.	117	New York	Washington	5:30 A.M.	10:05 A.M.	4 hr. 35 min.
e.	2041	Newark	Baltimore	4:30 P.M.	8:15 P.M.	3 hr. 45 min.
f.	2033	Jersey City	Aberdeen	8:10 A.M.	12:01 P.M.	3 hr. 51 min.
g.	7051	New York	Washington	12:01 A.M.	5:15 A.M.	5 hr. 14 min.
h.	2033	Wilmington	Washington	10:50 A.M.	1:50 P.M.	3 hr.
i.	2037	Newark	Washington	11:30 A.M.	5:00 P.M.	5 hr. 30 min.
j.	2057	New York	Baltimore	10:30 A.M.	2:00 P.M.	3 hr. 30 min.
k.	7125	New York	Baltimore	9:30 P.M.	1:00 A.M.	3 hr. 30 min.

3. Find the cost of each of the following one-way trips. Use the table on page 69.

	From	To	Cost
a.	San Antonio	Denver	$ 32.20
b.	Seattle	Washington	73.00
c.	New York	San Francisco	84.15
d.	Denver	Seattle	38.30
e.	Seattle	Los Angeles	33.20
f.	Atlanta	San Antonio	31.80
g.	Los Angeles	New York	84.15

Although the students encountered exercises on percent earlier in the work (page 45), it would be best to rewrite Exercises 1 and 2 in Group A. An understanding of percent is needed in order to do Exercise 4 of Group B.

4. Find the round-trip bus fare in each of the following exercises. Use the table on page 69.

From	To	One-Way Fare	Two-Way Fare	Discount	Round-Trip Fare
a. San Antonio	Los Angeles	$ 44.00	$ 88.00	$ 8.80	$ 79.20
b. Denver	Chicago	28.50	57.00	5.70	51.30
c. New York	Atlanta	28.10	56.20	5.62	50.58
d. Seattle	San Francisco	25.05	50.10	5.01	45.09
e. Denver	Washington	50.75	101.50	10.15	91.35
f. Chicago	New York	31.25	62.50	6.25	56.25

5. At what average speed would the buses travel to cover the distances shown in each of the following exercises? Find your answer to the nearest mile. (See Chapter 1, page 37.)

	Traveling Time	Distance Traveled	Average Speed
a.	2.5 hours	150 miles	60 mph
b.	4.5 hours	315 miles	70 mph
c.	6.5 hours	325 miles	50 mph
d.	3 hr. 30 min.	200 miles	57 mph
e.	7 hr. 30 min.	410 miles	55 mph
f.	5 hr. 30 min.	265 miles	48 mph

6. Determine the average speed to the nearest mile at which the buses have to travel in order to keep on schedule. Use the bus schedule on page 67.

	Trip Number	From	To	Distance Between Cities	Traveling Time	Average Speed
a.	2045	Newark	Baltimore	176 mi.	4 hr.	44 mph
b.	9	New York	Washington	224 mi.	4½ or 4.5 hr.	50 mph
c.	165	New York	Baltimore	188 mi.	3½ or 3.5 hr.	54 mph

C

1. The heading on the bus schedule on page 67 states that the nonstop trip from New York to Baltimore takes only 3 hours, 20 minutes approximately.

   a. How many of these nonstop trips are there during each weekday? 10

   b. At what time does each leave New York? 2:00 a.m., 5:30 a.m., 8:30 a.m., 10:30 a.m., 12:30 p.m., 2:30 p.m., 4:30 p.m., 6:30 p.m., 7:30 p.m., 9:30 p.m.

2. How much more time will it take the bus on Trip Number 2037 to travel between New York and Baltimore than it will take the bus on Trip Number 173? 55 min.

Review the concept of average speed with the purpose of showing that, for a bus to average 60 mph, it will frequently have to travel at higher rates than this in order to make up for those occasions when it must stop to pay highway tolls.

3. Use the bus schedule on page 67 to answer each of the following questions.

   a. How long does it take the bus on Trip Number 2033 to make the trip from New York to Newark? <u>45 min.</u>

   b. How long does it take the bus on Trip Number 173 to make the trip from New York to Newark? <u>35 min.</u>

   c. Why should more time be needed for Trip Number 2033? <u>On Trip Number 2033, the bus makes an extra stop in Jersey City.</u>

Unit 3: Traveling by Railroad

Train schedules are read in much the same way as bus schedules. The following schedule, however, contains an additional feature that you should examine. The hours on the left side of the table are read in the usual manner, that is, by starting at the top of the table and working your way down. Thus, Trip Number 17 leaves New York at 11:00 A.M., pulls into Newark at 11:16 A.M., and then goes on to Trenton, arriving there at 12:00 noon. The numbers on the right side of the table, however, are read in the reverse direction by starting at the bottom and running your finger up to the top of the table. For instance, Trip Number 42 leaves Washington at 3:50 A.M. and arrives in Baltimore at 4:32 A.M. From Baltimore it goes to Wilmington, arriving there at 5:35 A.M. It then makes a number of other stops along the way until it arrives in New York at 8 A.M.

READ DOWN				READ UP		
17	37	29		42	48	18
11 00	2 00	7 30	Lv New York Penna Sta. . . . .(PC)..(ET) N. Y. Ar	8 00	12 20	8 55
11 16	2 16	7 46	Newark. . . . . '. '. . . . . . . N. J.	7 43	12 05	8 40
12 00	2 59	8 29	Trenton. . . . . '. '. . . . . . . ''	6 56	11 20	7 55
12 27	3 26	8 57	North Philadelphia . . . . '. '. . . . . . . Pa.	6 25	10 52	7 27
12 36	3 35	9 06	Philadelphia (30th St. Sta.) . . . . ''	6 12	10 43	7 17
1 06	4 04	9 39	Wilmington. . . . . Del.	5 35	10 14	6 48
2 08	5 05	10 40	Baltimore Penna Sta.. . . . . .Md.	4 32	9 10	5 45
2 50	5 45	11 20	Ar Washington. . . . . D. C. Lv	3 50	8 30	5 00

■ I L L U S T R A T I O N 1 : How long does it take Trip Number 48 to travel from Baltimore to Newark?

● S O L U T I O N :

          Time of leaving Baltimore $= 9:10$ A.M.

          Time of leaving Newark $= 12:05$ P.M.

          Traveling time $= 12$ hrs. 5 min. $- 9$ hrs. 10 min.

                     $= 11$ hrs. 65 min. $- 9$ hrs. 10 min.

                     $= 2$ hrs. 55 min.

Here, again, a schedule is used that is read slightly differently than the previous two. The left side is read from top to bottom, while the right side is read in the reverse direction. These three should cover all the variations of transportation schedules in use.

▼EXPLANATION: This solution differs from the earlier ones only in that it is necessary for you to read the table from bottom to top. Note first that the train leaves Baltimore at 9:10 A.M. Then, by running your finger up the column for Trip Number 48, you discover that it arrives in Trenton at 12:05 P.M. The solution is then completed in exactly the same manner as in the earlier problems of finding the number of hours between two numerals in a time schedule.

Trains that carry people from suburban areas to a city offer their passengers the opportunity to save quite a bit of money on the purchase of commutation tickets. Although different railroad companies may have different plans, the usual commutation ticket is either of the weekly variety, or the monthly variety. With the former, a passenger may make as many trips as he wants to make during a particular week and, for this, he pays a flat fee. With the monthly commutation ticket the passenger may make as many trips as he wants to make during a

1-DAY ROUND TRIP, ONE WAY and COMMUTATION FARES

Subject to Change	Between NEW YORK (Pennsylvania Station) and			
	1-Day Round Trip	One-Way	Monthly Commutation	Weekly Commutation
Newark	—	$0.55	$19.35	$5.30
Elizabeth	$1.40	.91	27.60	7.60
Rahway	1.70	1.13	36.35	10.05
Avenel	1.90	1.25	37.95	10.50
Edgar	1.90	1.25	38.30	10.60
Woodbridge	1.90	1.25	38.30	10.60
Perth Amboy	2.05	1.36	38.70	10.70
South Amboy	2.20	1.45	39.45	10.95
Matawan	2.55	1.68	41.45	11.55
Hazlet	2.70	1.80	41.50	11.55
Middletown	2.85	1.89	42.70	11.90
Red Bank	3.20	2.13	43.35	12.10
Little Silver-Oceanport	3.40	2.25	43.95	12.25
Monmouth Park	—	2.35	—	—
Long Branch	3.75	2.47	44.50	12.40
Elberon	3.75	2.47	44.90	12.55
Allenhurst	3.90	2.58	45.10	12.60
No. Asbury Park	4.05	2.70	45.10	12.60
Asbury Park-Ocean Grove	4.05	2.70	45.20	12.60
Bradley Beach	4.05	2.70	45.30	12.65
Avon	4.20	2.79	45.35	12.65
Belmar	4.20	2.79	45.45	12.70
Spring Lake-Spring Lake Hgts.	4.40	2.93	45.65	12.75
Sea Girt	4.40	2.93	45.75	12.75
Manasquan	4.60	3.04	45.80	12.80
Pt. Pleasant Beach	4.60	3.04	46.00	12.85
Bay Head Junction	4.75	3.16	46.05	12.85

The term "commutation" was not explained in the writings above. On the possibility that some of the students may not be aware of its meaning, spend a few moments discussing this and also the word "commuter."

month. Here, again, the charge is a fixed amount. In both cases, the cost is a good deal less than the total cost of the individual trips, or the round-trip fares over the same period.

■ILLUSTRATION 2: Mr. Kerner lives in Avon and is employed in New York. He works 22 days during an average business month. How much can he save by purchasing a monthly commutation ticket rather than one-way tickets?

●SOLUTION:

Cost of monthly commutation ticket $= \$45.35$
Cost of one-way trip $= \$2.79$
Number of one-way trips in one day $= 2$
Number of one-way trips in 22 days $= 22 \times 2$
$$= 44$$
Cost of 44 one-way trips $= 44 \times \$2.79$
$$= \$122.76$$
Saving $= \$122.76 - \$45.35$
$$= \$77.41$$

▼EXPLANATION: The route of the trains on this line starts in New York and passes through each of the towns listed in the left-hand column. The first stop is Newark, followed by Elizabeth, Rahway, and so forth until the last town of Bay Head Junction is reached. Hence, to find the cost of the monthly commutation ticket from New York to Avon, run your finger down this column until it reaches Avon. After placing the edge of a piece of paper beneath this word, run your finger across the table until it comes to the column headed by the words "Monthly Commutation." The numeral your finger will be pointing to is $45.35—the cost of a monthly commutation ticket between New York and Avon. How is the cost of the one-way ticket found? Why was the cost of the one-way ticket doubled? Why aren't the towns in the table arranged in alphabetical order?

You may have wondered why the person in Illustration 2 did not buy 1 round-trip ticket each day rather than 2 one-way tickets. If he had done so, he might have saved at least a little money. Buying a round-trip ticket instead of 2 one-way tickets, however, is not always possible. Frequently, the railroad will insist that round-trip tickets be used only between the hours of 9:30 in the morning and 4:30 in the afternoon. The 1-day round-trip ticket is designed to attract the non-commuter into using the train to the city rather than a car. Furthermore, the railroads don't want such passengers to use the trains when most people are going to work. Hence, they restrict their traveling time to those hours when relatively few people are using the trains.

Illustration 2 points up the tremendous saving that can be had on the purchase of a monthly commutation ticket. Have some of the students obtain a rate table similar to the one on page 74. Use the local table to illustrate the saving that people in your community can have by purchasing commutation tickets.

EXERCISES   **A**

1. Determine the time at which each of the following trains pulls into the station indicated. Use the schedule on page 72.

	Trip Number	Station	Time
a.	17	North Philadelphia	12:27 P.M.
b.	37	Wilmington	4:04 P.M.
c.	17	Baltimore	2:08 P.M.
d.	29	Washington	11:20 P.M.

2. Determine the time at which each of the following trains pulls into the station indicated. Use the schedule on page 72.

	Trip Number	Station	Time
a.	42	Trenton	6:56 A.M.
b.	48	Wilmington	10:14 A.M.
c.	48	Newark	12:05 P.M.
d.	18	Philadelphia	7:17 P.M.

3. Find the time spent on each of the following train trips.

	Trip Number	From	To	Leaving Time	Arrival Time	Length Of Time
a.	37	New York	Wilmington	2:00 P.M.	4:04 P.M.	2 hr. 4 min.
b.	37	Trenton	Baltimore	2:59 P.M.	5:05 P.M.	2 hr. 6 min.
c.	29	North Philadelphia	Washington	8:57 P.M.	11:20 P.M.	2 hr. 23 min.
d.	17	Newark	Wilmington	11:16 A.M.	1:06 P.M.	1 hr. 50 min.
e.	42	Washington	New York	3:50 A.M.	8:00 A.M.	4 hr. 10 min.
f.	42	Baltimore	Newark	4:32 A.M.	7:43 A.M.	3 hr. 11 min.
g.	18	Wilmington	North Philadelphia	6:48 P.M.	7:27 P.M.	39 min.
h.	42	Philadelphia	Trenton	6:12 A.M.	6:56 A.M.	44 min.
i.	48	Philadelphia	Newark	10:43 A.M.	12:05 P.M.	1 hr. 22 min.
j.	48	Baltimore	New York	9:10 A.M.	12:20 P.M.	3 hr. 10 min.

4. Find the cost of a one-way ticket between New York and each of the following stations. Use the table on page 73.
   - a. Newark $ .55
   - b. Edgar $1.25
   - c. Hazlet $1.80
   - d. Red Bank $2.13
   - e. Allenhurst $2.58
   - f. Sea Girt $2.93

5. Find the cost of the weekly commutation ticket between New York and each of the following stations. Use the table on page 73.
   - a. Avenel $10.50
   - b. South Amboy $10.95
   - c. Long Branch $12.40
   - d. Bradley Beach $12.65
   - e. Belmar $12.70
   - f. Point Pleasant Beach $12.85

Care is used in Exercise 3 to include only those situations where the 0 hour is 12:00 midnight. You may want to select situations where the student will have to use 12:00 noon as the 0 hour.

6. How much will a person save by purchasing a 1-day round-trip ticket rather than 2 one-way tickets between New York and each of the following stations?

Station	1-Day Round Trip	One Way	Two Times One Way	Saving
a. Red Bank	$ 3.20	$ 2.13	$ 4.26	$ 1.06
b. Woodbridge	1.90	1.25	2.50	.60
c. Sea Girt	4.40	2.93	5.86	1.46
d. Middletown	2.85	1.89	3.78	.93
e. Elberon	3.75	2.47	4.94	1.19

7. How much will a person save by purchasing a weekly commutation ticket rather than 5 round-trip tickets for the week in traveling between New York and each of the following stations?

Station	Weekly Commutation	1-Day Round Trip	Five 1-Day Round Trips	Saving Or Loss
a. Elizabeth	$ 7.60	$ 1.40	$ 7.00	$ .60 (loss)
b. Perth Amboy	10.70	2.05	10.25	.45 (loss)
c. Little Silver	12.25	3.40	17.00	4.75 (saving)
d. Spring Lake	12.75	4.40	22.00	9.25 (saving)
e. Rahway	10.05	1.70	8.50	1.55 (loss)

8. Over the period of one year, a commuter will purchase either 50 weekly commutation tickets, or 12 monthly commutation tickets. How much can commuters save by buying the monthly tickets if they travel between New York and each of the following stations?

Station	Weekly Commutation	50 Weekly Commutations	Monthly Commutation	12 Monthly Commutations	Saving
a. Newark	$ 5.30	$ 265.00	$ 19.35	$ 232.20	$ 32.80
b. Hazlet	11.55	577.50	41.50	498.00	79.50
c. Bradley Beach	12.65	632.50	45.30	543.60	88.90
d. Allenhurst	12.60	630.00	45.10	541.20	88.80
e. Belmar	12.70	635.00	45.45	545.40	89.60

B

1. The distance from Baltimore to Newark is 176 miles. The train on Trip Number 48 leaves Baltimore on time, but arrives in Newark 5 minutes late.
   a. At what time did the train arrive in Newark?   12:10 p.m.
   b. How long did the trip take?   3 hrs.
   c. At what average speed, to the nearest mile, did the train have to travel in making this trip?   59 mph

2. Mr. Evans is planning to take the trip from New York to Washington. He is thinking of leaving sometime in the early afternoon.

a. If he takes Train Trip Number 37, how long will this trip take him? Use the train schedule on page 72.   <u>3 hr. 45 min.</u>

b. If he takes Bus Trip Number 171, how long will this trip take him? Use the bus schedule on page 67.   <u>4 hr. 35 min.</u>

c. How much time can he save by taking the train instead of the bus?   <u>50 min.</u>

3. Mr. Evans of Problem 2 decided he would also compare the cost of traveling by bus against the cost of traveling by train.

a. Find the cost of a one-way bus ticket between New York and Washington. Use the table on page 69.   <u>$9.15</u>

b. If the cheapest one-way train fare between New York and Washington is $10.65, how much can Mr. Evans save by traveling by bus?   <u>$1.50</u>

c. The railroad offers no discount on a round-trip ticket to Washington. The bus company offers a 10% discount rate off twice the one-way fare on this trip. How much would Mr. Evans save by purchasing a round-trip bus ticket instead of 2 one-way train tickets?   <u>$4.83</u>

Unit 4:   Traveling by Air

PART 1

Reading the flight schedule for an airline is pretty much the same as reading bus-line schedules designed for cities that are some distance apart. The symbols "Lv" and "Ar" are still abbreviations for the words "Leaving" and "Arriving." However, whereas the bus routes have "Trip Numbers," the flight routes have "Flight Numbers." There are, though, several very important differences between bus transportation and flight transportation other than speed and cost. There are no restrictions as to which seat you may occupy when traveling by bus, but there are very definite restrictions when traveling by airplane. The air traveler usually has three basic types of service available to him.

1. **First Class:** Special meals are provided for the traveler, with cocktails at no additional cost. The seats are wider, and there is much more legroom between the seats than on the other services. Also, there are fewer passengers per stewardess.

2. **Coach:** Meals are served at no cost, while cocktails must be bought. The quarters are much more cramped than on first-class service, both in elbowroom and in legroom.

3. **Economy Coach:** The service is much the same as on the coach flight, except that instead of having a meal provided, the passenger is offered only hot coffee.

Airlines vary on the services provided on the different class flights offered. Compare the services stated above to those of other airlines.

Commercial Transportation

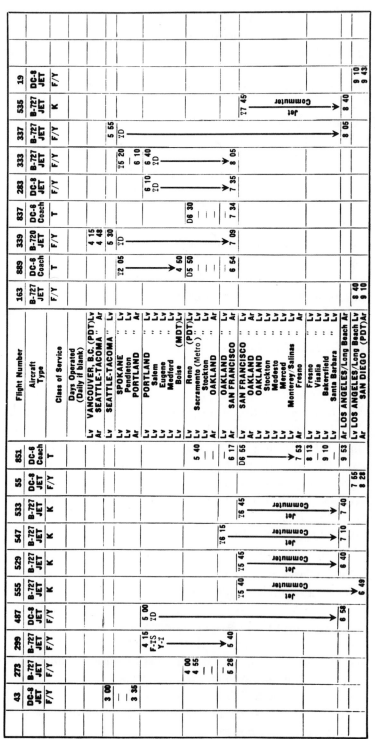

These flight schedules can be obtained from any travel agency or airline ticket office. Suggest to the students that they try to obtain one of their own to see in what way other schedules may differ from, or be comparable to, the above. They can also compare rates on similar flights.

Needless to say, the type of service you select is reflected in the cost of your plane ticket. Which of the three services is the most expensive? Why should it be?

Before looking at the cost of traveling by air, first examine a flight schedule. In the schedule at left, the third line shows the type of plane in which you will be traveling. Thus, for Flight Number 43, the plane is a DC-8 Jet, while for Flight Number 273, the plane is a B-727 Jet. In fact, all the planes used by this airline are jet-propelled planes except those indicated by the letter **T**. These planes are propeller-driven planes, and since they are much slower than the jet planes, they are used on the cheaper coach flights.

The letters in the fourth row of the schedule show the class of service as follows:

F: Jet First-Class Service
Y: Jet Coach Service
K: Jet Economy-Coach Service

Notice that you cannot always get the type of service you want. Whether you care for it or not, the only service you can get with this airline when flying out of San Francisco to Los Angeles at 5:45 in the afternoon is jet economy-coach service. If you don't happen to like that, you can only hope that there will be another airline that makes this same trip at the same time and that has the service you want. If there is none, then you either take the economy service, or stay home! Incidentally, the heavy type of all the numerals in this table, as in the bus schedules, tells you that these flights take place in the afternoon and evening hours.

■ILLUSTRATION 1: James Young left Vancouver for San Francisco on Flight Number 339.
    a. How long did this trip take him?
    b. How long was the stopover in Seattle?
●SOLUTION:
    (a) Time of leaving Vancouver = 4:15
        Time of arrival in San Francisco = 7:09
        Traveling time = 7 hr. 9 min. − 4 hr. 15 min.
                   = 6 hr. 69 min. − 4 hr. 15 min.
                   = 2 hr. 54 min.
    (b) Time of arrival in Seattle = 4:48
        Time of leaving Seattle = 5:30
        Stopover time = 5 hr. 30 min. − 4 hr. 48 min.
                = 4 hr. 90 min. − 4 hr. 48 min.
                = 42 min.

You might want to discuss with the class why the stopover time at some of the airports is quite lengthy, as in Illustration 1, while others are rather brief. Have them find stopover times in the table that are quite short.

▼EXPLANATION: To avoid making errors in reading the numerals in the flight schedule, it is best to place the edge of a piece of paper directly below the name of the city in which you are interested. In this case, it happens to be Vancouver. If you follow along the edge of the paper, you will come to the column for Flight Number 339. This flight leaves Vancouver at 4:15 in the afternoon. Notice that, in this table, the hours are separated from the minutes by a slightly larger than usual space. In the bus schedule, it was a period that separated the two. Now move the edge of the piece of paper down the column of cities until it is directly below San Francisco. Then, by again running your finger across to the column for Flight Number 339, you see that the plane arrives in San Francisco at 7:09. Finding the number of hours from 4:15 to 7:09 is done in exactly the same manner as before.

In Part (b), the term "stopover time" simply referred to the amount of time that the plane spent in Seattle from the moment it arrived until the moment it left. According to the schedule, Flight Number 339 landed at Seattle airport at 4:48 and did not take off again until 5:30. Hence, the difference between the arrival and departure times was the stopover time.

Suppose you now find out what travel by air is going to cost you. The following table gives the cost of air travel between various cities in the United States. What it does not include, though, is a federal tax of 8% that has to be added to the cost of each flight.

■ILLUSTRATION 2: Mr. McCloud made a round-trip flight from New York to San Diego to close a business deal.
   a. If he traveled jet first-class, how much would the trip have cost him?
   b. If he traveled jet coach, how much would the trip have cost him?
   c. How much could he have saved by traveling jet coach rather than jet first-class?

●SOLUTION:

$$(a) \quad \text{Air fare one way, first class} = \$160$$
$$\text{Round-trip fare, first class} = \$160 \times 2$$
$$= \$320$$
$$\text{Federal tax} = \$320 \times 8\%$$
$$= \$320 \times .08$$
$$= \$25.60$$
$$\text{Total cost, first class} = \$320 \times \$25.60$$
$$= \$345.60$$

Use the flight schedule on pages 79 to call attention to the letter D immediately to the left of the 6:55 time on Flight Number 851. Ask what this letter might mean. Also refer to the letters PDT after Reno and MDT after Boise and ask for an interpretation.

ONE-WAY JET FARE

		Las Vegas	Los Angeles	Miami	Minneapolis/St. Paul	New York/Newark	Omaha	Philadelphia	Pittsburgh	Portland	Salt Lake City	San Diego	San Francisco/Oakland	Seattle/Tacoma
Los Angeles	F	24.00	—	—	130.00	160.00	98.00	156.00	142.00	64.00	68.00	12.00	28.00	73.00
	Y	21.00	—	—	105.00	145.00	84.00	141.00	127.00	53.00	—	8.00	15.00	61.00
	K	13.00	—	—	—	—	—	—	—	—	—	7.00	13.50	—
Minneapolis/St. Paul	F	—	130.00	—	—	72.00	—	68.00	55.00	—	—	130.00	130.00	—
	Y	—	105.00	—	—	60.00	—	57.00	45.00	—	—	105.00	105.00	—
New York/Newark	F	149.00	160.00	—	72.00	—	80.00	11.00	28.00	160.00	134.00	160.00	160.00	160.00
	Y	133.00	145.00	—	60.00	—	67.00	10.00	24.00	145.00	119.00	145.00	145.00	145.00
Omaha	F	82.00	98.00	—	—	80.00	—	76.00	62.00	103.00	66.00	99.00	102.00	111.00
	Y	70.00	84.00	—	—	67.00	—	65.00	52.00	90.00	55.00	85.00	88.00	97.00
Philadelphia	F	146.00	156.00	—	68.00	11.00	76.00	—	23.00	156.00	132.00	156.00	156.00	156.00
	Y	130.00	141.00	—	57.00	10.00	65.00	—	20.00	141.00	116.00	141.00	141.00	141.00
Pittsburgh	F	133.00	142.00	76.00	55.00	28.00	62.00	23.00	—	142.00	119.00	142.00	142.00	142.00
	Y	117.00	127.00	65.00	45.00	24.00	52.00	20.00	—	129.00	104.00	127.00	127.00	129.00
Portland	F	83.00	64.00	—	—	160.00	103.00	156.00	142.00	—	52.00	71.00	44.00	14.00
	Y	71.00	53.00	—	—	145.00	90.00	141.00	129.00	—	42.00	60.00	36.00	13.00
San Diego	F	32.00	12.00	—	130.00	160.00	90.90	156.00	142.00	71.00	—	—	36.00	79.00
	Y	26.00	8.00	—	—	145.00	85.00	141.00	127.00	60.00	—	—	30.00	67.00
	K	—	7.00	—	—	—	—	—	—	—	—	—	20.00	—
San Francisco/Oakland	F	48.00	29.00	—	130.00	160.00	102.00	156.00	142.00	44.00	51.00	36.00	—	54.00
	f	37.00	15.00	—	105.00	145.00	88.00	141.00	127.00	36.00	41.00	30.00	—	43.00
	K	—	13.50	—	—	—	—	—	—	—	—	20.00	—	—
Seattle/Tacoma	F	91.00	73.00	—	—	160.00	111.00	156.00	142.00	14.00	62.00	79.00	54.00	—
	Y	78.00	61.00	—	—	145.00	97.00	141.00	129.00	13.00	49.00	67.00	43.00	—
Toronto, Ont.	F	128.00	149.00	—	54.00	—	61.00	—	—	150.00	112.00	149.00	153.00	150.00
	Y	113.00	115.00	—	45.00	—	51.00	—	—	121.00	98.00	115.00	134.00	121.00

(b) Air fare one way, coach = \$145

Round-trip fare, coach = \$145 × 2

= \$290

Federal tax = \$290 × 8%

= \$290 × .08

= \$23.20

Total cost, coach = \$290 + \$23.20

= \$313.20

(c) Saving = \$345.60 − \$313.20

= \$32.40

▼ EXPLANATION : Run your finger down the first column of the rate table until you come to New York. After placing a piece of paper along the row containing this city name, run your finger along the paper edge until you come to the column headed San Diego. Your finger will be pointing at the numerals \$160 and \$145. The upper numeral, \$160, is the cost of a one-way jet first-class flight. The lower numeral, \$145, is the cost of the one-way jet-coach flight. The round-trip cost is found simply by doubling the one-way fare, for the airlines give no discount on the purchase of a round-trip flight. Finding the federal tax on the fare of \$320 requires rewriting the percent numeral 8% as the decimal numeral .08. The product of \$320 and .08 gives the federal tax of \$25.60. When this is added to the fare of \$320, you find the total cost of the first-class flight to be \$345.60.

As a point of interest, note that the cost of travel by bus or train is not taxed by the federal government, whereas flight cost is taxed to the extent of 8%.

The coach fare of $313.20 is found in exactly the same manner. Finally, the difference between the first-class fare of $345.60 and the coach fare of $313.20 gives you a saving of $32.40.

EXERCISES   **A**

1. Find the arrival time in San Francisco of each of the following flight numbers. Use the flight schedule on page 78.

Flight Number	Arrival Time		Flight Number	Arrival Time
a.	273	5:26	c.	837	7:34
b.	851	6:17	d.	333	8:05

2. Find the time spent on each of the following flights. Use the flight schedule on page 78.

Flight Number	From	To	Leaving Time	Arrival Time	Length Of Time
a.	889	Spokane	Boise	2:05	4:50	2 hr. 45 min.
b.	283	Portland	San Francisco	6:10	7:35	1 hr. 25 min.
c.	547	Oakland	Los Angeles	6:15	7:10	55 min.
d.	851	Sacramento	Fresno	5:40	7:53	2 hr. 13 min.
e.	337	Seattle	Los Angeles	5:55	8:05	2 hr. 10 min.

3. Find the one-way fare between the points indicated. Do not include the federal tax. Use the fare table on page 81.

	From	To	Service	Fare
a.	Los Angeles	Portland	First Class	$ 64
b.	Pittsburgh	Miami	Jet Coach	65
c.	Seattle	Las Vegas	Jet Coach	78
d.	Portland	New York	First Class	160
e.	San Diego	San Francisco	Jet Economy-Coach	20

4. Find the round-trip cost between the points indicated. Include the 8% federal tax in your computation. Use the fare table on page 81.

	From	To	Service	One-Way Fare	Round-Trip Fare	Federal Tax	Total Cost
a.	San Diego	Los Angeles	First Class	$ 12	$ 24	$ 1.92	$ 25.92
b.	Newark	Portland	Jet Coach	145	290	23.20	313.20
c.	Pittsburgh	Philadelphia	Jet Coach	20	40	3.20	43.20
d.	Oakland	Pittsburgh	First Class	142	284	22.72	306.72
e.	Los Angeles	St. Paul	First Class	130	260	20.80	280.80

Problem 2 is designed to show a comparison between the cost of a first-class flight against a jet-coach flight. Have the students make other comparisons similar to this by using the fare table.

B

1. Mr. Manning missed Flight Number 533 out of San Francisco for Los Angeles and had to take Flight Number 851.

   a. How long would the trip have taken on Flight Number 533?

   55 min.

   b. How long did the trip take him on Flight Number 851?

   2 hr. 58 min.

   c. How much more time did he spend on Flight Number 851 than he would have on Flight Number 533?

   2 hr. 3 min.

   d. How much later did he arrive in Los Angeles by taking Flight Number 851 than he would have had he taken Flight Number 533?

   2 hr. 13 min.

   e. If Mr. Manning had waited for Flight Number 535, how long would he have had to wait after Flight Number 851 had left?

   50 min.

   f. How much earlier would Flight Number 535 have brought him into Los Angeles than Flight Number 851?

   1 hr. 13 min.

   g. How do you account for the fact that although Flight Number 535 left San Francisco later than Flight Number 851, it arrived in Los Angeles earlier?

   Flight Number 535 made no stops on route, while Flight Number 851 made two stops.

2. Fred Carpenter took a round-trip flight out of San Francisco for Saint Paul.

   a. How much would this flight have cost him if he had traveled first class? Include federal tax.

   $280.80

   b. How much would this flight have cost him if he traveled by jet coach? Include federal tax.

   $226.80

   c. How much would he save by traveling jet coach?

   $ 54.00

PART 2

Far fewer people travel by air on weekdays than on weekends. Therefore, to attract people to fly at times when they might not otherwise, most airlines offer bargain rates from Monday noon until Friday noon. Under the discount prices, the husband pays the usual cost. However, the fares for his wife and children are a good deal less. In fact, as you can see in the following table, the cost for each child is only one third the cost of the father's ticket when traveling by coach.

Ask the students if they can think of any conditions under which a person would take Flight 851 out of San Francisco for Los Angeles rather than Flight 535. (Refer to Problem 1.)

FAMILY–PLAN DISCOUNT

(From 12:00 noon Monday until 12:00 noon Friday)

		Fraction of Fare
First Class	Wife...................	¾
	Child Age 12–21..........	¾
	Child Age 2–11...........	½
Coach	Wife...................	⅔
	Child Age 2–21...........	⅓

■ ILLUSTRATION 1: Mr. Peabody took his wife and two children, ages 12 and 14, with him when he flew from Philadelphia to San Diego. They flew by jet coach, leaving on Monday evening and returning on Thursday evening. What was the total air transportation cost, including federal tax, on this trip? Use the rate table on page 81.

● SOLUTION:

$$\text{Mr. Peabody's fare} = \$141$$
$$\text{Mrs. Peabody's fare} = \tfrac{2}{3} \times \$141$$
$$= \$94$$
$$\text{Each child's fare} = \tfrac{1}{3} \times \$141$$
$$= \$47$$
$$\text{Both children's fares} = 2 \times \$47$$
$$= \$94$$
$$\text{Total one-way fare} = \$141 + \$94 + \$94$$
$$= \$329$$
$$\text{Federal tax one way} = \$329 \times 8\%$$
$$= \$329 \times .08$$
$$= \$26.32$$
$$\text{Total one-way transportation cost} = \$329 + \$26.32$$
$$= \$355.32$$
$$\text{Total two-way transportation cost} = 2 \times \$355.32$$
$$= \$710.64$$

▼ EXPLANATION: Since the trip was taken between 12:00 noon on Monday and 12:00 noon on Friday, Mr. Peabody was able to take advantage of the discount prices. From the table on page 81, you will find that the coach fare between Philadelphia and San Diego for Mr. Peabody is $141. The fare charged his wife is two thirds of this amount, according to the discount table, while each child's fare is one third of the $141. As you learned earlier, the federal tax is 8% of the total fare. When you add the tax of $26.32 to the $329, your sum is the total one-way transportation cost. How much would Mr. Peabody's fare have been had the family traveled first class? In that event, how much fare would he have had to pay for Mrs. Peabody? How is the total round-trip transportation cost found?

In Illustration 1, the federal tax was computed on the total one-way fare. Have the students determine the answer where they compute the tax on each person's fare separately. Ask them to justify why their answer should be the same as the one above. (Distributive law of multiplication over addition.)

Every airplane accident, whether large or small, gets so much publicity that far too many people feel that they are writing their own death warrant each time they step aboard a plane. Perhaps the thought that one just doesn't usually walk away from an airplane accident is what is troubling these people. However, statistics in the 1968 death-rate table which follows seem to indicate that these fears are groundless. In fact, they appear to say that you should be much more concerned about your safety when you drive your car, or when you are in the back seat of a taxi than when you board a plane. A little arithmetic tells you that the chance of meeting death in a car or taxi is more than 25 times greater than in a plane. How was this number reached?

The table clearly shows, if nothing else, that you are a great deal safer in the hands of a professional driver—other than a taxi driver—than when driving your own car. Notice how steeply the death rate drops when you leave your car at home and travel either by bus, train, or plane. Incidentally, the death rate on these last three varies slightly from year to year, so that it can't be said that it's safer to fly than it is to travel by bus or train. On a succeeding year, these three rates might simply reverse themselves. What can very definitely be said, though, is that traveling by any one of these public conveyances is much, much safer than traveling by automobile!

TRANSPORTATION—ACCIDENT DEATH RATES

Kind Of Transportation	Rate Per 100 Million Passenger Miles
Passenger Automobiles and Taxis	2.50
Passenger Automobiles on Turnpikes	1.30
Buses	0.20
Railroad Passenger Trains	0.16
Scheduled Domestic Air Transport Planes	0.09

And yet, despite the reassuring figures in this table, flight insurance companies do a brisk business in every airport in the country. People crowd around the counters where this insurance is sold. Or, if they do not want to wait, they can go to a vending machine where, for $2.50, it is possible to purchase $100,000 worth of flight insurance. Quite apparently, if a company is willing to charge so little for giving so much coverage, it must feel that the risk of an air accident is quite, quite small.

The flight insurance rates on page 86 are typical of those charged by most companies for airline trip-insurance. The principal sum is the amount of money given your *beneficiaries*. These are the people you

More current accidental death-rate tables can be found in such books as the *Information Please Almanac,* or the *World Almanac.*

RATE SCHEDULE

| Premium | Principal Sum | |
	One-way Trip	Round Trip
$ .50	$ 20,000	$15,000
.75	30,000	22,500
1.00	40,000	30,000
1.25	50,000	37,500
1.50	60,000	45,000
1.75	70,000	52,500
2.00	80,000	60,000
2.25	90,000	67,500
2.50	100,000	75,000

name in the policy to receive the insurance in the event an accident should befall the plane and you are killed. If you are not killed in an accident, there is still a possibility of collecting either part, or all, of the principal sum. This will depend on how badly you are injured.

Nature of Injury	Amount of Benefit
Loss of life, or both feet, or both hands, or both eyes	The principal sum
Loss of one hand and one foot	The principal sum
Loss of one hand and one eye, or one foot and one eye	The principal sum
Loss of one foot, or one hand	One half of the principal sum
Loss of one eye	One fourth of the principal sum

■ ILLUSTRATION 2: At the start of a one-way air trip, Mr. Traymore purchased $1 worth of insurance. The plane made a forced landing, during which one of Mr. Traymore's eyes was so badly injured that he lost the sight of it. How much did Mr. Traymore receive from the insurance company to compensate him for this loss?

● SOLUTION:

Principal sum for a $1 premium on a one-way trip = $40,000
Coverage for loss of one eye = ¼ × $40,000
= $10,000

▼ EXPLANATION: According to the rate schedule, a premium of $1 will purchase $40,000 worth of insurance on a one-way trip. The loss of one eye entitles Mr. Traymore to one fourth of this insurance, or

Students will often question why the loss of an eye should be worth only half of the loss of a hand or a foot. This decision is a value judgment based merely on what is believed to be the extent of the impairment of mobility caused by the loss of that part of the body.

$10,000. How much would Mr. Traymore have received had he lost both eyes? Why is the amount received for the loss of both eyes more than twice the amount received for the loss of one eye?

### EXERCISES					A

Do you recall how to do the computation in the following exercises? If not, you will probably want to refer to page 573 for help.

1. $\frac{1}{2} \times 20$ = 10	13. $\frac{3}{5} \times 45$ = 27
2. $\frac{1}{4} \times 12$ = 3	14. $\frac{3}{8} \times 32$ = 12
3. $\frac{1}{5} \times 30$ = 6	15. $\frac{4}{5} \times 60$ = 48
4. $\frac{1}{3} \times 42$ = 14	16. $\frac{7}{8} \times 56$ = 49
5. $\frac{1}{6} \times 84$ = 14	17. $\frac{1}{2} \times \$25$ = \$ 12.50
6. $\frac{1}{5} \times 345$ = 69	18. $\frac{1}{2} \times \$87$ = \$ 43.50
7. $\frac{1}{4} \times 764$ = 191	19. $\frac{1}{2} \times \$239$ = \$119.50
8. $\frac{1}{3} \times 594$ = 198	20. $\frac{1}{4} \times \$14$ = \$ 3.50
9. $\frac{2}{3} \times 15$ = 10	21. $\frac{1}{4} \times \$95$ = \$ 23.75
10. $\frac{3}{4} \times 16$ = 12	22. $\frac{1}{4} \times \$351$ = \$ 87.75
11. $\frac{2}{5} \times 20$ = 8	23. $\frac{3}{4} \times \$17$ = \$ 12.75
12. $\frac{5}{6} \times 12$ = 10	24. $\frac{3}{4} \times \$247$ = \$185.25

B

1. In each of the following exercises, the people traveled by air at a time when they could take advantage of the family-discount rates. Determine the fare for the person traveling with the husband or father.

	Fare of Father or Husband	Class of Traveling	Person Traveling	Fare
a.	$120	Coach	Child age 12	$ 40.00
b.	150	Coach	Child age 14	50.00
c.	240	Coach	Child age 10	80.00
d.	110	First Class	Child age 6	55.00
e.	144	First Class	Child age 10	72.00
f.	107	Coach	Child age 24	107.00
g.	180	Coach	Wife	120.00
h.	207	Coach	Wife	138.00
i.	152	First Class	Child age 15	114.00
j.	216	First Class	Wife	162.00
k.	117	First Class	Child age 7	58.50
l.	309	First Class	Child age 8	154.50
m.	145	First Class	Wife	108.75
n.	207	First Class	Wife	155.25
o.	343	First Class	Child age 17	257.25

It would be best to have the students do the exercises in Group A before attempting the exercises that follow them. This will give you an opportunity to see where their weaknesses may lie in finding the product of a fraction and a whole number -- a necessary prerequisite for doing Exercises B and C.

2. In each of the following exercises the people traveled by air at a time when they could take advantage of the family-discount rates. Determine the fare for the person traveling with the husband or father. Do not include the federal tax. Use the air-fare table on page 81.

From	To	Class Of Traveling	Fare of Father Or Husband	Person Traveling	Fare
a. Los Angeles	Omaha	Coach	$ 84.00	Child age 19	$ 28.00
b. New York	Pittsburgh	First Class	28.00	Child age 5	14.00
c. Portland	San Diego	Coach	60.00	Child age 14	20.00
d. San Francisco	Portland	Coach	36.00	Wife	24.00
e. San Diego	Philadelphia	Coach	141.00	Wife	94.00
f. Pittsburgh	Philadelphia	First Class	23.00	Wife	17.25
g. Seattle	Los Angeles	First Class	73.00	Child age 17	54.75
h. Pittsburgh	Seattle	First Class	142.00	Wife	106.50

3. In each of the following exercises, what is the amount of the principal sum of flight insurance that can be purchased?

	Premium	Type of Trip	Principal Sum
a.	$ .75	One-way	$ 30,000
b.	1.50	Round	45,000
c.	2.00	One-way	80,000
d.	2.50	Round	75,000

4. Each of the people in the following exercises was traveling by air. How much did either they, or their beneficiaries, receive as a result of an accident if they had purchased flight insurance for the premiums listed?

	Premium	Type Of Trip	Principal Sum	Extent Of Injury	Insurance Received
a.	$1.00	Round	$ 30,000	Death	$ 30,000
b.	1.75	One-way	70,000	Death	70,000
c.	2.50	One-way	100,000	Loss of one hand	50,000
d.	1.50	Round	45,000	Loss of one foot	22,500
e.	1.25	Round	37,500	Loss of one hand	18,750
f.	.50	Round	15,000	Loss of one eye	3,750
g.	2.25	Round	67,500	Loss of one eye	16,875

C

Travelers will frequently insure not only themselves against any injury that might occur to them as a result of an accident on a trip,

Exercises 3 and 4 should give the student some idea of the very large amount of protection he can purchase for a relatively small amount of money.

BAGGAGE AND PERSONAL EFFECTS INSURANCE

				AMOUNT OF INSURANCE								MAXIMUM
	$300.	$400.	$500.	$600.	$700.	$800.	$900.	$1,000.	$2,000.	$3,000.	$4,000.	$5,000.
TERM						PREMIUMS						.
1 Day	$ 1.00	$ 1.05	$ 1.10	$ 1.25	$ 1.30	$ 1.40	$ 1.45	$ 1.60	$ 2.40	$ 3.20	$ 4.00	$ 4.80
2 Days	1.25	1.40	1.60	1.70	1.95	2.10	2.25	2.40	3.65	4.85	6.05	7.25
3 Days	1.45	1.70	2.00	2.25	2.50	2.75	3.05	3.30	4.95	6.60	8.25	9.90
4 Days	1.70	2.10	2.40	2.75	3.10	3.40	3.80	4.15	6.20	8.25	10.35	12.35
5 Days	2.00	2.40	2.90	3.30	3.75	4.15	4.55	5.00	7.55	10.00	12.55	15.00
6-7 Days	2.25	2.75	3.30	3.80	4.35	4.85	5.40	5.85	8.75	11.65	14.55	17.50
8-9 Days	2.50	3.10	3.75	4.35	4.90	5.50	6.10	6.75	10.15	13.55	16.95	20.30
10-11 Days	2.75	3.40	4.15	4.85	5.50	6.20	6.90	7.60	11.40	15.20	18.95	22.75
12-13 Days	3.05	3.80	4.55	5.40	6.10	6.90	7.65	8.45	12.70	16.95	21.15	25.40
14-15 Days	3.30	4.15	5.00	5.85	6.75	7.60	8.45	9.30	13.95	18.60	23.25	27.90
16-17 Days	3.50	4.45	5.45	6.40	7.30	8.25	9.25	10.20	15.30	20.35	25.45	30.50
18-19 Days	3.80	4.85	5.85	6.90	7.90	8.95	9.95	11.00	16.50	22.00	27.50	33.00
20-21 Days	4.05	5.15	6.25	7.45	8.55	9.65	10.75	11.90	17.80	23.75	29.70	35.65
22-23 Days	4.35	5.50	6.75	7.90	9.15	10.35	11.55	12.70	19.05	25.40	31.80	38.10
24-25 Days	4.55	5.85	7.15	8.45	9.70	11.00	12.30	13.65	20.45	27.30	34.10	40.90
26-27 Days	4.85	6.20	7.60	8.95	10.35	11.70	13.10	14.45	21.70	28.95	36.20	43.40
28-29 Days	5.10	6.55	8.00	9.50	10.95	12.40	13.80	15.35	23.05	30.70	38.40	46.05
30 Da. to 1 Mo.	5.40	6.90	8.45	9.95	11.55	13.10	14.65	16.15	24.25	32.35	40.40	48.50

but, also, they will insure their baggage and personal effects against damage, loss, or theft during the trip. The table above is typical of most rate tables for this type of insurance.

1. Find the cost of the baggage and personal-effects insurance in each of the following exercises.

	Amount Of Insurance	Term In Days	Premium		Amount Of Insurance	Term In Days	Premium
a.	$300	4	$ 1.70	d.	$1,000	5	$ 5.00
b.	700	3	2.50	e.	3,000	27	28.95
c.	900	20	10.75	f.	4,000	19	27.50

2. If a person purchased insurance for between $1,000 and $2,000, the cost would be the premium for the first $1,000, plus one half the premium for anything over $1,000. Find the cost of baggage and personal-effects insurance in each of the following exercises.

	Amount Of Insurance	Term In Days	Premium On $1,000	Premium On Excess	½ Premium On Excess	Total Cost
a.	$1,300	1	$ 1.60	$ 1.00	$ .50	$ 2.10
b.	1,500	3	3.30	2.00	1.00	4.30
c.	1,800	24	13.65	11.00	5.50	19.15
d.	1,700	16	10.20	7.30	3.65	13.85
e.	1,400	22	12.70	5.50	2.75	15.45

It is extremely important that these exercises and all exercises in this text be discussed with the students from the point of view of them as consumers. Yes, an accurate answer is extremely important; but even more important is the meaning of the answer they have found.

3. If a person purchased insurance for between $2,000 and $3,000, the cost would be the premium for the first $2,000, plus one half the premium for anything over $2,000. Similar methods would be used for finding the cost of insurance between $3,000 and $4,000, or between $4,000 and $5,000. Find the cost of baggage and personal-effects insurance in each of the following exercises.

	Amount Of Insurance	Term In Days	Premium On Base Amount	Premium On Excess	½ Premium On Excess	Total Cost
a.	$2,500	14	$ 13.95	$ 5.00	$ 2.50	$ 16.45
b.	2,800	10	11.40	6.20	3.10	14.50
c.	3,600	16	20.35	6.40	3.20	23.55
d.	3,900	7	11.65	5.40	2.70	14.35
e.	4,700	25	34.10	9.70	4.85	38.95

D

1. Mr. Hardy flew by jet coach from Los Angeles to St. Paul on a business trip. He left on Tuesday and returned on Friday morning. Since his wife's parents lived in St. Paul, he took her and his son, age 9, along with him.
   a. How much was Mr. Hardy's round-trip fare? $210.00
   b. How much did he have to pay for his wife? $140.00
   c. How much did he have to pay for his son? $ 70.00
   d. What was the total fare for the entire family? $420.00
   e. What was the federal tax on the total fare? $ 33.60
   f. How much was the total flight cost for the family? $453.60

2. How much more would Mr. Hardy of Problem 1 have had to pay for this flight had the family traveled first class rather than jet coach?
   $173.25

3. During the year in which the transportation-accident death rate table was compiled, there were 630 hundred million passenger miles of air traveled. How many people were killed that year as a result of traveling by air on domestic scheduled flights? (See the death-rate table on page 85.)   56.70 or 57 people

Unit 5: Chapter Review and Test

In doing the computation for many of the following problems, it will be necessary for you to refer to the tables in this chapter.
1. Find the cost of renting each of the following cars for one day. Use the rate table on page 55 for Company A.

Problem 3 in Group B is quite difficult for the average student taking this course. It should be assigned only as an extra-credit problem.

Type Of Car	Base Rate	Number Of Miles	Cost Per Mile	Mileage Cost	Total Cost
a. Standard Sedan	$ 12.00	60	$ .12	$ 7.20	$ 19.20
b. Medium Convertible	15.00	87	.15	13.05	28.05

2. Mr. Amant rented a sports car for one week from Company B, whose rate table appears on page 55. He drove the car 450 miles during this period.

   a. How much did he pay the company for the rental of the car alone? $50.00

   b. How much did he pay the company in mileage cost? $36.00

   c. If the car averaged 15 miles to the gallon of gasoline, how many gallons of gasoline did he have to buy? 30

   d. If the average cost of each gallon of gasoline was 35.9¢, what did he have to pay for gasoline during the week? $10.77

   e. What was the total cost to Mr. Amant for renting the car that week? $96.77

3. The time in each of the following exercises is given in terms of normal recording. Rewrite them without using the letters A.M. or P.M.

	Time Normal Recording	Time New Recording		Time Normal Recording	Time New Recording
a.	3:00 A.M.	3:00	d.	2:00 P.M.	14:00
b.	7:20 A.M.	7:20	e.	5:30 P.M.	17:30
c.	9:12 A.M.	9:12	f.	9:43 P.M.	21:43

4. Nine hours and 15 minutes can be written as 8 hours and how many minutes? 75 min.

5. Find the time that has elapsed in each of the following exercises.

From	To	Time Elapsed		From	To	Time Elapsed
a. 4:20 A.M.	6:35 A.M.	2 hr. 15 min.	c.	8:30 A.M.	1:40 P.M.	5 hr. 10 min.
b. 2:45 P.M.	8:12 P.M.	5 hr. 27 min.	d.	10:58 A.M.	5:23 P.M.	6 hr. 25 min.

6. Determine the time it will take the bus that leaves Butler at 2:50 P.M. to arrive in Newark. Use the bus schedule on page 60.
   1 hr. 45 min.

7. A person takes bus Trip Number 2037 out of Jersey City for Washington. How long will this trip take him? Use the bus schedule on page 67.
   5 hr. 50 min.

8. What will be the cost of a round-trip ticket between Washington and San Antonio? Use the bus-rate table on page 69. $92.52

9. How long will it take the train that leaves Baltimore at 9:10 in the morning to arrive in Trenton? Use the schedule on page 72.
   2 hr. 10 min.

The odd-numbered problems on these two pages can be used as a review, while the even ones can be used for testing purposes.

10. Determine how much a person would save by purchasing a 1-day round-trip ticket from Belmar to New York instead of 2 one-way tickets. Use the rate table on page 73. $\underline{\quad \$ \quad 1.38 \quad}$

11. Mr. Richards commutes each day from his home in Elberon to his place of employment in New York. His working week is from Monday through Friday. How much can he save each week by purchasing a weekly commutation ticket instead of a one-way ticket? Use the table on page 73. $\underline{\quad \$ \quad 12.15 \quad}$

12. How long will it take the plane on Flight Number 333 to make the trip from Spokane to San Francisco? Use the flight table on page 78. $\underline{\text{2 hr. 45 min.}}$

13. What is the cost of a one-way jet first-class flight from Portland to Philadelphia? Include the federal tax. Use the table on page 81. $\underline{\text{\$168.48}}$

14. Mr. Coleman and his wife flew from San Diego to Oakland on Tuesday and returned on Thursday. They traveled on a jet-coach flight.
    a. What was the round-trip fare for Mr. Coleman? $\underline{\text{\$ 60.00}}$
    b. What was the round-trip fare for Mrs. Coleman? $\underline{\text{40.00}}$
    c. What was the total fare? $\underline{\text{\$100.00}}$
    d. What was the federal tax on this fare? $\underline{\text{\$ 8.00}}$
    e. What was the total cost for transportation? $\underline{\text{\$108.00}}$

15. How much flight insurance can be purchased for $2.25 on a one-way trip? $\underline{\text{\$90,000}}$

16. As a result of an accident on a round-trip business flight from Chicago to Houston, Mr. Gregory lost one hand. If he had purchased $2.00 worth of flight insurance before making the trip, how much compensation would he have received from the insurance company? $\underline{\text{\$30,000}}$

17. What is the cost of $800 worth of baggage and personal-effects insurance for a period of 28 days? Use the table on page 89. $\underline{\text{\$12.40}}$

18. Flight Number 337 out of Seattle to Los Angeles was 10 minutes early in arriving.
    a. How long did it take the plane to make the flight? $\underline{\text{2 hrs.}}$
    b. If the number of miles by air between Seattle and Los Angeles is 959, to the nearest mile, at what average speed was this plane traveling? $\underline{\text{480 mph}}$

CHAPTER 3

PURCHASING CONSUMER GOODS

At the present time, the nation's teen-agers are spending annually a little more than 20 billion dollars of their own money. When you consider the fact that this amounts to $1 out of every $10 spent on nonessential goods, you begin to realize that the teen-age market is keeping a lot of companies in business. By examining a few more bits of statistical information, you will discover that well over half of the high school population of today will be married before it reaches 21. Hence, the habits and attitudes you are developing now toward managing your money will be the same ones you will apply in just a few years when you may be married.

This chapter, perhaps more than any other in the text, is extremely important and timely to the student. Although he, personally, at this time of his life may not be involved in any other topic discussed, he is certainly a purchaser of goods for both himself and his family.

The easy-come, easy-go frame of mind may be fine when Dad's around to bail you out of debt. But all too soon you, yourself, will face the responsibility of making intelligent decisions on what to buy and, perhaps, even more important—when to buy. What with federal income tax and state income tax, every dollar you can save through wise money management is equivalent to about $1.25 in your earnings! It doesn't take much ability to spend money. To spend money intelligently, though, takes a little effort and just a little training. The purpose of this chapter is to take a look at a few of the things you might want to consider before making that purchase—whatever one you happen to be considering at the moment.

Unit 1:   Shopping at a Supermarket

PART 1

An interesting project that teachers frequently give their classes in consumer mathematics—in fact, your own class might be interested in doing this—is to make a list of some fifteen to twenty items such as the ones listed. Then, with this list in hand, the students are asked to visit three of the stores in their neighborhood and compare the prices of identical brand goods.

Comparison should be made between the prices of identical brands. Even in the same store, the same item—such as tuna fish—is canned by several different companies and sold at a variety of prices. Hence, it's important that, if a comparison of prices is to be made, it is made between the same brand and the same item in all stores.

Item	Brand	Weight	Price
Cornflakes	_____	12 oz. box	_____
Tuna Fish	_____	7 oz. can	_____
Laundry Bleach	_____	½ gal.	_____
Laundry Detergent	_____	1 lb. 4 oz. box	_____
Vegetable Juice	_____	1 qt. 4 oz. can	_____
Frozen French Fries	_____	12 oz. package	_____
Sugar	_____	5 lb. bag	_____
Salt	_____	1 lb. 10 oz. box	_____
Spaghetti	_____	1 lb. box	_____
Coffee	_____	1 lb. can	_____

The normal shopper could not go from supermarket to supermarket to compare prices before she made any purchase. Frequently, markets will run weekly specials—sometimes called come-ons—in which they drop prices quite drastically on some items in order to attract custom-

It is strongly urged that the students in the class undertake a comparison-shopping project similar to the one described above. If nothing else, have some go to one store to note the prices while other students go to a second store and do the same with identical products.

ers. Once they have the person in the store, they hope that she will purchase enough other items—possibly at higher prices than normal—to make up for any loss on the reduced specials. Unless a shopper starts out with list in hand of the best buys taken from advertisements of the several supermarkets in her area, she will probably waste a great deal of time and a great deal of gasoline trying to run down bargains.

It is possible, though, to save money by shopping wisely and yet do all your shopping in the same store. Purchase of a cheaper can of coffee does not mean the purchase of a poorer quality of coffee. Companies will often spend large sums of money to establish a good brand name for themselves. Once they have done this, they are in a position to create the impression that they should charge more than their competitors because their merchandise is of better quality. This may be far from the truth. Frequently, the quality of an item is a matter of personal taste. Enjoying one grade of coffee over another is more often dependent on your own taste than on a difference in price.

As a shopper, you have plenty to gain by taking a second look at the large economy-size package, whether it be of cornflakes or laundry detergent. The one problem you have to face is that fancy packaging has become a real art. All too often you find that the top quarter of the supergiant-size box contains nothing but air.

Thus, if you plan to save money shopping, you are faced with the prospect of having to read the fine print on the label. By law, the weights of the contents of every can, box, or bottle must appear on the label. The only way the manufacturers can outsmart you is by making the print too small to read—and this sometimes happens.

Being able to read the weight or capacity of the contents of a package is only part of the problem. You are still faced with the difficulty of interpreting what the measures mean. For instance, in the table on page 94, a number of the items are measured in terms of ounces, and yet these ounces mean different things in reference to different items. For example, the laundry detergent 1 pound is equivalent to 16 *ounces* in what is called avoirdupois measure. This is a standard of weights for items that are more or less classified as solid objects. However, in the case of vegetable juice, the 1 quart is equivalent to 32 *ounces* of liquid measure. This, of course, is a standard of measure for liquids. Thus, the term *ounce* is used as a measure of weight and also as a measure for volume or size.

There are only five different measures that appear on the labels of practically all the items that are sold in supermarkets. These are pounds, gallons, quarts, pints, and ounces. The relations between them are shown in the two tables on page 96.

To confuse the consumer even more, there are a number of companies that are showing the content weight in terms of grams. In all fairness, however, this information is usually accompanied by the weight in avoirdupois measure.

AVOIRDUPOIS MEASURE

1 pound (lb.)   =   16 ounces (oz.)

LIQUID MEASURE

1 gallon (gal.)	=	4 quarts (qt.)
1 quart	=	2 pints (pt.)
1 quart	=	32 ounces (oz.)

■ILLUSTRATION 1: How many ounces are there in 1 quart, 14 ounces?

▼EXPLANATION: According to the table of liquid measure, there are 32 ounces in a quart. Hence, by changing the 1 quart to 32 ounces and adding these to the 14 ounces, you can find the total number of ounces in 1 quart, 14 ounces.

●SOLUTION:

$$1 \text{ quart, 14 ounces} = 32 \text{ ounces} + 14 \text{ ounces}$$
$$= 46 \text{ ounces}$$

■ILLUSTRATION 2: A 1-pound, 9-ounce jar of applesauce can be purchased for 39 cents. What is the cost of each ounce of applesauce to the nearest tenth of a cent?

▼EXPLANATION: Since each pound is equivalent to 16 ounces, then the number of ounces in 1 pound, 9 ounces is 25. Hence, 25 ounces of applesauce cost 39 cents and, therefore, 1 ounce would be 1/25 of 39 cents. To find 1/25 of a number means to divide that number by 25.

●SOLUTION:

$$\text{Total weight} = 1 \text{ lb.} + 9 \text{ oz.}$$
$$= 16 \text{ oz.} + 9 \text{ oz.}$$
$$= 25 \text{ oz.}$$
$$\text{Cost of 25 oz.} = 39\cancel{c}$$
$$\text{Cost of 1 oz.} = 39\cancel{c} \div 25$$
$$= 1.56\cancel{c}, \text{ or } 1.6\cancel{c}$$

■ILLUSTRATION 3: Mrs. James purchased three cans of kernel corn for 46¢. How much would she have paid had she purchased only one can?

▼EXPLANATION: As in the previous illustration, if 3 cans cost 46¢, then 1 can would cost ⅓ the amount. Finding ⅓ of 46¢ involves dividing 46¢ by 3. However, dividing 46¢ by 3 gives you a quotient of 15⅓¢. It is not possible to give the dealer one third of a penny. Even though a mixed number involving one third as its fractional part is normally rounded off by dropping the one third, this is never done in the purchase of food. No matter how small the fraction of a penny may be in computing the cost of one can, the cost is always rounded off to

Some states are currently trying to enact laws whereby the dealer must display the cost of each item per unit measure, as is down in Illustration 2. Have the students investigate whether such a law has been enacted, or is pending in their state.

the next higher cent. Thus, 14¼¢ would be rounded off to 15¢; 29½¢ would be rounded off to 30¢; and the same for any other fraction. Can you see why the dealer would not want to drop the fraction of a penny?

●SOLUTION:

$$\text{Cost of 3 cans} = 46¢$$
$$\text{Cost of 1 can} = 46¢ \div 3$$
$$= 15⅓¢, \text{ or } 16¢$$

EXERCISES   A

Do you recall how to do the division in the following exercises? If not, you will probably want to refer to pages 593–594 for help. Determine the quotient correct to the nearest tenth of a cent.

1. 56¢ ÷ 9 = __6.2¢__	8. 114¢ ÷ 7 = __16.3¢__
2. 47¢ ÷ 5 = __9.4¢__	9. 146¢ ÷ 8 = __18.3¢__
3. 24¢ ÷ 7 = __3.4¢__	10. 159¢ ÷ 6 = __26.5¢__
4. 78¢ ÷ 8 = __9.8¢__	11. 56¢ ÷ 17 = __3.3¢__
5. 52¢ ÷ 6 = __8.7¢__	12. 95¢ ÷ 26 = __3.7¢__
6. 84¢ ÷ 3 = __28.0¢__	13. 107¢ ÷ 35 = __3.1¢__
7. 103¢ ÷ 9 = __11.4¢__	14. 126¢ ÷ 46 = __2.7¢__

B

1. Each of the following is expressed in terms of dollars. Rewrite them in terms of cents.

   a. $1.25 __125¢__   d. $4.06 __406¢__   g. $1 __100¢__
   b. $2.56 __256¢__   e. $2.09 __209¢__   h. $2 __200¢__
   c. $1.87 __187¢__   f. $7.62 __762¢__   i. $5 __500¢__

2. Write each of the following measures in terms of ounces only.

   a. 2 lb. __32 oz.__   e. 2 lb. 10 oz. __42 oz.__
   b. 5 lb. __80 oz.__   f. 4 lb. 1 oz. __65 oz.__
   c. 9 lb. __144 oz.__   g. 5 lb. 14 oz. __94 oz.__
   d. 1 lb. 3 oz. __19 oz.__   h. 9 lb. 7 oz. __151 oz.__

3. Write each of the following measures in terms of pints only.

   a. 3 qt. __6 pt.__   d. 7 qt. 1 pt. __15 pt.__
   b. 7 qt. __14 pt.__   e. 15 qt. 1 pt. __31 pt.__
   c. 2 qt. 1 pt. __5 pt.__   f. 27 qt. 1 pt. __55 pt.__

4. Write each of the following measures in terms of quarts only.

   a. 4 gal. __16 qt.__   e. 2 gal. 3 qt. __11 qt.__
   b. 8 gal. __32 qt.__   f. 5 gal. 2 qt. __22 qt.__
   c. 10 gal. __40 qt.__   g. ½ gal. __2 qt.__
   d. 1 gal. 1 qt. __5 qt.__   h. 2½ gal. __10 qt.__

Emphasize the need for an understanding of Exercise A before proceeding. Consumer comparison of food prices depends largely on the ability to compute unit prices. Similarly, unless a person can convert from one unit to another, as is required in B 1-5, any attempt at comparison is wasted effort.

5. Write each of the following measures in terms of ounces only.

   a. 1 qt. ____32 oz.____   e. 5 qt. 14 oz. ____174 oz.____
   b. 3 qt. ____96 oz.____   f. 9 qt. 6 oz. ____294 oz.____
   c. 8 qt. ____256 oz.____   g. 1 pt.   16 oz.
   d. 2 qt. 5 oz. ____69 oz.____   h. 3 pt.   48 oz.

6. What is the cost of each ounce of food in the following purchases?
   Find your answer to the nearest tenth of a cent.

	Total Cost	Number Of Ounces	Cost Per Ounce
a.	59¢	8	7.4 ¢
b.	37¢	6	6.2 ¢
c.	49¢	5	9.8 ¢
d.	76¢	9	8.4 ¢
e.	$1.62	14	11.6 ¢
f.	$1.97	26	7.6 ¢
g.	$2.05	37	5.5 ¢
h.	$3.19	18	17.7 ¢

7. What is the cost of each ounce of food in each of the following
   purchases? Find your answer to the nearest tenth of a cent.

	Total Cost	Weight Of Purchase	Number Of Ounces	Cost Per Ounce
a.	67¢	1 lb.	16	4.2 ¢
b.	84¢	2 lb.	32	2.6 ¢
c.	95¢	1 lb. 5 oz.	21	4.5 ¢
d.	$1.37	2 lb. 7 oz.	39	3.5 ¢
e.	$2.95	3 lb. 12 oz.	60	4.9 ¢
f.	$3.06	2 lb. 14 oz.	46	6.7 ¢

8. What is the cost of each ounce of food in the following purchases?
   Find your answer to the nearest tenth of a cent.

	Total Cost	Measure Of Contents	Number Of Ounces	Cost Per Ounce
a.	54¢	1 qt.	32	1.7 ¢
b.	76¢	2 qt.	64	1.2 ¢
c.	87¢	2 qt. 3 oz.	67	1.3 ¢
d.	$1.21	1 qt. 5 oz.	37	3.3 ¢
e.	$2.17	2 qt. 18 oz.	82	2.6 ¢
f.	$4.95	4 qt. 25 oz.	153	3.2 ¢

9. Prices in supermarkets are stamped on cans as 2/47¢, or 5/83¢, and
   so on. These prices are read as 2 cans for 47¢, or 5 cans for 83¢. How
   much will a person have to pay on the purchase of one can of each
   of the following items if they are marked as shown?

Marking On Can	Cost Per Can		Marking On Can	Cost Per Can	
a. 2/15¢	8	¢	g. 4/62¢	16	¢
b. 2/37¢	19	¢	h. 5/87¢	18	¢
c. 2/95¢	48	¢	i. 5/96¢	20	¢
d. 3/16¢	6	¢	j. 2/$1.15	58	¢
e. 3/95¢	32	¢	k. 3/$1.96	66	¢
f. 4/85¢	22	¢	l. 5/$2.16	44	¢

B

1. Frozen orange juice can be purchased at 5 cans for 86¢. How much would a person save by buying 5 cans at one time rather than 5 separate cans on 5 separate occasions?   4¢

2. How many ounces are there in 3 gallons, 2 quarts of a liquid?
            448 oz.

3. Peanut butter can be purchased in a 1-pound, 2-ounce jar at 67¢, or in a 1-pound, 12-ounce jar at 89¢.
   a. How much will a person have to pay per ounce if she purchases the smaller jar of peanut butter? Find your answer to the nearest tenth of a penny.   3.7¢
   b. How much will a person have to pay per ounce if she purchases the larger jar of peanut butter? Find your answer to the nearest tenth of a penny.   3.2¢
   c. How much can a person save on each ounce of peanut butter by purchasing the larger jar instead of the smaller jar? Find your answer to the nearest tenth of a penny.   .5¢

4. A certain brand of floor wax can be purchased in a 1-pint, 11-ounce container for 53¢, or in a larger container of 1 quart, 14 ounces at 85¢.
   a. How much will a person have to pay per ounce if she purchases the smaller container of floor wax? Find your answer to the nearest tenth of a penny.   2.0¢
   b. How much will a person have to pay per ounce if she purchases the larger container of floor wax? Find your answer to the nearest tenth of a penny.   1.8¢
   c. How much can a person save on each ounce of floor wax by purchasing the larger container instead of the smaller one? Find your answer to the nearest tenth of a penny.   .2¢

PART 2

A good deal of the difficulty in trying to shop wisely in a supermarket comes from a combination of the way items are marked for sale and

Often, the price of items will change, and only the new cans being placed on the shelves are marked with this new price. Alert the students to the fact that it might be wise to examine the prices on several cans before making their selection.

the peculiar weight of the contents. Thus, a certain brand of apple-sauce can be purchased in one of two sizes. In the 8-ounce container, the cost is 29 cents for 2 jars, while in the 15-ounce container, the cost is 67 cents for 3 jars. All too often the larger size is not necessarily the more economical buy, so you can't always use this as a guide.

In spite of the peculiar prices and odd weights, there is a way in which it is possible for you to compare the costs of the same item sold in two different sizes. This method, however, makes use of two mathematical principles. The first of these—the Product of Two Numbers Principle—was examined on page 36 of Chapter 1.

> The Product of Two Numbers Principle: If the product of two numbers is divided by one of these numbers, the quotient will be the other number.

The second principle that you need involves a relationship existing between two fractions. Before stating this principle, it might be a good idea to examine several illustrations to show that it seems justifiable. Consider, for instance, the two equal fractions

$$\tfrac{3}{4} \text{ and } \tfrac{6}{8}.$$

When we write them in the form of an equality, such as

$$\tfrac{3}{4} = \tfrac{6}{8},$$

the pair of numbers 3 and 8 are called opposites, and the same name is given to the pair of numbers 4 and 6.

$$\frac{3}{4} \diagdown\kern-1.2em\diagup \frac{6}{8}$$

The interesting thing about this is the fact that the product of 3 and 8 is exactly the same as the product of 4 and 6. Both products are 24. Now, should you take any other two equal fractions, such as $\tfrac{3}{5}$ and $\tfrac{9}{15}$, and again find the products of their opposites, you discover that here, too, these products are equal—they are both 45.

$$\frac{3}{5} = \frac{9}{15}$$

On the other hand, should you write down two fractions that are not equal—as, for example, $\tfrac{2}{3}$ and $\tfrac{4}{5}$—the products of what you might again call the opposites are not equal. In one case, the product is 10, while in the other, it is 12.

$$\frac{2}{3} \diagdown\kern-1.2em\diagup \frac{4}{5}$$

There are some students who may be familiar with the fact that the equality of two fractions is called a "proportion," and that the term "opposites" refers to the "means" or the "extremes" of the proportion. There is no reason why they cannot continue to use these terms.

Hence, it would appear that the following principle seems reasonable.

> The Equal Fraction Principle: If two fractions are equal, then the products of their opposites are also equal.

Our purpose in introducing these two principles is to enable you to compare the costs of the same item when packaged in two different containers. Before you can do this, however, it will be necessary for you to learn how you can find the replacement for **b** in an equation such as the following.

$$\frac{5}{6} = \frac{b}{18}$$

As you know from your earlier work in mathematics, the letter **b** is holding the place for some number which will make the fraction ⅚ equal to the fraction on the right side of the equal sign. The two principles just examined will help you find this replacement for **b**.

■ ILLUSTRATION: What number can be used as the replacement for **b** which will make the following equation true?

$$\frac{5}{6} = \frac{b}{18}$$

● SOLUTION:

$$\frac{5}{6} = \frac{b}{18} \qquad (1)$$
$$6 \times b = 18 \times 5 \qquad (2)$$
$$6 \times b = 90 \qquad (3)$$
$$b = 90 \div 6 \qquad (4)$$
$$b = 15 \qquad (5)$$

▼ EXPLANATION: By the Equal Fractions Principle, you know that if two fractions are equal, then the product of their opposites will also be equal. Hence, when 6 is multiplied by the placeholder **b**, this product should be equal to the product of 18 and 5. Thus:

$$\frac{5}{6} \diagdown\!\!\!\!\diagup \frac{b}{18}$$

This enables you to arrive at equation (2) from equation (1). To get equation (4), you made use of the Product of Two Numbers Principle. Since the product of the two numbers 6 and **b** is 90 [See step

The letter "b" in the illustration above is variously referred to—depending on the textbook author—as either a "placeholder" or a "variable." For the student taking this course, it would be best to use the term "placeholder," for experience seems to indicate that this appears to be more meaningful to him.

(3)], then when the number 6 is divided into the product, the quotient will be the other number **b**. This is exactly where step (4) comes from. Dividing 90 by 6 gives you 15 as the value of the placeholder **b**. To be doubly sure that your work is correct, replace the **b** by 15 and check to see whether the fraction 15/18 is equal to the fraction 5/6. By reducing 15/18 to its lowest terms, this immediately becomes evident.

EXERCISES

1. Find the replacement for **b** in each of the following equations.

a. $5 \times b = 15$ ___3___	j. $b \times 5 = 55$ ___11___	
b. $8 \times b = 24$ ___3___	k. $b \times 3 = 48$ ___16___	
c. $3 \times b = 27$ ___9___	l. $b \times 4 = 92$ ___23___	
d. $7 \times b = 42$ ___6___	m. $12 \times b = 108$ ___9___	
e. $9 \times b = 63$ ___7___	n. $14 \times b = 210$ ___15___	
f. $4 \times b = 48$ ___12___	o. $15 \times b = 165$ ___11___	
g. $b \times 2 = 12$ ___6___	p. $b \times 23 = 161$ ___7___	
h. $b \times 6 = 30$ ___5___	q. $b \times 31 = 372$ ___12___	
i. $b \times 8 = 64$ ___8___	r. $b \times 46 = 782$ ___17___	

2. Find the replacement for **b** in each of the following equations.

a. $b/2 = 9/6$ ___3___	h. $15/21 = b/7$ ___5___
b. $b/5 = 3/15$ ___1___	i. $22/18 = b/9$ ___11___
c. $b/4 = 25/20$ ___5___	j. $6/4 = b/16$ ___24___
d. $b/7 = 18/42$ ___3___	k. $40/21 = b/42$ ___80___
e. $b/6 = 18/54$ ___2___	l. $27/18 = b/54$ ___81___
f. $b/8 = 21/56$ ___3___	m. $5/3 = 15/b$ ___9___
g. $8/12 = b/3$ ___2___	n. $9/7 = 72/b$ ___56___

3. Find the replacement for **b** to the nearest cent in each of the following equations.

a. $7 \times b = 50\cancel{c}$ ___7.1¢___	g. $b \times 4 = 117\cancel{c}$ ___29.3¢___
b. $5 \times b = 48\cancel{c}$ ___9.6¢___	h. $b \times 3 = 157\cancel{c}$ ___52.3¢___
c. $8 \times b = 70\cancel{c}$ ___8.8¢___	i. $b \times 8 = 152\cancel{c}$ ___19.0¢___
d. $6 \times b = 82\cancel{c}$ ___13.7¢___	j. $14 \times b = \$2.16$ ___15.4¢___
e. $9 \times b = 85\cancel{c}$ ___9.4¢___	k. $23 \times b = \$1.56$ ___6.8¢___
f. $2 \times b = 67\cancel{c}$ ___33.5¢___	l. $31 \times b = \$2.29$ ___7.4¢___

4. Find the replacement for **b** to the nearest cent in each of the following equations.

a. $b/46\cancel{c} = 3/5$ ___27.6¢___	c. $b/93\cancel{c} = 5/8$ ___58.1¢___
b. $b/75\cancel{c} = 4/7$ ___42.9¢___	d. $b/127\cancel{c} = 7/12$ ___74.1¢___

Even for the student who has never been exposed to the "solution of an equation" in his elementary school mathematics, there are sufficient exercises here for the purposes of his needs in applying this information to comparison shopping.

e. $b/263¢ = 5/23$ ___57.2¢___
f. $b/282¢ = 4/27$ ___41.8¢___
g. $5/9 = b/\$1.08$ ___60.0¢___
h. $12/17 = b/\$1.28$ ___90.4¢___

i. $11/25 = b/\$2.14$ ___94.2¢___
j. $3/7 = 53¢/b$ ___123.7¢___
k. $14/26 = 87¢/b$ ___161.6¢___
l. $16/7 = \$1.23/b$ ___53.8¢___

PART 3

When a number is written in the form of a fraction, it can be interpreted in several ways. Usually you think of it as meaning only that it represents part of a quantity, such as one half (½) of an apple, or three quarters (¾) of a game, or two thirds (⅔) of a pie, and so on. However, a fraction can be thought of as representing the operation of division where the numerator is to be divided by the denominator. Thus, the fraction 15/5 can be interpreted as implying that 15 is to be divided by 5. Similarly for the fraction 30/6, the 30 is to be divided by 6.

There is still a third meaning for a fraction, which is the one that is important now. This one treats a fraction as a comparison where the numerator is being compared to the denominator. For instance, the fraction 8/4 expresses a comparison of the number 8 to the number 4. You can think of it as asking the question, "How does 8 compare with 4?" Should you actually divide 8 by 4, using the second interpretation of a fraction, you come up with the answer 2. This simply means that 8 is twice the size of 4.

Take this idea one step further and examine it in terms of the two-equal-fractions arrangement that you have just been studying. Thus, in the following equation:

$$\frac{6}{2} = \frac{24}{8}$$

the thought expressed is that "6 compares with 2 in exactly the same way that 24 compares with 8." That is to say, 6 is 3 times as large as 2, and 24 is also 3 times as large as 8. In general, then, whenever two fractions are written equal to each other, you can interpret this to mean that the numerator of the first fraction compares to the denominator of that fraction in the same way that the numerator of the second fraction compares to the denominator of that fraction.

In the illustration on page 101, where you were asked to find the replacement for **b** in the following equation:

$$\frac{5}{6} = \frac{b}{18}$$

This third meaning of a fraction as a comparison of two numerical quantities is called a "ratio." Ask the students if they have heard of this term. Numerical quantities can be compared, also, by the operation of subtraction rather than division.

what you were really doing was searching for a number that compared to 18 in the same manner that 5 compared to 6. The two principles on the Product of Two Numbers and the Equal Fractions enabled you to find this number without spending a lot of time just guessing at any and all numbers. It is these same two principles combined with the notion of a fraction being a comparison that will help you save money when shopping for food. While it seems a bit far-fetched, it really is not.

■ILLUSTRATION 1: A 9-ounce jar of beets can be purchased for 14¢. At this same rate per ounce, what is the cost of a 15-ounce jar of beets?

▼EXPLANATION: In doing a problem such as this, first draw up a comparison between the 9-ounce jar of beets and its cost of 14¢. Similarly, draw up a second comparison between the 15-ounce jar and its cost. Since the problem stated that the rate per ounce will be the same for the two jars, then the two fractions will have to be equal to each other. However, you do not know the cost of the 15-ounce jar. Hence, you use the placeholder **b** to represent this cost, and it is the value of **b** that you are searching for in this problem.

●SOLUTION:

"9 ounces compare to 14¢ in the same way that 15 ounces compare to b¢"

$$9/14¢ = 15/b$$
$$9 \times b = 15 \times 14¢$$
$$9 \times b = 210¢$$
$$b = 210¢ \div 9$$
$$b = 23\frac{1}{3}¢$$

Hence, the 15-ounce jar of beets would cost 23⅓¢, or approximately 24¢.

■ILLUSTRATION 2: A 24-ounce can of vegetable juice costs 30¢, while a 1-quart, 14-ounce can of the same brand costs 45¢. Which is the better of the two buys?

▼EXPLANATION: Before beginning the solution, it is best to state the amount of juice in both containers in ounces. This means changing the measure of the larger container from 1 quart, 14 ounces to 46 ounces. How were the 46 ounces obtained from 1 quart, 14 ounces? The plan is to set up a method for finding the cost of 46 ounces of vegetable juice by paying for it at the same price per ounce you have to pay for the 24-ounce can. That is to say, 24 ounces of juice compare to the price of 30 cents as 46 ounces compare to how much money? If this amount turns out to be more than 45¢, then you are better off with the larger can.

Mathematically speaking, it is not correct to say that 9 ounces is being compared to 14¢, for we can only compare quantities that are measured in the same unit. Experience in teaching consumer mathematics students has shown that the solution in Illustration 1 appears to be the best approach for them.

●SOLUTION:

$$24/30¢ = 46/\mathbf{b}$$
$$24 \times \mathbf{b} = 46 \times 30¢$$
$$24 \times \mathbf{b} = 1380¢$$
$$\mathbf{b} = 1380¢ \div 24$$
$$\mathbf{b} = 57½¢, \text{ or } 58¢$$

▼EXPLANATION (*continued*): It appears that if a person were to buy a 1-quart, 14-ounce can of vegetable juice and pay for it at the same rate that he paid for the 24-ounce can, the cost would be approximately 58¢. By buying the larger can for 45¢, he can save about 13¢.

■ILLUSTRATION 3: Frozen orange juice can be bought in a 6-ounce can at the rate of 5 cans for 89¢, or in a 12-ounce can at the rate of 3 cans for 97¢. Which is the better buy?

●SOLUTION:

Contents of the 5 smaller cans $= 5 \times 6$
$$= 30 \text{ ounces}$$
Contents of the 3 larger cans $= 3 \times 12$
$$= 36 \text{ ounces}$$
Hence, $30/89¢ = 36/\mathbf{b}$
$$30 \times \mathbf{b} = 36 \times 89¢$$
$$30 \times \mathbf{b} = 3204¢$$
$$\mathbf{b} = 3204¢ \div 30$$
$$\mathbf{b} = 106.8¢, \text{ or } 107¢$$

Thus, 30 ounces at 89¢ equal 36 ounces at approximately 107¢. Hence, the 36 ounces at 97¢ are a better buy than the 30 ounces at 89¢.

▼EXPLANATION: The first step in solving this problem is to find how many ounces of juice you actually get in each case. In the five smaller cans you get 30 ounces, while the total contents of the three larger cans is 36 ounces. As in Illustration 1, you now find the cost of the 36 ounces if purchased at the same rate per ounce as the 30 ounces. The price turns out to be 107¢. How much more is this than the price of the larger cans?

EXERCISES   A

1. The weight and price of a small can of vegetables given in each of the following exercises. The weight of a larger can is also given. If the larger can is bought at the same price per ounce as the smaller one, what is the cost of the larger can? Round off the cost in each case to the next higher penny.

In the solution to Illustration 1, page 104, should you prefer, you can express the comparison as 14¢/9 = b/15. In that way, each side of the equality represents the cost of 1 ounce of beets. The rest of the solution is identical to that shown.

	Weight of Contents Of Smaller Can	Cost Of Smaller Can	Weight of Contents Of Larger Can	Cost Of Larger Can
a.	6 oz.	15¢	8 oz.	20 ¢
b.	9 oz.	21¢	15 oz.	35 ¢
c.	10 oz.	35¢	16 oz.	56 ¢
d.	16 oz.	56¢	26 oz.	91 ¢
e.	21 oz.	98¢	36 oz.	168 ¢
f.	7 oz.	47¢	23 oz.	155 ¢
g.	9 oz.	69¢	17 oz.	131 ¢
h.	14 oz.	85¢	25 oz.	152 ¢
i.	12 oz.	$1.08	16 oz.	144 ¢
j.	18 oz.	$1.35	27 oz.	203 ¢
k.	1 lb. 2 oz.	63¢	1 lb. 10 oz.	91 ¢
l.	1 lb. 5 oz.	49¢	1 lb. 14 oz.	70 ¢
m.	2 lb. 3 oz.	$2.55	3 lb. 8 oz.	408 ¢
n.	4 lb. 7 oz.	$4.29	6 lb. 1 oz.	587 ¢

2. The weight and cost of a small can of vegetables are given in each of the following exercises. The weight and cost of a larger can of the same vegetables are also given. How much more would a person have to pay if he bought the larger can at the same rate per ounce as the smaller can? Round off the cost in each case to the next higher penny.

	Weight of Contents Of Smaller Can	Cost Of Smaller Can	Weight of Contents Of Larger Can	Cost Of Larger Can	Saving
a.	5 oz.	21¢	15 oz.	49¢	14 ¢
b.	4 oz.	30¢	10 oz.	61¢	14 ¢
c.	8 oz.	60¢	14 oz.	89¢	16 ¢
d.	14 oz.	91¢	22 oz.	119¢	24 ¢
e.	10 oz.	85¢	26 oz.	189¢	32 ¢
f.	15 oz.	95¢	27 oz.	139¢	32 ¢
g.	16 oz.	84¢	24 oz.	109¢	17 ¢
h.	9 oz.	$1.08	15 oz.	$1.54	26 ¢
i.	12 oz.	$1.28	21 oz.	$1.87	37 ¢
j.	7 oz.	93¢	12 oz.	$1.19	41 ¢
k.	15 oz.	86¢	23 oz.	$1.12	20 ¢
l.	12 oz.	$1.34	27 oz.	$2.59	43 ¢
m.	18 oz.	$1.07	32 oz.	$1.69	22 ¢
n.	1 lb. 2 oz.	72¢	1 lb. 14 oz.	$1.12	8 ¢
o.	1 lb. 4 oz.	95¢	2 lb. 4 oz.	$1.50	21 ¢
p.	2 lb. 1 oz.	$1.54	3 lb. 3 oz.	$1.99	39 ¢

3. In each of the following exercises, you are to determine which of the two buys is the better. You are to do this by finding what the cost of the larger amount would be if it is purchased at the same rate as the smaller amount.

a. One 8-ounce box of cornflakes for 20¢

or   Better by 10¢

One 18-ounce box of cornflakes for 35¢

Call the attention of the students to the fact that in Exercise 2, they must represent the cost of the item in "cents" before any effort is made to establish the equality.

b. One box of 48 tea bags for 55¢
   or
   One box of 100 tea bags for 99¢
   — Better by 16¢

c. Two 8-ounce cans of stewed tomatoes at 39¢
   or
   One 1-pound can of stewed tomatoes for 29¢
   — Better by 10¢

d. Two 7-ounce cans of peas for 33¢
   or
   Two 12-ounce cans of peas for 49¢
   — Better by 8¢

e. Five pounds of potatoes for 43¢
   or
   Twenty pounds of potatoes for $1.15
   — Better by 57¢

f. Two 12-ounce cans of vegetable juice for 29¢
   or
   One 1-quart, 14-ounce can of vegetable juice for 45¢
   Better by 11¢

g. Two 6-ounce cans of pineapple juice for 17¢
   or
   One 1-quart, 14-ounce can of pineapple juice for 29¢
   Better by 37¢

h. One 1-pound, 9-ounce jar of applesauce for 37¢
   or
   Two 15-ounce jars of applesauce for 45¢
   Same price

i. Two 9-ounce cans of creamed corn for 35¢
   or
   Two 1-pound, 1-ounce cans of creamed corn for 45¢
   Better by 22¢

j. One 1-pound, 2-ounce jar of peanut butter for 57¢
   or
   One 1-pound, 12-ounce jar of peanut butter for 89¢
   Same price

k. One 1-pint, 11-ounce can of floor wax for 53¢
   or
   One 1-quart, 14-ounce can of floor wax for 85¢
   Better by 6¢

l. Two 1-quart bottles of floor wax for 39¢
   or
   One 1-gallon bottle of floor wax for 50¢
   Better by 28¢

m. One 1-quart jar of starch for 19¢
   or
   One ½-gallon jar of starch for 35¢
   Better by 3¢

n. A 6-pack of tomato juice for 43¢ (5½ ounces in each can)
   or
   Three 1-quart, 14-ounce cans of tomato juice for $1
   Better by 80¢

The exercises here can be made more realistic if the students are required to bring in the actual prices and weights of some items from their local supermarkets.

B

1. At a supermarket, two quarts of milk cost 57¢, or a half gallon, 53¢. Mrs. Bradburn purchases 4 quarts of milk each day except Sunday.
   a. How much will she have to pay for the milk each day if she buys it by the quart?　　　　　　　　　　$1.14
   b. How much will she have to pay for the milk each day if she buys it by the half gallon?　　　　　　　　$1.06
   c. How much can she save in a week by buying milk by the half gallon rather than by the quart?　　　　$ .48
   d. How much can she save in one year by buying milk by the half gallon rather than by the quart?　　　$24.96

2. A box of powdered milk costs 83¢ at a supermarket. With the contents, it is possible to make 8 quarts of whole milk. Whole milk is sold here for 28¢ a quart. The Frost family uses 16 quarts of milk each week.
   a. What is the cost of the family's weekly milk supply if it uses fresh whole milk?　　　　　　　　　　$4.48
   b. What is the cost of the family's weekly milk supply if it uses powdered milk?　　　　　　　　　　$1.66
   c. How much money can the family save each week by buying powdered milk instead of fresh whole milk?　　$2.82
   d. How much can the family save in a year by buying powdered milk instead of fresh whole milk?　　　$146.64

Unit 2: Counting Change

The checker at the supermarket will normally not try to overcharge you, for he has nothing to gain. Any overcharge ends up in the supermarket's bank account, since the checker has to account for every penny he rings up on the cash register. However, checkers sometimes make mistakes. They are not necessarily careless, but price changes are made daily on many, many items, and keeping track of them is almost impossible. Then, too, prices stamped on containers are sometimes so badly blurred that they can easily be misread. Hence, it is a good idea to watch the register when poorly marked items are being rung up. In fact, it's a good idea to remember the prices of a number of items and spot-check to see if they are being charged correctly.

There is no point in deluding ourselves, or the students, into thinking that we can compute mentally with the speed of the register calculator. The best we can do is to make certain that the prices are rung up correctly, and then to check the slip at home.

You should take a moment while you are still at the cash register to make certain you receive the correct amount of change. Once you have walked away from the counter, it becomes embarrassing to return with money in hand to point out that you have been shortchanged. You may be troubled by the fact that you add rather slowly and feel uncomfortable about holding up a long line of people while you count your change.

It has been established that the best way to count change is by the additive method. Suppose you hand a cashier a $5 bill for a purchase of $2.36. She would start by giving you 4 cents and saying that $2.36 plus 4¢ is $2.40. To this, she would add 10¢, bringing the total to $2.50. This would be followed by a 50¢ piece so that you would now be up to $3.00. Then you would receive two $1 bills to bring the grand total to $5. Thus, your purchase, plus the change you received, would be equivalent to the $5 you gave the cashier.

Notice that, when counting change, it is not necessary to determine the actual amount of change. This amount could have been found by subtracting $2.36, the cost of the purchase, from $5, given in payment, for a difference of $2.64, your change. The chance of errors occurring in subtraction is much greater than in addition. Hence, it is advisable to add the change to the cost of the purchase until you reach the amount given in payment. Thus, if you add the change of 4¢, 10¢, 50¢, and, finally, two $1 bills, you will find that this comes to $2.64.

■ILLUSTRATION 1: How much change should be returned to a person who gave a $10 bill to pay for a $3.78 purchase?

▼EXPLANATION: Start with $3.78 and add just enough pennies to bring the total to an amount ending in either 0 or 5. In this case, you add 2 pennies to bring the total to $3.80. Then add the largest valued coins possible to bring the total to the nearest dollar amount. If you used nickels, you would have to have 4 of them to bring the amount to $4.00. However, only 2 dimes will bring you to $4.00. Hence, you use 2 dimes. You next add a $1 bill to bring the total to $5.00. Finally, you add a $5 bill to reach the $10 that was given in payment.

●SOLUTION:

Change given in payment of the $3.78 purchase
$$= 2¢ + 10¢ + 10¢ + \$1 + \$5$$

There are times when you have a pocketful of coins and have to pay for a purchase that amounts to $3.07. If you give the cashier a $5 bill, you will receive a $1 bill, plus 93¢, in change. Instead, you could give her $5 and 7¢ in change. By doing this, the change you receive from the cashier will be two $1 bills.

Some of the newer cash registers are so designed that they tell the cheekout clerk the difference between the amount given in payment for the purchase and the cost of the purchase. Have the students survey the markets in the area to see which ones have these newer registers.

In the event both bills and coins are given in payment of a purchase —unless the payment is the exact amount—it is best immediately to deduct the change given from the amount of the purchase. You then count out the change given you as if the purchase actually cost the smaller amount. Thus, if the cost is $2.27, and you give the cashier $5 and 2¢ as payment, you should immediately deduct the 2¢ from the $2.27 and think of the purchase price as $2.25 before counting the change. Similarly, if the cost is $8.55 and you give the cashier $10 and 5¢, you now think of the cost as $8.50. You also have to think that you gave only $10 in payment of the purchase. The extra 5¢ has already been subtracted to lower the price from $8.55 to $8.50.

■ ILLUSTRATION 2: Mr. Eddy gave a cashier $10.03 in payment of a $6.68 purchase. Use the table below to indicate how much change he should receive.

1¢	5¢	10¢	25¢	50¢	$1	$5	$10
		1	1		3		

▼ EXPLANATION: Immediately deduct 3¢ from $6.68 and think of the cost as $6.65 rather than $6.68. Also, think of the amount that Mr. Eddy gave the cashier as $10.00 rather than $10.03. Hence, adding 10¢ to $6.65 brings the total to $6.75. Another quarter will make the total $7.00 and three $1 bills will bring the final total to $10.

● SOLUTION:

1¢	5¢	10¢	25¢	50¢	$1	$5	$10
		1	1		3		

EXERCISES

1. Draw a table similar to the following and indicate how much change will be returned if a $1 bill is given for each of the purchases shown.

Amount Of Purchase	Change				
	1¢	5¢	10¢	25¢	50¢
85¢		1	1		
75¢				1	
67¢	3	1		1	
54¢	1		2	1	
36¢	4		1		1
28¢	2		2		1
19¢	1	1		1	1
6¢	4	1	1	1	1

The method described above for paying for an item is very often used by a purchaser. Unfortunately, he is often at a loss as to how to compute rapidly what change he should receive. An effort is made to clarify this.

2. Draw a table similar to the following and indicate how much change will be returned if a $5 bill is given for each of the purchases shown.

Amount Of Purchase	Change					
	1¢	5¢	10	25¢	50¢	$1
$4.50					1	
$4.16	4	1		1	1	
$4.02	3		2	1	1	
$3.78	2		2			1
$2.53	2		2	1		2
$1.89	1		1			3
98¢	2					4
59¢	1	1	1	1		4
25¢				1	1	4

3. Draw a table similar to the following and indicate how much change will be returned if the amount shown is given for each of the purchases listed.

Amount Of Purchase	Payment Made	Change							
		1¢	5¢	10¢	25¢	50¢	$1	$5	$10
62¢	$1.02	1	1	1					
83¢	$1.03		2						
54¢	$1.04					1			
26¢	$1.01				1	1			
$1.08	$5.08						4		
$1.17	$5.02		1		1	1	3		
$3.25	$5.25						2		
$2.62	$5.12					1	2		
$4.29	$10.04				1	1		1	
$1.57	$10.07					1	3	1	
$1.84	$10.09				1		3	1	

Unit 3: Computing the Discount on a Purchase

PART 1

During the past twenty years, discount houses have mushroomed. Originally, they were set up to sell name-brand hard goods such as refrigerators, freezers, radios, television sets, lawn mowers, and other appliances at prices much below what the local hardware store, or the large department store, was charging. At present, they are selling everything from food to pets. By now, it is difficult to tell whether the prices are really lower than those in the department store, or whether they are lower because of the quality of the product. In addition, the city department stores, to compete with the discount houses, have opened branches in large suburban shopping centers. Here they, too, offer daily bargains to attract the shopper.

Part of the confusion about determining how much of a bargain you are really getting arises from something called the manufacturer's list price, or the manufacturer's suggested price. This is the price at which the manufacturer suggests that stores sell his merchandise. Usually, this price is far higher than anyone would want to pay for the article. The merchant is in a position where he can quote the selling price in terms of relatively large discounts being granted from the list price. For instance, if the manufacturer's suggested price on a shirt is $6, the merchant can offer it at $4 and advertise a discount of $2. This makes it appear that you are being granted quite a saving. In reality, the shirt is probably worth only $4 to begin with, and it has been deliberately listed higher than it should have been.

Most reliable stores advertise their products in terms of the list price and the selling price. Hence, there is no question about what the manufacturer says you should pay and what you actually have to pay. Thus, the advertisement might appear as follows:

WINDOW SHADES IN WHITE OR EGGSHELL	
Manufacturer's List Price	Our Price
$2.49	$1.79

In this way, you know that you will be saving exactly 70¢ on each shade. There are a large number of merchants, though, who prefer to disguise their true sale prices. Their advertisements might appear as follows:

Sofas Usually Selling from $145 to $395 NOW Reduced 30% to 65%

Almost every newspaper on almost any day of the week will have a great number of advertisements similar to those above. The mails are also frequently flooded with this sales information. Students should be asked to bring a few of these advertisements to class.

Notice that nowhere does it say just how much you are going to pay for a sofa, nor is it possible to tell whether you will receive the 30% or the 65% on the one you happen to want! In cases such as this, you can be pretty certain that whatever you purchase will be reduced only the 30%, and possibly even less.

The purpose of this unit is to develop some method to determine whether the discount the merchant says you are receiving is really what you do receive. A discount is simply a reduction in the price of an article from what it had been priced at originally. Thus, in the case of the illustration of the window shades, since the original price was $2.49 and the new price is $1.79, the discount is 70¢.

In the illustration about the sofas, the 30% and 65% are the discount rates. As with any other percent values, they indicate the saving for each $100 in the list price of the article, rather than the saving itself. To see how to handle situations where the discount rate is given rather than the discount itself, it would be best to examine the following illustrations.

■ ILLUSTRATION 1: Mr. Samuels received a 15% discount on an FM radio that had been priced at $80. What discount did he receive?

▼ EXPLANATION: On page 589 of the review section at the back of the book, it is pointed out that the word "of" in phrases such as "25% of $90," or "23% of $94," and so on, implies the operation of multiplication between the two numbers. Since in this problem the discount is 15% of the $80, finding this discount involves nothing more than finding the product of 15% and $80. Before this can be done, however, it is necessary to change the numeral 15% from its percent form to its decimal form. What is the decimal numeral that is equivalent to 15%?

● SOLUTION:
$$\text{Discount} = 15\% \text{ of } \$80$$
$$= .15 \times \$80$$
$$= \$12.00$$

■ ILLUSTRATION 2: A desk that regularly sells for $120 can be bought during a sale at a discount rate of 20%. How much will a buyer have to pay for the desk if he purchases it during the sale?

● SOLUTION:
$$\text{Discount} = 20\% \text{ of } \$120$$
$$= .20 \times \$120$$
$$= \$24.00$$
$$\text{Selling Price} = \$120 - \$24$$
$$= \$96$$

▼ EXPLANATION: The discount is found in exactly the same way as in Illustration 1. Since the discount represents the amount the selling

The consumer mathematics student has a great deal less trouble in converting a percent discount rate to a decimal than to a fraction. Do this in all cases except for the 33-1/3% or the 66-2/3% rate. Applications of these rates are discussed on pages 118 and 119.

price was reduced, it is now only a matter of subtracting $24 from $120 to find the new selling price of the desk.

Your work on percent has taught you that 100% of any number is actually the number itself. For instance, finding 100% of 65 means multiplying 100% by 65. Before you can do this, of course, you have to rewrite the numeral 100% in its equivalent decimal form of 1.00. But 1.00 is just another way of writing the identity number for multiplication—this being 1. Hence, 100% times 65 is really 1 times 65, and this product is 65. In general, then, 100% of a number means 1 times the number, and this gives you the number itself.

Take another look at the solution in Illustration 2. When you found the selling price, what you were doing was subtracting the discount of $24 from the original value of $120. However, the discount is 20% of the original value, while the $120 can be thought of as 100% of the original value. Hence, you can express the selling price in Illustration 2 as follows:

Selling price = $120 − $24
         = 100% of original value − 20% of original value

But, 100% of the original value, minus 20% of the original value, is 80% of the original value. Thus, the selling price becomes as follows:

Selling price = 80% of original value

If the discount rate is 10% of the original value, then the selling price will be what percent of the original value? In general, if you know what percent the discount rate is, how can you find what percent of the original value the selling price will be?

How will this information help you? Well, it will enable you to determine the selling price of an article without first having to find the discount.

■ILLUSTRATION 3 : George Shaw was able to purchase a hammock listed at $14.99 at a discount rate of 40%. How much did he have to pay for the hammock?

●SOLUTION:
     Selling price = 100% of original price − 40% of original price
              = 60% of original price
              = 60% of $14.99
              = .60 × $14.99
              = $8.9940, or $8.99

▼EXPLANATION: Since George received a 40% discount rate off the 100% of the original price, he had to pay only 60% of the original price.

Unless your students happen to be somewhat above average, it might be best to avoid this method of computing the selling price of an article directly from the original list price and the discount rate.

Sixty percent of $14.99 is $8.99, the price he had to pay for the hammock. By the way, how large a discount did George receive?

EXERCISES   **A**

Do you recall how to find the answers in the following exercises? If not, you will want to refer to the pages indicated for help.

1. Change each of the following percent numerals to its equivalent decimal numeral. (See pages 583–584.)

a. 15% __.15__	d. 7% __.07__	g. 4.6% __.046__
b. 28% __.28__	e. 9% __.09__	h. 8.7% __.087__
c. 54% __.54__	f. 2% __.02__	i. 9.6% __.096__

2. Find the value of the following. (See page 589.)

a. 20% of 50 = __10.00__	f. 48% of 78 = __37.44__
b. 16% of 70 = __11.20__	g. 62% of 173 = __107.26__
c. 34% of 120 = __40.80__	h. 53% of 249 = __131.97__
d. 45% of 63 = __28.35__	i. 36% of 856 = __308.16__
e. 27% of 29 = __7.83__	j. 84% of 927 = __778.86__

B

1. Find the discount to the nearest penny on each of the following purchases.

	Original Price	Discount Rate	Discount
a.	$ 30.00	20%	$ 6.00
b.	50.00	40%	20.00
c.	75.00	10%	7.50
d.	60.00	35%	21.00
e.	18.00	25%	4.50
f.	45.00	18%	8.10
g.	22.50	15%	3.38
h.	8.75	12%	1.05
i.	19.75	25%	4.94
j.	4.99	50%	2.50
k.	37.85	28%	10.60
l.	49.95	34%	16.98
m.	109.85	10%	10.99
n.	257.50	22%	56.65

2. Find the discount to the nearest penny on each of the following purchases. After finding the discount, determine how much the buyer will have to pay for each purchase.

People will often use the terms "discount" and "discount rate" interchangeably. If at all possible, continually correct the students when they are in error.

	Original Price	Discount Rate	Discount	Selling Price
a.	$ 40.00	30%	$ 12.00	$ 28.00
b.	20.00	10%	2.00	18.00
c.	65.00	60%	39.00	26.00
d.	85.00	45%	38.25	46.75
e.	130.00	15%	19.50	110.50
f.	145.00	31%	44.95	100.05
g.	7.50	14%	1.05	6.45
h.	34.50	38%	13.11	21.39
i.	156.85	55%	86.27	70.58
j.	249.50	16%	39.92	209.58

3. Purchasers are granted the following discount rates. What percent of the selling price do they have to pay?

a. 20% __80%__   e. 15% __85%__   i. 6% __94%__
b. 10% __90%__   f. 25% __75%__   j. 14% __86%__
c. 30% __70%__   g. 45% __55%__   k. 32% __68%__
d. 40% __60%__   h. 50% __50%__   l. 41% __59%__

4. Without finding the discount, find the selling price to the nearest penny on each of the following purchases.

	Original Price	Discount Rate	Selling Price
a.	$ 10.00	10%	$ 9.00
b.	70.00	20%	56.00
c.	90.00	40%	54.00
d.	75.00	30%	52.50
e.	62.00	35%	40.30
f.	4.50	25%	3.38
g.	12.75	60%	5.10
h.	58.25	55%	26.21
i.	124.50	15%	105.83
j.	263.80	45%	145.09

C

1. A garden umbrella that usually sells for $29.99 is on sale at a discount rate of 35%.
   a. What discount is the purchaser being offered? Find your answer to the nearest penny.   __$10.50__
   b. How much will the purchaser have to pay for the umbrella?
                                                              __$19.49__

2. Men's nylon stretch socks that regularly sell for 79¢ a pair can be bought during a sale at three pairs for $1.75.
   a. How much would a buyer have to pay if he bought six pairs of socks at the regular price?   __$ 4.74__
   b. How much would a buyer have to pay if he bought six pairs of socks at the sale price?   __$ 3.50__

You might want to discuss with your students why merchants price articles at $1.98 rather than $2.00, or $29.99 rather than $30.00. Certainly the latter figures are much easier to use for computation.

c. How much could a buyer save by buying six pairs of socks during
   the sale? $1.24

3. Men's T-shirts regularly sell 3 for $4.50. During a spring sale, they
   are offered 3 for $2.75. How much can Mr. Forrest save on the pur-
   chase of a half dozen of these T-shirts if he buys them during the
   sale? $3.50

4. The usual selling price of men's pure linen initialed handkerchiefs
   at Mayer's Department Store is 59¢ each. At the time of its Father's
   Day sale, the store offered these same handkerchiefs 2 for 77¢.
   How much can a person save by buying a dozen of these handkerchiefs during the sale? $2.46

PART 2

In practically all cases, the rate of discount is expressed in a percent
form similar to the numerals used in Part 1 of this unit. There are times,
though, when the discount rate is written as a percent numeral that
involves a decimal. Thus, the discount rate offered might be 8.5%, or
15.25%, and so forth. These discount rates are treated no differently
than the earlier ones examined. Simply move the decimal point two
places to the left to change them from their percent form to their
equivalent decimal form. Thus, the decimal equivalent for 8.5% is .085
and for 15.25%, .1525.

Sometimes, though, you will find the discount rate expressed in a
form such as 12½%, or 16¼%, and the like. Whenever this happens, it is
best to change the fraction immediately to a decimal. In the case of
12½%, you would rewrite it as 12.5%, while 16¼% should be written as
16.25%. Except for one case, you will find that the majority of the fractions you will use will be either ¼, ½, or ¾. In the event their decimal
equivalents may have slipped your mind, they are as follows:

$$\tfrac{1}{4} = .25$$
$$\tfrac{1}{2} = .50$$
$$\tfrac{3}{4} = .75$$

■ ILLUSTRATION 1: Permanent-press, pre-cuffed dress slacks that
regularly sell for $9.95 a pair are dropped 18½% in price during a sale.
How much will a buyer have to pay for these slacks during the sale?

● SOLUTION:

$$\text{Discount} = 18\tfrac{1}{2}\% \text{ of } \$9.95$$
$$= 18.5\% \text{ of } \$9.95$$
$$= .185 \times \$9.95$$
$$= \$1.84075, \text{ or } \$1.84$$
$$\text{Selling price} = \$9.95 - \$1.84$$
$$= \$8.11$$

By actual division, have the students determine that the fraction numeral 1/4 is equivalent to
the decimal numeral .25; do the same for 1/2 and 3/4. As an extra-credit problem, have the
students show the converse, i.e., .25 is the equivalent of 1/4.

▼EXPLANATION: After changing the discount rate from the form 18½% to 18.5%, it was possible to complete the solution in the same manner as with the problems in Part 1 of this unit. Notice that in finding the selling price, the discount was computed first. Whenever the discount rate involves a mixed number, you usually will find this approach a good deal easier than computing the selling price directly.

As mentioned earlier, there is one discount rate involving a fraction that might give you a bit of trouble. This rate is 33⅓%. If you try to change the fraction ⅓ into a decimal as you did with the fractions ¼, ½, and ¾, you would simply get the repeating decimal .3333 ⋯. And this would cause no end of problems. Hence, the best thing to do in the event that the discount rate happens to be 33⅓% is to rewrite this numeral in its equivalent fractional form—33⅓% = ⅓. How can you show that the percent numeral 33⅓% and the fractional numeral ⅓ are equivalent forms of the same number? In the event you don't recall how this is done, you might refer to pages 583–584.

■ILLUSTRATION 2: Mrs. Parker waited for a sale to buy her vacuum cleaner. The regular price of the cleaner is $64.95. However, she was able to buy it at a saving of 33⅓%. How much did she have to pay for the cleaner?

●SOLUTION:

$$\text{Discount} = 33\tfrac{1}{3}\% \text{ of } \$64.95$$
$$= \tfrac{1}{3} \times \$64.95$$
$$= \$21.65$$
$$\text{Selling price} = \$64.95 - \$21.65$$
$$= \$43.30$$

▼EXPLANATION: After changing 33⅓% to the fractional numeral ⅓, the solution involves nothing more than finding the product of a fraction and a decimal. Here, again, it is best to find the discount before finding the selling price. If Mrs. Parker received a discount of ⅓ of the selling price, then what fraction of the selling price did she have to pay? What amount of money will this be?

Actually, the vacuum cleaner in Illustration 2 could have been advertised at a discount of ⅓ off the original price. In fact, many merchants prefer to advertise their discount rates in fractions rather than percents. They do this, however, only if the fractions happen to be ⅕, ¼, ⅓, ½, ⅔, or, possibly, ¾. If the fractions are any more involved than these, they prefer to use the percent form.

■ILLUSTRATION 3: At a closeout of kitchenware, a service for twelve people that regularly sells for $69.75 is offered at ⅔ off this price. How much will a buyer have to pay for this set?

Rarely, if ever, will any discount rather other than 33-1/3% and 66-2/3% be offered where the decimal equivalent is of the repeating form. Hence, for practical purposes, these are the only two that need to be considered.

●SOLUTION:

$$\text{Discount} = \tfrac{2}{3} \times \$69.75$$
$$= \$46.50$$
$$\text{Selling price} = \$69.75 - \$46.50$$
$$= \$23.25$$

▼EXPLANATION: Notice that the discount happens to be greater than the actual selling price. How do you account for this?

EXERCISES   A

Do you recall how to find the answers in the following exercises? If not, you will want to refer to the pages indicated for help.

1. Change each of the following percent numerals to its equivalent decimal numeral. (See pages 583–584.)
   a. 12.5% ___.125___   d. 52.9% ___.529___   g. 9.75% ___.0975___
   b. 23.7% ___.237___   e. 2.34% ___.0234___   h. 12.41% ___.1241___
   c. 46.1% ___.461___   f. 62.51% ___.6251___   i. 59.07% ___.5907___

2. Change each of the following percent numerals to its equivalent decimal numeral. (See pages 583–584.)
   a. 14½% ___.145___   e. 34¼% ___.3425___   i. 61¾% ___.6175___
   b. 42½% ___.425___   f. 56¼% ___.5625___   j. 5½% ___.055___
   c. 24½% ___.245___   g. 17¾% ___.1775___   k. 9¾% ___.0975___
   d. 10¼% ___.1025___   h. 27¾% ___.2775___   l. 4¼% ___.0425___

3. Find the product in each of the following exercises. (See page 589.)
   a. 16.5% × 40 = ___6.600___   f. 6.25% × 45 = 2.8125
   b. 20.5% × 56 = ___11.480___   g. 14.25% × 5.8 = ___.82650___
   c. 41.5% × 37 = ___15.355___   h. 43.25% × 1.50 = ___.648750___
   d. 18.5% × 128 = ___23.680___   i. 4.75% × .86 = ___.040850___
   e. 9.25% × 30 = ___2.7750___   j. 27.75% × 3.25 = ___.901875___

4. Find the product in each of the following exercises. (See page 589.)
   a. 12½% × 70 = ___8.75___   e. 15¼% × 10 = ___1.5250___
   b. 25½% × 92 = ___23.460___   f. 2¼% × 42.50 = ___.956250___
   c. 6½% × 1.34 = ___.08710___   g. 27¾% × 25 = 6.9375
   d. 3½% × 2.38 = ___.08330___   h. 42¾% × 5.70 = 2.436750

5. Find the product to the nearest penny in each of the following exercises. (See page 595.)
   a. ⅓ × $27 = ___$ 9.00___   h. ⅓ × $304.11 = ___$101.37___
   b. ⅓ × $84 = ___28.00___   i. ⅓ × $46 = ___15.33___
   c. ⅓ × $126 = ___42.00___   j. ⅓ × $85 = ___28.33___
   d. ⅓ × $252 = ___84.00___   k. ⅓ × $92 = ___30.67___
   e. ⅓ × $18.45 = ___6.15___   l. ⅓ × $116 = ___38.67___
   f. ⅓ × $20.67 = ___6.89___   m. ⅓ × $4.27 = ___1.42___
   g. ⅓ × $156.18 = ___52.06___   n. ⅓ × $18.46 = ___6.15___

To explore further the explanation for Illustration 3, ask the students such questions as, "For what discount rate will the discount and selling price be the same?" "In general, for what discount rate will the discount be greater than the selling price?" "Be less than the selling price?"

B

1. Buyers were offered a 33⅓% discount rate on each of the following purchases. Determine how much they had to pay for each article after first finding the discount to the nearest penny.

Article	Original Price	Discount	Cost to Purchaser
a. Tape Cartridge Player	$ 78.00	$ 26.00	$ 52.00
b. Portable Car Radio	96.00	32.00	64.00
c. Car Speaker Kit	10.95	3.65	7.30
d. Car Stereo Tape Player	79.95	26.65	53.30
e. Remote Control Switch	16.88	5.63	11.25
f. Solid-State Amplifier	32.95	10.98	21.97
g. Stereo Receiver	219.95	73.32	146.63
h. Matched Stereo System	419.95	139.98	279.97

2. How much will a person have to pay for each of the following purchases? First find the discount correct to the nearest penny.

	Original Price	Discount Rate	Discount	Cost
a.	$ 46.00	10.4%	$ 4.78	$ 41.22
b.	81.00	6.8%	5.51	75.49
c.	125.00	7.2%	9.00	116.00
d.	12.50	14.5%	1.81	10.69
e.	246.75	23.6%	58.23	188.52
f.	310.95	34.7%	107.90	203.05

3. How much will a person have to pay for each of the following purchases? First find the discount correct to the nearest penny.

	Original Price	Discount Rate	Discount	Cost
a.	$ 55.00	12½%	$ 6.88	$ 48.12
b.	90.00	30½%	27.45	62.55
c.	19.75	5½%	1.09	18.66
d.	68.95	23½%	16.20	52.75
e.	60.00	8¼%	4.95	55.05
f.	75.00	21¼%	15.94	59.06
g.	130.50	34¼%	44.70	85.80
h.	50.00	6¾%	3.38	46.62
i.	82.00	42¾%	35.06	46.94
j.	257.20	18¾%	48.23	208.97

C

1. When Fred Daniels purchased his solid-state 3-speed portable stereo tape recorder, he received a discount rate of 22½% on the selling price. What percent of the selling price did he have to pay for the tape recorder?   77½%

If you have not recently told the students not to write the answers to the exercises in their books, it might be advisable to do so now.

2. A discount of ¼ off the normal price is offered the buyer of a solid-state TV set during a sale. What fraction of the normal price will the buyer have to pay for the TV set?   <u>3/4</u>

3. A ball microphone is placed on sale at a discount rate of ⅕ off the regular price of $13.95.
   a. How much discount will a buyer receive?   <u>$2.79</u>
   b. How much will a buyer have to pay for this microphone if he buys it during the sale?   <u>$11.16</u>

4. The Radio Electronics Shop offers its customers a professional model 4-track stereo tape deck at $249, less a discount of ⅓ of this price. Its competitor, The Stereo Shop, is offering this same deck at $260.50, less 40% of this price.
   a. How much will a buyer have to pay if he purchases the tape deck at The Radio Electronics Shop?   <u>$166</u>
   b. How much will a buyer have to pay if he purchases the tape deck at The Stereo Shop?   <u>$156.30</u>
   c. How much can a person save by buying this tape deck in one store rather than the other?   <u>$9.70</u>

Unit 4: Computing the Discount Rate on a Purchase

When you first started looking into discounts and discount rates, you examined an advertisement on the sale of sofas that were originally priced from $145 to $395, but were reduced some 30% to 65%. At the time, there was some thought that perhaps most of the furniture was being sold at prices closer to the 30% discount rate than to the 65% rate. So that there is no question as to which rate you are receiving, you need some method of finding the discount rate when you know the original price and the sale price of the article.

The best place to begin is with the method used for finding the discount. Consider the case where the discount rate is 20% and the original price of the article is $30. To find the discount, you would proceed as follows:

$$\text{Discount} = 20\% \times \$30$$
$$\text{Discount} = .20 \times \$30$$
$$\text{Discount} = \$6$$

This can also be written in the following form:

$$.20 \times \$30 = \$6$$

When you look at this equation, you immediately begin to think in terms of the Product of Two Numbers Principle (see page 36). Recall

Discuss this topic with the students only if time permits. Computing the discount is far more important than computing the discount rate. This topic has interest in that it gives the student the means of ascertaining the honesty of a dealer who claims he is offering a certain discount rate.

that this principle stated that if the product of two numbers is divided by either of the numbers, the quotient will be the other number. For instance, the product of the two numbers 5 and 6 is 30. Hence, if you divide 30 by one of the two numbers, say, the number 6, the quotient will have to be the other number, that is, 5.

Thus: $5 \times 6 = 30$
Therefore: $5 = 30 \div 6$

Now in the preceding problem concerning the discount on an article, you had the following:

$$.20 \times \$30 = \$6$$

Hence, if you divide $6 by $30, the quotient is .20.

Thus: $.20 = \$6 \div \$30$ (1)

What does all this mean? If you go back to the wording of the problem, you will see that .20 is the discount rate expressed as a decimal numeral, while $6 is the discount and $30 is the original price of the article. Therefore, if you replace the numerals in equation (1) by the general terms they represent, you come up with the method for finding the discount rate.

Discount Rate = Discount ÷ Original Price

All you have to do to find the discount rate on the sale of an article is to divide the discount by the original price of the article. There is just one thing you must be careful of, though. The answer to your division computation will give you a decimal numeral. Hence, it will be necessary for you to change the decimal numeral to a percent numeral. How is this done?

■ ILLUSTRATION 1 : A pair of curtains that regularly sells for $14 was sold at a discount of $3. What discount rate was the purchaser receiving on this sale? Find your answer to the nearest whole number percent value.

● SOLUTION :

Discount Rate = Discount ÷ Original Price
= $3 ÷ $14
= .214
= 21.4%, or 21%

▼ EXPLANATION : The formula developed called for dividing the discount by the original price of the article. In this case, it means dividing $3 by $14. The quotient is found first as the decimal numeral .214, which is then changed to its equivalent percent numeral by moving

You might prefer to develop the discount-rate formula by using the general method applied to all percent situations, i.e., 20 compares to 100 as the $6 discount compares to the $30 original price. This will lead to the same formula as above.

the decimal point two places to the right. The 21.4 is rounded off to the nearest whole number 21, and hence the discount rate is 21%.

■ILLUSTRATION 2: A Yorkshire suit that regularly sells for $85 is priced at $69 during a sale. What discount rate will the purchaser receive when he buys this suit? Find your answer to the nearest whole number percent value.

▼EXPLANATION: Since the discount-rate formula calls for dividing the discount by the original price, your first task will have to be to find the discount in this problem. How can this be done? Once you know the discount, it is possible to complete the solution in exactly the same manner as in Illustration 1. A word of caution! Remember that in computing the discount rate, the discount must always be divided by the original value of the article and by no other number.

●SOLUTION:

$$\text{Discount} = \text{Original Value} - \text{Selling Price}$$
$$= \$85 - \$69$$
$$= \$16$$
$$\text{Discount Rate} = \text{Discount} \div \text{Original Value}$$
$$= \$16 \div \$85$$
$$= .188$$
$$= 18.8\%, \text{ or } 19\%$$

A great many factors help decide the selling price of an article. Of course, the merchant's cost of the article is extremely important. But, in addition to that, he has to think of the salaries of his employees, the store rent, his electric bill, his phone bill, and on and on. One of the things that enters into the picture is a rather peculiar one and has nothing to do with the profit he wants to make, or the bills he has to pay. It has something to do with what takes place in your mind when you see the price of an article. For instance, when you see an article marked $19.99, you tend to think that the price is around $19 rather than only one penny away from $20. Similarly, a stereo speaker selling for $99.98 appears to be a great deal cheaper than one selling for $100, and yet there is only a two-cent difference between them. Realizing the way people's minds work, a merchant prices articles a penny or two, or, sometimes, even five pennies, under a round number of dollars. To you, $17.95 is a better buy than $18, and $49.48 has a greater sales appeal than $50!

The tendency to price merchandise in this manner makes computation of discount rates a little more difficult. Hence, your best bet would be to round the price off to the nearest dollar, or, perhaps, to the nearest half-dollar, before finding the discount rate.

Emphasize repeatedly that the discount rate cannot be found unless the **discount** itself is known! In addition, stress that it is this discount that is divided by the **original** price of the article—**not** the selling price—in order to find the discount rate.

■ ILLUSTRATION 3: The Burns Brothers Shop is offering, for $9.98, a can opener that was originally priced at $12.99. What discount rate will a buyer receive on this purchase?

● SOLUTION:

$$\text{Original price} = \$12.99, \text{ or } \$13$$
$$\text{Selling price} = \$9.98, \text{ or } \$10$$
$$\text{Discount} = \$13 - \$10$$
$$= \$3$$
$$\text{Discount rate} = \$3 \div \$13$$
$$= .231$$
$$= 23.1\%, \text{ or } 23\%$$

▼ EXPLANATION: Both the original price of the can opener and the selling price are rounded off to the nearest dollar. This makes the discount approximately $3. The solution is then completed in the same manner as in Illustration 2. Had the exact numbers been used in the solution, the computation would have been much more difficult, and the answer would have been just about the same. Your work would have involved dividing $3.01 by $12.99, for a quotient of .232, which would still have been 23% when rounded off. How was the number $3.01 found?

EXERCISES   A

Do you recall how to find the answer in each of the following exercises? If not, refer to the pages indicated for help.

1. Change each of the following decimal numerals to its equivalent percent numeral. (See page 583.)

a. .35 _35%_	e. .04 _4%_	i. .362 _36.2%_
b. .62 _62%_	f. .07 _7%_	j. .543 _54.3%_
c. .41 _41%_	g. .01 _1%_	k. .042 _4.2%_
d. .17 _17%_	h. .09 _9%_	l. .074 _7.4%_

2. Write each of the following fractions as a decimal correct to the nearest thousandth. Then rewrite each decimal numeral as a percent numeral correct to the nearest whole number. The first exercise is completed for you. (See page 594.)

	Fraction	Decimal	Percent		Fraction	Decimal	Percent
a.	2/3	.667	67%	g.	17/23	.739	74%
b.	1/3	.333	33%	h.	41/74	.554	55%
c.	2/7	.286	29%	i.	2.50/6	.417	42%
d.	3/8	.375	38%	j.	4.75/9	.528	53%
e.	5/9	.556	56%	k.	4.25/12.50	.340	34%
f.	4/15	.267	27%	l.	7.40/52.50	.141	14%

See if the students can justify why the discount rate of an article can never exceed 100%

B

1. Determine the discount rate correct to the nearest whole-number percent value in each of the following exercises.

	Original Price	Discount	Discount Rate
a.	$ 5	$ 2	$\frac{40}{}$ %
b.	20	5	$\frac{25}{}$ %
c.	30	6	$\frac{20}{}$ %
d.	40	25	$\frac{63}{}$ %
e.	15	10	$\frac{67}{}$ %
f.	9	2	$\frac{22}{}$ %
g.	8	1	$\frac{13}{}$ %
h.	29	4	$\frac{14}{}$ %
i.	48	7	$\frac{15}{}$ %
j.	125	16	$\frac{13}{}$ %
k.	249	40	$\frac{16}{}$ %
l.	375	124	$\frac{33}{}$ %
m.	495	295	$\frac{60}{}$ %
n.	527	227	$\frac{43}{}$ %

2. Determine the discount rate correct to the nearest whole-number percent value on each of the following purchases.

Item	Original Price	Sale Price	Discount	Discount Rate
a. Foam Rubber Pillow	$ 9	$ 7	$ 2	22 %
b. Dacron Pillow	6	5	1	17 %
c. Serene Pillow	9	8	1	11 %
d. Down Pillow	22	18	4	18 %
e. Fortrel Suit	55	48	7	13 %
f. Sport Coat	40	28	12	30 %
g. Topcoat	75	58	17	23 %

3. Determine the discount rate correct to the nearest whole-number percent value on each of the following purchases.

Item	Original Price	Sale Price	Discount	Discount Rate
a. Alarm Clock	$ 8.50	$ 4.00	$ 4.50	53 %
b. Electric Hand Mixer	15.00	8.50	6.50	43 %
c. Electric Frypan	20.00	12.50	7.50	38 %
d. Electric Knife	28.50	14.50	14.00	49 %
e. Toaster	19.75	12.00	7.75	39 %
f. Electric Can Opener	16.75	8.50	8.25	49 %
g. Blender	29.75	19.25	10.50	35 %
h. Hood Dryer	37.25	24.75	12.50	34 %

4. Before determining the discount rate on each of the following purchases, round off both the original and the discount price to the nearest dollar. Find each answer correct to the nearest whole-number percent value.

Item	Original Price	Sale Price	Actual Discount	Discount Rate
a. 21" Weekender Bag	$ 14.98	$ 10.99	$ 3.99	27 %
b. 26" Pullman Bag	19.99	15.95	4.04	20 %
c. 29" Pullman Bag	23.95	17.98	5.97	25 %
d. Living-Room Suite	499.95	399.95	100.00	20 %
e. Reclining Chair	154.90	119.98	34.92	23 %
f. Sofa Bed	189.95	168.95	21.00	11 %

C

1. Girl's cotton knit polo shirts that regularly sell from $2.50 to $4.00 are placed on sale at $1.50 each.
   a. What discount rate would a purchaser receive if she bought a $2.50 polo shirt at the time of the sale? <u>40%</u>
   b. What discount rate would a purchaser receive if she bought a $4.00 polo shirt at the time of the sale? <u>63%</u>
2. A national magazine offered to sell 30 issues to subscribers for $3. The regular subscription rate is $5.77. However, if a person were to buy the 30 issues at a newsstand, he would have to pay $15.
   a. What discount rate would a person receive on this special offer over what he would have to pay if he purchased the magazine at a newsstand? <u>80%</u>
   b. What discount rate would a person receive on this special offer over what he would have to pay if he purchased the magazine at the regular subscription rate? <u>48%</u>
3. Before finding the discount rate on an article, it usually saves a great deal of time if the regular price and the sale price are rounded off either to the nearest dime, or the nearest quarter. To what amount would you round off each of the following prices?
   a. $1.49 <u>$1.50</u>   e. 39¢ <u>40¢</u>   i. $16.48 <u>$16.50</u>
   b. $1.74 <u>$1.75</u>   f. 69¢ <u>70¢</u>   j. $94.73 <u>$94.75</u>
   c. $2.24 <u>$2.25</u>   g. 88¢ <u>90¢</u>   k. $49.49 <u>$49.50</u>
   d. $1.58 <u>$1.60</u>   h. 19¢ <u>20¢</u>   l. $72.29 <u>$72.30</u>
4. No-iron dungarees that regularly sell for $7.19 can be bought during a sale at $3.74. What discount rate will Bob Perkins receive if he purchases a pair of these dungarees during the sale? Before computing your answer, round off the original selling price and the sale price respectively to the nearest dime and nearest quarter.
   <u>48%</u>
5. The Bradford Shop regularly sells men's socks for 85¢ a pair. During their 50th anniversary sale, they placed these socks on sale at 3 pairs for $1.75.

The method employed in Exercise 4 of Group B and Problem 4 above are quite accurate and far easier for computational purposes than working with the original numbers. Stress this approach, for prices are all too frequently given with "inconvenient" numbers.

a. How much would Tom Baxter have to pay for three pairs of these socks if he bought them when they were not on sale?

$2.55

b. What discount rate would Tom receive if he purchased these socks at the time of the sale? Find your answer to the nearest whole-number percent value.

31%

Unit 5: Installment Purchasing

Until now, our discussion has been limited only to the topic of buying the things you need. Paying for them was not discussed. Many people do not have the cash to buy many of the things they need—that is, the relatively large items such as a living-room suite, or a TV set, or a refrigerator, and so on. In fact, one of the first things you talked about at the outset of this course was how to buy an automobile if you didn't have the cash to pay for it.

There are several ways to avoid making immediate payment for merchandise you buy. Probably the most popular of these is the installment purchase. Your first reaction to this might be that a merchant would not be very anxious to sell merchandise if paid off in relatively small amounts over a long period of time. On the contrary! He is not only anxious to have you buy this way, but, in fact, he may very well urge you to do so. If he is successful in convincing you to buy the article on the installment plan, there is every chance that he will make more money on the installment overcharge than he does on the profit on the article itself.

Although each payment may be relatively small, the total is frequently a good deal more than you would have to pay if you paid for the article in one lump sum. People just do not take the time to determine how much extra they pay by choosing the small-monthly-payment plan. Needless to say, the merchant, until recently, didn't bother to tell them either. Within recent years, the federal government decided to pass a law requiring the dealer to tell the buyer exactly what rate of interest he is paying on the installment purchase. At the moment, your concern is how much extra you actually have to pay each time you make a purchase on the installment plan.

■ ILLUSTRATION 1: A 4-piece living-room suite that regularly sells for $325 can be bought on the installment plan for $20 down and $25 a month for 15 months. How much extra does an installment purchaser have to pay for this suite?

The "truth-in-lending" law requires the seller to notify the buyer the exact rate of interest being charged on the installment purchase. It does not, however, require the seller to state how much extra the buyer has to pay on the installment purchase over the cash purchase. This the buyer must determine.

▼ EXPLANATION: On the 15 monthly payments alone, the installment purchaser will be paying back 15 times $25, or $375. In addition to this, he made a down payment of $20. Hence, the total amount he paid for the suite is $375, plus $20, or $395. Since he could have had this same suite for a cash payment of $325, he paid an extra $70 for the privilege of paying off the cost over a 15-month period. How was the $70 found?

Incidentally, this $70 overpayment is known by a variety of names. Sometimes it is called the installment charge, or carrying charge, while at other times it is referred to as an interest charge. Whatever its name, this charge is the difference between what you would have to pay for the article when buying it on the installment plan and what you would have to pay for it if buying for cash.

● SOLUTION:

$$\text{Total of monthly installments} = 15 \times \$25$$
$$= \$375$$
$$\text{Installment price} = \$20 + \$375$$
$$= \$395$$
$$\text{Cash price} = \$325$$
$$\text{Installment charge} = \$395 - \$325$$
$$= \$70$$

■ ILLUSTRATION 2: Mr. Bamberg purchased a $480 refrigerator-freezer combination by making a 10% down payment and paying off the balance over a three-year period in equal monthly payments of $17.50. How much could Mr. Bamberg have saved had he purchased the refrigerator-freezer for the $480 cash price rather than on the installment plan?

● SOLUTION:

$$\text{Total of monthly installments} = 36 \times \$17.50$$
$$= \$630$$
$$\text{Down payment} = 10\% \times \$480$$
$$= .10 \times \$480$$
$$= \$48$$
$$\text{Installment price} = \$630 + \$48$$
$$= \$678$$
$$\text{Cash price} = \$480$$
$$\text{Installment charge} = \$678 - \$480$$
$$= \$198$$

▼ EXPLANATION: In the three-year period there are 36 monthly payments. How was the number 36 arrived at? Since each of the payments is $17.50, the total for all 36 is 36 times $17.50, or $630. Whenever the statement is made in business that a "10% down payment" has to be

Insist that students set up their solutions as in the solution above. The more careful they are in arranging their work neatly, the less chance there is for error. Furthermore, by outlining their work, it is easier for them to see not only what they have computed, but where they are going.

made, it means that 10% of the cash price is required before the buyer
can walk out with the merchandise. In this case, 10% of the cash price is
10% of $480. Finding 10% of $480 requires changing the numeral 10%
to the decimal numeral .10. Recall, also, that the word "of" implies the
operation of multiplication. Once the down payment is found, the rest
of the solution is completed in exactly the same manner as in Illustration 1.

EXERCISES   **A**

1. How large a down payment will have to be made on each of the
   following installment purchases?

	Cash Price	Percent Of Down Payment Required	Down Payment
a.	$ 250	10%	$ 25.00
b.	375	20%	75.00
c.	450	25%	112.50
d.	690	15%	103.50
e.	745	30%	223.50
f.	495	35%	173.25
g.	1,240	50%	620.00

2. How large a down payment—to the nearest penny—will have to be
   made on each of the following installment purchases?

	Cash Price	Percent Of Down Payment Required	Down Payment
a.	$ 72.50	10%	$ 7.25
b.	99.75	20%	19.95
c.	125.50	5%	6.28
d.	185.25	25%	46.31
e.	59.95	10%	6.00
f.	234.90	40%	93.96
g.	569.98	30%	170.99

3. How much will an installment purchaser have to pay under each of
   the following plans?

	Down Payment	Monthly Payments	Number of Months	Installment Price
a.	$ 50	$20	6	$ 170
b.	40	25	5	165
c.	75	15	9	210
d.	140	40	12	620
e.	69	18	15	339
f.	56	37	24	944
g.	18	16	36	594

The exercises in Group A are deliberately designed to guide the student step-by-step through
the process of first finding the down payment, then the installment price, and, finally, the
installment charge, which is really the ultimate goal.

4. How much will an installment purchaser have to pay under each of the following plans?

	Down Payment	Weekly Payments	Number of Weeks	Installment Price
a.	$3.00	$1.00	20	$ 23.00
b.	2.95	1.50	30	47.95
c.	4.50	1.25	52	69.50
d.	7.95	1.75	40	77.95
e.	8.25	2.45	38	101.35
f.	5.98	2.65	65	178.23

5. How much will an installment purchaser have to pay under each of the following plans?

	Down Payment	Monthly Payments	Number of Months	Installment Price
a.	$ 57.50	$15.50	8	$ 181.50
b.	69.75	18.75	10	257.25
c.	49.95	10.25	12	172.95
d.	120.50	25.50	24	732.50
e.	134.25	35.50	36	1,412.25
f.	129.95	34.50	18	750.95

6. How much extra will an installment purchaser have to pay when buying an article under each of the following plans?

	Down Payment	Monthly Payments	Number Of Months	Installment Price	Cash Price	Installment Charge
a.	$ 50	$10	5	$ 100	$ 90	$ 10
b.	25	5	20	125	95	30
c.	42	16	12	234	210	24
d.	75	23	30	765	605	160
e.	168	35	36	1,428	1,120	308
f.	212	42	24	1,220	1,005	215

7. How much extra will an installment purchaser have to pay when buying an article under each of the following plans?

	Down Payment	Monthly Payments	Number Of Months	Installment Price	Cash Price	Installment Charge
a.	$ 10.50	$ 5.00	8	$ 50.50	$ 42.00	$ 8.50
b.	18.75	6.00	10	78.75	68.75	10.00
c.	14.50	4.50	12	68.50	54.50	14.00
d.	67.95	10.00	24	307.95	267.95	40.00
e.	89.75	15.50	30	554.75	429.75	125.00
f.	105.98	36.50	18	762.98	705.98	57.00

8. How much extra will an installment purchaser have to pay when buying an article under each of the following plans?

As was done earlier where the students were required to distinguish between "discount" and "discount rate," now have them distinguish between "down payment" and "down-payment rate."

Cash Price	Down Payment (Rate)	Monthly Payments	Number Of Months	Installment Price	Installment Charge
a. $200	10%	$15	14	$ 230.00	$ 30.00
b. 150	20%	22	7	184.00	34.00
c. 180	25%	14	12	213.00	33.00
d. 175	30%	9	18	214.50	39.50
e. 450	15%	18	24	499.50	49.50
f. 675	40%	14	36	774.00	99.00

B

1. Mrs. Bradford could purchase a top-loading washer for $178 in cash. Unfortunately, she did not have the money to do this, so she made arrangements to put down a deposit of $28 and pay off the balance in 15 monthly payments of $12 each. How much extra did Mrs. Bradford have to pay by buying the washer on the installment plan? $ 30.00

2. The first thing Joe Brooks did on reaching 18 was to buy a motorcycle for $478.85. Since Joe didn't have the cash to pay, the dealer permitted him to make a down payment of $53.85 and pay off the rest in 30 monthly installments of $19.27 each. How much money could Joe have saved had he had the cash to pay for the motorcycle? $153.10

3. Mrs. Mallory bought her TV set from a door-to-door salesman by making no down payment, but agreeing to pay him $4.75 each week for a year. Had she taken the time to visit the discount house in her neighborhood, she would have found that this same set could be bought for $139.95 cash. How much money could Mrs. Mallory have saved had she had the cash and bought the set at a discount house? $107.05

4. After long years of pushing his lawn mower, Bob Cramer went out and bought a deluxe riding mower that could double as a snowplow during the winter season. If he had had the cash, the mower would have cost him $729. But he did not, so he arranged to make a 10% down payment and the rest he agreed to pay off monthly over a two-year period. The payments came to $35.15. How much greater is the installment price than the cash price? $187.50

5. A 120-watt matched solid-state stereo system can be bought for $319.95 cash. If the buyer doesn't have cash, the dealer is willing to arrange an easy-pay plan. This consists of making a down payment of 5% and weekly payments of $4.65 each over a two-year period. How much could a person save when buying this system if he did not take advantage of the easy-pay plan? $179.65

Many students have difficulty with the narrative problems. It might be best to assign those above as extra-credit problems. In reality, the exercises in Group B are the more important, for, normally, the practical situation will usually appear in outline form and not in narrative form.

Unit 6: The Charge Account

The large department stores have deferred-payment plans that are pretty much the same as those used in the monthly-installment plans. However, these stores don't like to use the term "installment buying," because, for some reason, this type of purchase has been thought to be beneath the dignity of the fashionable department stores. In recent years, though, they, too, have come to realize that it is possible for them to make more money on the deferred-payment plan than the actual profit on the merchandise itself. Hence, they, too, have entered the business of installment selling in a big way, except that they still refuse to call it by that name. They disguise the installment purchase by making up a variety of names for it, such as the following:

> The Revolving Charge Account
> The Permanent Budget Account
> The Convenient Budget Account

The idea behind these accounts, no matter what they are called, is to have the balance, or debt, paid off in monthly payments. A "small" service charge is added to the account each month. Now that the truth-in-lending law has been passed, customers must be informed what the charge is. The rate is 1% or 1½% per month on the unpaid balance, or even 2%, 2½%, or 3%, depending on what other stores in the area are charging and the section of the country in which the store is located.

There is no legal limit on the interest rate you can be charged on these accounts. The 1% per month rate seems like quite a small amount, but why not examine it more closely to see if this is the case? If you kept your money in a bank, the very highest rate the bank would be permitted to pay you under present law (other than in special accounts) is 5% per year. Now the 1% charge per month comes to 12% per year. Why? This is almost 2½ times the rate the bank can pay you. And if the service charge happens to be 3% per month, then, on a yearly basis, it would be 36%. This is seven times as much as the rate the bank can pay you. You can see that the revolving charge account was invented less for the convenience of the customer than for the profit of the department store.

At the time you inquire about the possibility of opening a charge account, you are usually asked to fill out a form similar to the one here. It is only after a check is made on how promptly you pay your bills that you are issued a credit card for the charge account.

This particular application blank has an interesting note in the lower-right corner. Notice that you are asked to check whether or not

As a class project, have the students check the department stores in their community to determine if there are any that do not permit the buyer to charge his purchases. As an outgrowth of this survey, draw up a comparison between the different credit plans.

you want to take out credit life insurance with this account. This insurance is the same type you examined at the time you were investigating the purchase of a car. You may remember that if you carried this insurance, in the event that you died before the car was fully paid for, the insurance company would pay off the balance of the debt. Credit insurance on a charge account is exactly the same. Should you die while a balance still remained in the account, this would be cleared up by the insurance company. The very last line of the application states that you have to make a monthly payment of 1/10 of 1% of the unpaid balance for this protection. Here is how some of these accounts operate.

DEPARTMENT STORE A

In this store, you simply tell the credit manager that you would like to have a revolving charge account of $100, $150, $200, $250, or $300. If you choose the $100 account, you will not be permitted to charge merchandise in excess of $100. In addition, each month you must make a payment of at least $10 on your debt. If the amount you owe the store drops below $10, then all you have to pay is whatever this amount happens to be.

There are many department stores that now insist that the charge-account customer carry credit insurance, for they do not want to incur the expense of trying to collect the balance of the debt from the deceased's family or relatives.

In the $150 account, the maximum you might charge is $150. Now your monthly payment will be at least $15 unless you manage to bring the debt below $15. In this event, you will pay only what you owe. What is the total amount you will be able to charge under the $200 account? How large will your monthly payments have to be?

No matter which of these accounts you choose, the "small service charge" is 1½% of the unpaid balance carried from the previous month's bill. Incidentally, there is no service charge on any purchases made during the current month.

■ILLUSTRATION 1: Mrs. Joan Clarke has a $250 charge account at Department Store A. The unpaid balance carried from the previous month's bill is $195.

    a. How large is Mrs. Clarke's monthly payment?
    b. How large is the service charge that is added to Mrs. Clarke's account?
    c. How much will Mrs. Clarke still owe on her account after she has made the monthly payment?

●SOLUTION:

$$(a) \text{ Monthly payment} = \$25$$
$$(b) \text{ Service charge} = 1\tfrac{1}{2}\% \times \$195$$
$$= 1.5\% \times \$195$$
$$= .015 \times \$195$$
$$= \$2.925, \text{ or } \$2.93$$
$$(c) \text{ Total of account at month's end} = \$195 + \$2.93$$
$$= \$197.93$$
$$\text{Balance still remaining} = \$197.93 - \$25$$
$$= \$172.93$$

▼EXPLANATION: Since this is a "$250 account," the amount of the cash monthly payment has to be $25. Hence, this is the answer to part (a). For part (b), the service charge is 1½% of the unpaid balance of $195. Before multiplying 1½% by $195, you first change the percent numeral from 1½% to 1.5%. Now by moving the decimal point two places to the left, this percent numeral can be rewritten in its equivalent form of .015 as a decimal numeral. Of course, the purpose of this is to enable you to multiply the number by $195. As you know, it is not possible to perform any of the operations when a number is expressed in its percent form. In answer to (c), you realize that the total debt at the end of the month consists of both the balance that had not been paid, plus the service charge for the month. This comes to $197.93. After subtracting the $25 that was paid, you find that Mrs. Clarke still owes this department store $172.93.

As explained earlier in a similar situation, do not have the students convert the mixed-number percent value to fractional form. The decimal form is far easier for most students, and particularly the student of consumer mathematics.

DEPARTMENT STORE B

This department store has set up a payment schedule to this effect.

SCHEDULE OF PAYMENTS

Highest Balance	Monthly Payment	Highest Balance	Monthly Payment
$ 20 to 100	$10	$551 to 600	$40
101 to 150	12	601 to 650	42
151 to 200	15	651 to 700	45
201 to 250	20	701 to 750	47
251 to 300	25	751 to 800	50
301 to 350	27	801 to 850	52
351 to 400	30	851 to 900	55
401 to 450	32	901 to 950	57
451 to 500	35	951 to 1,000	60
501 to 550	37		

If a person's balance during a particular month happened to be $317, then the smallest payment she could make would be $27. However, she can pay off any amount over that she cares to; in fact, she can pay off the entire debt of $317. What is the least payment that a charge-account customer can make during a month in which her balance is $637.24?

For the convenience of having a charge account in this store, you would pay a monthly service charge of 1½% on that part of the balance on your debt carried from the previous month's bill that was $500 or under, and only 1% on that part of the debt over $500.

■ ILLUSTRATION 2: Mrs. Riker's charge-account balance at Department Store B came to $739 after she paid her bill in February.

    a. How large a service charge was made against her account for the month of March?

    b. What was the smallest payment Mrs. Riker could make in March if there were no charge purchases that month?

● SOLUTION:

$$(a)\ \text{Service charge on first } \$500 = 1\tfrac{1}{2}\% \times \$500$$
$$= 1.5\% \times \$500$$
$$= .015 \times \$500$$
$$= \$7.50$$
$$\text{Balance of debt over } \$500 = \$739 - \$500$$
$$= \$239$$
$$\text{Service charge on amount over } \$500 = 1\% \times \$239$$
$$= .01 \times \$239$$
$$= \$2.39$$

You may want to prove for your students that 1% of a number can be determined by moving the decimal point in the number two places to the left of its original position. Some teachers prefer not to do this, for they fear that the process becomes purely mechanical for most students. The choice is yours to make.

$$\text{Total service charge} = \$7.50 + \$2.39$$
$$= \$9.89$$

(b) $\text{Total March bill} = \$739 + \$9.89$
$$= \$748.89$$

$$\text{Payment} = \$47$$

▼EXPLANATION: In determining the service charge in Part (a), you separate the computation into two sections. In the first of these, you find the service charge on the first $500 by computing 1½% of this amount. The remainder of the service charge is computed by determining 1% of the balance over the $500 amount. Since the total unpaid balance is $739, the amount over $500 is $239. On $239, 1% is $2.39. Hence, the total service charge is the sum of the two charges of $7.50 and $2.39, or $9.89. In finding the smallest possible payment for March, notice that the total bill of $748.89 falls between $701 and $750. Therefore, according to the "Schedule of Payments," the smallest payment that will be accepted by the store is $47.

DEPARTMENT STORE C

This department store is actually the one whose charge-account application appears on page 133. In this case, customers are allowed to charge purchases so long as the total remains under $1,000. Instead of following a schedule of payments, you are told that each month you must make a payment of at least 10% of the bill at the time of payment. You are also granted the option of purchasing credit insurance on your life at a cost of 1/10 of 1% of the unpaid balance carried from the previous month's bill. The monthly service charge here is also based on this unpaid balance, and is 2% of that amount.

■ILLUSTRATION 3: After paying her bill in September, the balance in Mrs. Porter's charge account at Department Store C was $237.

   a. What service charge will Mrs. Porter have to pay in October?
   b. How much will have to be added to Mrs. Porter's balance to pay for the cost of the credit insurance?
   c. What is the smallest payment Mrs. Porter can make on her charge account in October if she had no charge purchase in that month?

●SOLUTION:

(a) $\text{Service charge} = 2\% \times \$237$
$$= .02 \times \$237$$
$$= \$4.74$$

(b) $\text{Cost of insurance} = 1/10 \times 1\% \times \$237$
$$= 1/10 \times .01 \times \$237$$
$$= .001 \times \$237$$
$$= \$.237, \text{ or } \$.24$$

With each of the monthly rates charged, take time to point out how each compares with the rate of interest the student receives on his savings account; that is, a monthly charge of 2% is equivalent to an annual charge of 24%, which is almost 5 times the rate of 5% their bank is probably paying.

(c) Total bill for October $= \$237 + \$4.74 + \$.24$
$$= \$241.98$$
Minimum payment $= 10\% \times \$241.98$
$$= .10 \times \$241.98$$
$$= \$24.198, \text{ or } \$24.20$$

▼ EXPLANATION: The only computation above that might cause a little difficulty is that involving the cost of the insurance in Part (b). To find 1/10 of 1%, it is best to first rewrite 1% in its equivalent decimal form of .01. To get 1/10 of this number, simply divide .01 by 10. Thus:

$$\begin{array}{r} .001 \\ \hline 10)\overline{.010} \\ \underline{10} \\ 0 \end{array}$$

Therefore, $1/10 \times 1\% \times \$237$ becomes $.001 \times \$237$, and this product is $\$.237$. When $\$.237$ is rounded off to the nearest penny, the cost of the insurance turns out to be $\$.24$.

EXERCISES   **A**

If you do not recall how to do the computation in the following exercises, refer to page 573 for help. Write each of the products below as a decimal.

a. $\frac{1}{10} \times 1\%$ ___001___
b. $\frac{1}{2} \times 1\%$ ___.005___
c. $\frac{1}{4} \times 1\%$ ___.0025___

d. $\frac{1}{5} \times 1\%$ ___.0020___
e. $\frac{1}{8} \times 1\%$ ___.00125___
f. $\frac{1}{100} \times 1\%$ ___.0001___

B

1. Use the charge-account plans described for Department Store A on pages 133–134 to find the monthly payment on each of the following plans.
   a. The $100 plan ___$10___   c. The $150 plan ___$15___
   b. The $200 plan ___$20___   d. The $300 plan ___$30___
2. How large will the monthly service charge be on each of the following charge-account balances under the Department Store A plan on pages 133–134?
   a. $140 ___$2.10___   c. $86 ___$1.29___   e. $254.80 ___$3.82___
   b. $220 ___$3.30___   d. $132.40 ___$1.99___   f. $176.47 ___$2.65___

In the exercises of Part A, have the students convert 1% to the equivalent decimal form of 01 before attempting to divide. Use the method shown in the explanation to Illustration 3.

3. What balance will still remain after the monthly payment is made on each of the following charge accounts at Department Store A? No charge purchases were made during the current month.

	Balance From Previous Month	Type Of Account	Service Charge	Monthly Payment	Balance Still Remaining
a.	$ 80	$100	$ 1.20	$ 10	$ 71.20
b.	140	150	2.10	15	127.10
c.	220	250	3.30	25	198.30
d.	260	300	3.90	30	233.90
e.	145	200	2.18	20	127.18
f.	196	300	2.94	30	168.94
g.	234	250	3.51	25	212.51
h.	298	300	4.47	30	272.47

4. What are the smallest monthly payments that charge-account customers at Department Store B can make if their unpaid bills are as follows? (See page 135.)

a. $157 ___$15___
b. $234 ___$20___
c. $469 ___$35___
d. $723 ___$47___

e. $249.47 $ ___$20___
f. $358.31 ___$30___
g. $604.16 ___$42___
h. $918.12 ___$57___

5. How large will the monthly service charge be on each of the following charge-account balances at Department Store B?

	Balance From Previous Month	Charge On First $500 Or Less	Charge On Amount Over $500	Total Service Charge
a.	$400	$ 6.00	$ –	$ 6.00
b.	500	7.50	–	7.50
c.	800	7.50	3.00	10.50
d.	900	7.50	4.00	11.50
e.	750	7.50	2.50	10.00
f.	840	7.50	3.40	10.90
g.	645	7.50	1.45	8.95
h.	987	7.50	4.87	12.37
i.	712	7.50	2.12	9.62
j.	834	7.50	3.34	10.84

6. What balance will still remain after the smallest monthly payment possible is made on each of the following charge accounts at Department Store B? No charge purchases were made during the current month.

	Balance From Previous Month	Charge On First $500	Charge On Amount Over $500	Total Service Charge	Monthly Payment	Balance
a.	$600	$ 7.50	$ 1.00	$ 8.50	$ 40	$ 568.50
b.	870	7.50	3.70	11.20	55	826.20
c.	720	7.50	2.20	9.70	47	682.70
d.	960	7.50	4.60	12.10	60	912.10
e.	875	7.50	3.75	11.25	55	831.25

It would be best to have the students record their answers on lined paper where the exercises are outlined exactly as above The actual computation can be done on unlined paper. Both sheets of paper should be required of each student.

7. What are the smallest monthly payments that charge-account customers at Department Store C can make if their unpaid bills at the time of payment are as follows? (See page 136.)

a. $140 __$14.00__   e. $237.26 __$23.73__
b. $630 __$63.00__   f. $427.18 __$42.72__
c. $347 __$34.20__   g. $695.83 __$69.58__
d. $596 __$59.60__   h. $874.76 __$87.48__

8. How large will the monthly service charge be on each of the following charge-account balances at Department Store C?

a. $400 __$ 8.00__   e. $685 __$13.70__
b. $700 __$14.00__   f. $473 __$ 9.46__
c. $540 __$10.80__   g. $396 __$ 7.92__
d. $290 __$ 5.80__   h. $478 __$ 9.56__

9. The charge-account customers at Department Store C, whose unpaid balances are shown, had chosen to take out credit life insurance. How much did the insurance cost them for this month? (See page 136.)

a. $300 __$.30__   i. $623 __$ $.62__
b. $800 __$.80__   j. $731 __$.73__
c. $900 __$.90__   k. $298 __$.30__
d. $600 __$.60__   l. $487 __$.49__
e. $450 __$.45__   m. $312.45 __$.31__
f. $570 __$.57__   n. $533.82 __$.53__
g. $620 __$.62__   o. $649.72 __$.65__
h. $790 __$.79__   p. $158.07 __$.16__

10. What balance will remain after the smallest-possible monthly payment is made on each of the following charge accounts in Department Store C? No charge purchases were made during the current month. (See page 136.)

	Balance From Previous Month	Service Charge	Insurance Charge	Total Charge	Total Bill	Monthly Payment	Balance
a.	$200	$ 4.00	$ .20	$ 4.20	$ 204.20	$ 20.42	$ 183.78
b.	700	14.00	.70	14.70	714.70	71.47	643.23
c.	450	9.00	.45	9.45	495.45	45.95	413.50
d.	680	13.60	.68	14.28	694.28	69.43	624.85
e.	324	6.48	.32	6.80	330.80	33.08	297.72

In an exercise such as 10 above, unless the student outlines his work as shown, there is every likelihood that he will get lost somewhere in the process of finding each of the many parts of the solution.

C

1. Two charge-account customers at Department Store A (see pages 133–134) have exactly the same bill of $84.95. However, one has a "$100 account," while the other has a "$250 account." How much less will the first customer's payment be that month than the second customer's?   <u>$15.00</u>

2. Mrs. Jennings has a charge account at Department Store A (see pages 133–134). During the month of March, her bill was $18.85.
   a. If her account is a "$200 account," how much will her payment have to be?   <u>$18.85</u>
   b. If her account is a "$300 account," how much will her payment have to be?   <u>$18.85</u>
   c. If her account is a "$150 account," how much will her payment have to be?   <u>$15.00</u>

3. After making her May 1 payment, Mrs. Ellsworth's "$300 account" at Department Store A showed a balance of $240. She made no charge purchases during May.
   a. How large will her payment be on June 1?   <u>$30.00</u>
   b. How large will the service charge be for the month of May?   <u>$ 3.60</u>

   c. What is the total amount of merchandise that Mrs. Ellsworth will be able to charge during the month of June?   <u>$86.40</u>

Unit 7:   Chapter Review and Test

1. Write each of the following measures in terms of ounces only.
   a. 4 pounds <u>64 oz.</u>   b. 3 pounds, 5 ounces <u>53 oz.</u>
2. Write each of the following measures in terms of pints only.
   a. 5 quarts <u>10 pt.</u>   b. 6 quarts, 1 pint <u>13 pt.</u>
3. Write each of the following measures in terms of quarts only.
   a. 6 gallons <u>24 qt.</u>   b. 4 gallons, 3 quarts <u>19 qt.</u>
4. Write each of the following measures in terms of ounces only.
   a. 5 quarts, 7 ounces <u>167 oz.</u>   b. 2 pints, 10 ounces <u>42 oz.</u>
5. A can of creamed corn weighs 1 pound, 1 ounce. The cost of the can is 24¢. What is the cost per ounce of this creamed corn? Compute your answer to the nearest tenth of a penny.   <u>1.4¢</u>
6. Peach jelly sells at a supermarket at 3 jars for $1. How much will a customer probably have to pay for 1 jar?   <u>34¢</u>
7. Find the replacement for b in each of the following equations.
   a. $6 \times b = 48$ <u>8</u>   b. $b/3 = 16/12$ <u>4</u>

8. A 6-ounce box of breakfast flakes sells for 28¢. At the same rate per ounce, how much should a person have to pay for a 9-ounce box of the same flakes? <u>42¢</u>

9. An 8-ounce jar of beets costs 14¢. If a person purchased a 20-ounce jar of these same beets, he would have to pay 25¢. How much can a person save by buying the 20-ounce jar rather than by buying 20 ounces of beets at the same rate he paid for the 8-ounce jar? <u>10¢</u>

10. Mary Jamieson purchased $7.58 worth of food at the supermarket. She gave the checkout clerk a $10 bill in payment. Indicate the change that Mary received. Use a table similar to the one below.

1¢	5¢	10¢	25¢	50¢	$1	$5
2	1	1	1		2	

11. A television set that regularly sells for $184 was placed on sale at a 25% discount rate.
    a. How much discount did a person receive during the sale? <u>$46</u>
    b. How much did a person have to pay for the TV set if he purchased it during the sale? <u>$138</u>
    c. Show how you would find the sale price without first finding the discount. $184 × .75 = <u>$138</u>

12. During its storewide furniture sale, the Camden Company offered a set of porch furniture at 33⅓% off. If this porch furniture regularly sells for $237, how much will it cost during the sale? <u>$158</u>

13. An article that regularly sells for $20 can be purchased during a sale at a discount of $5. What discount rate is a purchaser receiving? <u>25%</u>

14. A $64.95 electric guitar can be purchased during a sale for $49.98. By rounding off each of these prices to the nearest dollar, find the discount rate to the nearest whole-number percent value. <u>23%</u>

15. Bruce Devlin purchased a typewriter that regularly sells for $137. Since he did not have the cash, he was permitted to buy it on the following terms:

$15 down and $8 per month for 18 months

How much could Bruce have saved had he had the cash to pay for the typewriter? <u>$22</u>

As suggested earlier, the odd-numbered problems can be used as a review, while the even-numbered ones can be used for testing.

16. Mr. Spellman has a $250 charge account at Department Store A.
(See pages 133–134.) After making his monthly payment in March,
his account showed a balance of $185.
   a. How large was Mr. Spellman's payment in April? $ 25.00
   b. How large was the service charge that was added to his account
      for March? $ 2.78
   c. How much still remained to be paid after he made his monthly
      payment in April? He made no charge purchases during the
      month of March. $162.78

CHAPTER 4

PERSONAL INCOME

There will be few experiences in your life that will give you more satisfaction than the first money you earn. New worlds will seem to open up before you—a convertible car, a 24-foot speedboat, a trip to Bermuda! It is only after you take a second look at the amount of the check that you settle for another necktie, or another blouse.

The way you receive your earnings depends frequently on the type of position you hold. If you fall into the managerial, or executive, group, you will probably receive an annual salary that is given to you in one of three ways:

1. Monthly
2. Semimonthly, that is, twice a month
3. Biweekly, that is, once every two weeks

If your experience is typical of most consumer-mathematics teachers, you will find that the topics covered in this chapter hold far more interest for the student than any others in the course. Many students at this age have just found their first job, or are in process of seeking it.

If you are not paid in this way, then your earnings may be based on any one, or a combination, of the following methods.

    1. Hourly basis
    2. Piece-rate basis
    3. Commission basis

Since most people will find themselves among the second group, it will be these three methods of computing earnings that will be examined in this chapter.

Unit 1: Earnings Computed on an Hourly Basis

Section 1: Regular Wages and Overtime Wages

The wages of the majority of workers are based on the number of hours that they work. Usually, they earn a certain salary per hour, and their earnings are computed in terms of the total number of hours they work during one week. Frequently, the labor organization that represents the employees of a company will have drawn up a contract with the managers of that company, stating what the hourly rates should be for these employees. Actually, the rate is not the same for everyone. The men on the custodial staff earn far less than the skilled draftsman, or the tool designer. The wages of all, however, are computed in exactly the same way.

■ILLUSTRATION 1: During the past week, Mr. Jenkins worked 37½ hours at the rate of $2.56 per hour. What were his earnings for the week?

●SOLUTION:

Rate for 1 hour = $2.56
Earnings for 37½ hours = 37½ × $2.56
= $96.00

▼EXPLANATION: There was very little involved in this problem other than finding the product of 37½ and $2.56. In doing the computation, you might find it best to change 37½ to 37.5 before multiplying.

Most wage contracts include an agreement in them that sets the total number of hours that an employee may work each week. If he works beyond that time, the agreement usually states that he will receive *time and a half* for the overtime work. This simply means that, for each of the overtime hours, his rate of pay will be 1½ times as large as the normal hourly pay rate. Thus, if the normal hourly rate is $2.00, then, for each hour of overtime work, the employee will receive 1½ times as much as this, or $3.00.

Notice that as in the case of the mixed-number percent value which was changed to a decimal equivalent, so, too, is the mixed numeral converted to the decimal numeral rather than the fraction numeral.

■ ILLUSTRATION 2: If the normal hourly wage rate is $3.47, what will the overtime wage rate be at time and a half?

● SOLUTION:

$$\text{Normal hourly wage rate} = \$3.47$$
$$\text{Time-and-a-half rate} = 1\frac{1}{2} \times \$3.47$$
$$= 1.5 \times \$3.47$$
$$= \$5.205$$

▼ EXPLANATION: There are two points of importance in the above solution. Notice that the 1½ was changed to the decimal 1.5 so that the computation would be easier. Also, the overtime pay rate of $5.205 was not rounded off to the nearest penny. No rounding off should be done until the total overtime salary is determined.

■ ILLUSTRATION 3: Mr. Sullivan is employed by a company where he is paid time and a half for all work beyond 38 hours per week. If his regular hourly rate is $2.69, how much will his earnings be during a week in which he worked 45 hours?

● SOLUTION:

$$\text{Regular hourly rate} = \$2.69$$
$$\text{Overtime hourly rate} = 1.5 \times \$2.69$$
$$= \$4.035$$
$$\text{Number of hours of overtime} = 45 - 38$$
$$= 7$$
$$\text{Regular salary} = 38 \times \$2.69$$
$$= \$102.22$$
$$\text{Overtime salary} = 7 \times \$4.035$$
$$= \$28.245, \text{ or } \$28.25$$
$$\text{Total salary} = \$102.22 + \$28.25$$
$$= \$130.47$$

EXERCISES   A

1. Find the time-and-a-half rate for each of the following regular hourly rates.

	Regular Hourly Rate	Time-and-a-Half Rate
a.	$3.00	$ 4.50
b.	5.00	7.50
c.	1.80	2.70
d.	2.50	3.75
e.	3.70	5.55
f.	2.64	3.96
g.	1.96	2.94
h.	3.38	5.07
i.	2.43	3.645
j.	3.87	5.805

Make certain that the students do not round off the hourly overtime rate to the nearest penny. It is only after the total overtime salary is computed that rounding off takes place. Rounding off at an early stage would change the overtime rate.

2. Determine the earnings of each of the following. None received overtime during the week.

	Hourly Rate	Hours Worked	Earnings
a.	$1.90	40	$ 76.00
b.	2.57	40	102.80
c.	3.85	38	146.30
d.	4.29	37	158.73
e.	2.37½	40	95.00
f.	2.84½	38	108.11
g.	2.384	39	92.98
h.	3.096	40	123.84
i.	2.76	37½	103.50
j.	2.18	38½	83.93
k.	2.83½	36½	103.48
l.	3.15½	35½	112.00

3. The regular hourly rate and the number of overtime hours of work are given below. Determine the overtime earnings of each if time and a half is paid for overtime work.

	Hourly Rate	Overtime Rate	Overtime Hours	Overtime Earnings
a.	$2.08	$ 3.12	2	$ 6.24
b.	3.24	4.86	3	14.58
c.	2.88	4.32	2½	10.80
d.	2.50	3.75	2¼	8.44
e.	1.96	2.94	4¾	13.97
f.	3.75	5.625	8	45.00
g.	2.67	4.005	14	56.07
h.	2.13	3.195	11	35.15
i.	2.71	4.065	5½	22.36
j.	3.45	5.175	7¼	37.52
k.	2.84½	4.2675	6	25.61
l.	4.06½	6.0975	12	73.17

4. The maximum number of hours that an employee should work under the regular hourly pay rate is given below. For work beyond this, he receives time-and-a-half pay. Compute the total earnings for the week for each of the following employees.

	Hourly Rate	Overtime Rate	Hours Worked	Maximum For Regular Rate	Regular Earnings	Overtime Hours	Overtime Earnings	Total Earnings
a.	$3.40	$ 5.10	42	40	$ 136.00	2	$ 10.20	$ 146.20
b.	2.80	4.20	48	40	112.00	8	33.60	145.60
c.	2.56	3.84	45	40	102.40	5	19.20	121.60
d.	3.08	4.62	41	38	117.04	3	13.86	130.90
e.	2.09	3.135	43	40	83.60	3	9.405	93.01

It is interesting to note that a number of unions have negotiated contracts involving fewer regular hours of work per week, and yet the employees continue to work the same number of hours they worked in the past. Ask the students why the unions negotiate these contract arrangements.

Hourly Rate	Overtime Rate	Hours Worked	Maximum For Regular Rate	Regular Earnings	Overtime Hours	Overtime Earnings	Total Earnings
f. 2.37	3.555	40	37	$ 87.69	3	$ 10.665	$ 98.36
g. 4.65	6.975	37	28	130.20	9	62.775	192.98
h. 2.18	3.27	41½	39	85.02	2½	8.175	93.20
i. 3.10	4.65	44¼	38	117.80	6¼	29.0625	146.86
j. 2.96	4.44	41	37½	111.00	3½	15.54	126.54
k. 3.24	4.86	44	38½	124.74	5½	26.73	151.47
l. 2.88	4.32	42½	35½	102.24	7	30.24	132.48
m. 2.65	3.975	41¾	37½	99.375	4¼	16.89375	116.27
n. 3.19	4.785	46¼	35½	113.245	10¾	51.43875	164.68

B

1. If Mr. Hunter works either Sundays or holidays, he receives double time for each hour of work. This means that he will receive twice as much for each hour of work on those days than he does at his regular hourly rate during the week. His regular hourly rate is $3.24 per hour. How much will he receive for a Sunday's work of 6½ hours? $ 42.12

2. Mr. Morely works for a firm where the normal work period is 38½ hours per week. He receives time and a half for overtime and double time for Sundays and holidays. His regular rate is $2.98 per hour.
   a. What will his normal weekly earnings be? $114.73
   b. What will he earn during a week in which he worked 42 hours? $130.38

   c. During the week in which he worked the 42 hours, he was also asked to work 5½ hours on Sunday. What were his total earnings for that week? $163.16
3. Mr. Morely of Problem 2 worked 36 hours during the week of the July 4th holiday. If 5 of the hours of work were on the holiday, what was his total salary for that week? $122.18
4. Mr. Morely's firm of Problem 2 considers both Thanksgiving Thursday and the Friday that follows it to be holidays. How much will Mr. Morely earn during the week of Thanksgiving, if of the 37 hours he worked, 4 were on Thursday and 7 were on Friday? $143.04

Section 2: Overtime Pay and Tardiness Deductions

Until now, time and a half has been interpreted to mean that for each hour of overtime work, the worker receives 1½ times the regular hourly pay rate. There is another interpretation for this, however, and

Not mentioned in this chapter is the bonus pay that many employees receive for working off hours, such as the night shift, or the midnight shift. Have your students check to determine whether the companies that employ their parents have this sort of arrangement.

that is, for each hour of overtime, he will receive 1½ hours of regular pay. Thus, 2 hours of overtime would be equivalent to 2 times 1½ hours of regular pay; 3 hours would be 3 times 1½ hours of regular pay. And, in general:

> If the number of overtime hours is multiplied by 1½, you will find the number of regular hours for which you will be paid.

Both of these methods of computation do—and should—lead to exactly the same amount of overtime earnings. The following illustrations will show why this is so.

■ ILLUSTRATION 1: Mr. Bryan's hourly salary is $2.58. What will his earnings be for 6 hours of overtime?

▼ EXPLANATION: By using the previous method, you would first multiply 1½ by $2.58 to determine the overtime hourly rate. This product would then be multiplied by the 6 hours, to give you the overtime earnings. Indicated below is what has to be done.

$$\text{Overtime rate} = \$2.58 \times 1\tfrac{1}{2}$$
$$\text{Overtime salary} = (\$2.58 \times 1\tfrac{1}{2}) \times 6$$

When examining $(\$2.58 \times 1\tfrac{1}{2}) \times 6$, you can see that by applying the associative law of multiplication, this can be rewritten as:

$$\$2.58 \times (1\tfrac{1}{2} \times 6)$$

That is, instead of finding the product by grouping the first two numbers, you are finding it by grouping the last two. By doing this, you will be multiplying the regular rate of $2.58 by 1½ times the number of overtime hours of work. This is exactly what the second method for computing the overtime salary is.

● SOLUTION:

$$\text{Number of actual overtime hours} = 6$$
$$\text{Number of earning overtime hours} = 6 \times 1\tfrac{1}{2}$$
$$= 9$$
$$\text{Overtime earnings} = 9 \times \$2.58$$
$$= \$23.22$$

Many salary agreements call for overtime wages to be paid on a daily basis rather than a weekly one. Thus, the arrangement may call for 7 hours of work per day over a 5-day week. Under these conditions, although a person may have worked less than 35 hours during a particular week, if he worked more than 7 hours during any one day of that week, he is entitled to overtime pay for that day.

It may be that many of your students are not familiar with the associative law of multiplication. If this is so, ask them to find the product of 2, 3, and 4 by grouping the numbers first as (2 x 3) x 4, and then as 2 x (3 x 4). Base the explanation of Illustration 1 on this example.

■ ILLUSTRATION 2: Mr. Morris works a 5-day week, 7 hours per day, at time and a half for all hours over the 7 in one day. If his hourly pay rate is $3.07, how much will he earn during a week in which his hours were as follows:

Monday	Tuesday	Wednesday	Thursday	Friday
6	9½	8	5	7

▼ EXPLANATION: On Tuesday, Mr. Morris worked 2½ hours overtime and on Wednesday he worked 1 hour overtime. Hence, during the entire week he worked 3½ hours overtime. The remaining hours—6 hours on Monday, 7 hours on Tuesday, 7 hours on Wednesday, 5 hours on Thursday, and 7 hours on Friday—are regular hours of work. By multiplying the 3½ hours by 1½, you will find the number of hours for which Mr. Morris will receive overtime salary. When this number is added to the number of regular hours of work, the sum will represent the total number of hours for which he will be paid.

● SOLUTION:

$$\text{Number of actual overtime hours} = 2\tfrac{1}{2} + 1$$
$$= 3\tfrac{1}{2}$$
$$\text{Number of earning overtime hours} = 1\tfrac{1}{2} \times 3\tfrac{1}{2}$$
$$= 1.5 \times 3.5$$
$$= 5.25$$
$$\text{Number of regular hours} = 6 + 7 + 7 + 5 + 7$$
$$= 32$$
$$\text{Total number of salary hours} = 32 + 5.25$$
$$= 37.25$$
$$\text{Total earnings} = 37.25 \times \$3.07$$
$$= \$114.3575, \text{ or } \$114.36$$

Employers are as unhappy about tardiness as teachers are. There is a difference, though, and that is that the employer has a way in which to combat this—he simply withholds part of your salary. On the whole, employers will often overlook a tardiness of as much as 15 minutes. When it runs over that, the amount they deduct will depend on the extent of the tardiness. Should tardiness become a habit, the employee may find that he no longer has a job.

A typical scale of wage loss for late arrival at work resembles the following:

MINUTES LATE	LOSS OF SALARY
First 15 minutes	No loss of salary
For each succeeding 10-minute period, or fraction thereof	¼ of an hour's salary

Notice that, in the explanation here, as in earlier examples, the mixed numerals were rewritten in their equivalent decimal form rather than in fraction form.

■ ILLUSTRATION 3: Steven Willard clocked in at 8:57 A.M. last Thursday. His workday is supposed to begin at 8:00 A.M. If he earns $2.86 per hour, how much will be deducted from his salary because of this tardiness?

▼ EXPLANATION: Steven was 57 minutes late on Thursday. For the first 15 of these, there is no loss of salary. This leaves 57 − 15, or 42 minutes to be accounted for. For each 10-minute period, or fraction of a 10-minute period in the 42 minutes, he will lose ¼ of an hour's salary. By dividing 10 into 42, you find that there are 4²⁄₁₀ 10-minute periods in 42 minutes. Hence, Steven will lose 5 quarter hours of salary. And since 5 times ¼ is 1.25, his salary loss will be 1.25 times $2.86. Incidentally, the phrase "clocked in at 8:57 A.M." means "reported to work at 8:57 A.M." The word "clocked" comes from the fact that an employee usually stamps the clock time on a card when he arrives at work.

● SOLUTION:

$$\text{Number of minutes tardy} = 57$$
$$\text{Number of minutes of salary loss} = 57 - 15$$
$$= 42$$
$$\text{Number of 10-minute periods} = 42 \div 10$$
$$= 4.2, \text{ or } 5$$
$$\text{Number of hours of salary loss} = 5 \times \tfrac{1}{4}$$
$$= 5/4$$
$$= 1.25$$
$$\text{Salary loss} = 1.25 \times \$2.86$$
$$= \$3.575$$
$$= \$3.58$$

EXERCISES   **A**

1. At time and a half for overtime, for how many hours will a person receive pay if he worked the following number of overtime hours?

	Actual Overtime Hours	Earning Overtime Hours
a.	2	3
b.	6	9
c.	10	15
d.	14	21
e.	7	10.5
f.	5	7.5
g.	9	13.5
h.	11	16.5
i.	8½	12.75
j.	6½	9.75
k.	4¼	6.375
l.	5¾	8.625

It is hoped that a possible peripheral outcome of exposure to this unit will be a greater interest on the part of students to report to school and to class at the required time. Emphasize that habits that they develop now may well carry over to their adult life and result in loss of income.

2. Each of the following employees is entitled to overtime pay for all the time they work over 8 hours per day. How many actual hours of overtime will each have during the week shown?

	Monday	Tuesday	Wednesday	Thursday	Friday	Overtime Hours
a.	8	5	9	7	12	5
b.	6	4	10	10	8	4
c.	8	8½	9	7	10	3.5
d.	6¼	7	8¼	8¼	8½	1
e.	10½	6	9½	8¼	8¼	4.5
f.	7	8¾	8½	9	8	2.25

3. Each of the following employees is entitled to overtime pay for all the time they work over 7 hours per day. How many hours of salary will each receive during the week shown below?

	Monday	Tuesday	Wednesday	Thursday	Friday	Regular Hours	Actual Overtime Hours	Earning Overtime Hours	Total Hours
a.	9	6	5	8	7	32	3	4.5	36.5
b.	7	7	7	7	9	35	2	3	38
c.	7	8	8	8	7	35	3	4.5	39.5
d.	7	9	7	7	9	35	4	6	41
e.	7	10	9	7	8	35	6	9	44
f.	6	7	10	7	9	34	5	7.5	41.5
g.	8	5	4	9	6	29	3	4.5	33.5
h.	7	8	7½	7	7½	35	2	3	38
i.	7	7½	7½	7½	7½	35	2	3	38
j.	8½	7½	7	7	8	35	3	4.5	39.5

4. Compute the overtime earnings for each of the following number of overtime hours. Use the method explained in Illustration 1 on page 148.

	Hourly Rate	Actual Overtime Hours	Earning Overtime Hours	Overtime Earnings
a.	$3.07	4	6	$ 18.42
b.	1.95	16	24	46.80
c.	2.29	10	15	34.35
d.	3.41	8	12	40.92
e.	1.84	3	4.5	8.28
f.	2.18	7	10.5	22.89
g.	2.96	15	22.5	66.60
h.	3.40	11	16.5	56.10
i.	2.25	3½	5.25	11.81
j.	4.23	5½	8.25	34.90
k.	3.94	2¼	3.375	13.30
l.	2.17	3¾	5.625	12.21

Make certain that the students express the "Earning Overtime Hours" as decimals before multiplying by 1.5 to determine the "Total Hours."

5. Each of the following employees is entitled to overtime pay for all time worked over 7 hours per day. How much will each earn during the week shown?

	M	T	W	Th	F	Regular Hours	Actual Overtime Hours	Earning Overtime Hours	Total Hours	Hourly Rate	Earnings
a.	7	7	7	7	8	35	1	1.5	36.5	$3.47	$126.66
b.	7	7	7	7	7	35	0	0	35	2.95	103.25
c.	7	6	7	5	7	32	0	0	32	2.06	65.92
d.	9	7	7	9	7	35	4	6	41	3.12	127.92
e.	8	7	7	8	7	35	2	3	38	1.85	70.30
f.	8	8	8	8	8	35	5	7.5	42.5	4.36	185.30
g.	9	7	9	8	7	35	5	7.5	42.5	4.94	209.95
h.	10	8	7	7	8	35	5	7.5	42.5	5.03	213.78

6. The employees of the Pure Oil Company are supposed to clock in at 8:00 A.M. If they are late, they are docked in salary in accordance with the table on page 149. How many quarter hours of salary will be lost by employees reporting at the following hours?

	Time Of Arrival	Minutes Late	Quarter Hours Of Salary Lost
a.	8:10	10	0
b.	8:14	14	0
c.	8:16	16	1
d.	8:28	28	2
e.	8:33	33	2
f.	8:57	57	5
g.	9:07	67	6
h.	9:25	85	7

7. How much salary will be lost by each of the following employees of the Pure Oil Company of Problem 6 if they clocked in at the hour shown?

	Time Of Arrival	Minutes Late	Quarter Hours Of Salary Lost	Hourly Wage	Salary Loss
a.	8:12	12	0	$3.56	$ 0
b.	8:18	18	1	2.68	.67
c.	8:26	26	2	3.24	1.62
d.	8:39	39	3	1.96	1.47
e.	8:42	42	3	2.57	1.93
f.	8:58	58	5	2.86	3.58
g.	9:15	75	6	3.40	5.10
h.	9:26	86	8	2.22	4.44

B

1. The workday at the Briggs Corporation normally ends at 4:30 in the afternoon. Should an employee work until 5:00, he receives no

When doing Exercises 6 and 7, have the students follow exactly the format of the solution to Illustration 3, page 150. The technique of determining the number of "quarter hours of salary lost" may be somewhat difficult for a few of the students.

extra pay for it. However, if he works beyond 5:00 P.M., he will receive ¼ hour at time-and-a-half pay for each 15 minutes of work, or part thereof, beyond 4:30. Thus, if he works until 4:56, he receives no overtime salary, but if he works until 5:02, he will receive ¾ of an hour at time-and-a-half salary. How many quarter hours of overtime salary will each of the following employees receive if they clock out at the time shown?

Time Of Leaving		Time Of Leaving	
a. 4:47	0	d. 5:57	6
b. 5:10	3	e. 4:53	0
c. 5:35	5	f. 6:18	8

2. Mr. Davenport works for the Briggs Corporation of Problem 1 at an hourly rate of $3.08. On Thursday, he worked until 6:25 P.M.
   a. How much overtime pay did he receive for the additional time he worked that day? $ 9.24
   b. How much regular salary did he receive for the day if he is employed on an 8-hour day? $24.64
   c. What were his total earnings for the day? $33.88

3. The Briggs Corporation of Problem 1 docks employees for tardiness in accordance with the table on page 149. The workday normally begins at 8:00 A.M. On Tuesday of this past week, Peter Marley clocked in at 8:42 A.M. and clocked out at 5:37 P.M. His hourly rate is $3.36.
   a. How much was he docked that day for being tardy? $ 2.52
   b. How much were his overtime earnings that day? $ 6.30
   c. Since he is employed on an 8-hour day, how much regular salary did he receive for the day? $24.36
   d. After deducting his loss for tardiness and adding his overtime pay, how much did he earn that day? $30.66

4. For how many hours will each of the following employees be paid if they work for the Briggs Corporation of Problem 1? Consider overtime, tardiness, and ½ hour for lunches for which they are not paid. Remember to multiply the overtime work by 1.5.

Clocked In	Clocked Out	Regular Hours	Tardiness	Actual Overtime Hours	Earning Overtime Hours	Total Hours
a. 8:00 A.M.	5:35 P.M.	8	0	1.25	1.875	9.875
b. 8:00 A.M.	4:35 P.M.	8	0	0	0	8
c. 8:10 A.M.	4:40 P.M.	8	0	0	0	8
d. 8:05 A.M.	5:25 P.M.	8	0	1	1.5	9.5
e. 8:18 A.M.	5:10 P.M.	8	.25	.75	1.125	8.875

In analyzing these problems for the students, use an approach similar to that shown in the solution to Illustration 3, page 150, except that now the divisor will be 15 rather than 10.

Unit 2: Earnings Computed on a Piece-Rate Basis

The situation that occurred as a result of the piecework wage system is an example of how an idea that appeared sound in theory turned out to be somewhat unsatisfactory in actual practice. Under this arrangement, an employee was paid only for the actual number of articles he produced. The feeling behind this was that the alert, competent, and energetic worker would be rewarded for the greater number of articles he was able to produce compared to the slow, lazy, or incompetent individual.

There is no question but that this pay basis increased production immensely. The only difficulty, though, was that in their haste to turn out a lot of articles, the employees were careless and slipshod in their work. Hence, a large percent of the items produced had to be either redone, or destroyed completely. This, for obvious reasons, upset company management. On the other hand, the unions that represented the employees were none too pleased either, for they felt this device was simply a deliberate attempt to drive men beyond their capacity. The increased rate of production led to an increase in the accident rate. Further, labor claimed that, as the men were able to turn out more articles, the amount of money that was given for each article was lowered. Hence, greater efficiency did not necessarily mean higher wages. In any event, both unions and management pretty much agree at present that the piece-rate wage system is not a very desirable way of paying employees.

There are still a number of small firms that use this wage system. Some of them employ people who do work at home. When the work is completed, the finished product is returned to the plant and the employee receives a fixed amount for each article.

■ILLUSTRATION 1: The Marshall Company pays its employees $2.59 for each article they produce. How much will a person earn during a week in which he was able to complete 47 articles?

●SOLUTION:
$$\text{Earnings} = 47 \times \$2.59$$
$$= \$121.73$$

▼EXPLANATION: The computation simply involved multiplying the number of articles produced by the amount received for each article. In the piece-rate wage system, there is no cause for concern with overtime or lateness, for the employee's earnings depend solely on how many articles he turns out.

In recent years, the management and labor of certain companies have agreed on a wage system that represents a combination of the hourly wage rate and the piece-rate method. In this plan, the employee receives a fixed hourly salary for each hour that he works. In addition, if he produces more than a certain number of articles during the week, he will receive a bonus for each such article produced. If he produces less, he loses nothing. Labor is pleased with this, for it knows that each worker will have at least a guaranteed minimum weekly income. Management finds that there are not only fewer accidents, but that greater care is taken in the production of the article.

■ILLUSTRATION 2: The Lacombe Corporation pays its employees an hourly wage of $3.17. In addition, for each article over 125 that the employee produces during a single week, he receives 87¢. How much will Charles Kaston earn during a week in which he worked 38 hours and produced 156 articles?

●SOLUTION:

$$\text{Hourly earnings} = 38 \times \$3.17$$
$$= \$120.46$$
$$\text{Number of articles over } 125 = 156 - 125$$
$$= 31$$
$$\text{Piecework earnings} = 31 \times \$.87$$
$$= \$26.97$$
$$\text{Total earnings} = \$120.46 + \$26.97$$
$$= \$147.43$$

EXERCISES   A

1. Each of the following employees was paid on a straight piecework basis. The number of articles each produced and the amount he received for each article is shown below. Determine the earnings of each for this week.

	Number Of Articles	Piecework Rate	Earnings
a.	176	62¢	$ 109.12
b.	248	47¢	116.56
c.	195	53¢	103.35
d.	469	29¢	136.01
e.	68	$1.84	125.12
f.	57	$2.06	117.42
g.	34	$4.19	142.46
h.	126	$1.15	144.90

2. All of the following employees worked on an hourly basis. In addition, they received a bonus for each article they produced over a

fixed number. Determine the bonus each employee received for the week shown.

	Fixed Number To Be Produced	Actual Number Produced	Bonus Articles	Bonus Per Article	Bonus
a.	100	96	0	42¢	$ 0
b.	100	117	17	47¢	7.99
c.	140	162	22	91¢	20.02
d.	150	159	9	86¢	7.74
e.	135	157	22	$1.17	25.74
f.	50	56	6	$3.24	19.44
g.	65	71	6	$2.76	16.56
h.	95	121	26	$1.08	28.08

3. All of the following employees worked on an hourly basis. In addition, they received a bonus for each article produced over a fixed number. Determine the earnings of each employee for the week shown.

	Number Of Hours	Hourly Rate	Regular Pay	Fixed Number To Be Produced	Actual Number Produced	Bonus Articles	Bonus Per Article	Bonus	Total Earnings
a.	40	$2.17	$ 86.80	150	140	0	46¢	$ 0	$ 86.80
b.	40	1.95	78.00	125	117	0	54¢	0	78.00
c.	40	2.53	101.20	140	164	24	82¢	19.68	120.88
d.	38	2.61	99.18	130	157	27	95¢	25.65	124.83
e.	37	2.86	105.82	120	168	48	81¢	38.88	144.70
f.	42	3.05	128.10	75	81	6	$1.12	6.72	134.82
g.	39	3.58	139.62	85	107	22	$1.29	28.38	168.00
h.	37½	2.98	111.75	115	139	24	$1.58	37.92	149.67

B

1. During the week of June 5, Mr. Faber produced the following number of articles each day.

Monday	Tuesday	Wednesday	Thursday	Friday
85	93	81	86	95

If he receives 32¢ for each article on a straight piecework basis, what were his earnings for the week? $140.80

2. Hillcrest Electronics pays its employees on a piece-rate basis of 36¢ per article. To discourage careless workmanship, the company deducts 45¢ from the earnings of an employee for each article that is rejected during inspection. How much did Mr. Metz receive during a week in which he produced 485 articles, but had 23 of these articles rejected? $164.25

Have the students arrange their work for Exercise 3 on lined paper. As with some of the earlier exercises, unless they follow a definite outline, they will very likely get lost part way through their solutions.

3. Mr. Hayes works for a firm where he is paid $2.76 per hour. In addition, he is granted a bonus of 18¢ for each article that he produces over 60 each day. What would be his earnings during a week in which he worked 37½ hours and produced the following number of articles daily?

Monday	Tuesday	Wednesday	Thursday	Friday
63	59	57	68	72

$107.64

4. The T and W Company uses the following graduated piecework weekly wage scale.

First 60 articles	75¢ each
Next 15 articles	82¢ each
Next 10 articles	91¢ each
All over 85 articles	$1.05 each

How much will each of the following employees earn during a week in which they produced the number of articles shown?

	Articles Produced	Earnings
a.	54	$ 40.50
b.	69	52.38
c.	72	54.84
d.	78	60.03
e.	83	64.58
f.	92	73.75
g.	109	91.60
h.	117	100.00

5. Mr. Quinn, who works for the T and W Company of Problem 4, produced an average of 96 articles each week. By carefully analyzing each step of his work, he was able to increase his production by 25%.
   a. How much did Mr. Quinn earn each week before he made a study of his work? $ 77.95
   b. By how many articles did Mr. Quinn increase his weekly production?   24
   c. How much did Mr. Quinn earn after changing his methods and increasing his production? $103.15
   d. How much more did Mr. Quinn earn each week as a result of this change? $ 25.20
   e. What percent more did Mr. Quinn earn each week as a result of this change?   32%

In Exercise 4, you may want the students to include more columns in their outlines of the solution. The headings of the columns should be: "Earnings at 75¢ Rate," "Earnings at 82¢ Rate," "Earnings at 91¢ Rate," and "Earnings at $1.05 Rate."

Unit 3: Earnings Computed on a Commission Basis

The third method for computing earnings is one in which the employee receives a certain percent of his sales. The people who earn their living in this manner are salesmen. They include the door-to-door salesmen who peddle magazines, brushes, vacuum cleaners, encyclopedias; telephone salesmen who try to get you to subscribe to magazines or newspapers; and even the great majority of car salesmen. All of them work on a straight commission basis—that is, their weekly earnings are based on a fixed percent of their total sales.

■ILLUSTRATION 1: Harvey Quimby is a salesman for the Atlantic Boat Corporation. His earnings are wholly on a commission basis. How much will he earn during a week in which his sales amounted to $5,460 and his commission rate is 4%?

●SOLUTION:
$$\text{Commission} = \$5,460 \times 4\%$$
$$= \$5,460 \times .04$$
$$= \$218.40$$

▼EXPLANATION: The computation for determining earnings on a commission basis is usually easier if the percent numeral is changed to its equivalent decimal form rather than to a fraction. As you learned earlier, a percent numeral is changed to a decimal numeral by moving the decimal point two places to the left in the percent form.

Just as there exists a wage basis that consists of a combination of the hourly wage system and the piece-rate system, so, too, is there one which combines the hourly wage system with the commission system. Employees who most frequently operate under this program are the salesclerks of large department stores. Not only do they receive an hourly wage but, also, a fixed percent of either their entire sales for the week, or that part of the sales over and above a certain amount.

■ILLUSTRATION 2: Jean Merrill works as a salesgirl for the South Shore Department Store at an hourly rate of $1.85 for a 45-hour week. In addition, she receives 1½% of all sales that she makes over $800 during one week. What are her earnings during a week in which she sells $2,100 worth of merchandise?

●SOLUTION:
$$\text{Hourly earnings} = 45 \times \$1.85$$
$$= \$83.25$$
$$\text{Sales over } \$800 = \$2,100 - \$800$$
$$= \$1,300$$

Here, too, have the students ask their relatives and friends to find out if any are receiving compensation on a commission basis. If possible, see if they can determine the real-estate brokerage rate in their area; also, if the rate differs for commercial property as against private homes.

$$\text{Commission on sales} = \$1,300 \times 1\tfrac{1}{2}\%$$
$$= \$1,300 \times .015$$
$$= \$19.50$$
$$\text{Total earnings} = \$83.25 + \$19.50$$
$$= \$102.75$$

▼EXPLANATION: The hourly earnings were found in the usual manner. The $800 was subtracted from $2,100, since the salesgirl's commission was based only on that part of the sales in excess of $800. To simplify the computation, the $1\tfrac{1}{2}\%$ was changed to the decimal .015 rather than to a fraction.

EXERCISES   A

1. All of the following employees work on a straight commission, based on their total sales. How much will each earn during a week in which total sales and commission rate were as shown?

	Total Sales	Commission Rate	Earnings
a.	$ 800	10%	$ 80.00
b.	500	18%	90.00
c.	960	22%	211.20
d.	745	16%	119.20
e.	873	9%	78.57
f.	1,376	9½%	130.72
g.	2,007	6¼%	125.44
h.	3,925	8¾%	343.44
i.	31,000	6%	1,860.00
j.	5,400	16½%	891.00

2. All of the following employees worked on an hourly basis. In addition, they received a commission on all their sales above the fixed amount shown. Determine the commission that each received, based on the information here.

	Total Sales For the Week	Commission Based On Sales Above Amount Shown Below	Commission Sales	Commission Rate	Commission
a.	$ 965	$ 800	$ 165.00	1%	$ 1.65
b.	842	750	92.00	2%	1.84
c.	6,254	5,000	1,254.00	3%	37.62
d.	1,686	1,250	436.00	2½%	10.90
e.	3,265	1,600	1,665.00	1¾%	29.14

3. All of the following employees worked on an hourly basis. In addition, they received a commission on all their sales above the fixed

As before, have all percent numerals expressed as decimal numerals and not as fraction numerals. In Exercises 1 and 2 you may want the students to insert an additional column where the commission rate is expressed as a decimal rather than as a percent.

amount shown. Determine the earnings for the week that each received, based on the information here.

Number Of Hours	Hourly Rate	Wages	Total Sales For the Week	Commission Based On Sales Above Amount Shown Below	Commission Sales	Commission Rate	Commission	Total Earnings
a. 44	$2.03	$ 89.32	$ 692	$ 600	$ 92	1%	$ .92	$ 90.24
b. 42	1.96	82.32	847	750	97	3%	2.91	85.23
c. 43	2.12	91.16	1,075	900	175	5%	8.75	99.91
d. 41½	2.18	90.47	1,524	1,200	324	3½%	11.34	101.81
e. 38½	2.04	78.54	1,386	1,000	386	2¾%	10.615	89.16
f. 40½	2.15	87.075	1,653	800	853	1¼%	10.6625	97.74

B

1. Kenneth Somers, a real estate agent, works on a straight commission of 7½% of the selling price of the property. He recently sold Mr. Glynn's home for $24,700.
   a. How much commission did Mr. Somers receive? _$1,852.50_
   b. How much of the $24,700 did Mr. Glynn receive? _$22,847.56_
2. Mr. Meding, an insurance broker, receives as his commission 55% of the first year's premium on a life insurance policy and 18% of the annual premium on an automobile insurance policy. How much did he earn during a week in which the first year's premiums on the life insurance that he sold amounted to $346 and the premiums on automobile insurance came to $427? _$ 267.16_
3. One of the authors of a textbook receives 3¼% of the sales of this book. How much did the author receive during a year in which 37,464 copies of the book were sold for $4.10 each? _$4,992.08_
4. The L. R. Meeker Company pays its salesmen a graduated commission, based on the following table:

For the first $800 of sales	6%
For the next $600 of sales	9%
For the next $500 of sales	10½%
In excess of $1,900 of sales	12½%

What will be the earnings of each of the following salesmen during a week in which their total sales were the amounts shown below?

	Sales	Earnings			Sales	Earnings
a.	$ 750	$ 45.00	e.		$1,342	$ 96.78
b.	900	57.00	f.		1,589	121.85
c.	1,600	123.00	g.		1,923	157.38
d.	2,400	217.00	h.		2,856	274.00

In Exercise 4, you may want the outline to include such columns as: "Commission at 9%," "Commission at 10½%," and Commission at 12½%."

5. Mary Cahill works as a salesclerk at Greeley Brothers Department Store, earning $1.76 per hour for a 42-hour week. In addition, she receives a 2% commission on all sales over $500 for the week. Her total salary this past week was $80.32.
   a. How much did her hourly earnings amount to for the week?

   $ 73.92

   b. How much of the $80.32 was commission? $ 6.40
   c. How much of her sales of the past week was over $500?

   $320.00

   d. What were her total sales for the week? $820.00

Unit 4: Payroll Deductions

Section 1: Income Tax Deductions

PART 1

When you get your first paycheck, you may be surprised by the amount you receive. It is a far cry from what you thought you had earned! The federal government, acting through your employer, takes a sizable chunk out of your salary. Since the amount taken is based on your income, it is called an income tax. The government's need for this tax will be discussed in the next chapter.

Some thirty years ago the members of the Congress decided that the government could not continue to collect taxes on an annual basis, as it had in the past. Too many people were not putting the money aside during the year to make their payment to the Treasury Department when it fell due at the end of the year. It was a matter of either developing some type of pay-as-you-go plan, or else fining or jailing a large part of the population for nonpayment of taxes. The income tax withholding program seemed the only solution. Under this plan, the employer deducts the tax from your salary, and, four times a year, he mails it to the Internal Revenue Service for you.

It was evident to the Congress that not all should be required to pay the same tax. The wealthier could afford to pay more to help run the government. Hence, they should be asked to contribute more. Also, the bachelor earning $150 a week has more money to spare than the husband earning the same wage, who has a wife and four children to support. Therefore, the income tax you must pay is dependent upon the following two factors:

1. The size of your income.
2. The number of people who rely on you for their support. Each of these is called an exemption.

Discuss with the students what is meant by the statement above that, "It was a matter of either developing some type of pay-as-you-go plan, or else fining or jailing a large part of the population for nonpayment of taxes."

Before the tax is computed on your weekly earnings, $13.50 is subtracted from these earnings for each exemption you claim. Thus, if your salary is $125 per week, and you have a wife, but no children, then you are entitled to 2 exemptions—one for yourself and one for your wife. Since $13.50 is deducted for each, the total deduction will be $27. Hence, your tax will be computed on what remains after the $27 is subtracted from your salary of $125, that is, on $98. In view of this, the more exemptions you have, the smaller is the amount on which the tax is computed.

To determine the tax, you have to refer to a table like the following. This table is distributed by the Internal Revenue Service and is available to any taxpayer.

TABLE 1. WEEKLY Payroll Period

(a) SINGLE person—including head of household:

If the amount of wages is: | The amount of income tax to be withheld shall be:

Not over $4 0

Over—	But not over—		of excess over—
$4	—$13	. . . . . . 14%	—$4
$13	—$23	. . . . . $1.26, plus 15%	—$13
$23	—$85	. . . . . $2.76, plus 19%	—$23
$85	—$169	. . . . . $14.54, plus 22%	—$85
$169	—$212	. . . . $33.02, plus 28%	—$169
$212	. . . .	$45.06, plus 33%	—$212

(b) Married person—

If the amount of wages is: | The amount of income tax to be withheld shall be:

Not over $4 0

Over—	But not over—		of excess over—
$4	—$23	. . . . . . 14%	—$4
$23	—$58	. . . . . $2.66, plus 15%	—$23
$58	—$169	. . . . $7.91, plus 19%	—$58
$169	—$340	. . . . $29.00, plus 22%	—$169
$340	—$423	. . . . $66.62, plus 28%	—$340
$423	. . . .	$89.86, plus 33%	—$423

■ILLUSTRATION: Robert Nordland works 39 hours each week at an hourly rate of $3.69. In addition to himself, he supports a wife and 3 children. How much is deducted from his salary each week for income tax purposes?

●SOLUTION:

$$\text{Earnings} = 39 \times \$3.69$$
$$= \$143.91$$

The table above can be found in the *Circular E—Employer's Tax Guide,* which is distributed by the Internal Revenue Service. You might want to check the current table against the one here. Although the tax has changed somewhat over the years, the method of computation has remained constant.

$$\text{Deduction for 5 exemptions} = 5 \times \$13.50$$
$$= \$67.50$$
$$\text{Taxable earnings} = \$143.91 - \$67.50$$
$$= \$76.41$$
$$\text{Tax} = \$7.91 + 19\% \times (\$76.41 - \$58)$$
$$= \$7.91 + 19\% \times \$18.41$$
$$= \$7.91 + \$3.50$$
$$= \$11.41$$

▼EXPLANATION: The earnings were found in the usual manner. Mr. Nordland has 5 exemptions—himself, his wife, and 3 children. Since each exemption gives him a deduction of $13.50, the deduction for 5 exemptions is 5 times as great. The taxable earnings are simply that part of his earnings on which he will have to pay the tax—that is, the difference that remains after the deductions have been subtracted from his total earnings. To find the tax itself, look at the lower half of the table for a married person. Since his taxable earnings are $76.41, and this number falls between $58 and $169, place a piece of paper along the row in which these two numerals appear. You then see that the tax will be $7.91, plus 19% of the amount of the taxable earnings over $58. The amount over $58 turns out to be $18.41. When this is multiplied by 19%, you get a product of $3.50. When you add this to $7.91, you find Mr. Nordland's tax to be $11.41.

EXERCISES   **A**

1. How large will the deduction be for the exemptions claimed by each of the following taxpayers?

	Number Of Exemptions	Deduction			Number Of Exemptions	Deduction
a.	1	$ 13.50		d.	4	$ 54.00
b.	0	0		e.	7	94.50
c.	3	40.50		f.	12	162.00

2. If a taxpayer is blind, he can claim an additional exemption. That is, instead of claiming 1 for himself, he can claim 2. Similarly, if his wife is blind, he can claim 2 for her also. How many exemptions can each of the following taxpayers claim?
   a. Mr. Howland is blind and supports only his son.   3
   b. Mr. Kilburn supports a blind wife and two children.   5
   c. Mr. Bolan is blind and supports a blind wife and one child.
                                                              5

Before assigning these exercises, devise oral questions similar to those in Exercises 2 and 3. These problems seem to appeal to the students.

3. If a taxpayer is 65 years old or over, he can claim an additional exemption. If his wife is 65 or over, he can claim an additional one for her, too. Thus, if both are over 65, a taxpayer can claim 4 exemptions for the two of them. How large will the deduction be for each of the following taxpayers?
   a. Husband over 65, wife under 65, 1 child   4
   b. Husband over 65, wife over 65, 2 children   6
   c. Husband under 65 and blind, wife under 65, 3 children   6
   d. Husband over 65 and blind, wife under 65   4
   e. Husband and wife both over 65 and both blind   6

4. If the earnings and exemptions are as shown, what are the taxable wages of each of the following people?

	Earnings	Exemptions	Deduction	Taxable Wages
a.	$ 90	2	$ 27.00	$ 63.00
b.	146	4	54.00	92.00
c.	172	0	0	172.00
d.	104.50	3	40.50	64.00
e.	114.76	5	67.50	47.26
f.	96.12	8	108.00	0

5. All of the following people are single and their taxable wages are as shown. How much tax will they have to pay weekly?

	Taxable Wages	Weekly Tax
a.	$ 10	$ .84
b.	18	2.01
c.	46	7.13
d.	107	19.38
e.	194	40.02
f.	2.56	0
g.	9.84	.82
h.	67.29	11.18
i.	148.16	28.44
j.	323.48	81.85

6. All of the following people are married and their taxable wages are as shown. How much tax will they have to pay?

	Taxable Wages	Weekly Tax
a.	$ 18	$ 1.96
b.	107	17.22
c.	194	34.50
d.	67.29	9.68
e.	148.16	25.04
f.	323.48	62.99

Since the terms "taxable wages" and "taxable income" are used quite frequently in both this chapter and the next, devote some time to making certain that the students understand their meaning. Although the work in this book requires no distinction between these terms, you may want to do this.

7. Compute the weekly tax deduction of each of the following tax-payers.

	Wages	Exemptions	Amount Exempted	Married Or Single	Taxable Wages	Tax
a.	$ 94.00	2	$ 27.00	Married	$ 67.00	$ 9.62
b.	107.00	3	40.50	Single	66.50	11.03
c.	62.00	1	13.50	Married	48.50	6.49
d.	84.00	1	13.50	Single	70.50	11.79
e.	149.75	2	27.00	Single	122.75	22.85
f.	226.18	4	54.00	Single	172.18	33.91
g.	241.39	5	67.50	Married	173.89	30.08
h.	429.84	6	81.00	Married	348.84	69.10

8. Compute the weekly tax deduction for each of the following tax-payers.

	Hourly Rate	Number Of Hours	Wages	Exemptions	Married Or Single	Taxable Wages	Tax
a.	$1.96	25	$ 49.00	0	Single	$ 49.00	$ 7.70
b.	3.58	37	132.46	1	Single	118.96	22.01
c.	3.12	41	127.92	3	Married	87.42	13.50
d.	4.56	38½	175.56	1	Single	162.06	31.49
e.	9.94	41½	412.51	2	Married	385.51	79.36

B

1. Mr. Jackson earns $2.98 per hour. During the week of July 17, he worked the following number of hours each day.

Monday   Tuesday   Wednesday   Thursday   Friday
   7   8   8   7½   8

Mr. Jackson has a wife who is blind and one child. How much will be deducted from this week's salary for income tax? $ 8.43

2. During the week of May 3, Walter Kraft worked 44 hours at time and a half for all work over 40 hours. His pay rate is $3.26 per hour. If he is single, but supports both of his parents, for which he receives one exemption for each, how much income tax will be deducted from his salary for this week? $19.92

3. Frances Midler is a salesgirl for Taylor's, Inc., a department store. She works at an hourly rate of $1.96, plus a 1½% commission on all sales over $500 each week. During the week of April 4, she sold $946 worth of merchandise and worked the following hours:

Monday   Tuesday   Wednesday   Thursday   Friday   Saturday
   8   8   6   10   8   4½

If Frances is single and supports only herself, how much was taken from her earnings for the week for income tax? $13.67

The problems in Group B might best be reserved for "extra-credit" work.

4. Longstreet and Sons pay their employees on a piece-rate basis of $1.18 for each article produced. During one week, one of their employees, who is 67 years of age and supports a wife who is 68, completed the following number of articles:

Monday	Tuesday	Wednesday	Thursday	Friday
14	17	15	18	21

How much will be deducted from this employee's salary for the week for income tax? $ 6.16

5. Harold Reed works at an hourly pay rate of $3.96, plus time and a half for all work over 8 hours a day. During the week of March 27, he worked the following hours:

Monday	Tuesday	Wednesday	Thursday	Friday
9	8	7	10	8

a. How much overtime pay did he earn for the week? $ 17.82
b. How much regular pay did he earn for the week? $154.44
c. What were his total earnings for the week? $172.26
d. If Harold were single and claimed 3 exemptions, how much would be taken from his salary for income tax? $ 24.83
e. If Harold were married and claimed 3 exemptions, how much would be taken from his salary for income tax? $ 21.92
f. How much would Harold have saved in income tax for that week had he been married rather than single? $ 2.91

PART 2

No large company—or even a small one—would ever think of determining the income tax deduction as you did in Part 1 of this section. This method is so time-consuming that a large firm would need an army of accountants simply to compute the withholding tax for the federal government. Those concerns that do not have electronic computers make use of an income tax withholding table that is provided for them by the Internal Revenue Service. As in the earlier table, this one, also, is composed of two parts—one for the employee who is single and the other for the employee who is married. Notice that the tables that appear on pages 168 and 169 are not complete. The part devoted to single persons starts with a wage of $58, while that for married persons starts with $76. The one distributed by the Internal Revenue Service begins with $0, and, hence, covers any weekly wage that a person might earn.

There are many firms that farm out their weekly payroll computation to computer consultants, for they find that the cost is less than employing their own staff of clerks and bookkeepers.

■ ILLUSTRATION: Robert Nordland works 39 hours per week at an hourly rate of $3.69. In addition to himself, he supports a wife and 3 children. How much is deducted from his salary each week for income tax purposes?

● SOLUTION:

$$\text{Earnings} = 39 \times \$3.69$$
$$= \$143.91$$

Number of exemptions = 5

Tax from table for married persons = $11.20

▼ EXPLANATION: After finding Mr. Nordland's salary to be $143.91, refer to the married persons' part of the table, for he is a married man. The easiest way of using this table is to ignore the first column headed by the words "At least." Then, run your finger down the second column titled "But less than" until you come to the first numeral greater than the weekly earnings. In this case, the weekly earnings are $143.91, and the first numeral greater than this in that column is 145. Place the edge of a piece of paper along this row and run your finger across to the column headed by the numeral 5, for this is the number of exemptions that Mr. Nordland can claim. Your finger will point to $11.20. This is the weekly tax that he will have to pay.

If you glance back at the illustration on page 163, you will discover that the Mr. Nordland in that problem is the same Mr. Nordland as in the one above. This time, however, he seems to be paying only $11.20 in income tax rather than the $11.41 found before! No error has been made, for both methods shown for computing the withholding tax give only an approximation of what the weekly tax deduction should be. Earlier it was pointed out that the Congress had agreed that income tax should be collected in small weekly amounts rather than in one yearly lump sum, as in the past. However, once each year the taxpayer must still fill out a form showing exactly the amount of tax he must pay on his yearly income. If this amount is less than the total of his weekly deductions, he sends the Internal Revenue Service a bill for his overpayment. If it is more, he sends a check for the difference. Hence, the Internal Revenue Service does not care which method is used for computing the weekly deductions, for it knows that at year's end it will eventually get exactly what the law requires from you.

EXERCISES   A

The income tax in these problems should be computed through the use of the tables on pages 168 and 169.

Emphasize the fact that income-tax deductions found either through the use of these tables, or the one on page 162, do not give the exact tax a person must pay. The purpose of the pay-as-you-go plan is to insure that a large part of that tax is paid before the end of the year—not the exact amount.

WEEKLY — SINGLE
PAYROLL PERIOD   PERSONS

And the wages are—		And the number of withholding exemptions claimed is—										
At least	But less than	0	1	2	3	4	5	6	7	8	9	10 or more
		The amount of income tax to be withheld shall be—										
$58	$59	$9.50	$7.00	$4.40	$2.00	$.10	$0	$0	$0	$0	$0	$0
59	60	9.70	7.20	4.60	2.20	.30	0	0	0	0	0	0
60	62	10.00	7.40	4.90	2.40	.50	0	0	0	0	0	0
62	64	10.40	7.80	5.30	2.70	.70	0	0	0	0	0	0
64	66	10.80	8.20	5.60	3.10	1.00	0	0	0	0	0	0
66	68	11.10	8.60	6.00	3.50	1.30	0	0	0	0	0	0
68	70	11.50	9.00	6.40	3.80	1.60	0	0	0	0	0	0
70	72	11.90	9.30	6.80	4.20	1.90	0	0	0	0	0	0
72	74	12.30	9.70	7.20	4.60	2.20	.30	0	0	0	0	0
74	76	12.70	10.10	7.50	5.00	2.50	.50	0	0	0	0	0
76	78	13.00	10.50	7.90	5.40	2.80	.80	0	0	0	0	0
78	80	13.40	10.90	8.30	5.70	3.20	1.10	0	0	0	0	0
80	82	13.80	11.20	8.70	6.10	3.60	1.40	0	0	0	0	0
82	84	14.20	11.60	9.10	6.50	3.90	1.70	0	0	0	0	0
84	86	14.60	12.00	9.40	6.90	4.30	2.00	.10	0	0	0	0
86	88	15.00	12.40	9.80	7.30	4.70	2.30	.30	0	0	0	0
88	90	15.40	12.80	10.20	7.60	5.10	2.60	.60	0	0	0	0
90	92	15.90	13.10	10.60	8.00	5.50	2.90	.90	0	0	0	0
92	94	16.30	13.50	11.00	8.40	5.80	3.30	1.20	0	0	0	0
94	96	16.80	13.90	11.30	8.80	6.20	3.70	1.50	0	0	0	0
96	98	17.20	14.30	11.70	9.20	6.60	4.00	1.80	0	0	0	0
98	100	17.60	14.70	12.10	9.50	7.00	4.40	2.10	.10	0	0	0
100	105	18.40	15.50	12.80	10.20	7.60	5.10	2.60	.60	0	0	0
105	110	19.50	16.60	13.70	11.20	8.60	6.00	3.50	1.30	0	0	0
110	115	20.60	17.70	14.70	12.10	9.50	7.00	4.40	2.10	.10	0	0
115	120	21.70	18.80	15.80	13.10	10.50	7.90	5.40	2.80	.80	0	0
120	125	22.80	19.90	16.90	14.00	11.40	8.90	6.30	3.80	1.50	0	0
125	130	23.90	21.00	18.00	15.00	12.40	9.80	7.30	4.70	2.30	.40	0
130	135	25.00	22.10	19.10	16.10	13.30	10.80	8.20	5.70	3.10	1.10	0
135	140	26.10	23.20	20.20	17.20	14.30	11.70	9.20	6.60	4.10	1.80	0
140	145	27.20	24.30	21.30	18.30	15.40	12.70	10.10	7.60	5.00	2.50	.60
145	150	28.30	25.40	22.40	19.40	16.50	13.60	11.10	8.50	6.00	3.40	1.30
150	160	30.00	27.00	24.00	21.10	18.10	15.20	12.50	10.00	7.40	4.80	2.40
160	170	32.20	29.20	26.20	23.30	20.30	17.40	14.40	11.90	9.30	6.70	4.20
170	180	34.70	31.40	28.40	25.50	22.50	19.60	16.60	13.80	11.20	8.60	6.10
180	190	37.50	33.70	30.60	27.70	24.70	21.80	18.80	15.80	13.10	10.50	8.00
190	200	40.30	36.50	32.80	29.90	26.90	24.00	21.00	18.00	15.10	12.40	9.90
200	210	43.10	39.30	35.60	32.10	29.10	26.20	23.20	20.20	17.30	14.30	11.80
210	220	46.10	42.10	38.40	34.60	31.30	28.40	25.40	22.40	19.50	16.50	13.70
220	230	49.40	44.90	41.20	37.40	33.60	30.60	27.60	24.60	21.70	18.70	15.80
230	240	52.70	48.20	44.00	40.20	36.40	32.80	29.80	26.80	23.90	20.90	18.00
240	250	56.00	51.50	47.10	43.00	39.20	35.50	32.00	29.00	26.10	23.10	20.20
250	260	59.30	54.80	50.40	46.00	42.00	38.30	34.50	31.20	28.30	25.30	22.40
260	270	62.60	58.10	53.70	49.30	44.80	41.10	37.30	33.50	30.50	27.50	24.60
270	280	65.90	61.40	57.00	52.60	48.10	43.90	40.10	36.30	32.70	29.70	26.80
280	290	69.20	64.70	60.30	55.90	51.40	47.00	42.90	39.10	35.40	31.90	29.00
290	300	72.50	68.00	63.60	59.20	54.70	50.30	45.80	41.90	38.20	34.40	31.20
300	310	75.80	71.30	66.90	62.50	58.00	53.60	49.10	44.70	41.00	37.20	33.40
310	320	79.10	74.60	70.20	65.80	61.30	56.90	52.40	48.00	43.80	40.00	36.20
320	330	82.40	77.90	73.50	69.10	64.60	60.20	55.70	51.30	46.80	42.80	39.00
330	340	85.70	81.20	76.80	72.40	67.90	63.50	59.00	54.60	50.10	45.70	41.80
340	350	89.00	84.50	80.10	75.70	71.20	66.80	62.30	57.90	53.40	49.00	44.60
350	360	92.30	87.80	83.40	79.00	74.50	70.10	65.60	61.20	56.70	52.30	47.90
		33 percent of the excess over $360 plus—										
$360 and over		93.90	89.50	85.10	80.60	76.20	71.70	67.30	62.80	58.40	54.00	49.50

See the comment at the bottom of page 162.

MARRIED — WEEKLY
PERSONS   PAYROLL PERIOD

And the wages are—		And the number of withholding exemptions claimed is—										
At least	But less than	0	1	2	3	4	5	6	7	8	9	10 or more
		The amount of income tax to be withheld shall be—										
$76	$78	$11.60	$9.00	$6.70	$4.70	$2.70	$.80	$0	$0	$0	$0	$0
78	80	11.90	9.40	7.00	5.00	3.00	1.10	0	0	0	0	0
80	82	12.30	9.80	7.30	5.30	3.30	1.40	0	0	0	0	0
82	84	12.70	10.10	7.60	5.60	3.60	1.70	0	0	0	0	0
84	86	13.10	10.50	8.00	5.90	3.90	1.90	.10	0	0	0	0
86	88	13.50	10.90	8.30	6.20	4.20	2.20	.30	0	0	0	0
88	90	13.80	11.30	8.70	6.50	4.50	2.50	.60	0	0	0	0
90	92	14.20	11.70	9.10	6.80	4.80	2.80	.90	0	0	0	0
92	94	14.60	12.00	9.50	7.10	5.10	3.10	1.20	0	0	0	0
94	96	15.00	12.40	9.90	7.40	5.40	3.40	1.50	0	0	0	0
96	98	15.40	12.80	10.20	7.70	5.70	3.70	1.70	0	0	0	0
98	100	15.70	13.20	10.60	8.10	6.00	4.00	2.00	.10	0	0	0
100	105	16.40	13.80	11.30	8.70	6.50	4.50	2.50	.60	0	0	0
105	110	17.30	14.80	12.20	9.70	7.30	5.30	3.20	1.30	0	0	0
110	115	18.30	15.70	13.20	10.60	8.10	6.00	4.00	2.00	.10	0	0
115	120	19.20	16.70	14.10	11.60	9.00	6.80	4.70	2.70	.80	0	0
120	125	20.20	17.60	15.10	12.50	10.00	7.50	5.50	3.50	1.50	0	0
125	130	21.10	18.60	16.00	13.50	10.90	8.40	6.20	4.20	2.20	.40	0
130	135	22.00	19.50	17.00	14.40	11.90	9.30	7.00	5.00	3.00	1.10	0
135	140	23.00	20.50	17.90	15.40	12.80	10.30	7.70	5.70	3.70	1.80	0
140	145	24.00	21.40	18.90	16.30	13.80	11.20	8.70	6.50	4.50	2.50	.60
145	150	24.90	22.40	19.80	17.30	14.70	12.20	9.60	7.20	5.20	3.20	1.30
150	160	26.40	23.80	21.30	18.70	16.10	13.60	11.00	8.50	6.30	4.30	2.30
160	170	28.30	25.70	23.20	20.60	18.00	15.50	12.90	10.40	7.80	5.80	3.80
170	180	30.30	27.60	25.10	22.50	19.90	17.40	14.80	12.30	9.70	7.30	5.30
180	190	32.50	29.60	27.00	24.40	21.80	19.30	16.70	14.20	11.60	9.10	6.80
190	200	34.70	31.80	28.90	26.30	23.70	21.20	18.60	16.10	13.50	11.00	8.40
200	210	36.90	34.00	31.00	28.20	25.60	23.10	20.50	18.00	15.40	12.90	10.30
210	220	39.10	36.20	33.20	30.30	27.50	25.00	22.40	19.90	17.30	14.80	12.20
220	230	41.30	38.40	35.40	32.50	29.50	26.90	24.30	21.80	19.20	16.70	14.10
230	240	43.50	40.60	37.60	34.70	31.70	28.80	26.20	23.70	21.10	18.60	16.00
240	250	45.70	42.80	39.80	36.90	33.90	30.90	28.10	25.60	23.00	20.50	17.90
250	260	47.90	45.00	42.00	39.10	36.10	33.10	30.20	27.50	24.90	22.40	19.80
260	270	50.10	47.20	44.20	41.30	38.30	35.30	32.40	29.40	26.80	24.30	21.70
270	280	52.30	49.40	46.40	43.50	40.50	37.50	34.60	31.60	28.70	26.20	23.60
280	290	54.50	51.60	48.60	45.70	42.70	39.70	36.80	33.80	30.90	28.10	25.50
290	300	56.70	53.80	50.80	47.90	44.90	41.90	39.00	36.00	33.10	30.10	27.40
300	310	58.90	56.00	53.00	50.10	47.10	44.10	41.20	38.20	35.30	32.30	29.30
310	320	61.10	58.20	55.20	52.30	49.30	46.30	43.40	40.40	37.50	34.50	31.50
320	330	63.30	60.40	57.40	54.50	51.50	48.50	45.60	42.60	39.70	36.70	33.70
330	340	65.50	62.60	59.60	56.70	53.70	50.70	47.80	44.80	41.90	38.90	35.90
340	350	68.00	64.80	61.80	58.90	55.90	52.90	50.00	47.00	44.10	41.10	38.10
350	360	70.80	67.10	64.00	61.10	58.10	55.10	52.20	49.20	46.30	43.30	40.30
360	370	73.60	69.90	66.20	63.30	60.30	57.30	54.40	51.40	48.50	45.50	42.50
370	380	76.40	72.70	68.90	65.50	62.50	59.50	56.60	53.60	50.70	47.70	44.70
380	390	79.20	75.50	71.70	67.90	64.70	61.70	58.80	55.80	52.90	49.90	46.90
390	400	82.00	78.30	74.50	70.70	66.90	63.90	61.00	58.00	55.10	52.10	49.10
400	410	84.80	81.10	77.30	73.50	69.70	66.10	63.20	60.20	57.30	54.30	51.30
410	420	87.60	83.90	80.10	76.30	72.50	68.80	65.40	62.40	59.50	56.50	53.50
420	430	90.50	86.70	82.90	79.10	75.30	71.60	67.80	64.60	61.70	58.70	55.70
430	440	93.80	89.50	85.70	81.90	78.10	74.40	70.60	66.80	63.90	60.90	57.90
440	450	97.10	92.70	88.50	84.70	80.90	77.20	73.40	69.60	66.10	63.10	60.10
450	460	100.40	96.00	91.50	87.50	83.70	80.00	76.20	72.40	68.70	65.30	62.30
460	470	103.70	99.30	94.80	90.40	86.50	82.80	79.00	75.20	71.50	67.70	64.50
470	480	107.00	102.60	98.10	93.70	89.30	85.60	81.80	78.00	74.30	70.50	66.70
480	490	110.30	105.90	101.40	97.00	92.60	88.40	84.60	80.80	77.10	73.30	69.50
490	500	113.60	109.20	104.70	100.30	95.90	91.40	87.40	83.60	79.90	76.10	72.30
500	510	116.90	112.50	108.00	103.60	99.20	94.70	90.30	86.40	82.70	78.90	75.10
510	520	120.20	115.80	111.30	106.90	102.50	98.00	93.60	89.20	85.50	81.70	77.90
520	530	123.50	119.10	114.60	110.20	105.80	101.30	96.90	92.40	88.30	84.50	80.70
530	540	126.80	122.40	117.90	113.50	109.10	104.60	100.20	95.70	91.30	87.30	83.50
540	550	130.10	125.70	121.20	116.80	112.40	107.90	103.50	99.00	94.60	90.10	86.30
550	560	133.40	129.00	124.50	120.10	115.70	111.20	106.80	102.30	97.90	93.40	89.10
560	570	136.70	132.30	127.80	123.40	119.00	114.50	110.10	105.60	101.20	96.70	92.30
		33 percent of the excess over $570 plus—										
$570 and over		138.40	133.90	129.50	125.00	120.60	116.20	111.70	107.30	102.80	98.40	93.90

1. All of the following persons are single and their weekly earnings are as shown. How much tax will be withheld from their salaries?

	Earnings	Exemptions	Tax
a.	$ 64.58	1	$ 8.20
b.	99.23	2	12.10
c.	163.28	0	32.20
d.	124.99	3	14.00
e.	125.01	3	15.00
f.	314.62	6	52.40
g.	352.84	2	83.40
h.	94.00*	1	13.90
i.	115.00	3	13.10
j.	280.00	5	47.00

* Find the first numeral larger than $94 in the "But less than" column.

2. All of the following persons are single and their weekly earnings are as shown. How much tax will be withheld from their salaries?

	Earnings	Exemptions	Tax
a.	$370.00	0	$ 97.20
b.	420.00	1	109.30
c.	480.00	2	124.70
d.	395.40	1	101.18
e.	432.85	3	104.64
f.	686.24	5	179.36

3. All of the following persons are married and their weekly earnings are as shown. How much tax will be withheld from their salaries?

	Earnings	Exemptions	Tax
a.	$ 76.81	0	$ 11.60
b.	123.57	2	15.10
c.	154.07	4	16.10
d.	273.12	5	37.50
e.	507.16	6	90.30
f.	96.00	0	15.40
g.	145.00	2	19.80
h.	530.00	4	109.10

4. All of the following persons are married, and their weekly earnings are as shown. How much tax will be withheld from their salaries?

	Earnings	Exemptions	Tax
a.	$590.00	0	$ 145.00
b.	642.00	2	153.26
c.	758.60	5	178.44
d.	843.27	8	192.98

It is very easy to err when using the tax table to do these problems. It is imperative that students use a guide to line up the row they are examining. In the event that they have lost the card distributed for this purpose earlier, insist that they obtain another.

5. Compute the weekly tax withheld for each of the following persons.

	Hourly Rate	Number Of Hours	Earnings	Exemptions	Married Or Single	Tax
a.	$2.07	42	$ 86.94	1	Single	$ 12.40
b.	1.89	35	66.15	0	Single	11.10
c.	2.64	37½	99.00	2	Married	10.60
d.	2.92	41½	121.18	3	Married	12.50
e.	2.14	38½	82.39	0	Married	12.70
f.	3.45	43	148.35	4	Single	16.50
g.	4.86	40½	196.83	5	Married	21.20
h.	5.94	34½	204.93	6	Married	20.50

B

1. Robert Reeves has a weekly income of $584.
   a. If he is single and claims 2 exemptions, how much will be withheld from his weekly earnings for income tax? $159.02
   b. If he is married and claims 2 exemptions, how much will be withheld from his weekly earnings for income tax? $134.12
   c. How much less will be withheld if he is married than if he is single? $ 24.90
2. Mrs. Evelyn Reilly earns $2.68 per hour as a typist. She works a 38½-hour week with no overtime. Since her husband claims her as an exemption, she claims no exemptions. How much will be withheld from her salary over a period of one year for income tax? $852.80
3. William Grady earns $3.74 per hour on a 38-hour week. He supports a wife and 2 children on his salary.
   a. If the computation for the withholding tax is made by using the table on page 162, how much will be taken from his salary?
   $ 13.63
   b. If the computation for the withholding tax is made by using the table on page 169, how much will be taken from his salary?
   $ 13.80
   c. How much more will be taken from his salary each week if one method of computation is used rather than the other? $ .17
4. The Frederick Knox Products Corporation pays its employees on a piecework basis according to the following weekly scale:

For the first 35 articles	$2.10 per article
For the next 10 articles	2.45 per article
For the next 15 articles	2.75 per article
For all over 60 articles	3.10 per article

If the question has not come up earlier, discuss with the students why anyone would want to claim no exemptions at all.

How much will be withheld in income tax for each of the following employees for the week shown below?

	Number Of Articles	Earnings	Exemptions	Married Or Single	Tax
a.	33	$ 69.30	1	Single	$ 9.00
b.	42	90.65	0	Married	14.20
c.	49	109.00	3	Married	9.70
d.	67	160.95	2	Single	26.20
e.	86	219.85	4	Married	27.50

5. Mr. Holmes works for the Frederick Knox Products Corporation of Problem 4. He is 67 years old and blind. His wife is 66 years old and is also blind. During the week of October 17, Mr. Holmes completed 74 articles. How much was withheld for income tax from his salary?

$16.70

Section 2: Social Security

PART 1

The federal government does not stop at just withholding part of your salary for income tax. It also takes another fraction of your earnings for social security. Before passage of the social security act, more than 90% of the people who were 65 or over had no way of supporting themselves. They became a financial burden on their children who, themselves, might be having difficulty making ends meet. The little that the children might have saved toward supporting themselves after retirement often went to aid their parents. Hence, people seemed to be caught up in a vicious cycle whereby each generation was chained to caring financially for the previous one, and, therefore, was not able to put enough aside for its own care.

In the late 1930's, the Congress decided to pass legislation whereby a certain fixed percent is taken from your salary and held for you until you reach retirement age. At that time, the money is returned to you in monthly allotments which will be described in a later chapter.

When people are young, they usually are unhappy about the social security deduction and grumble about it each time they look at their weekly paycheck. They somehow imagine that old age happens to other people—not to them. Or they think they will probably not live to collect the benefits of these weekly payments. But statistics show that they will probably reach retirement age and will need the help that is provided by the social security law. In fact, the closer they get to retirement, the more pleased they are that this money is waiting for them.

To bring the topic of social security closer to the students, ask if any of them are receiving social security payments and for what reason. Oddly enough, the students do not seem to be reluctant to discuss this openly in class. All too often the impression is that social security is only for the aged.

Deductions for social security are made in accordance with the following table. The rates have changed many times since the social security bill was first passed. And there is no reason to believe that they will remain as shown here through 1987. At present, though, these are the rates and these are the ones that concern you.

YEARS	RATE
1970	4.8%
1971–1972	5.2%
1973–1975	5.65%
1976–79	5.7%
1980–86	5.8%
1987 and after	5.9%

The law provides that deductions for social security must be made from that part of your earnings that are $7,800 per year, or less. Hence, if your earnings are less than $7,800 for one year, then 4.8% of the weekly salary will be deducted throughout the entire year. However, if your earnings exceed this amount, then deductions will be made from your weekly salary only until such time as the total earnings reach $7,800. For the remainder of the year, nothing will be deducted from your salary for social security contributions.

One other point of interest—you are not the only one who contributes to the fund for your retirement. For each dollar that you pay, your employer adds one of his own, and the two dollars are held in reserve for you.

■ILLUSTRATION 1: The hourly pay rate that Ralph Hopkins receives is $2.95. If he works a 42-hour week, how much will be taken from his earnings for social security?

●SOLUTION:

$$\text{Earnings} = 42 \times \$2.95$$
$$= \$123.90$$
$$\text{Social security deductions} = \$123.90 \times 4.8\%$$
$$= \$123.90 \times .048$$
$$= \$5.94720, \text{ or } \$5.95$$

▼EXPLANATION: The weekly wage of $123.90 was multiplied by the 4.8% rate. The product of $5.95 represents the social security tax deduction. Throughout your work, you will use the 4.8% rate. Incidentally, Mr. Hopkins' employer will add $5.95 to the $5.95 deducted from Ralph's earnings, and $11.90 will be sent to the Treasury Department.

■ILLUSTRATION 2: John Mason earns $186.40 each week. Which week of the year will be the first one in which no social security deduction will be taken from John's salary?

Check the current social security rate against that in the table above by calling the social security agency, usually listed under United States Government—Health, Education, and Welfare. Although the maximum of $7,800 and the rates may have changed, the computation method probably remains the same.

● SOLUTION:

Number of weeks during which social security payments will be made
$$= \$7,800 \div \$186.40$$
$$= 41.84$$
First week in which a payment will *not* be made = 43rd

▼ EXPLANATION: If a person earned $7,800 per week, then payments for social security would be made for 1 week only, for, in that 1 week, he would have reached the $7,800 maximum in his salary on which these payments are made for the entire year. If his earnings were $3,900 per week, then, in a period of 2 weeks, he would have made all the payments required of him. And if his earnings were $2,600 a week, then it would take 3 weeks. Notice that the number of weeks is found simply by dividing the weekly earnings into the $7,800.

In the case of Mr. Mason, who earns $186.40 each week, you divide this number into $7,800 to get 41.84. The numeral 41 of the 41.84 implies that 4.8% of his full salary is deducted for 41 weeks, while the .84 implies that 4.8% is taken from only 84/100 of his salary on the 42nd week. Hence, the first week in which deductions are not taken from his salary for social security is the 43rd week.

EXERCISES   A

1. How much will be deducted from each of the following salaries for social security? None of the employees who received these salaries has earned more than $7,800 prior to this date during the year.

	Weekly Salary	Social Security Tax		Weekly Salary	Social Security Tax
a.	$ 65	$ 3.12	f.	$ 74.60	$ 3.58
b.	87	4.18	g.	85.49	4.10
c.	124	5.95	h.	146.58	7.04
d.	237	11.38	i.	251.94	12.09
e.	354	16.99	j.	298.07	14.31

2. Which week of the year will be the first in which no social security tax will be taken from each of the following weekly salaries?

	Weekly Salary	First Week For No Deduction		Weekly Salary	First Week For No Deduction
a.	$200	40	f.	$268	31
b.	300	27	g.	185	44
c.	600	14	h.	194	42
d.	330	25	i.	209	39
e.	250	33	j.	236	35

In expanding upon the explanation to the solution, point out that the last full week of social security deductions will be the 41st. There will be a smaller deduction during the 42nd week, and no deduction during the 43rd week.

3. A person's take-home pay is the actual amount he receives after deductions have been subtracted from his earnings. How much will the take-home pay be for each of the following employees after income tax and social security deductions have been taken from their salaries? Use the income tax tables on pages 168 and 169.

	Weekly Earnings	Exemptions	Income Tax	Social Security	Take-Home Pay
a.	$137.00	2—Single	$ 20.20	$ 6.58	$ 110.22
b.	158.00	3—Married	18.70	7.58	131.72
c.	86.00	1—Single	12.40	4.13	69.47
d.	104.50	2—Married	11.30	5.02	88.18
e.	61.10	0—Single	10.00	2.93	48.17
f.	158.42	3—Married	18.70	7.60	132.12
g.	214.73	3—Single	34.60	10.31	169.82
h.	184.56	6—Married	16.70	8.86	159.00
i.	381.90	2—Single	92.33	18.33	271.24
j.	624.17	8—Married	120.68	29.96	473.53

4. Determine the take-home pay for each of the following employees after income tax and social security tax have been deducted. Each receives time and a half for all work over 40 hours per week. Use the income tax tables on pages 168 and 169.

	Hourly Earnings	Number Of Hours	Exemptions	Total Salary	Income Tax	Social Security	Take-Home Pay
a.	$1.80	40	0—Single	$ 72.00	$ 12.30	$ 3.46	$ 56.24
b.	1.95	40	1—Single	78.00	10.90	3.74	63.36
c.	2.98	40	4—Married	119.20	9.00	5.72	104.48
d.	2.54	38	2—Married	96.52	10.20	4.63	81.69
e.	2.93	39	0—Married	114.27	18.30	5.48	90.49
f.	2.67	42	2—Married	114.81	13.20	5.51	96.10
g.	3.24	44	3—Married	149.04	17.30	7.15	124.59
h.	3.58	41	4—Married	148.57	14.70	7.13	126.74
i.	3.94	41½	1—Single	166.47	29.20	7.99	129.28
j.	4.03	42½	5—Married	176.31	17.40	8.46	150.45

B

1. If a person earns $125 per week, how much more will be taken from his salary each week for social security in 1973 than in 1972? (Refer to the table on page 173.) $ .56

2. a. What is the largest annual salary from which social security deductions can be made? $7,800

   b. What is the largest amount that can be deducted from one person's earnings for social security during 1970? $374.40

3. Mr. Curran has a monthly income of $496.50. How much will be deducted from his salary for social security during one year? $285.98

When discussing Exercises 3 and 4, point up the fact that social security payments do not depend upon the number of exemptions claimed, as do the income tax payments.

4. Mr. Hamlin works an 8-hour day with time and a half for all work beyond 8 hours. His hourly rate is $4.17. If, besides himself, he lists his wife and 3 children as exemptions, how much is his take-home pay after deductions for social security and income taxes during the week in which he worked the following hours each day?

Monday	Tuesday	Wednesday	Thursday	Friday	
8	7	9	10	9	$159.34

5. Josephine Nivens works as a sales girl for Roll's Department Store, earning $1.88 per hour for a 43½-hour week. In addition, she receives a commission of 2½% on all sales over $850 that she makes during one week. Josephine is single, but claims both herself and her two parents as exemptions. How much will her take-home pay be, after deductions for social security and income taxes, during a week in which she sells $1,467 worth of merchandise? $ 83.34

PART 2

You probably realized, as you were doing the computation for the social security deductions in Part 1 of this section, that it was far too time-consuming. As in the case of the income tax deductions, the Treasury Department provides employers with tables that will tell them the amount to be deducted for social security. Where the income tax table gives only an approximation of the actual tax, the social security table gives the exact amount to be deducted had the wage been multipled by 4.8%.

Recall that the "At least" column of the income tax table was completely ignored when reading the table. Since it served no purpose, that column was deleted from this table so that a greater spread of wages could be included. Other than this, the social security table is read in the very same way as the income tax table is.

■ ILLUSTRATION : What will the social security tax be on a weekly wage of $120.17?

● SOLUTION :

Social security tax on $120.17 = $5.77

▼ EXPLANATION : As before, run your finger down the "But Less Than" column until you reach the first salary that is greater than $120.17. This appears in column (2), and the first such salary is $120.32. The numeral immediately to the right of $120.32 is the social security tax—$5.77. If you were to multiply $120.17 by the tax rate of 4.8%, the product would be the tax of $5.77 that you have just found.

In order to cover a wider range of wages in the table on page 177, the "At least" column was deleted. This column does appear in the table distributed by the Internal Revenue Service. In using the table, make certain that, if the wage appears in the table, the student continue to the first wage beyond it.

F.I.C.A. EMPLOYEE TAX TABLE—4.8% DEDUCTION

Wages— But Less Than	Soc. Sec. Tax	Wages— But Less Than	Soc. Sec. Tax	Wages— But Less Than	Soc. Sec. Tax	Wages— But Less Than	Soc. Sec. Tax	Wages— But Less Than	Soc. Sec. Tax
(1)		(2)		(3)		(4)		(5)	
$103.23	$4.95	$112.61	$5.40	$121.98	$5.85	$131.36	$6.30	$140.73	$6.75
103.44	4.96	112.82	5.41	122.19	5.86	131.57	6.31	140.94	6.76
103.65	4.97	113.03	5.42	122.40	5.87	131.78	6.32	141.15	6.77
103.86	4.98	113.23	5.43	122.61	5.88	131.98	6.33	141.36	6.78
104.07	4.99	113.44	5.44	122.82	5.89	132.19	6.34	141.57	6.79
104.28	5.00	113.65	5.45	123.03	5.90	132.40	6.35	141.78	6.80
104.48	5.01	113.86	5.46	123.23	5.91	132.61	6.36	141.98	6.81
104.69	5.02	114.07	5.47	123.44	5.92	132.82	6.37	142.19	6.82
104.90	5.03	114.28	5.48	123.65	5.93	133.03	6.38	142.40	6.83
105.11	5.04	114.48	5.49	123.86	5.94	133.23	6.39	142.61	6.84
105.32	5.05	114.69	5.50	124.07	5.95	133.44	6.40	142.82	6.85
105.53	5.06	114.90	5.51	124.28	5.96	133.65	6.41	143.03	6.86
105.73	5.07	115.11	5.52	124.48	5.97	133.86	6.42	143.23	6.87
105.94	5.08	115.32	5.53	124.69	5.98	134.07	6.43	143.44	6.88
106.15	5.09	115.53	5.54	124.90	5.99	134.28	6.44	143.65	6.89
106.36	5.10	115.73	5.55	125.11	6.00	134.48	6.45	143.86	6.90
106.57	5.11	115.94	5.56	125.32	6.01	134.69	6.46	144.07	6.91
106.78	5.12	116.15	5.57	125.53	6.02	134.90	6.47	144.28	6.92
106.98	5.13	116.36	5.58	125.73	6.03	135.11	6.48	144.48	6.93
107.19	5.14	116.57	5.59	125.94	6.04	135.32	6.49	144.69	6.94
107.40	5.15	116.78	5.60	126.15	6.05	135.53	6.50	144.90	6.95
107.61	5.16	116.98	5.61	126.36	6.06	135.73	6.51	145.11	6.96
107.82	5.17	117.19	5.62	126.57	6.07	135.94	6.52	145.32	6.97
108.03	5.18	117.40	5.63	126.78	6.08	136.15	6.53	145.53	6.98
108.23	5.19	117.61	5.64	126.98	6.09	136.36	6.54	145.73	6.99
108.44	5.20	117.82	5.65	127.19	6.10	136.57	6.55	145.94	7.00
108.65	5.21	118.03	5.66	127.40	6.11	136.78	6.56	146.15	7.01
108.86	5.22	118.23	5.67	127.61	6.12	136.98	6.57	146.36	7.02
109.07	5.23	118.44	5.68	127.82	6.13	137.19	6.58	146.57	7.03
109.28	5.24	118.65	5.69	128.03	6.14	137.40	6.59	146.78	7.04
109.48	5.25	118.86	5.70	128.23	6.15	137.61	6.60	146.98	7.05
109.69	5.26	119.07	5.71	128.44	6.16	137.82	6.61	147.19	7.06
109.90	5.27	119.28	5.72	128.65	6.17	138.03	6.62	147.40	7.07
110.11	5.28	119.48	5.73	128.86	6.18	138.23	6.63	147.61	7.08
110.32	5.29	119.69	5.74	129.07	6.19	138.44	6.64	147.82	7.09
110.53	5.30	119.90	5.75	129.28	6.20	138.65	6.65	148.03	7.10
110.73	5.31	120.11	5.76	129.48	6.21	138.86	6.66	148.23	7.11
110.94	5.32	120.32	5.77	129.69	6.22	139.07	6.67	148.44	7.12
111.15	5.33	120.53	5.78	129.90	6.23	139.28	6.68	148.65	7.13
111.36	5.34	120.73	5.79	130.11	6.24	139.48	6.69	148.86	7.14
111.57	5.35	120.94	5.80	130.32	6.25	139.69	6.70	149.07	7.15
111.78	5.36	121.15	5.81	130.53	6.26	139.90	6.71	149.28	7.16
111.98	5.37	121.36	5.82	130.73	6.27	140.11	6.72	149.48	7.17
112.19	5.38	121.57	5.83	130.94	6.28	140.32	6.73	149.69	7.18
112.40	5.39	121.78	5.84	131.15	6.29	140.53	6.74	149.90	7.19

See comment at the bottom of page 162.

If the wage itself appears in the table, you must still run your finger to the first salary that is *greater than* it. Thus, were you trying to determine the social security tax on a wage of $111.15, you would find that this numeral is in the table. However, you continue to move your finger to the next one beyond this, which is $111.36. The numeral at its right—$5.34—is the social security tax on $111.15.

It would be nice to say, and pleasing to the wage earner to hear, that the social security deduction is the last of the deductions taken from his earnings. But, unfortunately, this is not so. There are a great many others. Those most frequently included among them are retirement contribution, union dues, hospitalization, medical care, and government bonds. These deductions are handled so differently by different companies that it would be difficult to describe any general procedure that might fit all.

EXERCISES   A

1. Determine the social security tax on each of the following weekly salaries. Use the table on page 177. None of the employees who received these salaries has earned more than $7,800 prior to this date during the year.

	Weekly Salary	Social Security Tax		Weekly Salary	Social Security Tax
a.	$103.90	$ 4.99	f.	$129.00	$ 6.19
b.	104.21	5.00	g.	136.00	6.53
c.	112.62	5.41	h.	103.86	4.99
d.	120.84	5.80	i.	115.11	5.53
e.	125.03	6.00	j.	145.32	6.98

2. Determine the take-home pay for each of the following employees after income tax and social security deductions have been taken from their salaries. Use the tables on pages 168, 169, and 177 to compute the social security and income taxes.

	Weekly Earnings	Exemptions	Income Tax	Social Security	Take-Home Pay
a.	$105.50	1—Single	$ 16.60	$ 5.06	$ 83.84
b.	108.17	0—Married	17.30	5.19	85.68
c.	123.47	2—Married	15.10	5.93	102.44
d.	129.80	3—Single	15.00	6.23	108.57
e.	112.41	2—Single	14.70	5.40	92.31
f.	131.20	0—Single	25.00	6.30	99.90
g.	133.64	4—Married	11.90	6.41	115.33
h.	122.15	3—Married	12.50	5.86	103.79
i.	125.11	1—Married	18.60	6.01	100.50
j.	148.23	5—Married	12.20	7.12	128.91

Have the students compute 4.8% of the first three weekly salaries in Exercise 1 to see for themselves that the social security tax found by this method is identical with that found when using the table on page 177.

3. Determine the take-home pay for each of the following employees after social security and income taxes have been deducted. Use the tables for social security and income taxes on pages 168, 169, and 177.

	Hourly Rate	M	T	Days W	Th	F	Exemptions	Take-Home Pay
a.	$3.10	7	7	7	7	7	0—Single	$ 83.79
b.	3.45	7	8	8	7	7	2—Married	105.52
c.	3.75	7	7	10	8	7	0—Married	114.33
d.	3.59	7½	7½	8	8	9	4—Single	121.31
e.	3.94	7½	7½	7½	8½	7	4—Married	127.83
f.	3.12	9	9	9½	9	9	3—Married	118.85
g.	4.06	7¼	8¼	7	7	7	2—Married	121.28
h.	3.37	7¼	7½	8½	9	9	6—Married	124.64

4. Determine the take-home pay for each of the following employees after income tax and social security tax have been deducted. Each works on the piece-rate scale shown. Use the tables for social security and income taxes on pages 168, 169, and 177.

	Piece Rate	M	T	Number of Articles W	Th	F	Exemptions	Take-Home Pay
a.	$2.11	9	12	8	14	11	2—Married	$ 95.27
b.	$2.34	8	9	14	15	12	1—Single	106.01
c.	$2.58½	7	9	13	12½	12½	3—Married	117.49
d.	86½¢	23	29	21	27	29	4—Single	96.73
e.	65½¢	34	30	29	32	35	3—Single	89.57
f.	42.8¢	48	53	57	67	56	0—Single	91.70

B

1. If a person earns $118 weekly, what will be the total social security tax that will be taken from his salary during the period of one year? Use the social security table on page 177. $294.32

2. Mr. Norwood's weekly salary, both in 1968 and in 1970, was $147.50.
   a. In 1968, the social security tax rate was 4.4%. How much was deducted from Mr. Norwood's salary during that year for social security? $337.48
   b. How much was deducted in 1970? $368.16
   c. How much less was deducted in 1968 than in 1970? $ 30.68

3. If a person changes jobs during the year, then both employers will deduct social security tax from his salary until he has earned $7,800 from each. During a period of one year, Edwin Kirby worked for Kirch Furniture Company, earning $4,385, and for Jonathan Green Stores, Inc., earning $5,262.
   a. How much social security tax did he pay while an employee of the Kirch Furniture Company? $210.48

b. How much social security tax did he pay while an employee of the Jonathan Green Stores, Inc.? $252.58

c. What is the maximum amount he should have paid in social security tax for the entire year? (See Problem 2, page 175.)
                                                                $374.40

d. How much will have to be returned to Mr. Kirby by the Treasury Department? $ 88.66

4. In addition to social security tax and income tax deductions, each of the following employees has deductions for union dues, hospitalization, and retirement benefits. What is the take-home pay of each? Use the tables for social security and income taxes on pages 168, 169, and 177.

	Earnings	Exemptions	Union Dues	Hospitalization	Retirement Benefits	Take-Home Pay
a.	$127.54	2—Single	$3.24	$1.27	$ .84	$ 98.07
b.	104.95	1—Single	2.09	.93	.87	80.52
c.	134.16	3—Married	1.95	1.36	1.28	108.73
d.	144.28	5—Married	1.18	1.75	1.94	121.28
e.	148.44	0—Single	2.83	1.04	2.18	106.96

5. Clifford Liston earns $2.76 per hour for a 38-hour week with time and a half for all work over 38 hours. During the week of August 15, he worked 42 hours.

a. What were his total earnings for the week? $121.44

b. If he is 67 years old and his wife is 64 years old, how much will be deducted for income tax? $ 12.50

c. How much will be deducted for social security? $ 5.83

d. For retirement benefits, he pays 2½% of his salary, and for union dues, he pays .5% of his salary. How much is deducted for each?
                                    Retirement: $3.04; Union: $ .61

e. If the above are his only deductions, what is his take-home pay for the week of August 15? $ 99.46

Unit 5: Chapter Review and Test

1. What is the time-and-a-half rate if the regular hourly rate is as follows?
   a. $1.80 __$2.70__   b. $2.04 __$3.06__   c. $3.15 _$ 4.725_

2. If a person works 4 hours overtime at time and a half and his regular rate is $2.16, how much does he earn for these 4 hours?
                                                                $ 12.96

3. Mr. Marino normally works a 38-hour week with time and a half for overtime. What will his earnings be during a week in which he works 44 hours at $2.58 per hour? $121.26

Problem 3 of Group B affords you the opportunity to point out that 4.8% of a person's salary is taken out of the first $7,800 of earnings that he gets in each and every job he may hold during the year. His overpayment is credited to him when he files his income tax form.

4. a. If a person receives time and a half for all overtime work, how many regular hours salary will he receive for 8 hours of overtime work?   <u>12</u>

   b. How many regular hours salary will he receive for 5 hours of overtime work?   <u>7.5</u>

   c. Work on Sunday is usually paid at a double-time rate. How many regular hours salary will a person receive if he works 5½ hours on a Sunday?   <u>11</u>

5. Mr. Naylor earns $2.58 per hour. The firm he works for has a lateness penalty that is the same as the rate table on page 149. If Mr. Naylor is supposed to report for work at 9:00, but clocks in at 9:47, how much will be deducted from his salary?   <u>$ 2.58</u>

6. Edyth Cleveland works at the piece-rate basis of 87½¢ per article. How much will she earn during the week in which she completes the following number of articles?   <u>$ 88.38</u>

Monday	Tuesday	Wednesday	Thursday	Friday
15	18	26	23	19

7. Mrs. Deering works a 41-hour week on a salary of $2.14 per hour, plus a commission of 3½% on everything she sells in excess of $1,250 during the week. What were her earnings for the week of May 12 when she sold $1,948 worth of merchandise?   <u>$112.17</u>

8. a. Compute the income tax deduction for a single person who claimed 1 deduction and earned $158.40 per week. Use the table on page 168.   <u>$ 27.00</u>

   b. Compute the income tax deduction for a married person who claimed 3 deductions and earned $492.75 per week. Use the table on page 169.   <u>$100.30</u>

9. Compute the income tax deduction for Mr. Edgcomb, who is 69 years of age, blind, and supports a wife who is 66. His weekly earnings are $169.74. Use the table on page 169.   <u>$ 15.50</u>

10. How much social security tax will be taken from a person's earnings during a week in which his wages are $176.40?   <u>$ 8.47</u>

11. Determine the social security tax on each of the following weekly salaries. Use the social security tax table on page 177.
   a. $121.54 <u>$5.83</u>   b. $133.86 <u>$6.43</u>   c. $121.80 <u>$ 5.85</u>

12. If social security and income taxes are the only deductions that Mr. Baker has, what will his take-home pay be for the week shown here? He supports a wife and 4 children . His earnings are $3.08 an hour.   <u>$114.02</u>

Monday	Tuesday	Wednesday	Thursday	Friday
7	8	8½	8½	9

CHAPTER **5**

INCOME TAXES

Although part of your salary is withheld from you each week for income tax payments, you still have to fill out an income tax form once a year by April 15. As you learned, the weekly deductions are only a rough estimate of the actual amount you owe the federal government. Hence, the purpose of filing a return, that is, sending the Internal Revenue Service a statement of your income for the year, is to straighten out your account. When you complete one of the income tax forms, you may find that more withholding tax than necessary was deducted. When this happens—as it sometimes does—you are entitled to a refund. When you find that the total withholding deduction was not quite as large as the tax you owe, you must send a check covering the difference between what you should pay and what you did pay.

The graphs on page 183 show how the federal government spent the money that it collected during a recent year and where that money came from. Notice that the largest source is from the income tax peo-

A great many students are working at part-time jobs, and all too often many of them are paying a minimum of $5 to have someone complete an income tax form for them which they, themselves, could do in no more than 15 minutes time. Stress this idea with them.

ple pay. In fact, it accounts for 39¢ of every dollar collected by the government. On the other hand, the largest share of the money spent appears to go for national defense. During that year, some 45¢ of every dollar went for defense expenditures. The second largest slice of that dollar—about 25¢—went for unemployment benefits, retirement benefits, health programs, manpower training, war on poverty, medicare, and social security. There is no question but that the services that the government is called upon to provide are many and are needed. It is the small withholding contributions that each person makes that help support these programs.

Your Government Dollar

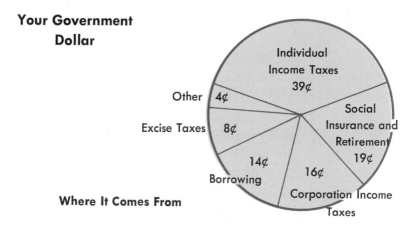

Where It Comes From

Where It Goes

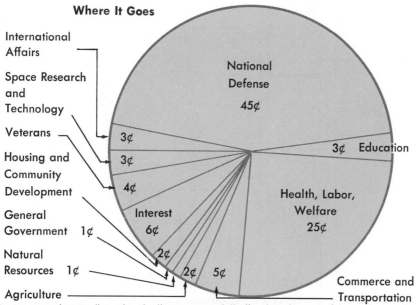

Devote some time to discussing the "government dollar"—where it comes from and where it goes. Of particular interest is the fact that less than half of it comes from individual income tax.

WAGE AND TAX STATEMENT

COPY C—For employee's records   19

INCOME TAX INFORMATION

Federal Income Tax Withheld	Wages¹ paid subject to withholding in 19	Other compensation ² paid in 19
$466.80 ①	$3,745.00 ②	③

SOCIAL SECURITY INFORMATION

F.I.C.A. Employee Tax Withheld ³	Total F.I.C.A. wages ⁴ paid in 19
$183.51 ④	$3,745.00 ⑤

EMPLOYEE NO.	No. Dependents *	1 Single 2 Married *
	1	1

Uncollected Employee Tax on Tips $

STATE OR MUNICIPAL INFORMATION

State Tax Withheld	City Tax Withheld

**

Name of State or City

Type or Print EMPLOYEE'S social security no., name and address below.

462-15-7583

Arthur T. Webb
547 Norman Road
Glenwood, Oregon

Type or Print **EMPLOYER'S** identification number, name and address

34-064837

General Electronics, Inc.
Highway 240
Glenwood, Oregon

*See Circ. E for sick pay reporting. **Gross wages for State if different from Federal.
1 Includes tips reported by employee. Amount is before payroll deductions or sick pay exclusion.

2 **Add this item to wages in figuring the amount to be reported as wages and salaries on your income tax return.**

3 One-eighth of this amount was withheld to finance the cost of Hospital Insurance Benefits. The remainder is for old-age, survivors, and disability insurance.

4 Includes tips reported by employee. If your wages were subject to social security taxes, but are not shown, these wages are the same as wages shown under "Federal Income Tax Information," but not more than $7,800.

Keep this copy as part of your tax records.

Form W-2 – U.S. Treasury Department, Internal Revenue Service APP.

The annual income tax returns that are sent to the Internal Revenue Service are filed on a report called Form 1040. How you complete this form depends not only on the size of your income, but also on the source of your income.

Unit 1:   Form 1040

Section 1:   Computation of Tax by the Internal Revenue Service

Shortly after January 1 each year, your employer types out four copies of Form W-2 shown at left. One he sends to the District Director of Internal Revenue so that he will know the amount of your earnings for the year and how much has been withheld from it both for income tax and social security tax. A second copy your employer keeps for his own records, while the remaining two he turns over to you. Of the two that you receive, one is for your records, while the other is attached to the income tax form that you send to the District Director of Internal Revenue. In this way, the District Director has a check on the accuracy of the information submitted to him.

Notice that the form on page 184 is marked "Copy C—For employee's records." This is the form that you keep for yourself. Except for this line, the other three forms are the same as this one. This Form W-2 will be examined in terms of the income of Arthur T. Webb, whose name appears on it.

1. The numeral in the box labeled ① represents the total of all the income tax that was withheld weekly from Mr. Webb's wages during the year.

2. The numeral in box ② is the total of wages paid Mr. Webb for that year by General Electronics, Inc.

3. Since he earned no other money from this company besides that reported in box ②, box ③ was left blank.

4. The letters F.I.C.A. in box ④ are abbreviations for the words Federal Insurance Contributions Act—another name for social security. Hence, the numeral that appears here represents the amount that was deducted from Mr. Webb's wages during the year for the social security tax.

5. In box ⑤, you find the same numeral as in box ②, for Mr. Webb had to pay social security tax on his entire income. Had he earned $9,745 during the year, then this amount would have appeared in the second box, while only $7,800 would have appeared in the fifth one. As you may recall, the reason for this is that social security deduc-

The Internal Revenue Service makes available to teachers in whatever numbers they might request a student publication entitled *Understanding Taxes—Teaching Taxes Program.* The content is current, and an effort is made to keep the writing at the student's level. It is somewhat more complex than this text.

tions are made only on the first $7,800 of a person's earnings. Since Mr. Webb earned less than $7,800, all of it was subject to the social security tax.

With the information from Form W-2 at his disposal, Mr. Webb was now in a position to complete his income tax form. He decided to permit the Internal Revenue Service to compute his tax for him. However, before he could reach this decision, he had to make certain his income was such that it fell within the two requirements that permitted this.

1. The first of these requirements specifies that the taxpayer's total income must be less than $5,000.
2. The second requirement states that less than $200 of his income must come from interest from money that he has invested.

Since Mr. Webb's only source of income was the money he had earned at General Electronics, Inc., he was able to ask the Internal Revenue Service to compute his tax. In view of this, he simply wrote the fill-ins for lines 1 through 15c and 19 while the IRS did the rest. (What do the letters IRS stand for?)

Each of the lines as Mr. Webb completed them will be examined separately.

1. Mr. Webb was single, so he placed a check mark in this square and left the squares for items 2, 3, 4, 5, and 6 blank. Were Mr. Webb married, he would probably have filed a *joint* return and indicated this by checking item 2. A joint return is one in which the husband and wife file the same form with the IRS. By so doing, they are granted certain advantages that usually result in a smaller tax payment than if they file separate returns.

7a. The information requested here concerns the number of exemptions Mr. Webb was claiming. Since he is neither 65 nor blind, he placed a check mark in the square under the word "Regular" and nothing in any of the other squares. At the far right of item 7, he wrote the numeral 1, for he had only 1 exemption he could claim.

8. Mr. Webb left this line blank, for he had no dependent children.

9. Mr. Webb left this line blank also, for he had no dependent relatives.

10. This line asks for the total number of exemptions claimed on lines 7, 8, and 9. Since Mr. Webb claimed only 1, himself, which he listed in answer to 7a, this numeral again appears on line 10.

If at all possible, make a master copy of Form 1040 on page 187, and then run off enough ditto copies for each of your students so that they will have the form constantly available for use throughout the teaching of this chapter.

Form 1040 Combined with Form 1040A

US Department of the Treasury / Internal Revenue Service
Individual Income Tax Return 19

For the year January 1–December 31, 19 , or other taxable year beginning _____ , 19 , ending _____ , 19 ___

Please print or type

Arthur T. Webb
547 Norman Road
Glenwood, Oregon

Your social security number
462 | 15 | 7583

Your occupation
Machinist

Spouse's social security number

Enter below name and address used on your return for 1968 (if same as above write "Same"). If none filed, give reason. If changing from separate to joint or joint to separate returns, enter 1968 names and addresses.
Same

Spouse's occupation

Name and address of employer at time of filing General Electronics, Inc., Glenwood, Oregon

Your Filing Status—(Check only one)
1. ☑ Single
2. ☐ Married filing joint return (even if only one had income)
3. ☐ Married filing separate return and spouse is also filing a return. If this item checked give spouse's social security number in space provided above and enter first name here ▶
4. ☐ Unmarried Head of Household
5. ☐ Surviving widow(er) with dependent child
6. ☐ Married filing separate return and spouse is not filing a return

Your Exemptions

Check boxes for exemptions which apply | Regular | 65 or over | Blind
7a **Yourself** . . . . | ☑ | ☐ | ☐ | Enter number of boxes checked ▶
7b **Spouse** (applies only if line 2 or line 6 is checked) . . . . . . | ☐ | ☐ | ☐

8 First names of your dependent children who lived with you   Enter number ▶

9 OTHER DEPENDENTS

(a) NAME—Enter figure 1 in the last column to right for each name listed (if more space is needed, use other side)	(b) Relationship	(c) Months lived in your home. See instructions, B–2.	(d) $600 or more income?	(e) Support you furnished. If 100% write "ALL."	(f) Support furnished by dependent and others
				$	$ ▶
					▶
					▶

10 Total exemptions from lines 7, 8, and 9 above . . . . ▶

Your Income

11 Wages, salaries, tips, etc. (Attach Form W–2 to back. If unavailable, explain on back) . | **11** | 3,745 | –

12a Dividends [Total before exclusion] $_____ [See item 2 on 1040–1] 12b Less Exclusion $_____ Balance ▶ | **12c**

13 Interest (Enter total here and if over $100, also list in Schedule B, Part II) . . . . | **13**

14 Other income: Total from attached schedules (check schedules used—C ☐, D ☐, E ☐, F ☐) . | **14**

15a Total [Add lines 11, 12c, 13 & 14] $ 3,745 , 15b Less Adjustments [See 1040–1] $ | Adjusted Gross income ▶ | **15c** | 3,745 | –

Your Tax and Surcharge

● If line 15c is $5,000 or more, go to Schedule T, to figure tax and surcharge. (Omit lines 16 and 17.)
● Go to Sch. T to figure tax and surcharge if you itemize deductions; or claim retirement income credit, foreign tax credit, or investment credit; or if you owe self-employment tax or tax from recomputing prior year investment credit (Omit lines 16 and 17.)
● If neither of above two items applies, go to Tax Tables instead of Sch. T. Complete lines 16, 17, & 18.

16 Tax from Tax Table (see tables on T–2 and T–3) . . . . . | **16** |

17 Tax surcharge on line 16 (see T–1 for tax surcharge tables) . | **17** |

18 Enter total of lines 16 and 17 OR amount from Schedule T, line 18, if applicable (check if from Tax Table A ☐, B ☐, C ☐; Tax Rate Sch. ☐, Sch. D ☐, or Sch. G ☐) . | **18** |

See 1040–1 for rules under which the IRS will figure your tax and surcharge.

Your Credits

19 Total Federal income tax withheld (attach Forms W–2 to back) | **19** | 466 | 80

20 Excess F.I.C.A. tax withheld (two or more employers—see R–2) . . . | **20** |

21 ☐ Nonhighway Federal gasoline tax, Form 4136; ☐ Reg. Inv., Form 2439 | **21** |

22 19 Estimated tax payments (include 19 overpayment allowed as a credit) | **22** |

23 Total (add lines 19, 20, 21, and 22) . . . . | **23** |

Make check or money order payable to Internal Revenue Service.

Balance Due or Refund

24 If line 18 is larger than line 23, enter BALANCE DUE. Pay in full with return ▶ | **24** |

25 If line 23 is larger than line 18, enter OVERPAYMENT ▶ | **25** |

26 Line 25 to be: (a) Credited on 19 estimated tax ▶ $; (b) Refunded ▶ $

Under penalties of perjury, I declare that I have examined this return, including accompanying schedules and statements, and to the best of my knowledge and belief it is true, correct, and complete.

Sign here

Arthur T. Webb   3/17/--
Your signature   Date

Signature of preparer other than taxpayer, based on all information of which he has any knowledge.   Date

Spouse's signature (if filing jointly, BOTH must sign even if only one had income)   Address

Please attach Copy B of Form W–2 to back

Please attach Check or Money Order here

Although Form 1040 has changed somewhat over the years, basically the technique of completing it has remained the same for many years. The student who can understand this one will have no trouble understanding whatever form may be current.

11. For line 11, Mr. Webb examined Form W-2 and saw that his wages were $3,745. It was this number that he wrote as the fill-in here.

12, 13, and 14. These lines call for other income that Mr. Webb might have had. Since he had no other income but that from General Electronics, Inc., he left these lines blank.

15a. This item is the total of all of Mr. Webb's income. Having written nothing but $3,745 on line 11, he repeated that amount here and again as the fill-in for 15c.

16, 17, and 18. Mr. Webb skipped these lines.

19. Mr. Webb wrote $466.80 as the fill-in for this line. This is the amount of income tax withheld from his earnings during the year. Mr. Webb learned this by examining the box marked 1 on Form W-2.

Mr. Webb then completed the form by signing his name at the bottom, left. He then placed this form, with Form W-2 attached, in an envelope and mailed them to the office of the District Director for his state. The employees of the IRS will complete lines 16, 17, and 18, and shortly thereafter, Mr. Webb will receive a check for the overpayment he made, or a bill for the amount he still owes.

EXERCISES

Complete lines 1 through 15 and 19 of Form 1040 from the following information.

	Withholding Tax	Wages	Type Of Return
a.	$382	$3,400	Single—1 Exemption
b.	$475	$3,750	Single—1 Exemption
c.	$173	$2,157	Single—1 Exemption
d.	$507	$4,900 & $0	Joint—Husband and wife
e.	$258	$4,736 & $0	Joint—Husband, wife, 2 children
f.	$302 & $79	$3,875 & $1,100	Joint—Husband, wife, 1 child

Section 2:   Computation of Tax by Taxpayer Where Income Is Less than $5,000

At this time, lines 16, 17, and 18 of Form 1040 are going to be examined somewhat more carefully. In Section 1, employees of the Internal Revenue Service were allowed to determine the fill-ins for these lines. This can be done only if your income is less than $5,000. However, most people prefer to compute the tax themselves so that they

Since you may not have sufficient copies of Form 1040 to distribute to the students, the next best thing is to have them use lined paper on which the lines are numbered from 1 through 15 and 19. Then have the students refer to the actual form on page 187 for the information pertaining to the lines.

know immediately whether the government is indebted to them, or if the reverse is true.

For computing the actual income tax, the government provides tables similar to those shown on page 190. These tables can be used only if your total income is less than $5,000. Notice, also, that neither of these tables is complete, for both should begin with salaries of $0. In addition, there should be a third table that is designed for married persons who file separate returns. Since very few married persons have anything to gain by filing separate returns, this table was not included.

■ILLUSTRATION 1: Compute the income tax that Mr. Camper must pay on an income of $4,765. Mr. Camper is married and has 3 children. He is filing a joint return.

●SOLUTION:

Tax on $4,765 on a joint return with 5 exemptions = $151

▼EXPLANATION: Since Mr. Camper is a married man filing a joint return, you refer to Tax Table B, which is designed for a return such as this. As in earlier tables, you ignore the "At least" column and run your finger down the "But less than" column until you come to the first numeral larger than 4,765. It is 4,800. Place the edge of a piece of paper along the row containing this numeral. Then move your finger across the row until it comes to rest under the column headed by the numeral 5, which indicates the number of exemptions that Mr. Camper has claimed. Your finger should be pointing to $151.

The $151 is the amount that Mr. Camper would owe the government were there no additional tax to be paid. This second tax is based on the $151. A tax that is computed on the basis of another tax is called a *surcharge tax*. To find the additional tax Mr. Cooper will have to pay, refer to the surcharge tables on page 192. The one you need now is Table 2 for married persons filing a joint return. As before, run your finger down the "But less than" column until you come to the first number greater than $151. This turns out to be the first number in the table—$293—while the numeral immediately to its right, $0, gives you the surcharge tax Mr. Camper has to pay. Hence, his total tax is $151. What would the surcharge tax have been had the base tax been $337? $409? $475?

■ILLUSTRATION 2: Complete lines 11 through 25 for Arthur T. Webb, who has earned $3,745 during the year. The withholding tax during the year came to $466.80. Arthur is single and claims only himself as an exemption.

In the event the surcharge tax is no longer in force at the time you are teaching this topic, you may want to delete this from the computation. Be careful, however, for the answers in the *Teacher's Annotated Edition* will not be the same as those found without the surcharge tax.

Tax Tables for Persons With Incomes Under $5,000

TAX TABLE A—For Single Persons

| If your total income is— | | And the number of exemptions is— | | | | | |
At least	But less than	1	2	3	4	5	6 (If 7 or more there is no tax)
		Your tax (before surcharge) is—					
$2,450	$2,475	$236	$124	$23	$0	$0	$0
2,475	2,500	240	128	26	0	0	0
2,500	2,525	244	132	30	0	0	0
2,525	2,550	248	136	33	0	0	0
2,550	2,575	253	139	37	0	0	0
2,575	2,600	257	143	40	0	0	0
2,600	2,625	261	147	44	0	0	0
2,625	2,650	265	151	47	0	0	0
2,650	2,675	270	155	51	0	0	0
2,675	2,700	274	159	54	0	0	0
2,700	2,725	278	163	58	0	0	0
2,725	2,750	282	167	61	0	0	0
2,750	2,775	287	171	65	0	0	0
2,775	2,800	291	175	68	0	0	0
2,800	2,825	295	179	72	0	0	0
2,825	2,850	299	183	76	0	0	0
2,850	2,875	304	187	79	0	0	0
2,875	2,900	308	191	83	0	0	0
2,900	2,925	312	195	87	0	0	0
2,925	2,950	316	199	91	0	0	0
2,950	2,975	322	203	94	0	0	0
2,975	3,000	327	207	98	0	0	0
3,000	3,050	333	213	104	4	0	0
3,050	3,100	342	221	111	11	0	0
3,100	3,150	350	229	119	18	0	0
3,150	3,200	359	238	126	25	0	0
3,200	3,250	367	248	134	32	0	0
3,250	3,300	376	255	141	39	0	0
3,300	3,350	385	263	149	46	0	0
3,350	3,400	393	272	157	53	0	0
3,400	3,450	402	280	165	60	0	0
3,450	3,500	410	289	173	67	0	0
3,500	3,550	419	297	181	74	0	0
3,550	3,600	427	306	189	81	0	0
3,600	3,650	436	315	197	89	0	0
3,650	3,700	445	324	205	96	0	0
3,700	3,750	453	334	213	104	4	0
3,750	3,800	462	343	221	111	11	0
3,800	3,850	470	353	229	119	18	0
3,850	3,900	479	363	238	126	25	0
3,900	3,950	487	372	246	134	32	0
3,950	4,000	496	381	255	141	39	0
4,000	4,050	504	390	263	149	46	0
4,050	4,100	513	399	272	157	53	0
4,100	4,150	521	407	280	165	60	0
4,150	4,200	530	416	289	173	67	0
4,200	4,250	538	424	297	181	74	0
4,250	4,300	547	433	306	189	81	0
4,300	4,350	556	442	315	197	89	0
4,350	4,400	564	450	324	205	96	0
4,400	4,450	573	460	334	213	104	4
4,450	4,500	581	467	343	221	111	11
4,500	4,550	590	476	353	229	119	18
4,550	4,600	598	484	362	238	126	25
4,600	4,650	607	493	372	246	134	32
4,650	4,700	615	501	382	255	141	39
4,700	4,750	624	510	391	263	149	46
4,750	4,800	633	519	400	272	157	53
4,800	4,850	641	527	410	280	165	60
4,850	4,900	650	536	419	289	173	67
4,900	4,950	658	545	429	297	181	74
4,950	5,000	667	553	438	306	189	81

TAX TABLE B—Married Filing Jointly

| If your total income is— | | And the number of exemptions is— | | | | | |
At least	But less than	2	3	4	5	6 (If 7 or more there is no tax)
		Your tax (before surcharge) is—				
$2,450	$2,475	$121	$23	$0	$0	$0
2,475	2,500	124	26	0	0	0
2,500	2,525	128	30	0	0	0
2,525	2,550	131	33	0	0	0
2,550	2,575	135	37	0	0	0
2,575	2,600	138	40	0	0	0
2,600	2,625	142	44	0	0	0
2,625	2,650	146	47	0	0	0
2,650	2,675	149	51	0	0	0
2,675	2,700	153	54	0	0	0
2,700	2,725	157	58	0	0	0
2,725	2,750	161	61	0	0	0
2,750	2,775	164	65	0	0	0
2,775	2,800	168	68	0	0	0
2,800	2,825	172	72	0	0	0
2,825	2,850	176	75	0	0	0
2,850	2,875	179	79	0	0	0
2,875	2,900	183	82	0	0	0
2,900	2,925	187	86	0	0	0
2,925	2,950	191	89	0	0	0
2,950	2,975	194	93	0	0	0
2,975	3,000	198	96	0	0	0
3,000	3,050	204	102	4	0	0
3,050	3,100	211	109	11	0	0
3,100	3,150	219	116	18	0	0
3,150	3,200	226	123	25	0	0
3,200	3,250	234	130	32	0	0
3,250	3,300	241	137	39	0	0
3,300	3,350	249	144	46	0	0
3,350	3,400	256	151	53	0	0
3,400	3,450	264	159	60	0	0
3,450	3,500	271	166	67	0	0
3,500	3,550	279	174	74	0	0
3,550	3,600	286	181	81	0	0
3,600	3,650	294	189	88	0	0
3,650	3,700	302	196	96	0	0
3,700	3,750	310	204	102	4	0
3,750	3,800	318	211	109	11	0
3,800	3,850	326	219	116	18	0
3,850	3,900	334	226	123	25	0
3,900	3,950	342	234	130	32	0
3,950	4,000	350	241	137	39	0
4,000	4,050	358	249	144	46	0
4,050	4,100	365	256	151	53	0
4,100	4,150	372	264	159	60	0
4,150	4,200	380	271	166	67	0
4,200	4,250	387	279	174	74	0
4,250	4,300	394	286	181	81	0
4,300	4,350	401	294	189	88	0
4,350	4,400	408	302	196	95	0
4,400	4,450	415	310	204	102	4
4,450	4,500	422	318	211	109	11
4,500	4,550	430	326	219	116	18
4,550	4,600	437	334	226	123	25
4,600	4,650	444	342	234	130	32
4,650	4,700	451	350	241	137	39
4,700	4,750	459	358	249	144	46
4,750	4,800	467	366	256	151	53
4,800	4,850	474	374	264	159	60
4,850	4,900	482	382	271	166	67
4,900	4,950	489	390	279	174	74
4,950	5,000	497	398	286	181	81

The lines completed in the solution above are the only ones that the bulk of your students will be concerned with over the next few years. Lines such as 12a, 12b, and 13 are discussed later in this chapter. There is no reason why you should not talk briefly about each of the blank lines at this point.

●SOLUTION:

11. Wages	11.	$3,745
12a. Dividends $_____		
12b. Less Exclusion $_____	Balance 12c.	_____
13. Interest	13.	_____
14. Other Income	14.	_____
15a. Total $3,745		
15b. Less Adjustments $_____		
	Adjusted Gross Income 15c.	3,745
16. Tax from Tax Table	16. 453	
17. Tax Surcharge	17. 45	
18. Total Tax	18.	498
19. Total Federal Income Tax Withheld	19. 467	
20. Excess FICA Tax Withheld	20. _____	
21. Gasoline Tax	21. _____	
22. Estimated Tax Payments	22. _____	
23. Total	23.	467
24. If line 18 is larger than line 23, enter BALANCE DUE	24.	31
25. If line 23 is larger than line 18, enter OVERPAY-MENT	25.	_____

▼EXPLANATION: Mr. Webb has no income from any source other than his wages. Hence, the fill-in for line 11 is $3,745, while lines 12, 13, and 14 are left blank, and his total income for line 15 is the same as that for line 11. In view of the fact that Mr. Webb is single, you refer to Tax Table A, where you find that the first income greater than $3,745 is $3,750. The tax for an income of $3,745, where there is but one exemption, is $453, which is recorded as the fill-in for line 16. The surcharge on $453 for a single person is $45. Where was this found? And, hence, the total tax for line 18 is $498.

To lessen the drudgery of computation, the IRS permits you

(a) to drop off any amount that is less than 50¢
(b) and to increase to the next dollar any amount from 50¢ through 99¢

Since the withholding tax amounted to $466.80, this was rounded off to $467, which is the fill-in for line 19. Lines 20, 21, and 22 do not pertain to Mr. Webb, so they were left blank. Hence, line 23, which is the total tax already paid by Mr. Webb for the year, was only the $467 that was withheld. The $31 on line 24 is the difference between

The tables on these two pages appear in the package mailed to taxpayers at the outset of each year. It will save a great deal of ruffling of pages if a master copy can be made of them and ditto copies given to the students. Sections of these tables also appear in the publication *Understanding Taxes*.

19__ Tax Surcharge Tables

TABLE 1—Single Taxpayers and Married Persons Filing Separate Returns

If your tax is at least:	But less than	Your tax surcharge² is:	If your tax is at least:	But less than	Your tax surcharge² is:
0	$148	0	$395	$405	$40
$148	153	$1	405	415	41
153	158	2	415	425	42
158	163	3	425	435	43
163	168	4	435	445	44
168	173	5	445	455	45
173	178	6	455	465	46
178	183	7	465	475	47
183	188	8	475	485	48
188	193	9	485	495	49
193	198	10	495	505	50
198	203	11	505	515	51
203	208	12	515	525	52
208	213	13	525	535	53
213	218	14	535	545	54
218	223	15	545	555	55
223	228	16	555	565	56
228	233	17	565	575	57
233	238	18	575	585	58
238	243	19	585	595	59
243	248	20	595	605	60
248	253	21	605	615	61
253	258	22	615	625	62
258	263	23	625	635	63
263	268	24	635	645	64
268	273	25	645	655	65
273	278	26	655	665	66
278	283	27	665	675	67
283	288	28	675	685	68
288	295	29	685	695	69
295	305	30	695	705	70
305	315	31	705	715	71
315	325	32	715	725	72
325	335	33	725	735	73
335	345	34			
345	355	35			
355	365	36	If $735 or more multiply your tax by .10		
365	375	37			
375	385	38			
385	395	39			

TABLE 2—Married Taxpayers Filing Joint Returns and Certain Widows and Widowers

If your tax is at least:	But less than	Your tax surcharge² is:	If your tax is at least:	But less than	Your tax surcharge² is:
0	$293	0	$488	$493	$40
$293	298	$1	493	498	41
298	303	2	498	503	42
303	308	3	503	508	43
308	313	4	508	513	44
313	318	5	513	518	45
318	323	6	518	523	46
323	328	7	523	528	47
328	333	8	528	533	48
333	338	9	533	538	49
338	343	10	538	543	50
343	348	11	543	548	51
348	353	12	548	553	52
353	358	13	553	558	53
358	363	14	558	563	54
363	368	15	563	568	55
368	373	16	568	573	56
373	378	17	573	578	57
378	383	18	578	585	58
383	388	19	585	595	59
388	393	20	595	605	60
393	398	21	605	615	61
398	403	22	615	625	62
403	408	23	625	635	63
408	413	24	635	645	64
413	418	25	645	655	65
418	423	26	655	665	66
423	428	27	665	675	67
428	433	28	675	685	68
433	438	29	685	695	69
438	443	30	695	705	70
443	448	31	705	715	71
448	453	32	715	725	72
453	458	33	725	735	73
458	463	34			
463	468	35			
468	473	36	If $735 or more multiply your tax by .10		
473	478	37			
478	483	38			
483	488	39			

the amount Mr. Webb should have paid in tax—$498—and the amount he did pay—$467. It is this $31 that he must pay the government. In the event that line 18 had been $460, then the government would owe Mr. Webb $7. Had this occurred, the $7 would have been the fill-in for line 25, and line 24 would have been left blank. Should this have been the case, Mr. Webb would have indicated on line 26 whether he wanted this amount credited to him, or returned to him. What does "credited to him" mean?

EXERCISES　　　　　　　　A

The Tax Tables on page 190 and the Tax Surcharge Tables on this page are to be used for the following problems.

1. Determine the base income tax that each of the following taxpayers will have to pay. This is the tax before the surcharge is added.

	Total Income	Type Of Return	Number Of Exemptions	Base Tax
a.	$2,546	Single	2	$ 136
b.	3,027	Single	4	4
c.	4,376	Single	7	0
d.	3,948	Joint	3	234
e.	4,269	Joint	4	181
f.	4,756	Joint	2	467
g.	4,597	Joint	6	25
h.	2,975	Single	1	327
i.	4,000	Single	3	263
j.	4,650	Joint	4	241

2. Determine the surcharge tax on each of the following base taxes.

	Base Tax	Type Of Return	Surcharge Tax
a.	$162	Single	$ 3
b.	217	Single	14
c.	123	Single	0
d.	261	Single	23
e.	184	Single	8
f.	245	Single	20
g.	280	Single	27
h.	760	Single	76
i.	850	Single	85
j.	327	Joint	7
k.	412	Joint	24
l.	491	Joint	40
m.	264	Joint	0
n.	528	Joint	48
o.	446	Joint	31
p.	390	Joint	20
q.	820	Joint	82
r.	980	Joint	98

3. Determine the total income tax (base tax plus surcharge tax) that each of the following taxpayers will have to pay.

	Total Income	Type Of Return	Number Of Exemptions	Base Tax	Surcharge Tax	Total Tax
a.	$2,658	Single	3	$ 51	$ 0	$ 51
b.	2,514	Single	2	132	0	132
c.	3,346	Joint	2	249	0	249
d.	4,827	Joint	4	264	0	264
e.	3,741	Single	3	213	14	227
f.	2,945	Single	2	199	11	210
g.	4,468	Joint	3	318	6	324
h.	4,893	Joint	2	482	38	520
i.	4,679	Single	1	615	62	677
j.	4,328	Single	2	442	44	486
k.	3,927	Single	1	487	49	536

The design of these exercises was to break Form 1040 down to bite-size chunks that could be digested easily by the students. It is hoped that by the time they reach Exercise 5, they will understand the complete picture.

4. Determine the balance due, or overpayment, for each of the following taxpayers. Indicate whether your answer is a refund or an additional payment.

	Total Income	Type Of Return	Number Of Exemptions	Base Tax	Surcharge Tax	Total Tax	Withholding Tax	Balance Due Or Overpayment
a.	$3,458	Single	1	$410	$41	$451	$422	$29 Bal. due
b.	3,754	Single	3	221	15	236	237	1 Refund
c.	4,093	Single	2	399	40	439	371	68 Refund
d.	4,468	Joint	2	422	26	448	438	10 Bal. due
e.	4,957	Joint	4	286	0	286	304	18 Refund
f.	2,675	Single	3	54	0	54	59	5 Refund

5. Complete lines 11 through 25 of Form 1040 as shown in the illustration on page 191. The information for each of the taxpayers follows.

	Base Tax	Surtax		Income Man	Woman	Types Of Return	Number Of Exemptions	Tax Withheld		Total Tax	Balance D or Overpaym
a.	$556	$56	a.	$4,324		Single	1	$532	a.	$612	$80 Bal.
b.	381	38	b.		$3,968	Single	2	387	b.	419	32 Bal.
c.	390	20	c.	4,916	0	Joint	3	401	c.	410	9 Bal.
d.	430	28	d.	0	4,531	Joint	2	412	d.	458	46 Bal.
e.	350	12	e.	3,962	700	Joint	3	365	e.	362	3 Over
f.	271	0	f.	4,231	625	Joint	4	293	f.	271	22 Over

B

1. Mr. Bedford earned $4,256.84 during the past year. Mrs. Bedford, who had a part-time job, earned $473.95. In addition, they had a savings account that paid them $84.21 in interest. They have one child, Doris, who is in the third grade. If the Bedfords file a joint return, how much income tax will they have to pay for the year?

$374 + $17 = $391

2. Form W-2 of William Johnstone showed the following:

Federal income tax withheld	Wages paid subject to withholding	Other compensation	FICA employee tax withheld	Total FICA wages
$267.32	$4,698.24	—	$225.51	$4,698.24

Mr. Johnstone is 67 years of age, while his wife is 68. Use this information to complete lines 11 through 25 of Form 1040 for Mr. Johnstone. (See page 191.)   Total Tax = $241; Balance due = $26

In doing Exercise 5 in Group A and the problems in Group B, use an approach similar to that described at the bottom of page 188.

3. Ronald McCoy is single and blind. He supports only himself. On January 7, he received the following Form W-2 information from his employer.   <u>Total Tax = $433 + $43 = $476; Balance due = $64</u>

Federal income tax withheld	Wages paid subject to withholding	Other compen- sation	FICA employee tax withheld	Total FICA wages
$412.17	$4,258.63	—	$204.41	$4,258.63

Use this information to complete lines 11 through 25 for Ronald.

4. Fred Willard has a wife and 3 children. His weekly salary is $94.42.
   a. Use the table on page 162 to determine the withholding tax that will be taken from his salary each week.   <u>$3.40</u>
   b. How much will be withheld from Mr. Willard's salary during the period of one year?   <u>$176.80</u>
   c. How much is Mr. Willard's annual salary?   <u>$4,909.84</u>
   d. Use the table on page 190 to determine what Mr. Willard's income tax will be on this annual income.   <u>$174.00</u>
   e. Will Mr. Willard receive a refund from the Internal Revenue Service, or does he have a balance still to pay? What is this amount?   <u>Refund: $2.80 or $3.00</u>

Section 3: Computation of Tax by Taxpayers Using the Standard Deduction

In Section 2, you learned that a person could use the Tax Table when filing his income tax return only if his income were less than $5,000. In this section, you will learn one way of completing Form 1040 if your income happens to be greater than $5,000.

For the person having an income greater than $5,000, the Internal Revenue Service supplies him with two schedules. One is a Tax Computation Schedule that explains exactly what computation is necessary to determine the fill-in for line 18 of Form 1040—the tax line. (See the form on page 196.) Of the 18 lines on the Tax Computation Schedule, only the first 10 are used by most taxpayers. Lines 11 through 17 are usually left blank. When this happens, line 18 is simply a repetition of line 10. Since this is so, the material in this book pertaining to the Tax Computation Schedule will be concerned with only the first 10 lines. The second schedule needed for completing Form 1040 is the Tax Rate Schedule, which shows the tax rate for any income. This schedule appears on page 197.

If your students are somewhat below average in their mathematical ability, it may be best to omit Sections 3 and 4 and go directly to Unit 2 on page 209.

SCHEDULE T
(Form 1040)
Department of the Treasury
Internal Revenue Service

Tax Computation

▶ If no entry is made on line 14, line 16, or line 17, keep this for your records
▶ If entry is made on line 14, line 16, or line 17, attach to form 1040

Name as shown on Form 1040 | Social Security Number

1 Your adjusted gross income (from line 15c, Form 1040) . . . .
Note.—If your adjusted gross income is less than $5,000 and you choose to take the standard deduction instead of itemizing your deductions, omit lines 2, 3, 4, and 5. Find your tax in the appropriate table (A or B on T–2 or C on T–3). **Enter tax on line 6 below.**

2 Enter on the line at the right the amount of your deduction figured under one of the following methods:

    a If you itemize deductions, enter the total from Schedule A, line 17
        OR
    b Figure your standard deduction as follows:
        (1) Enter 10 percent of line 1 but do not enter more than $1,000 ($500 if married and filing separately) . . $
        (2) Enter the sum of: $200 ($100 if married and filing separately) plus $100 for each exemption claimed in line 10 of Form 1040, but do not enter more than $1,000 ($500 if married and filing separately) . . $

Enter the larger of b(1) or b(2) on the line at the right. If your spouse files a separate return, determine your deduction in the same manner that she (he) has.

3 Subtract the amount on line 2 from the amount on line 1 and enter the balance here . . . .
4 Enter number of exemptions claimed on line 10, Form 1040, ... Multiply this number by $600, and enter the amount here . . . .
5 Subtract the amount on line 4 from the amount on line 3 and enter the balance here. This is your taxable income. Figure tax on this amount by using the appropriate Tax Rate Schedule (I, II, or III) on T–1. **Enter tax on line 6 below** . . . .
6 Tax . . . .
7 If you claim the retirement income credit, enter amount from Schedule R, line 12, here . . . . . .
8 Subtract line 7 from line 6 . . . .
9 Tax surcharge. If line 8 is less than $735, find surcharge from tax surcharge tables on T–1. If line 8 is $735 or more, multiply amount on line 8 by .10 and enter result here . . . .

10 Total (Add lines 6 and 9) . . . .

11 Retirement income credit from Schedule R, line 17 (attach Schedule R) . . . . . .
12 Investment credit (attach Form 3468) . . . .
13 Foreign tax credit (attach Form 1116) . . . .

14 Total credits (add lines 11, 12, and 13) . . . .

15 Income tax (subtract line 14 from line 10) . . . .

16 Self-employment tax (attach Schedule SE) . . . .

17 Tax from recomputing prior-year investment credit (attach Form 4255) . . . .

18 Total tax (add lines 15, 16, and 17). Enter here and on line 18, Form 1040 (make no entry on line 16 or 17, Form 1040). Attach Sch. T to Form 1040 only if you made an entry on line 14, 16, or 17 above . .

The 10% standard deductions usually cause the students no trouble at all. They do, however, have a little more trouble grasping the method of computing the minimum standard deductions. Use a number of different-sized families to test the students orally on this type of deduction.

Tax Rate Schedules

Schedule I—Single Taxpayers and Married Persons Filing Separate Returns				Schedule II—Married Taxpayers Filing Joint Returns and Certain Widows and Widowers (See B–2)			
If the amount on line 5, Schedule T is:		Enter on line 6, Schedule T:		If the amount on line 5, Schedule T is:		Enter on line 6, Schedule T:	
Not over $500....14% of the amount on line 5.				Not over $1,000....14% of the amount on line 5.			
Over—	But not over—		of excess over—	Over—	But not over—		of excess over—
$500	$1,000	$70+15%	$500	$1,000	$2,000	$140+15%	$1,000
$1,000	$1,500	$145+16%	$1,000	$2,000	$3,000	$290+16%	$2,000
$1,500	$2,000	$225+17%	$1,500	$3,000	$4,000	$450+17%	$3,000
$2,000	$4,000	$310+19%	$2,000	$4,000	$8,000	$620+19%	$4,000
$4,000	$6,000	$690+22%	$4,000	$8,000	$12,000	$1,380+22%	$8,000
$6,000	$8,000	$1,130+25%	$6,000	$12,000	$16,000	$2,260+25%	$12,000
$8,000	$10,000	$1,630+28%	$8,000	$16,000	$20,000	$3,260+28%	$16,000
$10,000	$12,000	$2,190+32%	$10,000	$20,000	$24,000	$4,380+32%	$20,000
$12,000	$14,000	$2,830+36%	$12,000	$24,000	$28,000	$5,660+36%	$24,000
$14,000	$16,000	$3,550+39%	$14,000	$28,000	$32,000	$7,100+39%	$28,000
$16,000	$18,000	$4,330+42%	$16,000	$32,000	$36,000	$8,660+42%	$32,000
$18,000	$20,000	$5,170+45%	$18,000	$36,000	$40,000	$10,340+45%	$36,000
$20,000	$22,000	$6,070+48%	$20,000	$40,000	$44,000	$12,140+48%	$40,000
$22,000	$26,000	$7,030+50%	$22,000	$44,000	$52,000	$14,060+50%	$44,000
$26,000	$32,000	$9,030+53%	$26,000	$52,000	$64,000	$18,060+53%	$52,000
$32,000	$38,000	$12,210+55%	$32,000	$64,000	$76,000	$24,420+55%	$64,000
$38,000	$44,000	$15,510+58%	$38,000	$76,000	$88,000	$31,020+58%	$76,000
$44,000	$50,000	$18,990+60%	$44,000	$88,000	$100,000	$37,980+60%	$88,000
$50,000	$60,000	$22,590+62%	$50,000	$100,000	$120,000	$45,180+62%	$100,000
$60,000	$70,000	$28,790+64%	$60,000	$120,000	$140,000	$57,580+64%	$120,000
$70,000	$80,000	$35,190+66%	$70,000	$140,000	$160,000	$70,380+66%	$140,000
$80,000	$90,000	$41,790+68%	$80,000	$160,000	$180,000	$83,580+68%	$160,000
$90,000	$100,000	$48,590+69%	$90,000	$180,000	$200,000	$97,180+69%	$180,000
$100,000	....	$55,490+70%	$100,000	$200,000	....	$110,980+70%	$200,000

■ILLUSTRATION 1: Mr. and Mrs. Fletcher filed a joint return showing a total income of $8,463, with 5 exemptions. Complete the first ten lines of the Tax Computation Schedule with this information.

●SOLUTION:

1. Your adjusted gross income $8,463
2. Deductions
    a. Itemized
    b. Standard
      (1) 10% Standard $846
      (2) Minimum Standard $700   846
3. Subtract line 2 from line 1   7,617
4. Number of exemptions   5
    Multiply this number by 600   3,000
5. Subtract line 4 from line 3   4,617
6. Tax   737
7. Retirement income credit   _____
8. Subtract line 7 from line 6   _____
9. Tax surcharge   74
10. Total   811

▼EXPLANATION:

1. The fill-in for this line is simply the Fletcher's total income.

2. A person is permitted to make certain deductions from his total income so as to lessen the amount of money on which he has to pay a

tax. These deductions include donations to charitable institutions, real estate taxes, and others that will be explained more fully in the next section. The government, however, feels that the total of these deductions will amount to about 10% of a person's income. Hence, rather than have you go through the trouble of listing each of your deductions and how much each amounts to, you are permitted automatically to deduct 10% of your income as the 10% standard deduction. In the problem here, 10% of $8,463 comes to $846.30. Since 30¢ is less than 50¢, you drop it and write $846 as the fill-in for line 2.

There is another standard deduction that you are permitted to use that is called the minimum standard deduction. It is found by first multiplying the number of exemptions by $100 and then adding $200 to this product. In the case of the Fletchers of this illustration, there were 5 exemptions. When this number is multiplied by $100, the product is $500. When $200 is added to this, it will give a total deduction of $700. Since the taxpayer is permitted to take either of these two standard deductions, the Fletchers would have been foolish to have selected the $700 deduction, for it is much the smaller. However, had there been 7 exemptions in the Fletcher family, then the minimum standard deduction would have been $700 plus $200, or a total of $900. In view of the fact that this is larger than $846, the $900 deduction would have been used. At no time, though, are you permitted a standard deduction that is greater than $1,000. Thus, were there 12 exemptions in the family, only $1,000 would be permitted as a standard deduction, and not $1,200 plus $200, or $1,400.

3. By subtracting $846 from $8,463, you find the fill-in for line 3.

4. The $3,000 on this line comes from the product of $600 times 5, which is the number of exemptions the Fletchers claimed. In the preceding chapter, when examining the weekly income, you learned that a person did not have to pay income tax on his entire salary, but only on that part of his salary that remained after $13.50 was subtracted for each exemption. So, too, when computing the tax at this time, you find that the taxpayer is permitted to deduct $600 from his income for each of his exemptions. It is only on the difference that remains that the tax is determined. His exemptions, or, as they are also called, his dependents, would, of course, include not only his wife, but his children, too, if they are under 19. Should the child be over 19, he is still considered an exemption if he is a full-time student for at least 5 months a year.

5. The fill-in for this line comes from subtracting $3,000 from $7,617. It is on $4,617 that the tax is computed.

Emphasize the fact that neither of the standard deductions can exceed $1,000. Deductions greater than this amount are discussed in the next section.

6. To find the fill-in for line 6, examine the Tax Rate Schedules. Since the Fletchers are filing a joint return, refer to Schedule II where you discover that $4,617 falls between $4,000 and $8,000. Hence, you start by writing down $620, which is the tax that must be paid on the first $4,000. The tax on the remaining $617 is determined by finding 19% of the $617. This comes to $117.23. Since the 23¢ is less than 50¢, you drop it and add only the $117 to the $620, for a total of $737. This is the base tax the Fletchers must pay.

7. and 8. These lines are used only by people who are retired.

9. The surcharge for this line is found as before by examining the Tax Surcharge Table. Since $737 does not appear in the table, it is necessary to determine 10% of $737. This turns out to be $73.70, which is rounded off to $74.

10. The fill-in here is the total tax that Mr. Fletcher must pay. It is the sum of the base tax and the surcharge tax.

EXERCISES   A

1. Compute the minimum standard deduction in each of the following situations.
    a. Husband, wife, 3 children all under 19—joint return $ 700
    b. Husband, wife—joint return $ 400
    c. One man—single return $ 300
    d. One man supporting 2 younger brothers and sisters who are all under 19 years of age—single return $ 600
    e. Husband, wife, 8 children (all under 19)—joint return $1,000
2. Compute the 10% standard deduction for each of the following:

	Total Income	10% Standard Deduction
a.	$5,600	$ 560
b.	6,300	630
c.	7,950	795
d.	6,840	684
e.	8,463	846
f.	9,258	926

3. How much can be deducted for exemptions in each of the following tax returns?
    a. One man (age 56) filing a single return—no dependents $ 600
    b. Husband (age 42) and wife (age 41) $1,200

As in the exercises in the previous section, an effort is made to present the tax computation schedule in very small segments working ultimately toward Exercise 7, where the pupils see the entire picture.

c. Husband (age 35), wife (age 34), and 3 children of ages 5, 8, and 10 $3,000
d. Husband (age 43), wife (age 41); wife is blind   1,800
e. Husband (age 67), wife (age 62)   1,800
f. Husband blind (age 69), wife (age 70)   3,000
g. Husband (age 46), wife (age 45), children of 16, 18, and 22; the child of 22 is working.   2,400

4. Line 5 of the Tax Computation Schedule is given in each of the following problems. Compute the tax for line 6 by using the Tax Rate Schedules.

	Line 5	Type Of Return	Tax (Line 6)
a.	$ 800	Joint	$ 112
b.	1,700	Joint	245
c.	300	Single	42
d.	900	Single	130
e.	3,500	Joint	535
f.	3,500	Single	595
g.	5,620	Single	1,046
h.	7,340	Single	1,465
i.	6,930	Joint	1,177
j.	7,468	Single	1,497
k.	8,123	Single	1,664
l.	8,754	Joint	1,546

5. Line 5 of the Tax Computation Schedule is given in each of the following problems. Compute the tax for line 6 by using the Tax Rate Schedules.

	Line 5	Type Of Return	Tax (Line 6)
a.	$ 16,200	Single	$ 4,414
b.	27,300	Single	9,719
c.	36,750	Single	14,823
d.	89,340	Single	48,141
e.	126,400	Single	73,970
f.	16,200	Joint	3,316
g.	39,400	Joint	11,870
h.	47,620	Joint	15,870
i.	126,400	Joint	61,676
j.	275,000	Joint	163,480

6. The taxable income, which is the fill-in for line 5 of the Tax Computation Schedule, is shown as follows. Determine the tax on line 6, the tax surcharge on line 9, and the total on line 10. Use the tables on pages 197 and 192.

Exercise 5 was introduced to show the students how large a tax is paid by individuals with relatively substantial incomes. As a point of interest, compare Exercise e with Exercise i. Also of interest to the student is the point that the taxpayer in j pays a greater amount in tax than remains for himself.

Taxable Income	Type Of Return	Tax (Line 6)	Tax Surcharge (Line 9)	Total Tax (Line 10)
a. $ 7,500	Single	$ 1,505	$ 151	$ 1,656
b. 8,200	Single	1,686	169	1,855
c. 9,600	Single	2,078	208	2,286
d. 11,000	Single	2,510	251	2,761
e. 9,000	Joint	1,600	160	1,760
f. 12,400	Joint	2,360	236	2,596
g. 16,500	Joint	3,400	340	3,740
h. 22,300	Joint	5,116	512	5,628

7. Complete the first six lines of the Tax Computation Schedule with the following information. Use either the 10% standard deduction, or the minimum standard deduction—whichever is the greater.

	Total Income	Number Of Exemptions	Type Of Return	Tax (Line 6)
a.	$8,000	3	Joint	$ 886
b.	9,000	1	Single	1,505
c.	7,500	2	Joint	915
d.	8,640	6	Joint	653
e.	6,640	6	Joint	328
f.	9,375	4	Single	1,139
g.	8,156	3	Single	286
h.	5,942	7	Joint	118

B

1. Both Mr. and Mrs. Hutchins are working, and they find that it is to their advantage to file separate returns. What is the minimum standard deduction for Mr. Hutchins if he claims himself and their three children as exemptions? $ 600

2. Mr. Gebhard earned $6,270 last year, while his wife earned $3,140. These earnings were their only source of income. They have two children attending school.

   a. If they filed a joint return, how much would their tax be?
   $1,114

   b. If they filed separate returns where Mr. Gebhard claimed the two children as exemptions, what would their total tax be? (See Tax Rate Schedule I.)
   $1,114

   c. If they filed separate returns where Mrs. Gebhard claimed the two children as exemptions, what would their total tax be? (See Tax Rate Schedule I.)
   $1,161

   d. Under which method of filing would the tax be the least, and by how much?   Either under method (a) or method (b) by $47

3. Mr. Spencer's taxable income, that is, the amount on line 5 of the Tax Computation Schedule, is $150,000.
   a. How much tax would he have to pay on this amount if he were single? $90,490 + 9,049 = $99,539
   b. How much tax would he have to pay on this amount if he were married and filed a joint return? $76,980 + $7,698 = $84,678
   c. How much more would he have to pay under the single return than under the joint return? $14,861

4. A single taxpayer reported a taxable income of $250,000 (line 11d).
   a. How much income tax did he have to pay?$160,490 + $160,049 = $176,5
   b. How much of the $250,000 was he able to keep? $73,461

5. a. How much money in income tax will a single taxpayer have to pay on each taxable dollar that he earns more than $100,000 during the year?   70¢ + 7¢ = 77¢
   b. How much money will a single person be able to keep for himself of each taxable dollar that he earns more than $100,000 during the year?   23¢

Section 4:   Filing Form 1040 When Deductions Are Itemized

Earlier you learned that the government permits you to make certain deductions so that you do not have to pay a tax on your entire income. It was also stated that the deductions of the average taxpayer did not exceed either the 10% standard deduction, or the minimum standard deduction. Hence, the Internal Revenue Service permits the taxpayer automatically to take either of these deductions so as to save him the time and effort needed to fill out a much longer form. However, if the deductions do amount to more than either of the standard deductions, the taxpayer would be foolish not to list them, for he might save himself some money by doing so. Before going further, it would be best to take a look at just what deductions can be made.

Deductions for Contributions

You can deduct gifts to:

Churches, including assessments
Salvation Army, Red Cross, CARE
United Funds and Community Chests
Nonprofit schools and hospitals

You cannot deduct gifts to:

Relatives, friends, other individuals
Political organizations or candidates
Social clubs
Labor unions

As in several earlier exercises, Problems 3, 4, and 5 were designed to show the amount of tax paid by a person whose earnings fall in the high-income brackets.

You can deduct gifts to:

Veterans' organizations

Boy Scouts, Girl Scouts, and other similar organizations

Nonprofit organizations primarily engaged in conducting research or education for the alleviation and cure of diseases and disabilities such as cancer, cerebral palsy, cystic fibrosis, diseases of the heart, diabetes, hemophilia, mental illness and mental retardation, multiple sclerosis, muscular dystrophy, poliomyelitis, tuberculosis, etc.

You cannot deduct gifts to:

Chambers of commerce

Propaganda organizations

Deductions for Interest Payments

You can deduct interest on:

Your personal note to a bank or an individual

A mortgage on your home

A life insurance loan, if you pay the interest in cash

Delinquent taxes

You cannot deduct interest on:

Indebtedness of another person, when you are not legally liable for payment of the interest

A gambling debt or other nonenforceable obligation

A life insurance loan, if interest is added to the loan and you report on the cash basis

Deductions for Payment of Taxes

You can deduct these taxes:

Real estate taxes

State and local gasoline taxes

General sales tax

State and local income taxes

Personal property taxes

You cannot deduct these taxes:

Any federal excise taxes on your personal expenditures, such as taxes on theater admissions, furs, jewelry, cosmetics, transportation, telephone, gasoline, etc.

Federal social security taxes

Hunting licenses, dog licenses

Auto inspection fees, tags, drivers licenses

Water taxes

Taxes paid by you for another person

Alcoholic beverage, cigarette, and tobacco taxes

It is interesting to discuss the items above with the students and to ponder such questions as to why certain items are considered deductible, while others are not. By no means should the student be required to memorize this material.

Deductions for Accident or Theft Losses

You can deduct losses on:	You cannot deduct losses on:
Property such as your home, clothing, or automobile destroyed or damaged by fire	Personal injury to yourself or another person
Property, including cash, which is stolen from you	Accidental loss by you of cash or other personal property
Loss or damage of property by flood, lightning, storm, explosion, or freezing	Property lost in storage or in transit
	Damage by rust, gradual erosion or deterioration
	Animals or plants damaged or destroyed by disease

Of the deductions listed above, the only one that requires a little care in handling is the one on accident or theft losses. To begin with, you must realize that only those losses that are not covered by insurance are deductible. Thus, if, during an accident, your car was damaged to the extent of $275 and the insurance company paid the entire cost of the repairs, then you could deduct nothing for this loss when itemizing your deductions. However, if you had to pay the $275 yourself, then you still would not be permitted to deduct this entire amount from your income when filing your return. Only that part of the loss over $100 can be deducted. Hence, in this case, you can deduct $175 rather than $275. Had the loss been less than $100, then you could not make any deduction.

The decision as to whether or not to list deductions when filing a tax return is quite easy to make. You simply list all of your deductions. If the sum is greater than both of the standard deductions, then you should itemize your deductions. Thus, if the sum of the deductions is $742, while the 10% standard deduction is $953 and the minimum standard deduction is $600, then, by all means, the 10% standard deduction should be used.

■ ILLUSTRATION 1: Mr. Sprague has a wife and four children. His income for the year was $13,462. The total of his deductions was $1,150. Should he itemize his deductions, or take one of the standard deductions?

● SOLUTION:

Minimum standard deduction = $200 + 6 × $100 = $800
10% standard deduction = $1,000
Itemized deductions = $1,150

Hence, Mr. Sprague should itemize his deductions.

▼ EXPLANATION: The only thing odd about the solution above is the fact that the 10% standard deduction is $1,000. Although 10% of the in-

Compare the deductible policy here with the $100-deductible charge that they examined at the time that they studied automobile insurance. The government may be paying a large part of a loss not covered by insurance, depending on the income bracket in which the individual may be.

come of $13,462 equals $1,346.20, recall that you are permitted to deduct no more than $1,000 on either of the standard deductions. Hence, it would be to Mr. Sprague's advantage to itemize his deductions, for the $1,150 is greater than both standard deductions.

■ ILLUSTRATION 2: Mr. Martin's earnings during the past year were $9,647. He has a wife and three children. In itemizing his deductions he found that they included:

North Church	$217	Real estate tax	$654
United Fund	$ 86	State income tax	$136
Red Cross	$ 10	Interest on mortgage	$185

While the family was away from home one evening, thieves stole jewelry. The loss, which amounted to $394, was not covered by insurance. How much income tax did Mr. Martin have to pay for the year?

▼ EXPLANATION: The first question to be answered is whether or not to itemize the deductions. The minimum standard deduction is $200 + 5 × $100 = $700, while the 10% standard deduction is 10% of $9,647, or $964.70. In finding the sum of the itemized deductions, you begin by subtracting $100 from the theft of $394 for a difference of $294. When this is added to the other deductions, you have a total of $1,582. Since itemizing deductions gives you by far the greatest total deduction, then it is this method that Mr. Martin should use. To find the tax that the Martins will have to pay, you will have to complete lines 1 through 10 of the Tax Computation Schedule. The fill-ins for these lines appear in the solution below. For the information concerning each of these lines, refer to the Tax Computation Schedule on page 196. A joint return was filed.

● SOLUTION:

Line 1:	$9,647	Line 6:	822.35, or 822
Line 2:	1,582	Line 7:	_____
Line 3:	8,065	Line 8:	_____
Line 4:	3,000	Line 9:	82
Line 5:	5,065	Line 10:	904

There are just two more lines on Form 1040 that bear examination before leaving this topic. These are lines 12 and 13. For item 12a, the taxpayer has to list all the *dividends* he has received during the year. In a later chapter, you will learn that dividends are simply a share in the profit of a company of which the taxpayer is a part owner. Of the dividends he receives, all but $100 of that amount is taxable. In a case where the dividends come to $238, you would first subtract $100 from

Emphasize the point that a person whose itemized deductions exceed $1,000 should know immediately that this is the type of deduction he should take and not the standard deductions. Neither of the latter can be greater than $1,000.

this amount, and it would be only on the remaining $138 that tax would have to be paid. The $138 is the fill-in for item 12c of Form 1040, while $100 is the fill-in for item 12b. In a joint return, the husband is permitted to deduct $100 from *his* dividends, and the wife is permitted to deduct $100 from *her* dividends. If his dividends are $130 and hers $108, then each can deduct $100, leaving $30 for him and $8 for her, or a total of $38 on which to pay tax. However, if his dividends are $200 and hers only $38, then his deduction would still amount to $100, while hers would be only $38, for a total deduction of $138. Hence, they would have to pay tax on $100 of their combined dividends.

The fill-in for line 13 is quite simple. It is the total interest you have received on all your bank accounts and also any interest you may have received from people who have borrowed money from you. If this total is less than $100, you leave line 13 blank. If, however, it is more than $100, you must enter the *entire* amount on line 13.

EXERCISES   A

1. How much of the dividends in each of the following "single" returns is taxable?
   a. $467 ___$367___   b. $957 ___$857___   c. $85 ___$0___

2. How much of the dividends in each of the following "joint" returns is taxable?

	Husband's Dividends	Wife's Dividends	Husband's Taxable Dividends	Wife's Taxable Dividends	Total Taxable
a.	$342	$256	$ 242	$ 156	$ 398
b.	196	107	96	7	103
c.	412	0	312	0	312
d.	0	212	0	112	112
e.	124	58	24	0	24
f.	93	268	0	168	168
g.	59	43	0	0	0

3. Use the information below to complete lines 11 through 15 of Form 1040.

	Total Wages	Dividends His	Dividends Hers	Interest	Line 15c
a.	$ 7,300	$ 0	—	$140	$7,440
b.	6,900	—	$180	120	7,100
c.	8,500	150	120	—	8,570
d.	9,100	240	60	80	9,320
e.	12,600	70	730	260	13,490
f.	14,900	97	63	580	15,480

In doing Exercise 3, use an approach similar to that described at the bottom of page 188.

4. None of the following losses was covered by insurance. How much will the taxpayer be permitted to deduct from his income for each of these when filing his tax return?

a. $267 __$167__   c. $49 __$0__
b. $342 __$242__   d. $102 __$2__

5. Determine whether the taxpayer should itemize his deductions, take the 10% standard deduction, or take the minimum standard deduction. In making your decision, show the amount for each of the three. Use the information below.

	Total Income	Total Of Itemized Deductions	Exemptions	Minimum Standard	10% Standard	Answer
a.	$ 7,346	$ 523	7	$ 900	$ 735	Min.
b.	8,520	741	3	500	852	10%
c.	9,342	802	8	1,000	934	Min.
d.	8,634	965	4	600	863	Item.
e.	12,685	1,025	8	1,000	1,000	Item.
f.	16,394	926	5	700	1,000	10%

6. Write the fill-ins for lines 1 through 6 of the Tax Computation Schedule. Use the information below.

	Total Income	Total Of Itemized Deductions	Exemptions	Type Of Return	Tax (Line 6)
a.	$ 8,346	$ 967	4	Joint	$ 806
b.	7,465	893	2	Single	992
c.	12,374	1,158	4	Joint	1,560
d.	16,258	1,940	5	Joint	2,110
e.	24,395	3,658	1	Single	6,136

7. After computing the total tax (line 10 of the Tax Computation Schedule), determine the "Balance Due" or "Overpayment" for each of the following taxpayers.

	Total Income	Total Of Itemized Deductions	Exemptions	Type Of Return	Total Tax (Line 10)	Income Tax Withheld	Balance Due Or Overpayment
a.	$ 7,540	$ 850	3	Single	$ 975	$ 850	$125 Bal. due
b.	9,370	1,180	4	Joint	1,056	1,545	489 Overpayment
c.	14,500	1,840	1	Single	3,137	3,312	175 Overpayment
d.	19,680	3,420	6	Joint	2,668	3,014	346 Overpayment

In doing Exercises 6 and 7, use an approach similar to that described at the bottom of page 188. In both of these exercises, the itemized deductions listed are more advantageous to the taxpayer than either of the standard deductions.

B

1. When Mr. Stark itemized his deductions, he found that they were the following:

Real estate tax	$542	Salvation Army	$25
Church	$46	Community Chest	$40
Interest on a loan	$80	Interest on mortgage	$154
State gasoline tax	$47	State income tax	$121

Mr. Stark is married and has four children. If his income for the year was $8,647, should he itemize his deductions, or take one of the standard deductions? Justify your answer by comparing the deductions. 10% Standard = $865; minimum standard = $800; Itemized = $1,055; therefore, itemize.

2. Deductions for medicine are permitted in accordance with the following rule:

> The amount of the total drug bill that exceeds 1% of the income is deductible.

Thus, if the income is $9,200, then 1% of it is $92. Hence if the drug bill for the year is $104, $12 of this is deductible. How much of each of the following drug bills is deductible?

	Total Drug Bill	Total Income	1% Of Total Income	Amount Deductible
a.	$ 95	$7,460	$ 75	$ 20
b.	86	5,595	56	30
c.	157	9,310	93	64
d.	34	8,942	89	0

3. Deductions for medical and dental expenses are permitted in accordance with the following rule:

> The amount of the total medical and dental bill that exceeds 3% of the income is deductible.

How much of each of the following total medical and dental bills is deductible?

	Total Medical And Dental Bill	Total Income	3% Of Total Income	Amount Deductible
a.	$367	$ 8,750	$ 263	$ 104
b.	794	14,520	436	358
c.	256	10,300	309	0
d.	932	12,840	385	547

Because of the deductible clause on drug costs and medical and dental costs, there are relatively few people who can take advantage of this deduction.

4. Determine the total deduction for drugs and medical and dental bills for each of the following incomes:

	Total Drug Bill	Total Medical And Dental Bill	Total Income	Amount Deductible
a.	$126	$546	$9,340	$ 299
b.	164	367	8,596	187
c.	56	675	7,420	452
d.	89	140	6,390	25

Unit 2: State Income Tax

Computation of a state income tax is often very much the same as that of the federal income tax. A taxpayer is frequently allowed certain deductions like those granted by the federal government. The difference between his total income and these deductions is called his net income. Also, the net income is reduced still further by the personal exemptions that he is permitted for each of his dependents. Each of the 35 states that raises money through this means has established its own rate table for determining the tax. Three of these are as follows. In each case, the income shown is the net income.

ARKANSAS

Tax Rates		Exemptions
On 1st $3,000:	1%	Single: $17.50 reduction in tax
On 2nd $3,000:	2%	Married: $35 reduction in tax
On next $5,000:	3%	Head of household: $35 reduction in tax
On next $14,000:	4%	Each dependent: $6 reduction in tax
On balance:	5%	

HAWAII

Tax Rates		Exemptions
Not over $500:	2.25%	For each exemption allowed on federal income tax: $600
On next $500:	3.25%	Blindness: $5,000 in place of all other exemptions
On next $500:	4.5%	
On next $500:	5%	
On next $1,000:	6.5%	
On next $2,000:	7.5%	
On next $5,000:	8.5%	
On next $4,000:	9.5%	
On next $6,000:	10%	
On next $10,000:	10.5%	
Over $30,000:	11%	

NORTH CAROLINA

Tax Rates		Exemptions
On 1st $2,000:	3%	Single: $1,000
On next $2,000:	4%	Married: $2,000
On next $2,000:	5%	Head of household: $2,000
On next $4,000:	6%	Each dependent: $300
Over $10,000:	7%	Blindness: An additional $1,000

The three states of Arkansas, Hawaii, and North Carolina were selected because their approach to the collection of state income tax was typical of the methods employed by all states that have an income tax law.

■ILLUSTRATION 1: How much state income tax would Mr. Thomas have to pay on a net income for $8,250 if he lived in Arkansas? Mr. Thomas has a wife and four children.

●SOLUTION:

$$
\begin{array}{lll}
\text{Net income} & = & \$8,250 \\
\text{Tax on 1st \$3,000} = \$3,000 \times 1\% = \$30.00 & - & 3,000 \\
\hline
& & 5,250 \\
\text{Tax on 2nd \$3,000} = 3,000 \times 2\% = 60.00 & - & 3,000 \\
\hline
& & 2,250 \\
\text{Tax on next \$2,250} = 2,250 \times 3\% = 67.50 & - & 2,250 \\
\hline
\text{Tax on} \quad \$8,250 \qquad\qquad = \$157.50 & & 0
\end{array}
$$

Reduction for Mr. Thomas = $35
Reduction for 5 dependents = 30

Total reduction   = $65.00
    Tax due   = $92.50

▼EXPLANATION: There are a few states whose tax plan is similar to that of Arkansas. Rather than reduce the net salary by a certain amount for each exemption, the actual tax itself is reduced by a sum that is based on the number of these exemptions. Since Mr. Thomas is married, he is permitted a $35 reduction for himself in his tax. Then, for each of his dependents, of which there are five—his wife and four children—he can reduce his tax by another $6. Hence, for himself and his five dependents, he has a total reduction of $65. When this is subtracted from the tax of $157.50 on an income of $8,250, he is left with a balance of only $92.50 to pay. Notice that at the far right of the Solution a running tally was kept of the net income that still remained to be taxed. This is the same device used earlier in finding the cost of gas, electricity, or water.

■ILLUSTRATION 2: If Mr. Thomas of Illustration 1 moves to Hawaii, how much greater will his state tax be on the same income?

●SOLUTION:

Deduction for 6 exemptions = 6 × $600 = $3,600
Taxable income = $8,250 − $3,600   = $4,650

$$
\begin{array}{lll}
\text{Tax on 1st} \quad \$500 = \$500 \times 2.25\% = \$11.25 & - & 500 \\
\hline
& & 4,150 \\
\text{Tax on next} \quad \$500 = 500 \times 3.25\% = 16.25 & - & 500 \\
\hline
& & 3,650
\end{array}
$$

The format used above for outlining the solution to the problems may appear a bit cumbersome, but it does enable a student to keep track of the income on which he has already computed the tax and on the amount that still remains.

Tax on next $500 = 500 \times 4.5\% = $ 22.50 | $-$ 500

3,150

Tax on next $500 = 500 \times 5\% = $ 25.00 | $-$ 500

2,650

Tax on next $1,000 = 1,000 \times 6.5\% = $ 65.00 | $-$ 1,000

1,650

Tax on next $1,650 = 1,650 \times 7.5\% = $ 123.75 | $-$ 1,650

Tax on $4,650   = \$263.75 | 0

Amount to be paid in Hawaii = $263.75
Amount to be paid in Arkansas = $-$92.50
Additional Hawaii tax = $\overline{\$171.25}$

▼ EXPLANATION: In Arkansas, the deductions for exemptions are made on the tax itself. In Hawaii, the deductions for exemptions are made in exactly the same way as they were earlier when computing the federal income tax. The deductions in Hawaii are taken from the person's income before the tax is computed.

EXERCISES   A

1. How much state income tax do the following people have to pay if they live in Hawaii?

	Net Income	Number Of Exemptions	Tax
a.	$ 1,000	1	$ 9.00
b.	1,400	1	21.00
c.	2,300	1	60.00
d.	4,700	2	177.50
e.	5,340	4	136.10
f.	6,850	5	203.75
g.	9,370	4	457.45
h.	12,400	3	772.00

2. How much state income tax do the following people have to pay if they live in North Carolina?

	Net Income	Number of Exemptions	Tax
a.	$ 1,800	Single person	$ 24.00
b.	2,600	Single person	48.00
c.	3,900	Married person plus 1 dependent	48.00
d.	5,700	Married person plus 3 dependents	92.00
e.	6,500	Married blind person plus 2 dependents	96.00
f.	9,340	Head of household plus 4 dependents	248.40
g.	14,600	Married person plus 2 dependents	620.00

3. How much state income tax do the following people have to pay if they live in Arkansas?

	Net Income	Number of Exemptions	Tax
a.	$ 2,600	Single	$ 8.50
b.	4,700	Single	46.50
c.	3,940	Married plus 2 dependents	1.80
d.	6,850	Married plus 1 dependent	74.50
e.	7,320	Head of household plus 3 dependents	76.60
f.	12,000	Single	262.50
g.	13,500	Married plus 5 dependents	275.00

B

1. a. Two men have exactly the same net income and the same number of dependents, but one is married, while the other is classified as the "head of a household." Will one pay a smaller state income tax than the other if they live in Arkansas? Justify your answer.   No; both receive a deduction of $35.

   b. Would there be any difference in their taxes if they lived in North Carolina?   No

2. Mr. Fields is an unmarried blind man who has no dependents. His net income last year was $7,314.

   a. If he lived in Hawaii, how much state income tax did he have to pay? $ 95.41

   b. If he lived in North Carolina, how much would his state income tax have been? $205.70

   c. How much more—or less—would he have had to pay in North Carolina than in Hawaii? $110.29 more

3. In Arkansas, how much more state income tax would a married man with two dependents have to pay than one with four dependents if they both had exactly the same net income? Assume that the net income of each would require a tax of more than $100. $ 12 more

4. How much more—or less—would a single person with no dependents and a net income of $16,000 have to pay in state income tax if he lived in North Carolina rather than in Arkansas? $407.50 more

5. A married man who is blind and has three dependents has a net income of $4,340. Compare the tax he would have to pay in Hawaii with that which he would have to pay in North Carolina.
   Hawaii: $0; North Carolina: $13.20

Unit 3:   Chapter Review and Test

1. Determine the federal income tax to be paid by each of the following persons. Use the tax tables on page 190 and the Tax Surcharge Table on page 192.

	Annual Income	Type Of Return	Number Of Exemptions	Base Tax	Surcharge Tax	Total Tax
a.	$3,540	Single	3	$ 181	$ 7	$ 188
b.	4,690	Joint	4	241	0	241
c.	3,750	Single	1	462	46	508

2. Use the tax table for determining the "Balance Due" or "Overpayment" for the following taxpayer.

Income Husband	Wife	Type Of Return	Number Of Exemptions	Tax Withheld Husband	Wife
$4,360	$510	Joint	4	$301	$46

   Base tax: $271; surtax: $0; total tax: $271; overpayment: $76

3. a. What is the minimum standard deduction for a family consisting of a husband, a wife, and three children? $ 700
   b. What is the 10% standard deduction for a family with an income of $8,375? $ 838
   c. What is the largest minimum standard deduction that can be taken? $1,000
4. If line 5—the taxable income—of the Tax Computation Schedule is $6,300, find the tax for line 6 by using the tax rate schedules on page 197. This income was reported on a joint return. $1,057
5. How much can be deducted for exemptions when filing a federal income tax return by the following families?
   a. Husband blind (age 37), wife (age 35), children of ages 15, 12, and 9 $3,600
   b. Husband (age 69), wife (age 66), child age 20 who is in college $3,000
6. Use the following information to complete the first 6 lines of the Tax Computation Schedule. (See page 196.)

	Total Income	Number Of Exemptions	Type Of Return	Deductions	
a.	$7,000	1	Single	10% standard deduction	$1,064
b.	8,400	7	Joint	Minimum standard deduction	501

By using parts of these exercises for a review and the remainder for a test, this unit can easily be used for both purposes.

7. Mr. Mortenson owned stock on which he received dividends of $85 during the past year. His wife also received dividends of $342 on stock that she owned. In addition, they had two bank accounts that paid them $437 in interest during the year. How much of this income was taxable? $0 + $242 + $437 = $679

8. Mr. Schilling's car was damaged to the extent of $175 during an automobile accident. He carried no insurance to cover the damage to his car. How much of this loss could he use as a deduction when filing his federal income tax return? $75

9. Use the information below to determine whether the taxpayer should itemize his deductions, take the 10% standard deduction, or take the minimum standard deduction. Justify your answer.

	Total Income	Total Of Itemized Deductions	Exemptions	10% Standard	Minimum Standard	Answer
a.	$ 6,400	$ 496	2	$ 640	$400	10% standard
b.	9,500	1,410	5	950	700	Item.
c.	14,400	1,200	4	1,000	600	Item.

10. Mr. Robbins' itemized deductions on an income of $9,200 came to $1,250. When he filed his Form 1040 return, he reported a wife and three children as dependents. What fill-ins did Mr. Robbins have for lines 1 through 10 of the Tax Computation Schedule?
    Base tax: $801; surtax: $80; total tax: $881

11. The Keeler family lives in Arkansas. It consists of Mr. Keeler, his wife, and three teen-age children. If Mr. Keeler's net income last year was $8,750, how much state income tax did he have to pay? (See page 197 for the tax tables.) $113.50

CHAPTER 6

BANKING—
THE SAVINGS ACCOUNT

If you think back a few years, you may recall that one day a week your teacher would announce: "Today is banking day." With that, pupils would deposit with her anything from a penny to a dollar or two. The purpose behind the school banking program is twofold:

1. It is to make the students aware of the need for thrift and to develop the habit of saving regularly—a habit that may possibly carry over into adult life.
2. It is designed to show students how small deposits made regularly over a long period of time can add up to a sizable sum of money.

If your school happens to have a banking program, survey the students to determine how many of them participate in the program and how regular their deposits are. If the school does not, check to see if any of the students have ever banked money under such a program.

There seems to be some question about how habit-forming saving money can actually be. But, there is no question about the fact that the small deposits made weekly eventually add up to sizable amounts.

In recent years, banks have been trying to outdo each other to attract depositors. At first, they started by giving away ballpoint pens, or transistor radios, or ladies' umbrellas, or other inexpensive gifts to new depositors. People, though, soon tired of withdrawing money from one bank to deposit it in another simply for a pen. It wasn't long, therefore, before banks turned to raising rates offered on savings accounts to attract depositors. The banks, of course, want more and more depositors; for the more money that comes in, the more they can lend. It is only through lending money that they can exist and earn a profit. As expected, as each bank increased the rate it was offering depositors, its competitors either met this rate, or outdid it.

This practice could not continue indefinitely, for every state has laws that govern the amount of interest a bank can charge a borrower. Thus, if by law no more than $6 per year for each $100 can be charged for lending money, then a bank certainly cannot pay a depositor $7 per year for each $100 deposited. Obviously, if this were done, the bank would lose $1 per year on every $100. To stop this upward spiral, the government passed a law limiting most banks to a rate of interest of $5 per $100 per year.

What the rate of interest means and how changes in it affect your savings will be but two of the topics discussed in this chapter.

Unit 1: Completing a Deposit Slip

The deposit slips of most banks or savings and loan associations are pretty much the same as the one shown here. Some prefer to have the depositor's address appear immediately under his name rather than separated by the deposit as on this slip. All have one line for "Bills," another line for "Coin," and several lines where "Checks" can be listed separately. Since, normally, a deposit will not contain items other than these, nothing else appears other than the word "Total." At the top of the slip, the depositor records his account or book number. Most banks are now equipped with computers, and computers operate with numbers rather than names. Even were this not so, you would still be known as a number at the bank, for it is far easier to file information numerically than by name. In addition, some people have the same first, last, and even middle name, too! The purpose of recording your name on the slip serves as a cross-check after your account card has been found by number.

In a few states, the interest rate can be greater than the $5 per $100 per year noted above. Also, under certain special time savings accounts, the rates can be greater than the 5%.

The vertical line on the deposit slip that separates "Dollars" from "Cents" is purely a safety device. Banks learned long ago that people were rather careless in the way they placed the decimal points in a column of numerals. Hence, the total deposited was sometimes recorded incorrectly. To help people write the numerals in the proper position, the line was inserted to replace the decimal point. The numerals to the left of the line record the number of dollars, while those to the right indicate the number of cents. This is a common device that is used on many accounting forms.

■ILLUSTRATION: Mr. Demarest deposited 4 ten-dollar bills, 6 five-dollar bills, 8 one-dollar bills, 2 half-dollars, 3 quarters, 7 dimes, one check for $18.62, and another for $146.17. How was the deposit slip filled out?

●SOLUTION:

	Dollars	Cents
Bills	78	00
Coin	2	45
Checks	18	62
	146	17
Total	245	24

This may be the first time that the students have encountered the use of the vertical line as a means of separating the dollars from the cents. Point out that this device is used in most bookkeeping forms, bills, and the like.

▼EXPLANATION: Neither bills nor coins are listed separately. The total of the 4 ten-dollar bills, 6 five-dollar bills, and 8 one-dollar bills came to $78. This numeral was then recorded in the "Dollars" column in line with the word "Bills." Similarly, the total of the coins is $2.45. The $2 appears in the "Dollars" column, while the 45¢ is recorded in the "Cents" column. Checks are listed separately, for if reference has to be made to the deposit slip, it is easy to spot whether the amount of each check was recorded correctly. Finally, the total of the entire deposit—$245.24—appears at the bottom.

EXERCISES   A

Complete each of the following deposit slips.

1.

	Dollars	Cents
Bills	45	00
Coin		67
Checks	124	78
Total	170	45

2.

	Dollars	Cents
Bills	93	00
Coin		81
Checks	56	24
Total	150	05

3.

	Dollars	Cents
Bills	59	00
Coin		96
Checks	135	42
	258	17
Total	453	55

4.

	Dollars	Cents
Bills	186	00
Coin	1	85
Checks	39	51
	347	62
Total	574	98

5.

	Dollars	Cents
Bills	285	00
Coin	14	62
Checks	495	25
	106	19
	84	36
Total	985	42

6.

	Dollars	Cents
Bills	547	00
Coin	28	15
Checks	1,246	50
	912	47
	350	25
Total	3,084	37

B

Draw deposit slips similar to those in Part A, above, and complete them by using the following information.
1. Deposited: 6 ten-dollar bills, 8 five-dollar bills, 4 one-dollar bills, 1 half-dollar, 3 quarters, 4 dimes, 1 check for $46.50. $152.15

Rather than have the students draw deposit slips, it would be well if these could be dittoed, or if, perhaps, they could be obtained from a local bank.

2. Deposited: 3 ten-dollar bills, 12 five-dollar bills, 9 one-dollar bills, 2 half-dollars, 2 quarters, 7 dimes, 4 nickels, 1 check for $126.75, 1 check for $37.50. $265.65

3. Deposited: 2 twenty-dollar bills, 5 ten-dollar bills, 7 one-dollar bills, 15 quarters, 23 dimes, 8 nickels, 14 pennies, 1 check for $85.72, 1 check for $67.30, 1 check for $140. $396.61

4. Deposited: 4 twenty-dollar bills, 3 ten-dollar bills, 15 one-dollar bills, 12 half-dollars, 20 quarters, 25 dimes, 15 nickels, 40 pennies, 1 check for $217.20, 1 check for $86.30, 1 check for $109.25. $552.40

5. Deposited: 8 twenty-dollar bills, 14 ten-dollar bills, 25 five-dollar bills, 20 one-dollar bills, 20 half-dollars, 25 quarters, 50 dimes, 25 nickels, 200 pennies, 1 check for $150, 1 check for $53.40, 1 check for $117.60. $790.50

Unit 2:   The Interest Formula

Section 1:   Monthly Periods of Time

Although money was originally deposited in a bank for safekeeping, those days have long passed. The present-day depositor is much more interested in how much his money will earn for him in a particular bank than in whether that bank is a safe place for his money. In return for leaving his money in a bank, the depositor is paid for its use in terms of the size of his account. The amount he receives is quoted as a percent value, such as, perhaps, 4% or 5% per annum. This simply means that if money is kept on deposit for a period of an entire year, the bank will pay the depositor $4 for each $100, or, if the rate is 5%, then the payment will be $5 for each $100.

The $4 per $100 per year, that is, the 4% per annum, is called the annual rate of interest. Hence, if a person has $200 on deposit, he will receive $4 for each $100, or a total of $8. This $8, called interest, is added to his account automatically at the end of the year. Just as people earn money by working, so, too, does money earn money by working. The bank puts a depositor's money to work by lending it to individuals, or, possibly, by buying bonds. The earnings that the bank passes on to the depositor for the use of his money is, as stated above, interest.

Many banks pay their depositors interest every half year rather than annually. The rate of interest, however, is still advertised on an annual basis where the sign in a bank window says "4% per annum." Thus, if the deposit is $300 and if interest is given once a year, the payment will be $12 at the close of the year. Since interest is paid every half year—semiannually—the amount the depositor receives is $6 for the half year. It would seem, then, that finding the half-yearly payment is simply a matter of multiplying the annual interest by ½. Similarly, if a bank paid interest every quarter of a year—and the majority of banks are now doing this—then the quarterly payment would be found by multiplying the annual interest by ¼. In the situation just examined, where the annual interest is $12, the quarterly amount will be one fourth of this, or $3.

Since all interest payments are dependent on the annual interest payment, it would be best to examine how this can be found when the numbers are not quite so simple as those in the previous paragraph. In finding the answer to such questions as, "What is 4% of $128?" you may recall that it is merely necessary to replace the word "of" by the multiplication sign and then determine the product of 4% and $128. On some occasions, it is advisable to convert the 4% to its equivalent decimal numeral, .04, while on others, it will serve your purpose better to rewrite it as the fractional numeral, 4/100.

The question you now face appears different from the one above, "What is the annual interest on $128 that is deposited at 4% for a period of one year?" However, when reworded, it turns out to be exactly the same, "What is 4% of $128?" Hence, finding the annual interest reduces itself to computing the product of the amount of money on deposit, called the *principal*, with the annual rate of interest. This is frequently written as:

$$\text{Interest} = \text{Principal} \times \text{Interest Rate}$$

or, in the form of a formula as:

$$I = P \times R$$

■ ILLUSTRATION 1 : Find the interest on $836 for a period of one year if the annual interest rate is 5%.

● SOLUTION :

$$
\begin{aligned}
I &= P \times R \\
&= \$836 \times 5\% \\
&= \$836 \times 5/100 \\
&= \$4{,}180/100 \\
&= \$41.80
\end{aligned}
$$

▼ EXPLANATION : The interest rate of 5% can be written either as .05 or 5/100. The fraction is used here simply because it applies more closely to the material about to be developed. The quotient of 4,180 and 100 was found by moving the decimal point two places to the left in the numeral 4,180.

Notice that a special point is made of writing the percent numeral as a fraction numeral rather than a decimal numeral. This was deliberately done so that it would fall more readily into line with the evaluation of the formula: I = P x R x T.

In the illustration on page 220, it was specially noted that the interest rate of 5% was an annual rate. Since interest rates are always quoted for a period of one year—unless otherwise stated—there will be no need to point this out again.

Had the bank in this illustration paid interest every half year, then one half of the $41.80 would have been the semiannual payment. And if payments were made every quarter of a year, then one fourth of the $41.80 would have been the quarterly interest payment. Rather than first compute the annual interest and then one half or one quarter of that amount, both steps can be expressed as a single process by writing the interest formula as:

$$I = P \times R \times T$$

where the "T" is either the fraction ½ or ¼, depending on whether the interest is paid semiannually or quarterly. As before, the "P times R" represents the annual interest. Furthermore, the "T," or "Time," can be 1/12 if interest is given monthly. Then you would want to find one twelfth of the annual interest. Or the "T" can be 2/12 if the interest is given once every two months. Then you would want to find two twelfths of the annual interest. And, similarly, the fractions would be 3/12 for once each three months, and 4/12 for once each four months. As a matter of fact, the quarterly payments are actually made once each three months. Hence, the fraction for the quarterly payments should be 3/12. But this reduces to ¼ in any event, so it does not matter whether the interest payments are considered as having been made quarterly, or once every three months. The same is true of payments made either semiannually or every six months.

■ILLUSTRATION 2 : Find the semiannual interest payment on $1,248 if the interest rate is 4%.

●SOLUTION:

$$I = P \times R \times T$$
$$= \$1,248 \times 4\% \times \frac{\text{half-year}}{2}$$
$$= \$1,248 \times \frac{\cancel{4}}{100} \times \frac{1}{\cancel{2}}$$
$$= \$2,496/100$$
$$= \$24.96$$

▼EXPLANATION: By finding the interest for the half year immediately, it was possible to simplify the computation by reducing the fractions before multiplying.

The last sentence on page 220 refers to the possibility of finding the quotient of 4,180 and 100 by moving the decimal point two places. Verify with the students that this is not only true of this situation, but of any other that involves division by 100. Permit them to use this principle.

■ILLUSTRATION 3: Find the quarterly interest payment on $3,420 if the interest rate is 4¾%.

● SOLUTION:

$$I = P \times R \times T$$
$$= \$3{,}420 \times 4\tfrac{3}{4}\% \times \text{quarterly}$$

$$= \$\overset{855}{\cancel{3{,}420}} \times \frac{19}{400} \times \frac{1}{\underset{1}{\cancel{4}}}$$

$$= \$16{,}245/400$$
$$= \$40.6125, \text{ or } \$40.61$$

▼EXPLANATION: The only part of the solution that might have caused any concern is the changing of 4¾% to 19/400. At first it is necessary to rewrite 4¾% as 19/4%. Then, using the meaning of percent, the 19/4% is expressed as 19/4/100, which is then changed to 19/400.

EXERCISES   A

If you do not recall how to do the computation in the following exercises, you will probably want to refer to the pages indicated for additional help.

1. Change each of the following percent numerals to a fraction and reduce the fraction to lowest terms. (See page 583.)

a. 5%	1/20		i. 4½%	9/200	
b. 10%	1/10		j. 5½%	11/200	
c. 50%	1/2		k. 3½%	7/200	
d. 40%	2/5		l. 6½%	13/200	
e. 75%	3/4		m. 4¼%	17/400	
f. 4%	1/25		n. 5¼%	21/400	
g. 3%	3/100		o. 6¾%	27/400	
h. 6%	3/50		p. 2¾%	11/400	

2. Find the product in each of the following exercises. (See page 574.)

a. $20 \times \tfrac{3}{4} \times \tfrac{1}{5}$	=	3
b. $60 \times \tfrac{2}{3} \times \tfrac{3}{4}$	=	30
c. $10 \times \tfrac{3}{5} \times \tfrac{1}{2}$	=	3
d. $500 \times \tfrac{4}{100} \times \tfrac{1}{2}$	=	10
e. $800 \times \tfrac{5}{100} \times \tfrac{1}{4}$	=	10
f. $900 \times \tfrac{6}{100} \times \tfrac{1}{3}$	=	18
g. $800 \times \tfrac{17}{400} \times \tfrac{1}{2}$	=	17
h. $1{,}200 \times \tfrac{21}{400} \times \tfrac{1}{3}$	=	21
i. $3{,}000 \times \tfrac{11}{400} \times \tfrac{2}{3}$	=	55

Conversion of a percent numeral such as 4¾% to its equivalent fraction form of 19/400 is not a simple one for the students to understand. Develop this procedure very slowly. Do not continue with the work until Exercises i through p of A are thoroughly understood.

B

1. Find the interest in each of the following exercises. The interest is paid once each year.

	Principal	Interest Rate	Interest
a.	$ 600	5%	$ 30.00
b.	800	4%	32.00
c.	1,200	3%	36.00
d.	5,600	4%	224.00
e.	3,250	5%	162.50
f.	6,745	3%	202.35
g.	900	4½%	40.50
h.	1,600	5½%	88.00
i.	2,800	5¼%	147.00
j.	3,600	4¼%	153.00
k.	4,800	3¾%	180.00
l.	5,320	4¾%	252.70

2. Find the semiannual interest in each of the following exercises.

	Principal	Interest Rate	Interest		Principal	Interest Rate	Interest
a.	$ 400	4%	$ 8.00	e.	$6,000	4½%	$ 135.00
b.	1,500	5%	37.50	f.	8,200	5½%	225.50
c.	5,400	3%	81.00	g.	3,200	4¼%	68.00
d.	7,325	4%	146.50	h.	4,800	3¼%	78.00

3. Find the quarterly interest in each of the following exercises.

	Principal	Interest Rate	Interest		Principal	Interest Rate	Interest
a.	$5,345	4%	$ 53.45	e.	$3,200	5¼%	$ 42.00
b.	2,296	5%	28.70	f.	4,000	4¼%	42.50
c.	6,400	4½%	72.00	g.	2,112	3¾%	19.80
d.	7,200	5½%	99.00	h.	7,520	4¾%	89.30

4. If interest is paid for the period of time shown, determine the interest on each of the following deposits.

	Principal	Interest Rate	Period for Which Interest Is Computed	Interest
a.	$9,000	4%	1 month	$ 30.00
b.	8,400	5%	1 month	35.00
c.	6,300	4%	2 months	42.00
d.	3,700	6%	2 months	37.00
e.	2,500	4½%	2 months	18.75
f.	5,700	3½%	4 months	66.50
g.	3,300	4¼%	4 months	46.75
h.	6,720	4¾%	4 months	106.40

Most of these exercises (but not all) were so designed that, after reducing the fractions, it was possible to have only the number 100 remaining in the denominator. The computations can then be completed by moving a decimal point.

C

1. Mr. Rossner had a deposit of $3,675 in a bank that paid 4.87% interest annually.
   a. How much interest did Mr. Rossner receive at the end of the year? (Hint: Rewrite 4.87% as a decimal.) $\underline{\$\ 178.97}$
   b. If no deposits or withdrawals were made during the year, how much money did Mr. Rossner have in this account at the close of the year? $\underline{\$3,853.97}$

2. The Greensboro Savings Bank pays interest annually at the rate of 4⅞%. George Wells has $5,600 deposited in this bank.
   a. How much interest will Mr. Wells receive at the end of one year? $\underline{\$\ 273.00}$
   b. If interest is paid semiannually, how much interest will Mr. Wells receive at the end of one half year? $\underline{\$\ 136.50}$

3. Kenneth Stagg has $14,600 on deposit in a bank that pays interest semiannually.
   a. How much interest will he receive at the end of one half year if the interest rate is 5%? $\underline{\$\ 365.00}$
   b. How much interest will he receive at the end of one half year if the interest rate is 4½%? $\underline{\$\ 328.50}$
   c. How much more will he receive at the 5% rate than at the 4½% rate? $\underline{\$\ \ \ 36.50}$

4. How much more interest will a person receive during an interest period in which he has $20,000 on deposit at a bank that pays 5% interest rate rather than 4%? Both banks pay interest quarterly. $\underline{\$\ \ \ 50.00}$

Section 2:   Daily Periods of Time

Only rarely does a person have exactly the same amount of money on deposit in a bank during the entire interest period. More often he will deposit money during the period, or, possibly, withdraw money, or perhaps even do both. In past years, banks would give interest only on money that had been in the account for the entire interest period. That is, if a bank paid interest every six months—on June 1 and December 1 —then only the money that was in the account on June 1 would receive interest on December 1. And, similarly, only the money in the account on December 1 would receive interest the following June 1. Recently, however, a number of banks have begun to pay interest from the day of deposit until the end of the interest period. Thus, if interest is paid

With the introduction of the computer into banking operations, many banks offer their depositors interest from the day of deposit to the day of withdrawal. Prior to the day of the computer, the task involved in these computations would have made this offering impossible.

on June 1 and December 1, then a person depositing money on April 12 would receive interest on this deposit from that date until June 1. Or if the deposit is made on July 8, then the interest would be paid on the number of days from that date until December 1.

The interest formula that was developed in Part 1 for monthly periods can be used equally well for daily periods. In the earlier problems, it was necessary for you to determine what fractional part of a year 6 months happened to be, or 3 months, or 2 months, and so forth. This was done by dividing each of these numbers by 12, for there are 12 months in a year. Thus, 6 months is 6/12 or ½ of a year; 3 months is 3/12 or ¼ of a year. Once this was known, then the yearly interest was simply multiplied by 6/12 if interest was given every 6 months, or by 3/12 if interest was given every 3 months; or by 2/12 if given every 2 months. Now you are faced with the problem of having to determine what fractional part of a year a certain number of days happens to be. To do this, of course, it is necessary to know the number of days in a year.

When banks first began to give interest on deposits, all the computation was done by hand. This was a long and tedious process. To ease the task somewhat, the banks used 360 days in a year instead of the actual 365. It shortened the labor of computation, for 360 is an easier divisor than 365. Although banks now use tables, computers, or calculators to do the arithmetic for them, most still use the 360-day year. Unless otherwise stated, the same will be done in this book.

Consider now the case of a man who deposited money at a bank 60 days before the end of the interest period. As before, the interest will first be found for a period of one year. Then, since interest accumulated for only 60 days, he will be given but 60/360 of the year's interest. The "Time" in the interest formula

$$I = P \times R \times T$$

will now be the fractional part of the year represented by the number of days in question. When the formula was first applied, the "Time" was the fractional part of the year represented by the number of months in question. In both cases, therefore, the "T" in the formula is that fractional part of the year for which interest is being sought. The illustrations that follow should help to clear up any questions.

■ ILLUSTRATION 1: Find the interest on $800 if it is kept in a bank at 5% for a period of 60 days.

It is interesting to note that a goodly number of banks will use the 360-day year in lending money, while they will use the 365-day year in giving interest to the depositors. As an extra-credit assignment, see if any of your better students can show why a bank would do this.

● SOLUTION:

$$I = P \times R \times T$$

$$= \$800 \times 5\% \times \frac{60}{360}$$

$$= \$\overset{8}{800} \times \frac{5}{\underset{1}{100}} \times \frac{\overset{1}{60}}{\underset{6}{360}}$$

$$= \frac{\$40}{6}$$

$$= \$6.666 \text{ or } \$6.67$$

▼ EXPLANATION: The product of $800 with 5% is the interest for one full year. However, the money had been in the bank for only 60 days. Hence, the depositor is entitled to only 60/360 of the year's interest. Therefore, the annual interest represented by $800 × 5/100 must still be multiplied by 60/360.

■ ILLUSTRATION 2: Find the interest on $2,640 that was deposited at a bank 24 days before the end of the interest period. The bank pays an annual interest rate of 4½% to its depositors.

● SOLUTION:

$$I = P \times R \times T$$

$$= \$2,640 \times 4\tfrac{1}{2}\% \times 24/360$$

$$= \$2,640 \times \frac{\overset{3}{\cancel{9}}}{\underset{100}{\cancel{200}}} \times \frac{\overset{\overset{1}{\cancel{2}}}{\cancel{24}}}{\underset{\underset{10}{\cancel{30}}}{\cancel{360}}}$$

$$= \frac{\$7,920}{1,000}$$

$$= \$7.92$$

▼ EXPLANATION: As in Illustration 1, the fractional part of the year represented by 24 days is 24/360 of a year. The 4½% is changed to 9/200, and then the fractions are reduced as much as possible before multiplying. Notice that once the denominators of the fractions are either 10 or 100, they are not reduced any further. These numbers are not changed since, as you know, division by 10, 100, or 1,000 is done simply by moving the decimal point.

Use a number of numerical illustrations to verify the last sentence on this page.

EXERCISES   A

Find the interest for the period of time shown for each of the following deposits.

	Principal	Interest Rate	Number Of Days	Interest
1.	$1,200	4%	60	$ 8.00
2.	1,800	6%	120	36.00
3.	4,500	5%	40	25.00
4.	2,300	6%	90	34.50
5.	1,440	4½%	30	5.40
6.	5,600	4½%	36	25.20
7.	1,850	5½%	72	20.35
8.	3,600	4¼%	54	22.95
9.	1,880	5¼%	108	29.61
10.	2,880	4¼%	150	51.00
11.	3,670	4¾%	144	69.73
12.	4,672	5¾%	126	94.02

B

1. Mr. Green deposited $756 at a bank that paid interest at a rate of 4% from the day of deposit. If the deposit was made 50 days before interest was given, how much interest did the $756 earn for the period? $ 4.20

2. Howard Cramer had $4,000 on deposit at the Regional Savings Bank, which paid interest semiannually at 5%. Ninety days before the end of the interest period Howard deposited $600 to his account.
   a. How much interest did he receive on the $4,000 for the half year? $100.00

   b. How much interest did he receive on the $600 for the 90 days? $ 7.50

   c. What was the total interest for the period? $107.50

3. The Cranford National Bank has an interest rate of 4% and interest is paid quarterly. At the beginning of a quarterly period, Mr. Tomkins had $2,600 in his savings account. Sixty days before the end of the period, he deposited $900, and forty days before the end, he deposited $270.
   a. How much interest did he receive on the $2,600? $ 26.00
   b. How much interest did he receive on the $900? $ 6.00
   c. How much interest did he receive on the $270? $ 1.20
   d. What was the total interest that he received for the period? $ 33.20

Have the students express percent numbers such as 4½% immediately in the fraction numeral form of 9/200 without going through the intermediate steps of showing how the fractional form was obtained.

Unit 3:   Finding Interest With the Aid of Tables

Section 1:   The Timetable

You may have noticed in the preceding section that you were always told the exact number of days that the money had been in the bank. Normally, though, all that would be known is the date that the money had been deposited and the date when the interest was to be paid. Then, someone would have to determine the number of days from one date to the other. Thus, if the deposit was made on March 17 and interest was to be paid on June 1, before the interest could be computed, an employee of the bank would have to find the number of days from March 17 to June 1. One way of doing this, of course, is to count the days. This method not only takes far too much time, but it offers too many opportunities for making errors. To avoid both of these problems, the following table is usually resorted to.

Notice that each of the days of the year is numbered. As an illustration, February 6 is the 37th day of the year, while April 15 is the 105th

TIMETABLE

Day of Month	Jan.	Feb.	March	April	May	June	July	Aug.	Sept.	Oct.	Nov.	Dec.
1	1	32	60	91	121	152	182	213	244	274	305	335
2	2	33	61	92	122	153	183	214	245	275	306	336
3	3	34	62	93	123	154	184	215	246	276	307	337
4	4	35	63	94	124	155	185	216	247	277	308	338
5	5	36	64	95	125	156	186	217	248	278	309	339
6	6	37	65	96	126	157	187	218	249	279	310	340
7	7	38	66	97	127	158	188	219	250	280	311	341
8	8	39	67	98	128	159	189	220	251	281	312	342
9	9	40	68	99	129	160	190	221	252	282	313	343
10	10	41	69	100	130	161	191	222	253	283	314	344
11	11	42	70	101	131	162	192	223	254	284	315	345
12	12	43	71	102	132	163	193	224	255	285	316	346
13	13	44	72	103	133	164	194	225	256	286	317	347
14	14	45	73	104	134	165	195	226	257	287	318	348
15	15	46	74	105	135	166	196	227	258	288	319	349
16	16	47	75	106	136	167	197	228	259	289	320	350
17	17	48	76	107	137	168	198	229	260	290	321	351
18	18	49	77	108	138	169	199	230	261	291	322	352
19	19	50	78	109	139	170	200	231	262	292	323	353
20	20	51	79	110	140	171	201	232	263	293	324	354
21	21	52	80	111	141	172	202	233	264	294	325	355
22	22	53	81	112	142	173	203	234	265	295	326	356
23	23	54	82	113	143	174	204	235	266	296	327	357
24	24	55	83	114	144	175	205	236	267	297	328	358
25	25	56	84	115	145	176	206	237	268	298	329	359
26	26	57	85	116	146	177	207	238	269	299	330	360
27	27	58	86	117	147	178	208	239	270	300	331	361
28	28	59	87	118	148	179	209	240	271	301	332	362
29	29		88	119	149	180	210	241	272	302	333	363
30	30		89	120	150	181	211	242	273	303	334	364
31	31		90		151		212	243		304		365

Inquire of the students if they notice under what condition the table above could not be used. See if they can suggest what slight alteration would have to be made so that the table could be applied to leap year.

day of the year. To find that February 6 is the 37th day of the year, simply run your finger down the column headed by the words "Day of Month" until you reach the numeral 6. Place a piece of paper along this row and run your finger along the edge of the paper until it comes to the column headed by "Feb." The numeral your finger will be pointing to is 37. This implies that February 6 is the 37th day of the year. How would you show that April 15 is the 105th day of the year?

With this background, finding how many days there are from February 6 to April 15 is a relatively easy matter. You need simply to subtract 37 from 105. The difference of 68 is the number of days from the first date to the second.

■ILLUSTRATION 1: How many days are there from March 6 to June 1?

●SOLUTION:

>Day of year represented by March 6: 65
>Day of year represented by June 1: 152
>Number of days from March 6 to June 1 $= 152 - 65$
>$\qquad\qquad\qquad\qquad\qquad\qquad\qquad\qquad = 87$

■ILLUSTRATION 2: How much interest will a person receive on a deposit of $840 that was made on April 2? The interest rate paid by the bank is 5%, while the interest period ends on July 1.

●SOLUTION:

>Day of year represented by April 2: 92
>Day of year represented by July 1: 182
>Number of days from April 2 to June 1 $= 182 - 92$
>$\qquad\qquad\qquad\qquad\qquad\qquad\qquad\qquad = 90$

$$\text{Interest} = P \times R \times T$$
$$= \$840 \times 5\% \times 90/360$$
$$= \overset{210}{\cancel{\$840}} \times \frac{5}{100} \times \frac{\overset{1}{\cancel{90}}}{\underset{\underset{1}{\cancel{4}}}{\cancel{360}}}$$
$$= \frac{\$1050}{100}$$
$$= \$10.50$$

▼EXPLANATION: Through the use of the timetable, it was found that April 2 is the 92nd day of the year, while July 1 is the 182nd day of the year. After determining that there were 90 days from the first of these dates to the second, the interest was computed in exactly the same manner as before.

Take time to check to see if the students still have the card they were given to use as a guide when lining up numerals in a table. If it is lost, either provide them with another, or insist that they obtain another.

EXERCISES   A

1. Use the timetable on page 228 to find the number of days from the first date to the second in each of the following exercises. Both dates occurred during the same year, which was not a leap year.

	Period of Time		Number
	From:	To:	Of Days
a.	January 6	May 3	117
b.	January 17	April 4	77
c.	February 13	June 1	108
d.	March 15	May 31	77
e.	February 23	September 5	194
f.	August 12	August 29	17
g.	July 2	October 21	111
h.	April 17	November 2	199
i.	June 12	December 1	172
j.	March 19	June 1	74

2. The interest periods of the Guardian National Bank end on June 1 and December 1. Deposits were made on each of the following dates. For how many days during that period did these deposits collect interest?

	Date	Number Of Days		Date	Number Of Days
a.	February 14	107	e.	May 2	30
b.	April 7	55	f.	September 6	86
c.	July 8	146	g.	October 14	48
d.	August 23	100	h.	January 18	134

3. The State Savings Bank issues interest quarterly on February 1, May 1, August 1, and November 1. Deposits were made on each of the following dates. For how many days during the first period did these deposits collect interest?

	Date	Number Of Days		Date	Number Of Days
a.	January 4	28	f.	July 9	23
b.	February 17	73	g.	September 30	32
c.	June 25	37	h.	March 1	61
d.	April 11	20	i.	May 23	70
e.	August 28	65	j.	October 5	27

4. The Bank of Colorado gives interest twice each year on June 30 and December 31. If the annual rate of interest is 5%, how much interest did each of the following deposits receive for the period during which it was made?

You should find that your students enjoy doing the exercises above, for most students seem to. To avoid their constantly having to turn pages, you may want to make a master copy of the timetable and then distribute dittoed forms to the students.

	Deposit	Date	Number Of Days	Interest
a.	$1,800	May 1	60	$ 15.00
b.	900	April 1	90	11.25
c.	2,400	May 25	36	12.00
d.	3,600	January 31	150	75.00
e.	1,500	September 2	120	25.00
f.	800	October 20	72	8.00
g.	1,450	March 14	108	21.75
h.	2,690	November 25	36	13.45

5. The Clearwater Bank and Trust Company pays interest quarterly at 4% on January 31, April 30, July 31, and October 31. How much interest did each of the following deposits receive for the period during which it was made?

	Deposit	Date	Number Of Days	Interest
a.	$ 750	March 1	60	$ 5.00
b.	950	May 20	72	7.60
c.	900	September 13	48	4.80
d.	3,300	May 8	84	30.80
e.	765	January 19	12	1.02

B

1. Use the timetable on page 228 to find the number of days from the first date to the second date. The second date occurs in the year following the first.

	Period Of Time From:	To:	Number Of Days
a.	December 15	January 12	28
b.	December 3	January 17	45
c.	November 14	January 23	70
d.	November 5	January 31	87
e.	October 17	February 1	107
f.	September 25	February 14	142

2. The First National Savings Bank of Delaware gives interest at 5% on March 1 and September 1 of each year. How much interest did each of the following deposits earn for the period during which it was made?

	Deposit	Date	Number Of Days	Interest
a.	$ 720	December 1	90	$ 9.00
b.	672	November 1	120	11.20
c.	1,440	December 13	78	15.60
d.	2,680	October 26	126	46.90

Do not assign the exercises above before explaining to the students how the table can be used for finding the number of days from a date in one year to a date in the following year.

3. Bruce Taylor made two deposits at the Springfield Trust Company during a semiannual interest period. The first deposit of $480 was made on January 25, and the second of $320 was made March 20. The annual interest rate is 4½%, paid on May 31 and November 30.
   a. How much interest did Mr. Taylor receive on the $480 deposit for the period until May 31? $ 7.56
   b. How much interest did Mr. Taylor receive on the $320 deposit for the period until May 31? $ 2.88
   c. What was the total interest that Mr. Taylor received on both deposits? $10.44

Section 2: The Simple Interest Table

SIMPLE INTEREST ON $1
Rates

Days	4%	4¼%	4½%	4¾%	5%	5½%	6%
1	$.0001111	$.0001181	$.000125	$.0001319	$.0001389	$.0001528	$.0001667
2	.0002222	.0002361	.000250	.0002639	.0002778	.0003056	.0003333
3	.0003333	.0003542	.000375	.0003958	.0004167	.0004583	.0005000
4	.0004444	.0004722	.000500	.0005278	.0005556	.0006111	.0006667
5	.0005556	.0005903	.000625	.0006597	.0006944	.0007639	.0008333
6	.0006667	.0007083	.000750	.0007917	.0008333	.0009167	.0010000
7	.0007778	.0008264	.000875	.0009236	.0009722	.0010694	.0011667
8	.0008889	.0009444	.001000	.0010556	.0011111	.0012222	.0013333
9	.0010000	.0010625	.001125	.0011875	.0012500	.0013750	.0015000
10	.0011111	.0011806	.001250	.0013194	.0013889	.0015278	.0016667
11	.0012222	.0012986	.001375	.0014514	.0015278	.0016806	.0018333
12	.0013333	.0014167	.001500	.0015833	.0016667	.0018333	.0020000
13	.0014444	.0015347	.001625	.0017153	.0018056	.0019861	.0021667
14	.0015555	.0016528	.001750	.0018472	.0019444	.0021389	.0023333
15	.0016667	.0017708	.001875	.0019792	.0020833	.0022917	.0025000
16	.0017778	.0018889	.002000	.0021111	.0022222	.0024444	.0026667
17	.0018889	.0020069	.002125	.0022431	.0023611	.0025972	.0028333
18	.0020000	.0021250	.002250	.0023750	.0025000	.0027500	.0030000
19	.0021111	.0022431	.002375	.0025069	.0026389	.0029028	.0031667
20	.0022222	.0023611	.002500	.0026389	.0027778	.0030556	.0033333
21	.0023333	.0024792	.002625	.0027708	.0029167	.0032083	.0035000
22	.0024444	.0025972	.002750	.0029028	.0030556	.0033611	.0036667
23	.0025555	.0027553	.002875	.0030347	.0031944	.0035139	.0038333
24	.0026666	.0028333	.003000	.0031667	.0033333	.0036667	.0040000
25	.0027778	.0029154	.003125	.0032986	.0034722	.0038194	.0041667
26	.0028889	.0030694	.003250	.0034306	.0036111	.0039722	.0043333
27	.0030000	.0031875	.003375	.0035625	.0037500	.0041250	.0045000
28	.0031111	.0033056	.003500	.0036944	.0038889	.0042778	.0046667
29	.0032222	.0034236	.003625	.0038264	.0040278	.0044306	.0048333
30	.0033333	.0035417	.003750	.0039583	.0041667	.0045833	.0050000

The accuracy of these tables is far greater than you may want to use with your students. Very little will be lost should you prefer to have them round off each number to the nearest ten thousandth.

Deposits are rarely made in nice round numbers such as those that were used in the previous sections. More often the deposits will be in amounts such as $243.70 or $1,695.26. Because of this, the difficulty in computation increases many times over what you have been doing when finding interest. Since most banks have thousands upon thousands of accounts for which interest must be determined, they frequently use computers. Those that cannot afford either to purchase or rent a computer will make use of a table such as the one below. This table shows the interest that accumulates on $1 for periods ranging from 1 day to 60 days at various rates of interest. A bank that offers interest quarterly will need a table that covers a period of from 1 to 90 days, for there are 90 days in a quarter of a year. Similarly, a bank where interest is given semiannually will need a table covering 180 days.

SIMPLE INTEREST ON $1

Rates

Days	4%	4¼%	4½%	4¾%	5%	5½%	6%
31	$.0034444	$0036597	$.003875	$.0040903	$.0043056	$.0047361	$.0051667
32	.0035555	.0037778	.004000	.0042222	.0044444	.0048889	.0053333
33	.0036666	.0038958	.004125	.0043542	.0045833	.0050417	.0055000
34	.0037777	.0040139	.004250	.0044861	.0047222	.0051944	.0056667
35	.0038889	.0041319	.004375	.0046180	.0048611	.0053472	.0058333
36	.0040000	.0042500	.004500	.0047500	.0050000	.0055000	.0060000
37	.0041111	.0043681	.004625	.0048819	.0051389	.0056528	.0061667
38	.0042222	.0044861	.004750	.0050139	.0052778	.0058056	.0063333
39	.0043333	.0046042	.004875	.0051458	.0054167	.0059583	.0065000
40	.0044444	.0047222	.005000	.0052778	.0055556	.0061111	.0066667
41	.0045555	.0048403	.005125	.0054097	.0056944	.0062639	.0068333
42	.0046666	.0049583	.005250	.0055417	.0058333	.0064167	.0070000
43	.0047777	.0050764	.005375	.0056736	.0059722	.0065694	.0071667
44	.0048888	.0051944	.005500	.0058056	.0061111	.0067222	.0073333
45	.0050000	.0053125	.005625	.0059375	.0062500	.0068750	.0075000
46	.0051111	.0054306	.005750	.0060694	.0063889	.0070278	.0076667
47	.0052222	.0055486	.005875	.0062014	.0065278	.0071806	.0078333
48	.0053333	.0056667	.006000	.0063333	.0066667	.0073333	.0080000
49	.0054444	.0057847	.006125	.0064653	.0068056	.0074861	.0081667
50	.0055555	.0059028	.006250	.0065972	.0069444	.0076389	.0083333
51	.0056666	.0060208	.006375	.0067292	.0070833	.0077917	.0085000
52	.0057777	.0061389	.006500	.0068611	.0062222	.0079444	.0086667
53	.0058888	.0062569	.006625	.0069931	.0073611	.0080972	.0088333
54	.0060000	.0063750	.006750	.0071250	.0075000	.0082500	.0090000
55	.0061111	.0064931	.006875	.0072569	.0076389	.0084028	.0091667
56	.0062222	.0066111	.007000	.0073889	.0077778	.0085556	.0093333
57	.0063333	.0067292	.007125	.0075208	.0079167	.0087083	.0095000
58	.0064444	.0068472	.007250	.0076528	.0080556	.0088611	.0096667
59	.0065555	.0069653	.007375	.0077847	.0081944	.0090139	.0098333
60	.0066666	.0070833	.007500	.0079167	.0083333	.0091667	.0100000

As a point of interest, call to the student's attention that the interest on $1 at 6% for a period of 60 days turns out to be 1¢. Have them generalize from this as to what the interest on any amount would be at an interest rate of 6% for 60 days.

■ILLUSTRATION 1: A deposit of $483 was made 37 days before the close of an interest period. How much interest did the depositor receive on the $483 for that period if the annual rate of interest paid by the bank was 4¾%?

▼EXPLANATION: To find the interest on $1 for 37 days, run your finger down the column headed by the word "Days" until you reach the numeral 37. Place the edge of a piece of paper along the row containing this numeral. Then run your finger along the edge of the paper until it reaches the column headed by the numeral "4¾%." Your finger will be pointing to $.0048819—the amount of interest that will accumulate on $1 over a period of 37 days at an interest rate of 4¾%. To find the interest on $483 for this period, simply multiply $.0048819 by 483.

●SOLUTION:

Interest on $1 @ 4¾% for 37 days = $.0048819
Interest on $483 @ 4¾% for 37 days = 483 × $.0048819
= $2.3579577, or $2.36

■ILLUSTRATION 2: Raymond Parks deposited $562.50 on April 17 at the Broadway Trust Company, which pays an annual interest rate of 5%. If the interest period closed on May 31, how much interest did Mr. Parks receive on this deposit?

●SOLUTION:

Day of year represented by April 17: 107
Day of year represented by May 31: 151
Number of days from April 17 to May 31 = 151 − 107
= 44
Interest on $1 @ 5% for 44 days = $.0061111
Interest on $562.50 @ 5% for 44 days = 562.50 × $.0061111
= $3.437493750, or $3.44

▼EXPLANATION: The table on page 228 is used to find the number of days from April 17 to May 31. This turns out to be 44. With this information, you use the table on pages 232–233 and complete the problem in the same manner as in Illustration 1.

It is possible to use the interest table to find the interest on $1 at 6% for 90 days, although 90 days does not appear in the table. Can you explain how this can be done?

EXERCISES   **A**

1. Find the interest on $1 for each set of conditions shown below. Do not round off any answer to the nearest cent.

It is quite apparent from the number of digits encountered in the answers above that this work may prove to be somewhat tedious to some of your students. As suggested before, to ease their burden have them round off the numbers in the table to the nearest ten thousandth.

	Number Of Days	Rate Of Interest	Interest
a.	46	4%	$ .0051111
b.	18	4½%	.002250
c.	53	4¼%	.0062569
d.	27	5½%	.0041250
e.	8	5%	.0011111
f.	41	4¾%	.0054097
g.	36	4¼%	.0042500
h.	11	5½%	.0016806
i.	23	4½%	.002875
j.	58	5%	.0080556

2. Find the interest on each of the following deposits under the conditions shown. Round off each answer to the nearest cent.

	Deposit	Number Of Days	Rate Of Interest	Interest on $1	Interest
a.	$2,000	37	4¼%	$ .0043681	$ 8.74
b.	1,700	56	5%	.0077778	13.22
c.	3,420	25	4¾%	.0032986	11.28
d.	650	46	4%	.0051111	3.32
e.	925	16	5½%	.0024444	2.26
f.	764	33	4½%	.004125	3.15
g.	4,315	41	5%	.0056944	24.57
h.	1,007	29	4¾%	.0038264	3.85
i.	802	52	4¼%	.0061389	4.92
j.	685	11	5½%	.0016806	1.15

3. The interest period at the Dearborn Mutual Bank and Trust Company closes on August 30. The annual rate of interest paid by this bank is 4¾%. How much interest will each of the following deposits receive for the period if deposited on the date shown?

	Deposit	Date Of Deposit	Number Of Days	Interest on $1	Interest
a.	$ 275	July 14	47	$ .0062014	$ 1.71
b.	354	July 5	56	.0073889	2.62
c.	1,240	August 2	28	.0036944	4.58
d.	962	July 23	38	.0050139	4.82

4. Find the interest for each of the following deposits for the period in which the deposit was made.

	Deposit	Date Of Deposit	Interest Period Closes	Rate Of Interest	Number Of Days	Interest On $1	Interest
a.	$ 740	May 17	June 30	4½%	44	$ .005500	$ 4.07
b.	254	April 8	June 1	4%	54	.0060000	1.52
c.	480	August 23	September 30	5%	38	.0052778	2.53
d.	3,250	January 17	March 1	4¾%	43	.0056736	18.44
e.	2,130	October 14	November 30	4¼%	47	.0055486	11.82
f.	295	July 6	August 1	5½%	26	.0039722	1.17

5. Find the interest on each of the following deposits for the period in which the deposit was made.

	Deposit	Date Of Deposit	Interest Period Closes	Rate Of Interest	Number Of Days	Interest On $1	Interest
a.	$ 625	December 3	January 1	5%	29	$.0040278	$ 2.52
b.	1,050	December 12	January 30	4½%	49	.006125	6.43
c.	975	December 28	February 1	4¾%	35	.0046180	4.50
d.	2,345	December 15	January 31	5½%	47	.0071806	16.84

B

1. The table on pages 232–233 can be used to find interest on deposits for periods of time other than from 1 through 60 days. For instance, the interest on $1 at 4½% for 70 days is found by adding the interest for 60 days ($.007500) to the interest for 10 days ($.001250), for a total of $.008750 in interest for 70 days. Find the interest on $1 under the following conditions. Do not round off your answer to the nearest cent.

	Number Of Days	Rate Of Interest	Interest
a.	80	4%	$ .0088888
b.	90	5%	.0125000
c.	65	4½%	.0081250
d.	85	4¼%	.0099987
e.	73	5%	.0101389
f.	86	5½%	.0131389
g.	105	4%	.0116666
h.	112	4¼%	.0132222

2. Find the interest on each of the following deposits under the conditions shown. Round off each answer to the nearest cent.

	Deposit	Number Of Days	Rate Of Interest	Interest on $1	Interest
a.	$ 460	80	5%	$ .0111111	$ 5.11
b.	2,310	100	4½%	.012500	28.88
c.	1,540	115	4%	.0127777	19.68
d.	3,546	89	4¾%	.0117431	41.64

3. Peter Fleming deposited $342 at his bank on February 17. Interest was paid semiannually on June 1 and December 1 at the rate of 4¾%. How much interest did Mr. Fleming receive on the $342 for the interest period during which this money was deposited? $4.69

4. Mr. Daniels deposited $576 on July 17 and $428 on August 26 at the Central Savings and Loan Association, which has an interest rate of 5%. Interest is paid on April 1 and October 1 of each year.
   a. How much interest did Mr. Daniels receive for the interest period on the $576 deposit? $6.08

Although possible, it is not advisable, to have the students use the Simple Interest Table when the number of days is greater than 120. Before undertaking the exercises in Group B, ask the students what combination of days they would use to find the interest for such periods as 95 days, 110 days, etc.

b. How much interest did Mr. Daniels receive for the interest period on the $428 deposit? $2.14

c. What was the total interest that Mr. Daniels received on both
deposits for the interest period? $8.22

Unit 4: Finding the Interest on a Savings Account for an Interest Period

Thus far you have learned how to compute the interest on deposits made to a savings account when these deposits occur during the interest period. In addition, you have learned how to determine interest on savings where interest was paid either semiannually or quarterly. It appears, then, that the only thing left to investigate is what happens to the interest on money that is withdrawn during the interest period.

Different banks have different ways of treating the interest on withdrawals. The most common procedure is to assume that the amount withdrawn had never been on deposit at any time during the interest period. Consider the case of a person who has $600 on deposit in a bank which gives interest on March 1 and September 1 of each year. If he should withdraw $200 on August 15, he will lose the interest on the $200 for the entire 6-month interest period, that is, he will receive interest as though he had had only $400 on deposit during these 6 months. If he withdrew $500, on how much money would he receive interest for the 6-month period?

■ ILLUSTRATION: Harry Wilson had $695 on deposit at the Tri-State Bank and Trust Company at the beginning of the 6-month interest period. On August 17, he withdrew $220. This was the only withdrawal or deposit made to this account during the 6 months. If the bank paid interest at 4½% on June 1 and December 1, how much interest was added to Mr. Wilson's account on December 1?

● SOLUTION:

Amount of money on which interest was paid during the 6 months

$$= \$695 - \$220$$
$$= \$475$$
$$I = P \times R \times T$$
$$= \$475 \times 4\tfrac{1}{2}\% \times \text{semiannually}$$
$$= \$475 \times \frac{9}{200} \times \frac{1}{2}$$
$$= \frac{\$4275}{400}$$
$$= \$10.6875, \text{ or } \$10.69$$

It was noted earlier that many banks offer interest from day of deposit to day of withdrawal. However, the majority still add interest to their accounts in accordance with the method discussed here.

▼EXPLANATION : Since any withdrawal is viewed by the bank as if the money had not been in the account at any time during the period, it is necessary to subtract the $220 from the $695. The difference of $475 draws interest for the interest period of one half year. When applying the interest formula, the 4½% is changed to the fractional numeral of 9/200, while the numeral used for the time is ½.

The methods of computation you have just learned round out your background on interest payments to savings accounts. In summary it can be said:

1. Withdrawals from an account during an interest period are subtracted from the amount on deposit at the beginning of the period before interest is computed. Interest on the balance is computed either quarterly, or semiannually, depending on how often the bank makes interest payments.

2. Deposits to an account during an interest period draw interest from the day of deposit until the close of the period.

■ILLUSTRATION 2 : Fred Tobin had $2,650 on deposit at the Gerard Savings Bank on April 1, which is the beginning of a quarterly period. During this period the account had the following activity:

> May 17: Deposit of $475
> May 30: Deposit of $290
> June 6: Withdrawal of $725

If the annual interest rate is 5%, how much did Mr. Tobin have on deposit on June 30 at the close of the interest period?

● SOLUTION :

Amount on which interest was paid for the three months
$= \$2,650 - \$725$
$= \$1,925$
$I = P \times R \times T$
$\quad = \$1,925 \times 5\% \times \frac{1}{4}$
$\quad = \$24.06$
Number of days from May 17 to June 30 $= 181 - 137$
$\qquad\qquad\qquad\qquad\qquad = 44$
Interest on $475 @ 5% for 44 days $= 475 \times \$.0061111$
$\qquad\qquad\qquad\qquad\qquad = \$2.90$
Number of days from May 30 to June 30 $= 181 - 150$
$\qquad\qquad\qquad\qquad\qquad = 31$
Interest on $290 @ 5% for 31 days $= 290 \times \$.0043056$
$\qquad\qquad\qquad\qquad\qquad = \$1.25$
Total interest $= \$24.06 + \$2.90 + \$1.25$
$\qquad\qquad\quad = \$28.21$

If the students were told to round off the numbers in the Simple Interest Table to the nearest ten thousandth earlier, then they should do the same at this time.

Money on deposit on June 30
$$= (\$2,650 - \$725) + \$475 + \$290 + \$28.21$$
$$= \$2,718.21$$

▼EXPLANATION: The solution can be thought of as being separated into four parts. In the first of these, the interest formula is used to compute the interest for the quarterly period on $1,925. This is the balance that remained after the withdrawal of $725 was subtracted from the amount on deposit at the beginning of the period. The second part of the solution is concerned with finding the interest on the deposit of $475 made on May 17. The tables on pages 228 and 232–233 are both used in finding this interest. Similarly, for part three these tables are again used to determine the interest for the deposit made on May 30. Finally, in part four, the withdrawal ($725) is subtracted from the amount in the account on April 1 ($2,650), and to this difference is added the two deposits ($475 and $290), and the total interest ($28.21).

EXERCISES   A

1. Interest is paid semiannually on each of the following accounts. Withdrawals during this period are shown. How much interest was added to each account at the end of this semiannual period?

	Amount on Deposit At Beginning Of Period	Withdrawals	Interest Rate	Interest
a.	$3,400	$600	4%	$ 56.00
b.	2,900	$500	5%	60.00
c.	5,200	$1,200	4½%	90.00
d.	3,475	$835	4½%	59.40
e.	2,693	$425, $108	5½%	59.40
f.	4,987	$350, $597	5½%	111.10
g.	7,349	$549, $2,000	4¾%	114.00

2. Interest is paid quarterly on each of the following accounts. Withdrawals during this period are shown. How much interest was added to each account at the end of this quarterly period?

	Amount on Deposit At Beginning Of Period	Withdrawals	Interest Rate	Interest
a.	$2,500	$500	4%	$ 20.00
b.	4,150	$470	4½%	41.40
c.	3,754	$350, $524	4¼%	30.60
d.	5,308	$760, $860	4¾%	43.80

The students will probably find the exercises above somewhat difficult. Do only enough of the exercises to acquaint the students with the technique.

3. Interest is paid semiannually on each of the following accounts. Deposits during this period are shown. These deposits were made the number of days before the end of the period, as indicated. How much interest was added to each account at the end of this semiannual period?

	Amount on Deposit At Beginning Of Period	Deposit	Interest Rate	Number Of Days	Interest
a.	$1,800	$ 700	4%	50	$ 39.89
b.	4,500	600	4½%	42	104.40
c.	5,200	480	5½%	37	145.71
d.	3,600	1,200	4¼%	26	80.18

4. Interest is paid quarterly on each of the following accounts. Deposits during this period are shown. These were made the number of days before the end of the period, as indicated. How much interest was added to each account at the end of this quarterly period?

	Amount on Deposit At Beginning Of Period	Deposit	Interest Rate	Number Of Days	Interest
a.	$2,400	$900	5%	45	$ 35.63
b.	6,500	850	4%	53	70.01
c.	1,740	625	4½%	34	22.24
d.	3,580	735	5½%	29	52.49

5. Interest is paid semiannually on each of the following accounts. Withdrawals and deposits during this period are shown. The deposits were made the number of days before the end of the period, as indicated. How much interest was added to each account at the end of this semiannual period?

	Amount on Deposit At Beginning Of Period	Withdrawal	Deposit	Number Of Days	Interest Rate	Interest
a.	$3,900	$300	$600	40	4%	$ 74.67
b.	2,800	400	520	35	5%	62.53
c.	1,750	310	450	52	4%	31.40
d.	4,630	830	725	27	4½%	87.95
e.	7,200	500	930	18	5½%	186.81
f.	5,300	800	640	46	5½%	128.25

B

1. Raymond Trent had $6,200 on deposit at the Cornwall Trust Company on August 1, which is the beginning of a quarterly period.

The end of the period is October 31. During the quarter, Raymond's account showed a deposit of $240 on September 14.

   a. How much interest did he receive for this quarterly period if the bank has an annual interest rate of 4%? $ 63.25

   b. How much did Raymond have on deposit on November 1?

                                        $6,503.25

2. On May 1, George White had $4,500 on deposit in his account at the Wayside Trust Company, which has an annual interest rate of 5% paid semiannually on May 1 and November 1. During this six-month period, his account showed the following activity:

> June 27: Withdrawal of $1,600
> September 14: Deposit of $320

How much interest did Mr. White receive for this period?

                                        $ 74.63

3. The Mutual Savings Bank of Bayside has an annual interest rate of 4½%, which it pays its depositors quarterly. One of its accounts showed the following activity for the quarter beginning March 1 and ending May 31.

> March 1: Amount on deposit, $1,400
> March 17: Withdrawal of $250
> April 6: Deposit of $620
> May 3: Withdrawal of $350

   a. How much interest was added to this account for this quarterly period? $ 13.26

   b. How large was this account on June 1? $1,433.26

Unit 5: Compound Interest

Section 1: Computing Compound Interest by Formula

The savings accounts in almost all banks and savings and loan associations in the United States are covered by federal insurance. In the event that a bank, for some reason, is unable to return to its depositors the money that belongs to them, then the federal government sees to it that the depositors are repaid. However, this insurance covers only that part of any single account up to $20,000. Thus, in an account of $24,000, $20,000 of it would be insured, while the remaining $4,000 would not be. If the bank where this amount was deposited could not pay the depositor the $24,000, then $20,000 of this would eventually be returned to him through the Federal Deposit Insurance Corpora-

Actually, the government agency that insures the bank deposits is different from the one that covers savings and loan deposits. Basically, however, the protection under both agencies is quite the same.

tion. The amount over $20,000, which in this case is $4,000, would not be returned to the depositor, for it is not insured. If the depositor had had $27,000 in this bank, how much would have been returned to him?

If he had had but $4,000 in this bank, how much would he have received?

Because deposits are insured only to a maximum of $20,000, people will frequently bring their account up to about $18,000 and then make no further deposits to it. By doing this they feel that should disaster befall the bank, they will not lose their money. The $18,000, though, continues to collect interest over the years. Of importance to you now is the question of how large this account will grow in the future. This can best be shown through the following illustration.

■ILLUSTRATION 1: The Bank of Fairfield has an annual interest rate of 4%. Interest is credited to accounts only once each year. If neither withdrawals nor deposits are made to a $13,000 account at this bank over a 3-year period, how much will be on deposit in this account at the end of the 3 years?

●SOLUTION:

Interest for the first year:
$$I = P \times R \times T$$
$$= \$13,000 \times 4/100 \times 1$$
$$= \$520$$
Amount on deposit at the end of the first year:
$$A_1 = \$13,000 + \$520$$
$$= \$13,520$$
Interest for the second year:
$$I = P \times R \times T$$
$$= \$13,520 \times 4/100 \times 1$$
$$= \$540.80$$
Amount on deposit at the end of the second year:
$$A_2 = \$13,520 + \$540.80$$
$$= \$14,060.80$$
Interest for the third year:
$$I = P \times R \times T$$
$$= \$14,060.80 \times 4/100 \times 1$$
$$= \$562.43$$
Amount on deposit at the end of the third year:
$$A_3 = \$14,060.80 + \$562.43$$
$$= \$14,623.23$$

You may want to point out to the students that a husband and wife, by having separate accounts, a joint account, and two trust accounts—one in each name—can have five separate accounts insured for $20,000, or a total of $100,000 of insured money in a single bank.

▼EXPLANATION: Since interest was given only once each year, then the replacement for the "Time" in the interest formula was 1. During the first year, the $13,000 earned $520 in interest. Because the account was dormant, that is, no money was deposited in it, nor was any withdrawn, then, during the second year, the account showed both the original $13,000, plus the first year's interest of $520, or a total of $13,520. Hence, the second year's interest was computed on this $13,520, and it was $540.80. This was $20.80 more than was earned the first year. The additional interest came from the fact that not only the $13,000 earned interest during the second year, but the first year's interest of $520 also earned interest for the depositor. Thus, the total on deposit during the third year was $14,060.80. This was made up of the principal of $13,520 from the second year, plus the interest of $540.80 that it had earned. The third year's interest of $562.43 was even more than that of the second year. This was as it should be, for the second year's interest was now helping to earn money for the depositor during the third year. In this example, the account received $42.43 more in interest during the third year than it did during the first. The extra interest came from the interest that had been added to the account during the first two years.

When interest on an account is permitted to earn interest on itself, as in the illustration above, this process is called *compounding interest.* The banks that do this say they are issuing compound interest. Since banks pay interest either semiannually or quarterly, the process that was used in the example just completed would have to be changed slightly. Rather than the "Time" being 1, it would be ½ if interest were given semiannually, or ¼ if given quarterly.

■ILLUSTRATION 2: If the Bank of Fairfield in Illustration 1 compounds interest (pays interest) semiannually, how large will the account of $13,000 be at the end of the 3-year period?

●SOLUTION:

Amount on Deposit	Interest Earned
1st ½ year: $13,000	$13,000 × 4/100 × ½ = $260
2nd ½ year: $13,000 + $260 = $13,260	$13,260 × 4/100 × ½ = $265.20
3rd ½ year: $13,260 + $265.20 = $13,525.20	$13,525 × 4/100 × ½ = $270.50
4th ½ year: $13,525.20 + $270.50 = $13,795.70	$13,795 × 4/100 × ½ = $275.90
5th ½ year: $13,795.70 + $275.90 = $14,071.60	$14,071 × 4/100 × ½ = $281.42
6th ½ year: $14,071.60 + $281.42 = $14,353.02	$14,353 × 4/100 × ½ = $287.06

Amount on deposit at the end of 3 years = $14,353.02 + $287.06
= $14,640.08

Now that banks are operating with the aid of computers, many of them are offering interest compounded daily. Actually, this is an excellent advertising device only, for there is very, very little more that a depositor can gain by having interest compounded daily rather than quarterly.

▼EXPLANATION: There are 6 half-yearly periods in the 3 years. Interest is computed on each by using the interest formula in which the replacement for the "Time" is ½. Had the interest been paid quarterly, then the replacement for the "Time" in the formula would have been ¼. In finding the interest payment, only the whole number of dollars on deposit is used. The number of cents, no matter how large it may be, is dropped. Thus, for the 4th one half year the interest should have been computed on $13,795.70 rather than on the $13,795 that was used. It was computed on the dollars only to simplify computation. At most, the loss to the depositor by this method can be only 2¢ per period.

Before leaving this problem, it might be interesting to you to compare the amount of interest the account earned over the three-year period, when interest was compounded semiannually, with what it earned when interest was compounded annually. How large was the account at the end of three years when interest was given only once each year? (See Illustration 1, page 242.) How large was the account at the end of three years when interest was given twice each year? (See Illustration 2, page 243.) How much more will a person earn over a 3-year period by having an account of $13,000 in a bank at a 4% interest rate compounded semiannually rather than annually?

EXERCISES   A

1. Each of the following accounts is permitted to remain dormant over the period shown. How large will each account be at the end of the period if interest is compounded annually?

	Amount on Deposit At Beginning of Period	Interest Rate	Period Of Years	Amount on Deposit At End of Period
a.	$6,000	4%	2	$ 6,489.60
b.	5,000	3%	3	5,463.62
c.	9,000	5%	3	10,418.60
d.	8,000	4½%	2	8,736.20
e.	4,000	4¼%	2	4,347.23
f.	5,000	5½%	2	5,565.13

2. Each of the following accounts is permitted to remain dormant over the period shown. How large will each account be at the end of the period if interest is compounded semiannually?

	Amount on Deposit At Beginning of Period	Interest Rate	Period Of Years	Amount on Deposit At End of Period
a.	$4,000	4%	1	$ 4,161.60
b.	3,600	3%	1½	3,764.43
c.	4,800	4½%	1	5,018.43
d.	7,200	5½%	1	7,601.45

The exercises here are typical of the new time savings accounts that have recently been made available to depositors. In these accounts, the depositor is not permitted either to add or withdraw any money from his savings over a period of a year in some cases, or two years in other cases.

3. Each of the following accounts is permitted to remain dormant over the period shown. How large will each account be at the end of the period if interest is compounded quarterly?

	Amount on Deposit At Beginning of Period	Interest Rate	Period Of Years	Amount on Deposit At End of Period
a.	$8,000	4%	½	$ 8,160.80
b.	8,400	5%	½	8,611.31
c.	9,600	4½%	½	9,817.22
d.	6,400	4¾%	½	6,552.90

B

1. Mr. Sherman had $5,000 in an account at the Western Savings and Loan Association, where interest is compounded semiannually at 5%. If Mr. Sherman neither added to, nor withdrew any money from, this account for a period of 1 year, how much interest did his savings earn? $253.13
2. The Neighborhood Savings Institution pays an annual interest rate of 4%.
   a. How much will a dormant account of $7,000 earn in interest over a two-year period if interest is compounded annually? $571.20
   b. How much will this account earn over the two-year period if interest is compounded semiannually? $577.00
   c. How much more will be earned if interest is compounded semiannually rather than annually? $ 5.80
3. Tom Baker has a $3,200 savings account at the Lakewood Bank and Trust Company where interest is paid at an annual rate of 4%. During the period of one year, he makes no deposits or withdrawals from this account.
   a. How much interest will this account earn if interest is compounded semiannually? $129.28
   b. How much interest will this account earn if interest is compounded quarterly? $129.92
   c. How much would Mr. Baker gain over the year if interest were compounded quarterly rather than semiannually? $ .64

Section 2: Computing Compound Interest by Table

A few years ago, the pastor of a church was going over some very old records. Among them he found a letter that was written by an officer in the British army during the Revolution to the colonial pastor. It seems that while transporting weapons from one point to another, some British soldiers had damaged a fence that belonged to the church. In the letter, the officer had assured the pastor that the British government would pay $25 at the close of the war to cover this damage. Unfortunately, the debt was never paid.

Newspapers published this story widely. They raised the interesting point as to how much the $25 indebtedness might now have grown at an interest rate of 5%, compounded annually. When you consider how long it took you to do the problems in the first part of this section, where the period of time was but 3 or 4 years at most, you can imagine the difficulty involved in this computation where the interest has to be compounded over a 190-year period! As you have probably guessed by now, much of the tedious computation that you had to struggle through could be shortened by the use of tables, such as the one that appears on page 247. This table is designed to tell you how much $1 will amount to at various rates of interest, compounded annually after a period of time from 1 to 50 years.

■ILLUSTRATION 1: One dollar is deposited in a bank that pays a 4% interest rate, compounded annually. If this account remains dormant for 15 years, into how much money will the $1 grow to be?

▼EXPLANATION: Run your finger down the column headed by the word "Years" until it comes to rest at the numeral 15. Place the edge of a piece of paper along the row containing this numeral. Then run your finger across this row until it comes to the column headed by the numeral 4%. The numeral 1.8009 that your finger is pointing at represents the amount of money that $1 will grow to be after a period of 15 years at an interest rate of 5% compounded annually.

●SOLUTION:

Value of $1 @ 4% after 15 years = $1.8009, or $1.80

It is just one simple step from finding what $1 will amount to by using this table to finding what any number of dollars will amount to. After determining how much $1 will be worth after a period of time, it is merely necessary to multiply that number by whatever the amount may have been on deposit.

■ILLUSTRATION 2: Mr. Donald Prell opened an account with $5,300 at the Valley Savings Bank and allowed that account to remain dormant. If interest is compounded annually at 5½%, how large will this account be at the end of 18 years?

●SOLUTION:

Value of $1 @ 5½% after 18 years = $2.6215
Value of $5,300 @ 5½% after 18 years = 5,300 × $2.6215
= $13,893.95

Before turning to page 248 to see the end of the story concerning the debt incurred by the British government during the Revoluntionary War, you might want to ask the students what their guess would be as to the size of the debt at the present time.

COMPOUND INTEREST TABLE

Rate

Years	1%	1¼%	2%	2¼%	2½%	4%	5%	5½%	6%
1	1.0100	1.0125	1.0200	1.0225	1.0250	1.0400	1.0500	1.0550	1.0600
2	1.0201	1.0252	1.0404	1.0455	1.0506	1.0816	1.1025	1.1130	1.1236
3	1.0303	1.0380	1.0612	1.0690	1.0769	1.1249	1.1576	1.1742	1.1910
4	1.0406	1.0509	1.0824	1.0931	1.1038	1.1699	1.2155	1.2388	1.2625
5	1.0510	1.0641	1.1041	1.1177	1.1314	1.2167	1.2763	1.3070	1.3382
6	1.0615	1.0774	1.1262	1.1428	1.1597	1.2653	1.3401	1.3788	1.4185
7	1.0721	1.0909	1.1487	1.1685	1.1887	1.3159	1.4071	1.4547	1.5036
8	1.0829	1.1045	1.1717	1.1948	1.2184	1.3686	1.4775	1.5347	1.5938
9	1.0937	1.1183	1.1951	1.2217	1.2489	1.4233	1.5513	1.6191	1.6895
10	1.1046	1.1323	1.2190	1.2492	1.2801	1.4802	1.6289	1.7081	1.7908
11	1.1157	1.1464	1.2434	1.2773	1.3121	1.5395	1.7103	1.8021	1.8983
12	1.1268	1.1608	1.2682	1.3060	1.3449	1.6010	1.7959	1.9012	2.0122
13	1.1381	1.1753	1.2936	1.3354	1.3785	1.6651	1.8856	2.0058	2.1329
14	1.1495	1.1900	1.3195	1.3655	1.4130	1.7317	1.9799	2.1161	2.2609
15	1.1610	1.2048	1.3459	1.3962	1.4483	1.8009	2.0789	2.2325	2.3966
16	1.1726	1.2199	1.3728	1.4276	1.4845	1.8730	2.1829	2.3553	2.5404
17	1.1843	1.2351	1.4002	1.4597	1.5216	1.9479	2.2920	2.4848	2.6928
18	1.1961	1.2506	1.4282	1.4926	1.5597	2.0258	2.4066	2.6215	2.8543
19	1.2081	1.2662	1.4568	1.5262	1.5987	2.1068	2.5270	2.7656	3.0256
20	1.2202	1.2820	1.4859	1.5605	1.6386	2.1911	2.6533	2.9178	3.2071
21	1.2324	1.2981	1.5157	1.5956	1.6796	2.2788	2.7860	3.0782	3.3996
22	1.2447	1.3143	1.5460	1.6315	1.7216	2.3699	2.9253	3.2475	3.6035
23	1.2572	1.3307	1.5769	1.6682	1.7646	2.4647	3.0715	3.4262	3.8197
24	1.2697	1.3474	1.6084	1.7085	1.8087	2.5633	3.2251	3.6146	4.0489
25	1.2824	1.3642	1.6406	1.7441	1.8539	2.6658	3.3864	3.8134	4.2919
26	1.2953	1.3812	1.6734	1.7834	1.9003	2.7725	3.5557	4.0231	4.5494
27	1.3082	1.3985	1.7069	1.8235	1.9478	2.8834	3.7335	4.2444	4.8223
28	1.3213	1.4160	1.7410	1.8645	1.9965	2.9987	3.9201	4.4778	5.1117
29	1.3345	1.4337	1.7758	1.9065	2.0464	3.1187	4.1161	4.7241	5.4184
30	1.3478	1.4516	1.8114	1.9494	2.0976	3.2434	4.3219	4.9840	5.7435
31	1.3613	1.4698	1.8476	1.9935	2.1500	3.3731	4.5380	5.2581	6.0881
32	1.3749	1.4881	1.8845	2.0381	2.2038	3.5081	4.7649	5.5473	6.4534
33	1.3887	1.5067	1.9222	2.0840	2.2589	3.6484	5.0032	5.8524	6.8406
34	1.4026	1.5256	1.9607	2.1308	2.3153	3.7943	5.2533	6.1742	7.2510
35	1.4166	1.5446	1.9999	2.1788	2.3732	3.9461	5.5160	6.5138	7.6861
36	1.4308	1.5639	2.0399	2.2278	2.4325	4.1039	5.7918	6.8721	8.1473
37	1.4451	1.5835	2.0807	2.2779	2.4933	4.2681	6.0814	7.2501	8.6361
38	1.4595	1.6033	2.1223	2.3292	2.5557	4.4388	6.3855	7.6488	9.1543
39	1.4741	1.6233	2.1647	2.3816	2.6196	4.6164	6.7048	8.0695	9.7035
40	1.4889	1.6436	2.2080	2.4352	2.6851	4.8010	7.0400	8.5133	10.2857
41	1.5038	1.6642	2.2522	2.4900	2.7522	4.9931	7.3920	8.9815	10.9029
42	1.5188	1.6850	2.2972	2.5460	2.8210	5.1928	7.7616	9.4755	11.5570
43	1.5340	1.7060	2.3432	2.6033	2.8915	5.4005	8.1497	9.9967	12.2505
44	1.5493	1.7274	2.3901	2.6619	2.9638	5.6165	8.5572	10.5465	12.9855
45	1.5648	1.7489	2.4379	2.7218	3.0379	5.8412	8.9850	11.1266	13.7646
46	1.5805	1.7708	2.4866	2.7830	3.1139	6.0748	9.4343	11.7385	14.5905
47	1.5963	1.7929	2.5363	2.8456	3.1917	6.3178	9.9060	12.3843	15.4659
48	1.6122	1.8154	2.5871	2.9096	3.2715	6.5705	10.4013	13.0653	16.3939
49	1.6283	1.8380	2.6388	2.9751	3.3533	6.8333	10.9213	13.7838	17.3775
50	1.6446	1.8610	2.6916	3.0420	3.4371	7.1067	11.4674	14.5420	18.4202

Questions on how long it takes money to double or triple itself at various rates of interest when compounded annually should be asked when examining the table. In particular have the students notice that it takes half the time at 4% that it does at 2%.

▼EXPLANATION: The value of $1 at 5½% for a period of 18 years equals $2.6215. Since $5,300 is 5,300 times as large as $1, then the $5,300 will have grown to 5,300 times as large as $2.6215. Hence, the product of these two numbers, $13,893.95, is the amount that was in the account after 18 years. It is interesting to notice that this is more than twice the original deposit. If the original deposit had been $5,000, what would you do to find the size of the account at the end of the 18 years?

It is not too difficult to compute the interest on the $25 debt that the British government failed to pay some 190 years ago. The compound interest table appears to be of value only if the period of time is 50 years or less. You can attack the problem, however, by breaking up the 190-year period into several parts. First, you can find the value of the $25 after 50 years. Knowing this amount, you can then find how much that will amount to after the next 50 years. This answer will represent the value of $25 after 100 years. This process can then be repeated for another 50 years, and, finally, for the last 40 years, thus making a total of 190 years. This solution is outlined below.

Value of $25 @ 5% for 50 years = 25 × $11.4674
= $286.69
Value of $286 @ 5% for next 50 years = 286 × $11.4674
= $3,279.68
Value of $3,279 @ 5% for next 50 years = 3,279 × $11.4674
= $37,601.60
Value of $37,601 @ 5% for last 40 years = 37,601 × $7.0400
= $264,711.04

Needless to say, the British government did not pay the $264,711.04 that it owed the church! It did, however, pay off the original $25 debt.

EXERCISES   **A**

1. How much will $1 be worth after the period of years shown if interest is compounded annually at each of the following rates?

	Rate	Years	Value		Rate	Years	Value
a.	4%	25	$ 2.67	g.	4%	10	$ 1.48
b.	2%	25	1.64	h.	1%	40	1.49
c.	5%	20	2.65	i.	5%	8	1.48
d.	2½%	40	2.69	j.	1¼%	32	1.49
e.	4%	12	1.60	k.	6%	5	1.34
f.	2%	24	1.61	l.	2¼%	20	1.56

In the computation above, the numbers were rounded off by dropping the fractional parts of a dollar. This might easily account for a great deal more money over the 190-year period.

2. Each of the following accounts remained dormant for the period of time shown. How large will each account be at the end of the period if interest is compounded annually?

	Amount on Deposit At Beginning of Period	Interest Rate	Period Of Years	Value of $1	Amount on Deposit At End of Period
a.	$ 4,500	5%	8	$ 1.4775	$ 6,648.75
b.	6,200	4%	14	1.7317	10,736.54
c.	7,450	6%	10	1.7908	13,341.46
d.	12,600	5½%	23	3.4262	43,170.12
e.	300	5%	50	11.4674	3,440.22
f.	1,850	2½%	35	2.3732	4,390.42
g.	4,342	2%	42	2.2972	9,974.44
h.	6,935	1%	18	1.1961	8,294.95
i.	16,250	1¼%	30	1.4516	23,588.50
j.	23,900	2¼%	16	1.4276	34,119.64

3. How much interest will each of the following accounts earn over the period shown if interest is compounded annually?

	Amount on Deposit At Beginning of Period	Interest Rate	Period Of Years	Value of $1	Amount on Deposit At End of Period	Interest
a.	$6,000	4%	12	$ 1.6010	$ 9,606.00	$ 3,606.00
b.	8,000	5½%	20	2.9178	23,342.40	15,342.40
c.	3,400	6%	16	2.5404	8,637.36	5,237.36
d.	7,500	5%	34	5.2533	39,399.75	31,899.75
e.	2,750	1%	45	1.5648	4,303.20	1,553.20
f.	9,325	2¼%	27	1.8235	17,004.14	7,679.14

4. How much will $1 be worth after the period of years shown below if interest is compounded annually at the following rates?

	Rate	Years	Value of $1 After 50 Years	Value
a.	4%	60	$ 7.11	$ 10.52
b.	5%	80	11.47	49.57
c.	6%	75	18.42	79.06
d.	2½%	100	3.44	11.82

B

1. If you run your finger down the 4% column on the compound interest table on page 247, you will discover that the first numeral that appears as $2 or over is the numeral $2.0258. This occurs at the 18th year. You can interpret this to mean that $1 becomes approximately $2 at a 4% interest rate compounded annually. Another way of looking at this is to say that money doubles itself in 18 years at an interest rate of 4% compounded annually.

Problem 4 should be assigned only to the more capable students. Note that the technique of using this table for years not in the table involves the operation of multiplication, while in the use of the Simple Interest Table, finding interest on days not in the table involves the operation of addition.

How long will it take money to at least double itself at each of the following rates if interest is compounded annually?

a. 5% 15 years   c. 4% 18 years   e. 2¼% 32 years
b. 2½% 29 years   d. 2% 36 years   f. 5½% 13 years

2. How long will it take money to at least triple itself at each of the following rates if interest is compounded annually?

a. 2½% 45 years   b. 4% 29 years   c. 5½% 21 years

3. Mr. Jackson deposited $5,000 at the Industrial Savings Bank, which paid interest annually. The account remained dormant for a period of 15 years, after which he withdrew the money.

a. How much money would Mr. Jackson have received had the rate of interest been 4%? $ 9,004.50

b. How much money would Mr. Jackson have received had the rate of interest been 5%? $10,394.50

c. How much more would he have received at the 5% rate than at the 4% rate? $ 1,390.00

4. Fifty dollars was deposited at a bank that paid a 5% interest rate, compounded annually. If the account remained dormant for a period of 75 years, how large would the account be at the end of that period? $ 1,941.66

Section 3: The Compound Interest Table for Periods Other than Annual

As you know, banks do not compound interest only once a year, but rather twice a year (semiannually), or four times a year (quarterly). Hence, the compound interest table on page 247 is of very little use unless it can be shown that it can be applied under conditions other than when interest is compounded annually. To show that this can be done, consider the following two problems.

1. An account of $2,000 is permitted to remain dormant for a period of 2 years. If interest is compounded semiannually at 4%, how large will this account be at the end of the 2 years?

●SOLUTION:
Principal for 1st ½ year = $2,000
Interest for 1st ½ year
    = $2,000 × 4% × ½ = $40

❖ ❖ ❖

2. An account of $2,000 is permitted to remain dormant for a period of 4 years. If interest is compounded annually at 2%, how large will this account be at the end of the 4 years?

●SOLUTION:
Principal for 1st year = $2,000
Interest for 1st year
    = $2,000 × 2% × 1 = $40

❖ ❖ ❖

These two problems were set up in juxtaposition so that the students might match up principal with principal and interest with interest in each succeeding period.

Principal for 2nd ½ year = $2,040   Principal for 2nd year = $2,040
Interest for 2nd ½ year   Interest for 2nd year
   = $2,040 × 4% × ½ = $40.80   = $2,040 × 2% × 1 = $40.80

      ✿ ✿ ✿   ✿ ✿ ✿

Principal for 3rd ½ year   Principal for 3rd year
        = $2,080.80   = $2,080.80
Interest for 3rd ½ year   Interest for 3rd year
   = $2,080 × 4% × ½ = $41.60   = $2,080 × 2% × 1 = $41.60

      ✿ ✿ ✿   ✿ ✿ ✿

Principal for 4th ½ year   Principal for 4th year
        = $2,122.40   = $2,122.40
Interest for 4th ½ year   Interest for 4th year
   = $2,122 × 4% × ½ = $42.44   = $2,122 × 2% × 1 = $42.44

      ✿ ✿ ✿   ✿ ✿ ✿

Principal at end of 2 years   Principal at end of 4 years
        = $2,164.84   = $2,164.84

It is very evident that the principal and interest for both of the problems are exactly the same for each succeeding period. The only difference is that, in the illustration on the left, when computing the interest, it was necessary to multiply 4% by ½, while in the illustration on the right, it was necessary to multiply 2% by 1. Since these two products:

$$4\% \times \tfrac{1}{2} = 2\% \quad \text{and} \quad 2\% \times 1 = 2\%$$

give exactly the same answer, it appears that:

    a. Finding the amount on deposit at the end of 2 years, if interest is compounded twice each year at 4%,

is the same as

    b. finding the amount on deposit at the end of 4 years if interest is compounded once each year at 2%.

The important point to notice in these two statements is that the number of years has been doubled while the rate has been cut in half.

If possible, have the students extrapolate from the illustrations above and state the general principle that appears at the top of page 252.

This illustration suggests the much broader principle that:

> Interest compounded semiannually at a fixed rate
> for a certain number of years

> **is the same as**

> interest compounded annually at half the fixed rate
> for twice the certain number of years.

As an example:

> Interest compounded at 6% semiannually for 5 years

> **is the same as**

> interest compounded at 3% annually for 10 years.

What words should replace the blank spaces in the following statement? "Interest compounded semiannually at 3% for 8 years is the same as interest compounded annually at _____% for _____ years."

With this principle as a background, you are now in a position to apply the compound interest table to situations where interest is compounded semiannually rather than annually.

■ ILLUSTRATION 1: Mr. Carlson deposited $4,800 at the State Bank of Utah, which pays an interest rate of 5% compounded semiannually. If the account remains dormant for a period of 15 years, how much money will Mr. Carlson have in this account at the end of this period?

● SOLUTION:

> Interest compounded semiannually at 5% for 15 years

> **is the same as**

> interest compounded annually at 2½% for 30 years.

> Value of $1 @ 2½% after 30 years = $2.0976
> Value of $4,800 @ 2½% after 30 years = 4,800 × $2.0976
>   = $10,068.48

▼ EXPLANATION: Once you have changed the interest from being compounded semiannually at 5% for 15 years to being compounded annually at 2½% for 30 years, the rest of the solution is completed in exactly the same way as earlier.

The method just used for changing semiannual interest payments to annual interest payments can be applied equally well for changing

After examining the principle above and applying it to Illustration 1, try to have the students anticipate what the next step of the work will be, i.e., setting up of a principle for using the table which applies when interest is compounded quarterly.

quarterly payments to annual payments. Where before you halved the interest rate and doubled the years, now when the interest is given quarterly, you take one fourth of the interest rate and multiply the years by four. The principle now appears as:

Interest compounded quarterly at a fixed rate for a certain number of years

is the same as

interest compounded annually at one quarter the fixed rate for four times the certain number of years.

As an example:

Interest compounded at 6% quarterly for 5 years

is the same as

interest compounded at 1½% annually for 20 years.

What words should replace the blank spaces in the following statement? "Interest compounded quarterly at 8% for 12 years is the same as interest compounded annually at _____% for _____ years."

■ILLUSTRATION 2: A savings account at the Del Rio Savings and Loan Association had an original deposit of $2,700, after which no activity was recorded on the account for a period of 8 years. This savings and loan association paid a 5% annual interest rate, compounded quarterly. How much money will be recorded to the account at the end of the 8 years?

●SOLUTION:

Interest compounded quarterly at 5% for 8 years

is the same as

interest compounded annually at 1¼% for 32 years.

Value of $1 @ 1¼% after 32 years = $1.4881
Value of $2,700 @ 1¼% after 32 years = $2,700 × $1.4881
                                     = $4,017.87

▼EXPLANATION: As in Illustration 1, once you have changed the interest from being compounded quarterly to interest being compounded annually, then the compound interest table can be applied exactly as before. Perhaps the most difficult part of the computation in this problem is concerned with dividing 5% by 4. This is 1¼%.

In the principle above, the primary objective is to have the students realize that the interest rate is divided by 4, while the time is multiplied by 4.

EXERCISES   A

1. If each of the following interest rates is changed from one which is compounded semiannually to one which is compounded annually, what will the annual rate and period of time have to be?

    a. 6% compounded semiannually for 4 years   3% for 8 years
    b. 8% compounded semiannually for 12 years   4% for 24 years
    c. 5% compounded semiannually for 10 years   2½% for 20 years
    d. 3% compounded semiannually for 26 years   1½% for 52 years
    e. 4½% compounded semiannually for 15 years   2¼% for 30 years

2. If each of the following interest rates is changed from one which is compounded quarterly to one which is compounded annually, what will the annual rate and period of time have to be?

    a. 4% compounded quarterly for 8 years   1% for 32 years
    b. 8% compounded quarterly for 12 years   2% for 48 years
    c. 6% compounded quarterly for 6 years   1½% for 24 years
    d. 5% compounded quarterly for 10 years   1¼% for 40 years

3. What will be the value of $1 if interest accumulates under each of the following conditions?

	Frequency At Which Interest Is Compounded	Number Of Years	Rate Of Interest	Value of $1 At Close of Period
a.	Semiannually	6	4%	$ 1.27
b.	Semiannually	12	5%	1.81
c.	Semiannually	11	2%	1.24
d.	Semiannually	16	2½%	1.49
e.	Semiannually	23	4½%	2.78
f.	Quarterly	5	8%	1.49
g.	Quarterly	9	4%	1.43
h.	Quarterly	12	10%	3.27
i.	Quarterly	7	5%	1.42
j.	Quarterly	2	9%	1.19

4. Each of the following accounts was opened with the deposit shown below. After making this deposit, the person permitted the account to remain dormant for the period indicated. How large will each of these accounts be at the end of these periods?

	Original Deposit	Interest Compounded	Number Of Years	Interest Rate	Value of $1	Account At End Of Period
a.	$2,000	Semiannually	5	4%	$ 1.2190	$ 2,438.00
b.	3,000	Semiannually	9	2%	1.1961	3,588.30
c.	5,000	Semiannually	14	5%	1.9965	9,982.50
d.	4,500	Semiannually	20	12%	10.2857	46,285.65
e.	7,300	Semiannually	25	2½%	1.8610	13,585.30
f.	6,000	Quarterly	3	4%	1.1268	6,760.80

In order to decrease the opportunities for errors, have the students set up Exercises 1 and 2 as follows: 6% compounded semiannually for 4 years

is the same as

_____ compounded annually for _____ years.

	Original Deposit	Interest Compounded	Number Of Years	Interest Rate	Value of $1	Account At End Of Period
g.	9,000	Quarterly	11	8%	$ 2.3901	$ 21,510.90
h.	3,600	Quarterly	7	10%	1.9965	7,187.40
i.	7,350	Quarterly	4	5%	1.2199	8,966.27
j.	4,920	Quarterly	12	9%	2.9096	14,315.23

B

1. The Bank of Dearborn pays an annual interest rate of 5% to its depositors. Mr. Sloane opened an account there with a deposit of $5,000, and then he allowed the account to remain dormant for a period of 10 years.

    a. How much money would Mr. Sloane have in the account at the end of the 10-year period if interest is compounded semiannually? $8,193.00

    b. How much money would Mr. Sloane have in the account at the end of the 10-year period if interest is compounded quarterly? $8,218.00

    c. How much would Mr. Sloane gain over this period if interest is compounded quarterly rather than semiannually? $ 25.00

2. The Savings Bank of Verona offers two different accounts. One is called an "Investment Account," in which money can be deposited only in $1,000 amounts. The other is a "Regular Account," where deposits can be made in any amount. The rate of interest paid on an "Investment Account" is 5%, while that on a "Regular Account" is 4%. Interest is compounded quarterly in both cases. A person opened an account with $20,000. If this account remained dormant for 8 years, how much better off would the depositor be had he taken out an "Investment Account" rather than a "Regular Account"? $2,264.00

3. How much interest will accumulate on each of the following accounts if they remain dormant for the period of time shown?

	Original Deposit	Interest Compounded	Number Of Years	Interest Rate	Interest
a.	$3,700	Semiannually	8	5%	$1,792.65
b.	9,850	Semiannually	12	4½%	6,978.73
c.	7,400	Quarterly	7	4%	2,377.62
d.	8,340	Quarterly	6	5%	2,897.32

4. A deposit of $5,000 lays dormant for a period of 30 years. If the bank pays an interest rate of 4% compounded semiannually, how large will this account be at the end of this period? (See page 247.) $16,405.30

Unit 6: Growth of Regular Deposits

This chapter opened by pointing out that one of the purposes of school banking was to try to train you to develop the habit of making regular deposits. It might be well at this point to find out just how rapidly money does grow under these conditions. To make the situation as simple as possible, consider only that case in which deposits are made only once each year, and where interest is added to the account only once each year, also. In circumstances where interest is compounded quarterly and deposits are made weekly, the problem not only becomes quite involved, but also a bit beyond the scope of the work here. Examine the situation where deposits of $2,000 are made annually at a bank that pays a yearly interest rate of 4%. During the first year, there will be only $2,000 in the account, for this is the amount of the first deposit. At the end of the first year, however, interest will have been added to the account.

First year's interest: $I = P \times R \times T$
$$= \$2,000 \times 4\% \times 1$$
$$= \$80$$

Hence, after the first year, the amount on deposit will be the original $2,000, plus the $80 in interest, or a total of $2,080. Now, with the beginning of the second year, another $2,000 is deposited, bringing the savings account up to $4080. Thus, at the close of this second year, the bank will compute the interest on the $4,080.

Second year's interest: $I = P \times R \times T$
$$= \$4,080 \times 4\% \times 1$$
$$= \$163.20$$

By adding the second year's interest of $163.20 to the second year's bank balance of $4,080, you get the total amount of money ($4,243.20) on deposit at the close of the second year. The process repeats itself —another deposit of $2,000 followed by another interest payment, and on and on. How much money would be on deposit during the third year? How much interest will this money earn during the third year? Hence, how much money will be on deposit at the end of the third year? And, finally, how large will the account be after the new deposit is made at the beginning of the fourth year?

The computation is not really very difficult, but it is rather long. By now, it should be apparent that whenever the arithmetic process repeats itself as it does here, there are usually tables available. The one to be used here is on page 257. This table was designed to show how

The once-a-year deposit would be typical of the annuity or the insurance premium rather than a deposit to a savings account. Banks do make arrangements with depositors to transfer money periodically from checking accounts to savings accounts.

large $1 deposits made annually would grow at interest rates of 4%, 4½%, and 5%. To prepare this table, someone had to do the computation for $1 that was being done for $2,000.

■ILLUSTRATION 1: Deposits of $1 are made annually over a period of 15 years. If interest is compounded annually at 5%, how large will the account be at the end of this period?

GROWTH OF $1 ANNUAL DEPOSITS

Years	Rate		
At End of:	4%	4½%	5%
1	1.0400	1.0450	1.0500
2	2.1216	2.1370	2.1525
3	3.2465	3.2782	3.3101
4	4.4163	4.4707	4.5256
5	5.6330	5.7169	5.8019
6	6.8983	7.0192	7.1420
7	8.2142	8.3800	8.5491
8	9.5828	9.8021	10.0266
9	11.0061	11.2882	11.5779
10	12.4864	12.8412	13.2068
11	14.0258	14.4640	14.9171
12	15.6268	16.1599	16.7130
13	17.2919	17.9321	18.5986
14	19.0236	19.7841	20.5786
15	20.8245	21.7193	22.6575
16	22.6975	23.7417	24.8403
17	24.6454	25.8551	27.1324
18	26.6712	28.0636	29.5390
19	28.7781	30.3714	32.0660
20	30.9692	32.7831	34.7193
21	33.2480	35.3034	37.5052
22	35.6179	37.9370	40.4305
23	38.0826	40.6892	43.5020
24	40.6459	43.5652	46.7271
25	43.3117	46.5706	50.1135
26	46.0842	49.7113	53.6691
27	48.9676	52.9933	57.4026
28	51.9663	56.4230	61.3227
29	55.0849	60.0071	65.4388
30	58.3283	63.7524	69.7608

▼EXPLANATION: This table is read in the same manner as the compound interest table. Run your finger down the "Years" column until you reach the numeral 15. Then move your finger along the row containing the 15 until it comes to the column headed by the numeral 5%. The numeral $22.6575 that you are pointing to represents how much

"Growth" tables such as the one above can be set up in different ways. This one is designed to show the amount on deposit at the end of a specific period prior to the moment when the new deposit is made. It was felt that the student would understand this better than any other arrangement.

money you would have had you deposited $1 annually for 15 years at
a bank that paid a 5% interest rate. How much of the $22.66 did you
deposit over the 15 years? How much of the $22.66 is interest?

● SOLUTION:

Value of annual deposits of $1 @ 5% over 15 years = $22.6575, or
$22.66

■ ILLUSTRATION 2: Annual deposits of $2,000 are made over a 25-
year period. If interest is compounded annually at 4%, how large will
the account be at the end of this period?

● SOLUTION:

Value of annual deposits of $1 @ 4% over 25 years = $43.3117
Value of annual deposits of $2,000 @ 4% over 25 years
= 2,000 × $43.3117
= $86,623.40

▼ EXPLANATION: As with the compound interest table, once you have
found the value for an annual deposit of $1, it is simply a matter of
multiplying this answer by 2,000 to find the value for an annual deposit of $2,000. Incidentally, do not round off any number found in the
table until you have completed all the computation. Then round off
your answer to the nearest cent. Can you explain why this should be
done in this manner? Notice that in the 25-year period, the person
would have deposited 25 times $2,000, or $50,000. How much interest
would he have received over the 25-year period?

EXERCISES   A

1. Deposits of $1 are made annually over the following period of years.
   If interest is compounded annually, how large will each account be
   at the close of the period?

	Interest Rate	Period Of Years	Value Of Account At Close Of Period
a.	4%	8	$ 9.58
b.	4%	19	28.78
c.	4½%	23	40.69
d.	4½%	29	60.01
e.	5%	17	27.13
f.	5%	30	69.76

2. The following deposits are made annually over the period of years
   shown. If interest is compounded annually, how large will each
   account be at the close of the period?

As part of the analysis of Illustration 2, point out that the amount of interest accumulated over
the period is almost as great as the amount deposited over the years. Also call to pupils' attention that whereas some of the early deposits have doubled in value, interest on later ones is
relatively small.

	Annual Deposits	Interest Rate	Period Of Years	Value Of $1 Deposits	Value Of Account At Close Of Period
a.	$ 400	5%	12	$ 16.7130	$ 6,685.20
b.	900	5%	18	29.5390	26,585.10
c.	500	5%	25	50.1135	25,056.75
d.	650	4%	9	11.0061	7,153.97
e.	1,300	4%	16	22.6975	29,506.75
f.	2,500	4%	27	48.9676	122,419.00
g.	3,420	4%	30	58.3283	199,482.79
h.	4,350	4½%	10	12.8412	55,859.22
i.	1,275	4½%	15	21.7193	27,692.11
j.	3,525	4½%	25	46.5706	164,161.37

3. The following deposits are made annually over the period of years shown. If interest is compounded annually, how much interest will these accounts have earned over the period of years?

	Annual Deposits	Interest Rate	Period Of Years	Value Of $1 Deposits	Value Of Account At Close Of Period	Interest Accumulated Over the Period
a.	$ 800	4%	10	$ 12.4864	$ 1,989.12	$ 9,989.12
b.	800	5%	10	13.2068	2,565.44	10,565.44
c.	3,000	4½%	6	7.0192	3,057.60	21,057.60
d.	2,500	4½%	18	28.0636	25,159.00	70,159.00
e.	1,400	4%	22	35.6179	19,065.06	49,865.06
f.	1,600	5%	28	61.3227	53,316.32	98,116.32

B

1. On the day George was born, his father began to put aside $500 each year to pay for George's college education. The money was deposited annually in a bank that paid a 4½% interest rate, compounded annually. On George's 19th birthday, his father made the last deposit of $500 and then turned the account over to George. How much money was in the account at that time? $15,685.70

2. On the day that Mr. Roberts was 35 years old, he and his wife decided to deposit $400 each year on his birthday so that they would have their own retirement fund when Mr. Roberts retired at 65. Their deposits were made at a bank where interest was compounded annually.

   a. How much money will be in their account on Mr. Roberts' 65th birthday if the annual rate of interest is 4%? The last deposit was made on that day. $23,731.32

   b. How much money will be in their account on Mr. Roberts' 65th birthday if the annual rate of interest is 5%? $28,304.32

The situation explained in Problem 1 of Group B is one that frequently occurs at the present time because of the high cost of a college education. Equally as often, parents will purchase life insurance with this same goal in mind.

c. How much better off financially would the Roberts have been had the bank paid 5% rather than 4%? $ 4,573

3. Each Christmas for 25 years, Mr. Riley and the other employees of the Arco Drill Company received a bonus of $250. Instead of spending the money, he deposited it in a special bank account to which he made no other deposits. Interest was compounded annually at 4½%.

   a. How large was the account at the end of the 25-year period?
                                                                                   $11,642.50

   b. How much interest had been added to the account over the period of years? $ 5,392.50

4. a. Without using the table on page 257, determine how much money a person would have in the bank at the end of 4 years if he deposited $5,000 annually at 4% compounded annually. $22,081.60

   b. Determine how much money a person would have in the bank at the end of four years if he deposited $5,000 annually at 4% compounded annually. Use the table on page 257. $22,081.50

   c. Can you explain why your answers to the preceding two questions are not the same?   Numbers in table were rounded off.

Unit 7:   Chapter Review and Test

A

1. Complete each of the following deposit slips.

a.	Dollars	Cents		b.	Dollars	Cents
Bills	56	00		Bills	182	00
Coin		96		Coin	5	68
Checks	84	50		Checks	76	43
					153	69
Total	141	46		Total	417	80

2. Find the interest on each of the following accounts. Interest payments are made over the periods shown.

	Principal	Interest Rate	Period	Interest
a.	$ 700	5%	Annually	35.00
b.	800	4½%	Annually	36.00
c.	1,400	5%	Semiannually	35.00
d.	2,000	5½%	Semiannually	55.00
e.	2,400	6%	Quarterly	36.00
f.	1,600	4½%	Quarterly	18.00

In answer to Problem 3 a, the question may be raised as to whether the 26th bonus payment had been added to the account. The problem is so worded as to try to have the students realize that the 26th payment is not to be added.

3. Find the interest on each of the following deposits for the period of time shown.

	Principal	Interest Rate	Period In Days	Interest
a.	$ 900	6%	60	$ 9.00
b.	500	3%	120	5.00
c.	4,000	5%	36	20.00
d.	2,000	4½%	72	18.00
e.	3,600	5¼%	40	21.00

4. Find the number of days between the dates in each of the following exercises. Use the timetable on page 228.
   a. From June 17 to December 2 of the same year. 168 days
   b. From October 14 to January 31 of the following year. 109 days

5. Use the Simple Interest Table on pages 232–233 to find the interest on each of the following deposits. Round off each answer to the nearest cent.

	Deposit	Number of Days	Interest Rate	Interest on $1	Interest
a.	$4,000	35	5½%	$ .0053472	$ 21.39
b.	2,500	56	4¾%	.0073889	18.47
c.	6,000	80	4½%	.010000	60.00

6. Find the interest on each of the following deposits for the period in which the deposit was made. In finding your answer, use both the timetable and the Simple Interest Table.

	Deposit	Date Of Deposit	Interest Period Closes	Interest Rate	Number Of Days	Interest On $1	Interest
a.	$ 600	May 2	June 30	5%	59	$ .0081944	$ 4.92
b.	5,000	November 17	December 31	4½%	44	.005500	27.50
c.	4,500	June 5	July 31	4¾%	56	.0073889	33.25

7. Each of the following accounts remained dormant for the period of time shown. How large will the account be at the end of the period if interest is compounded annually? In finding your answer, use the Compound Interest Table on page 247.

	Amount On Deposit At Beginning Of Period	Interest Rate	Period Of Years	Value of $1	Amount On Deposit At End Of Period
a.	$6,000	5%	24	$ 3.2251	$ 19,350.60
b.	8,500	5½%	45	11.1266	94,576.10

As in other chapter closing units, part of this can be used for review and the remainder for testing.

8. Each of the following accounts remained dormant for the period of time shown. How large will the account be at the end of the period if interest is compounded periodically as indicated? In finding your answer, use the Compound Interest Table on page 247.

	Original Deposit	Interest Compounded	Years	Interest Rate	Value of $1	Account At End Of Period
a.	$6,000	Semiannually	8	4%	$ 1.3728	$ 8,236.80
b.	3,000	Semiannually	17	5%	2.3153	6,945.90
c.	8,000	Quarterly	12	4%	1.6122	12,897.60

9. The following deposits are made annually over the period of years shown. If interest is compounded annually, how large will each account be at the close of the period? In finding your answer, use the table on page 257.

	Annual Deposits	Interest Rate	Period Of Years	Value Of $1 Deposits	Account At End Of Period
a.	$ 200	4%	16	$ 22.6975	$ 4,539.50
b.	800	4½%	22	37.9370	30,349.60
c.	1,400	5%	28	61.3227	85,851.78

B

In finding your answer to each of the following problems, use whatever tables in this chapter you feel are necessary.

1. On March 1, the first day of an interest period, Mr. Johnson had $2,600 on deposit at the Second National Bank of Greensville, which pays an interest rate of 4%. On March 26, he withdrew $200, while on April 12, he deposited $1,000. The quarterly interest period closes on May 31. In computing interest, the bank deducts all withdrawals made during the period from the amount on deposit at the beginning of the period, and it gives interest on all deposits from the day of deposit. How much money did Mr. Johnson have in this account on June 1? $3,429.44

2. An $8,000 savings account remained dormant over a period of 10 years in a bank where interest is compounded semiannually at 5%. How much interest was added to this account over the 10-year period? $5,108.80

3. Mr. Arben opened a savings account with a $10,000 deposit, and then he permitted the account to remain dormant over a period of 20 years. The bank paid an interest rate of 5%. How much more will

Mr. Arben have in his account at the end of the 20 years if interest is compounded semiannually rather than annually? $ 318

4. At 20, George West decided that when he reached 40, he would take a trip around the world. To prepare for this, he planned to deposit $400 annually at a bank that paid an interest rate of 4½% compounded annually.

a. At the end of 20 years, how much money did George have for his world trip?
$13,113.24

b. How much more would George have had if he had kept his money in a bank that paid 5% compounded annually? $ 774.48

CHAPTER 7

BANKING SERVICES

All too soon you reach the age where, around the first of each month, your mail is flooded with bills for gas, electricity, rent, dental payments, automobile payments, insurance payments, and so on. It is not possible to ignore these bills for very long. Eventually you go to each of your creditors and pay your debts in cash. After several years of doing this, you decide that there must be an easier way of paying bills than by making these monthly rounds. Of course there is. These bills can be paid by checks through the mails. Checking accounts, however, cost money, and it is this cost that will be considered now.

Unit 1: Checking Accounts

Section 1: The Cost of a Checking Account

There are thousands upon thousands of banks in the United States, and each of them appears to have its own system of charges for its checking-account services. In fact, quite frequently, even a single bank

It would hardly be an exaggeration to say that there are as many different checking-account plans as banks. Each one seems to want to add its own personal touch to its own program. Fortunately, there's also a great deal of similarity in these plans, which make the three here somewhat typical.

will have several different types of checking accounts for its depositors, depending on whether they are businessmen, or private individuals, or want to keep large balances in their accounts, or just a few dollars to pay off an occasional small bill. There is, though, some similarity among the variety of charges made for checking accounts. Costs differ from bank to bank, but basically the computation of this cost falls into one of the three patterns described here.

A. The Special-Checking-Account Plan

Computing the cost to maintain this type of account is relatively easy. Usually there is a maintenance charge of 50¢ per month. In addition, you are required to pay 10¢ for every check that you write. When the special checking account was first made available, the people using it had to purchase their checks in advance at 10¢ per check. Sometimes people made errors in writing out a check, and the check had to be destroyed. Since 10¢ had already been paid for the check, this money was lost each time a check was torn up and thrown away. The banks now charge the depositor 10¢ per check only after the check has been returned to the bank for payment.

∎ILLUSTRATION 1: Peter Welch has a special checking account at the Mayfair Trust Company. During the past month, he wrote 9 checks. How much will be charged against his checking account if this bank uses the plan described above?
●SOLUTION:

$$\text{Monthly maintenance charge} = \$.50$$
$$\text{Charge for 9 checks} = 9 \times \$.10$$
$$= \$.90$$
$$\text{Total charge} = \$.50 + \$.90$$
$$= \$1.40$$

B. The Flat-Payment Plan

Under this plan you are permitted to write all the checks you want, assuming you have money in the bank to cover them, of course, and the only charge is $2 per year. However, in order to take full advantage of this plan, you must keep a minimum balance of $300 in your checking account. If the balance happens to drop between $200 and $300, then for the month in which this occurs you will be charged $1. If you allow the balance to fall below $200, then during that month you have to pay a service charge of $2.

The names used here to describe these three plans are actually the names given to these or similar plans by many banks.

■ ILLUSTRATION 2: Walter Bryan has a checking account at a bank that uses the flat-payment plan. During two months of last year, Mr. Bryan permitted the balance in his account to reach $225. On four other months, it dropped to as low as $110. For the remainder of the year, a balance was maintained that was above $300. What was the total amount of money that Mr. Bryan had to pay for issuing checks last year?

● SOLUTION:

Cost for 2 months in which the balance was $225 = 2 × $1
= $2
Cost for 4 months in which the balance was $110 = 4 × $2
= $8

Basic service charge for the year = $2
Total cost for the year = $2 + $8 + $2
= $12

Actually, the person who has a checking account under the flat-payment plan frequently gets the impression that his only cost for maintaining this account is $2 per year so long as he keeps the balance above $300. This is not quite correct, for there is a hidden cost that he should know about. By keeping $300 constantly on deposit in the checking account, he cannot have this same $300 in his savings account, where it might earn interest at the rate of perhaps 4%, or 5%, a year. This loss of interest should be considered as part of the cost of having this type of account.

■ ILLUSTRATION 3: A person maintains an average balance of $450 in his checking account over a period of a year. If he had had this money in his savings account, it would have drawn 4% interest, compounded annually. How much interest did this person lose on the $450 over the period of the year?

● SOLUTION:

$$I = P × R × T$$
$$= \$450 × 4\% × 1$$
$$= \$450 × 4/100 × 1$$
$$= \$18.00$$

▼ EXPLANATION: Since interest is compounded annually, finding the interest is just a matter of applying the interest formula where the "Time" is 1 year. If the bank had paid interest that was compounded semiannually or quarterly, it would be best to do the computation by the method shown on page 252.

The purpose of Illustration 3 is to show students that the cost of a checking account is far more than the $2 yearly he pays under the Flat-Payment Plan, or the 10¢ per check under the Special-Checking-Account Plan. He must not forget that he is losing interest on the money in the checking account.

C. The Analysis Plan

This plan is a bit more involved than the previous two. To determine the monthly charge, it is necessary to refer to a table such as the following. Notice that the word "Items" appears in the headings of the third and fourth columns. An item, when used in reference to a checking account, implies either a check that is drawn against the account, or a deposit that is made to the account. Thus, if a person wrote 7 checks during a month in which he made 2 deposits, he would be charged with 9 items for that period.

Minimum Balance	Basic Charge	Items Allowed	Charge Per Additional Item
Under $100.00	75¢	10	5¢
$100.00 to $199.99	50¢	10	5¢
$200.00 to $299.99	25¢	10	5¢
$300.00 to $399.99	0	15	5¢
$400.00 and over	0	20	5¢

■ ILLUSTRATION 4: Mr. Young issued 17 checks during September. During this period he made 4 deposits. When examining his checkbook, he found that the smallest amount of money he had in his checking account during September was $247.56. If his bank used the "analysis plan" for computing the cost, how much was his checking account charge for the month?

● SOLUTION:

$$\text{Basic charge} = 25\text{¢}$$
$$\text{Number of items during month} = 17 + 4$$
$$= 21$$
$$\text{Number of items that will be charged} = 21 - 10$$
$$= 11$$
$$\text{Charge for additional items} = 11 \times 5\text{¢}$$
$$= 55\text{¢}$$
$$\text{Total charge} = 25\text{¢} + 55\text{¢}$$
$$= 80\text{¢}$$

▼ EXPLANATION: Mr. Young's lowest balance for the month was $247.56. Since this fell between $200.00 and $299.99, the basic charge was 25¢. Also, under this balance he was permitted to have 10 items at no additional charge. However, Mr. Young had issued 17 checks and made 4 deposits, or a total of 21 items. For each item over 10, he had to pay 5¢. Since there were 11 items over the 10 that were free, he had to pay 11 times 5¢, or 55¢. By adding the basic charge of 25¢ to the additional charge of 55¢, you get the total charge of 80¢.

In the Analysis Plan, the bank is making an effort to compensate the depositor in some way for the interest lost by not keeping this money in a savings account. The interest earned by the minimum balance is used to offset the basic cost and item cost of the checking account.

EXERCISES   A

The plans referred to in the following problems are the ones described on the preceding pages.

1. Use the Special-Checking-Account Plan to find the charge for the month in each of the following exercises.

	Number Of Checks Issued	Charge			Number Of Checks Issued	Charge
a.	12	$ 1.70		d.	23	$ 2.80
b.	17	2.20		e.	14	1.90
c.	8	1.30		f.	38	4.30

2. Use the Flat-Payment Plan to find the charge for the month in each of the following exercises. Do not consider the yearly charge when finding your answer.

	Minimum Balance For the Month	Charge			Minimum Balance For the Month	Charge
a.	$462.75	$ 0.00		d.	163.48	$ 2.00
b.	249.52	1.00		e.	87.25	2.00
c.	304.16	0.00		f.	203.12	1.00

3. Use the Analysis Plan to find the charge for the month in each of the following exercises.

	Minimum Balance For the Month	Number Of Checks Issued	Number Of Deposits Made	Charge
a.	$473.26	18	0	$ 0.00
b.	314.65	19	0	0.20
c.	415.18	32	0	0.60
d.	347.09	27	0	0.60
e.	256.12	24	0	0.95
f.	207.91	36	1	1.60
g.	141.52	17	1	0.90
h.	183.40	42	3	2.25
i.	76.57	35	2	2.10
j.	54.21	48	4	2.85

4. If interest is compounded annually, how much interest will be lost during the year by keeping the following average balance in a checking account rather than a savings account?

	Average Balance	Interest Rate	Interest			Average Balance	Interest Rate	Interest
a.	$600	5%	$ 30.00		e.	325	5%	$ 16.25
b.	500	4%	20.00		f.	976	4%	39.04
c.	800	4½%	36.00		g.	472	4½%	21.24
d.	450	5½%	24.75		h.	676	4¼%	28.73

The students usually have no difficulty with the exercises above and enjoy doing them. Exercise 4 serves the dual role as a review of the compound interest table and as a means of showing the students how much interest is lost by depositing money in a checking account rather than a savings account.

B

1. At the bank where Mr. Pierson has both a checking account and a savings account, interest is paid to a savings-account depositor at the rate of 4½% compounded semiannually. How much interest will Mr. Pierson lose over the period of one year if he keeps an average balance of $950 in his checking account throughout the year? (Use the table on page 247 and the method described on pages 250–253.)
<u>$43.23</u>

2. Mr. Quigly kept an average balance of $600 in his checking account during the past year. If this money had been deposited in his savings account, he would have received 5% interest, compounded quarterly. How much money did Mr. Quigly lose last year by keeping this money in his checking account?   <u>$30.54</u>

3. Mr. Kemp had a checking account at a bank that used the Flat-Payment Plan for computing the cost. During the past year, the minimum balance in his checking account for each month was as follows:

January $627	April $259	July $485	October $712
February $302	May $523	August $192	November $410
March $146	June $267	September $317	December $252

What was the total amount that Mr. Kemp had to pay to maintain this checking account during the past year?   <u>$9</u>

4. During the month of October, the balance in Mr. Langley's checking account dropped to $227.34. He issued 26 checks during the month.
   a. If the checking account was in a bank that used the Special-Checking-Account Plan, what would the charge have been?
   <u>$3.10</u>
   b. If the checking account was in a bank that used the Analysis Plan, what would the charge have been?   <u>$1.05</u>
   c. How much could he have saved by using one of these plans rather than the other?   <u>$2.05</u>

5. Mr. Morley's checking account is in a bank that uses the Flat-Payment Plan. During the past year, he maintained an average balance of $620, and he never permitted the balance to drop below $300. Had the money been in a savings account, he would have received 4½% interest, compounded semiannually. What was the total cost of maintaining this account last year? Include both the loss of interest and the charge on the checking account.   <u>$30.21</u>

Problems 3 and 4 in the above group should not be passed by.

Section 2: Writing Checks

Now that you have learned what the cost of maintaining a checking account can be, it might be well to take some time to learn how to write a check. The form of most checks is very much the same as the one here. The only differences might be the position of the check number and the date. On this check these items appear on the top line. Often they appear at the far right of the check, with the check number on the first line and the date directly below it.

NEWARK, N. J. _June 16_____ 19—No. 481

THE NATIONAL BANK   55-584 / 212

PAY
TO THE
ORDER OF George Evans $23 48/100

Twenty-three and   48/100   DOLLARS

FRED CROSS
Fred Cross

The purpose of a check number is to help you find the check easily at some later date if you want to refer to it. The name of the person to whom you are giving the check—and who will receive cash for it—is written after the words, "Pay to the Order of." Directly after that appears the amount of the check. This amount is written in Arabic numerals. The dollar part of the amount—in this case $23—is written quite large, while the cents part immediately after it is written over the numeral 100. The numeral 2 in the 23 is written as close as possible to the dollar sign. The fraction line in $\frac{48}{100}$ must also be written as close to the numeral 3 in the 23 as possible. The purpose of this is to prevent a dishonest person from writing another numeral or two into the amount of the check that might increase the size of the check. If this were done, however, the person would, in some way, have to change the written form of the number that appears on the next line so as to agree with the changed numeral. This might prove to be somewhat difficult. Obviously the purpose of writing out the amount of the check on the center line is to lessen the chance of having the check

While the writing of checks is a relatively simple matter, there are many adults who seem to be both fearful and ignorant of how it is done. The purpose of this unit is to help the student overcome any such fears he may harbor. Experience has shown that they thoroughly enjoy this section.

altered. The use of the wavy line that appears here is to prevent any possible change being made in the amount of the check. Finally, the person who writes out the check, and from whose bank account the money will be withdrawn, signs his name in the lower right-hand corner.

If the check had been for exactly twenty-three dollars, then the numeral would appear as $23\frac{00}{100}$, while the written form would be:

$$\text{"Twenty-three and} \sim\sim\sim \frac{00}{100} \sim\sim\sim \text{Dollars"}$$

Two zeros must appear in the numerator of the fraction. If only one were written there, a 9 could be inserted in front of it, making the amount 90¢ rather than 0¢, as it was meant to be. Similarly, if the amount were twenty-three dollars and four cents, then the numeral should be written as $23\frac{04}{100}$ where a zero appears before the 4 in the numerator of the fraction. Were just the 4 to appear in the numerator, then by writing a 9 before it, the amount could easily be changed to 94¢. By doing this, the dishonest person would gain 90¢. This seems like a rather small amount over which to be dishonest, but such changes do occur on the face of checks.

Each time a check is written, you also record, for your own information, the number of the check, the date of issue, the name of the person for whom it was written, and the amount of the check. This record appears on a page of the checkbook, and often resembles the illustration on page 272. If the checkbook from which this illustration was taken were opened before you, there would be three checks on the page at the right, and the record pertaining to these three checks would appear on the page at the left. Thus, for check #481, the date that it was written was June 16, 19__. It was made payable to George Evans. The amount Mr. Evans received was $23.48. Notice that the words "Repair for TV set" appear below the name George Evans. Although this information does not appear on the check, it is written here to remind you who George Evans happens to be and why you had paid him $23.48.

The $81.56 that appears in the lower right-hand corner is the sum of the amounts for which the three checks on this page were drawn. This numeral appears again in the lower-left corner, to the right of the words "Less Checks Drawn." It was rewritten here, for you are about to subtract the $81.56 from the "Total Balance and Deposits." This is the amount that would have been in the checking account had the

Keeping an account of checks issued and an accurate reading of the checkbook balance has been an endless supply of amusing material for the comic writer. Perhaps through the work here the student can be shown that keeping these records is not nearly so difficult as they have been led to believe.

DATE	DEPOSITS	RECORD OF CHECKS AS DRAWN	AMOUNT
	BALANCE FORWARD 427 18	No. 481 DATE June 16 19 — PAY TO George Evans (Repair for TV set)	23 48
6 18	75 —	No. 482 DATE June 19 19 — PAY TO Public Utilities, Inc. (Electric and gas bill)	16 25
		No. 483 DATE June 20 19 — PAY TO Trion Lumber Co. (Lumber for shelving)	
	TOTAL BALANCE AND DEPOSITS 5 0 2 18		41 83
	LESS CHECKS DRAWN 81 56		
	BALANCE FORWARD 4 2 0 6 2	TOTAL CHECKS DRAWN	81 56

three checks never been written. At the top-left corner of the page is
the numeral $427.18. This is the balance that was in the checking ac-
count before check #481 was made out for George Evans. On June
18, $75 was deposited to the checking account, thus bringing the total
of the original balance of $427.18 and this deposit to $502.18. After
deducting the $81.56 from this amount, you get a balance of $420.62

The students must be impressed with the fact that unless they check all their computations
at least once, they are leaving too much latitude for errors errors that carry over to the page
of the checkbook.

in the checking account. The $420.62 is now written at the top-left corner of the next page of the checkbook in exactly the same position as the $427.18.

EXERCISES   A

1. From your local bank you may be able to obtain a number of blank checks. If not, draw check forms similar to the one on page 270 and then write a check for each of the following. Fill in your own check number and date.

	Issued to:	Amount	Issued by:
a.	Smith Brothers Oil Company	$64.50	Eugene Farrell
b.	Richard Peterson	17.86	Edward Hawkins
c.	William Helms, Inc.	3.49	David Claire
d.	Leonard Motors	136.25	Bernard Mosby
e.	Henry Schmidt	47.00	Leslie Meehan
f.	Firemen's Insurance Company	168.00	John Williams
g.	May's Transport Company	31.05	Philip Jackson
h.	Dorothy Hamilton	214.09	Herman Feder
i.	Joseph Day	302.45	Charles Morrison
j.	Carr's Service Station	104.52	James Seton

2. Draw forms similar to the one on page 272. After recording the information for each set of the following checks, complete each form by finding the balance to be forwarded to the following page of the checkbook.

a. Balance brought forward: $227.89
   Checks issued: May 9, Service Bureau Corp., $56.20
                   May 12, Arthur Myers, $19.45
                   May 14, Joseph Nadler, $7.84 $144.40
b. Balance brought forward: $509.18
   Checks issued: February 14, Alex Nagy, $173.50
                   February 14, Robert Linnon, $15.20
                   February 15, Exclusives, Inc., $90.89 $229.59
c. Balance brought forward: $294.06
   Checks issued: July 26, Lionel Hoppler, $81.55
                   July 26, Gerald Pittman and Co., $175.20
                   July 28, Paul Underwood, $62.37
   Deposit: July 27, $114.75 $ 89.69

You may find that the local banks are unwilling or unable to supply as many checks as you may need. In that event, either draw a check on a stencil or ditto-master and distribute the mimeographed material to the students. It might be best to write the word "SAMPLE" prominently on the stencil form.

 d. Balance brought forward: $413.82
  Checks issued: October 3, Turnpike Sales, $49.95
       October 3, Grace Newhouse, $71.50
       October 4, Oliver Holder, $118.27 $490.95
  Deposit: October 4, $316.85
 e. Balance brought forward: $712.58
  Checks issued: April 12, Internal Revenue Service, $424.70
       April 14, Home Oil Company, $88.42
       April 15, Thompson's Dairy, $23.60
  Deposits: April 12, $55.00 $337.36
     April 15, $106.50
 f. Balance brought forward: $1,241.20
  Checks issued: June 4, Hanlon and Wilson, $394.25
       June 8, Fred Austin, $226.92
       June 10, Stephen Morrow, $471.88
  Deposits: June 5, $192.37
     June 8, $247.50
     June 10, $86.87 $674.89

Section 3: Reconciling the Checking Account Statement

Periodically—usually once a month—the bank sends a statement such as the one on page 275. The information that appears on this form includes:

1. The checks you have written that have been cashed during the month
2. The deposits you have made
3. The service charges the bank has made against your account (See Section 1 of this unit.)
4. And, finally, the balance of your checkbook account

Your first reaction may be to put the statement into a desk drawer and forget it. However, it would be better if you had second thoughts about the matter and checked the balance that the bank statement showed against the one that you have recorded in your own checkbook. If the two do not agree, there is always the slight possibility that the computers at the bank may be in error. The chance of this, though, is quite remote.

There are other reasons why you should want to compare your checkbook balance with that of the bank's. If nothing else, the monthly service charge for issuing checks would not have appeared in your own

Reconciling the checkbook's balance with the bank's statement of that balance tends to frighten students at the outset, but they do get a great deal of satisfaction when they discover the two to be the same. This is no different than the way all of us feel whenever that happens!

Mr. William Allyn
53 Somerset Road
Westbrook, N. Y.

4

VOUCHERS ENCLOSED 6

CHECKS	DEPOSITS	DATE	BALANCE
AMOUNT BROUGHT FORWARD		AUG 29	856.41
83.21		SEP 2	773.20
41.50		SEP 9	731.70
273.20		SEP 11	458.50
	320.50	SEP 16	779.00
9.14		SEP 17	769.86
	104.20	SEP 29	874.06
.85 s.c.			873.21

KEY

EC—ERROR CORRECTED   SC—SERVICE CHARGE - PREVIOUS MONTH
RT—RETURN ITEM   LS—LIST
CC—CERTIFIED CHECK   DM—DEBIT MEMO
DC—DEPOSIT CORRECTION   CM—CREDIT MEMO

PLEASE EXAMINE THIS STATEMENT
UPON RECEIPT AND REPORT ANY
DIFFERENCES AT ONCE

YOUR BALANCE
IS THE LAST AMOUNT PRINTED
IN THIS COLUMN

National, State, and County
Banking Company

records. And you would want to deduct this amount from your account. In addition, there will be times when you write a check while away from home and then forget to record the information in your checkbook upon returning home. In the same way, a deposit that you may have made in the morning might be completely forgotten some eight hours later when you are back home again. Each of these will, of course, tend to make your bank balance different from that shown in the bank's records.

Chances are it is that forgotten check that was written when the person could not record the information which causes so much distress when reconciling the checkbook. To avoid this, people frequently make a note of the check and place a note in a pocket where it cannot be overlooked.

In addition to this, there is still another factor that may make the two accounts differ. Quite often there are a few checks that you wrote that were not cashed before the statement was mailed to you. In view of this, the bank balance will be much higher than yours. The process of comparing your records with those of the bank is called reconciling a bank statement.

■ ILLUSTRATION: Reconcile the checkbook balance with the bank statement balance based on the following information.

    Balance recorded in the checkbook: $423.78

    Balance recorded on the bank statement: $509.09

    Checks written that have not yet cleared the bank: $14.67, $29.50, $5.84

    Service charge for the period: $1.45

    Check written but never recorded: $19.75

    Deposit made but never recorded: $56.50

● SOLUTION:

Reconciling the Two Statements

Checkbook balance:	$423.78	Bank balance:		$509.09
Add deposit not recorded:	56.50	Deduct outstanding		
	480.28	checks:	14.67	
Deduct:			29.50	
Forgotten			5.84	50.01
check:	19.75			
Service charge: 1.45	21.20			
Actual				
checkbook balance: $459.08		Actual bank balance:		$459.08

▼ EXPLANATION: The objective of reconciling the checkbook balance with the bank balance is not only to see if an error has been made, but also to determine exactly what your actual checkbook balance is. This quite simply means how much money you have in the checking account. Hence, both the checkbook balance and the bank balance are examined specifically toward showing that the actual amount of money you have in your checking account is the same as the amount of money that the bank should have recorded there. The left side of the solution is devoted to computing the actual checkbook balance, while the right side is for the actual bank balance. In examining the left side, notice that a deposit of $56.50 had not been recorded at the time it was made. Hence, the balance of $423.78 had to be increased by $56.50. In addition, the person had written a check for $19.75 and had failed to record this in his checkbook. This means that he really has $19.75 less in his checking account than he thought he had. Further, the service

There are many ways that people use to reconcile their own balance with that of the bank's — and most of them are fine. The method presented above has the feature of showing the actual amount of money still remaining in the account on which checks can be drawn.

charge for the month was $1.45. Taking both the service charge and the forgotten check into account, the actual amount of the checkbook balance should be $21.20 less than the $480.28. The difference between $480.28 and $21.20, which is $459.08, is the actual checkbook balance.

In the right section of the solution you can see that there is but one thing that can affect the bank balance, and that is the item called outstanding checks. These are the checks that the person has written, but, as yet, the checks have not cleared the bank, that is, they have not reached the bank. Since the bank is not aware that they have even been written, the amount of these checks has not been subtracted from its balance. On the other hand, in but a few days these checks will be presented to the bank for payment, and hence the actual bank balance should be less than the $509.09 shown. In fact, the amount that must be deducted is $50.01. This is the sum of the three outstanding checks. Thus, when $50.01 is subtracted from the bank balance of $509.09, you find that the actual bank balance of $459.08 is the same as the actual checkbook balance.

EXERCISES   A

When doing the problems in this set of exercises, draw reconciliation forms similar to the one on page 276.

Reconcile the bank balance with the checkbook balance in each of the following exercises.

	Bank Balance	Checkbook Balance	Service Charge	Outstanding Checks	Actual Balance
1.	$246.50	$203.90	$ .60	$43.20	$ 203.30
2.	512.40	446.45	.85	$66.80	445.60
3.	604.70	588.00	1.20	$17.90	586.80
4.	393.20	389.10	.85	$4.95	388.25
5.	827.60	745.55	1.45	$83.50	744.10
6.	752.20	685.60	1.10	$43.20, $24.50	684.50
7.	629.74	555.77	.90	$57.25, $17.62	554.87
8.	483.12	449.34	.65	$9.48, $24.95	448.69
9.	279.06	226.43	1.05	$46.52, $7.16	225.38
10.	941.82	869.50	1.75	$16.58, $4.69, $52.80	867.75

B

1. Reconcile the checkbook balance with the bank balance, using the following information.
   Checkbook balance: $694.23   Bank balance: $620.63
   Checks written that have not cleared the bank: $12.75
   Service charge: $1.15
   Check written but never recorded: $85.20   Actual balance: $607.88

In doing the exercises here, although no special forms are needed, it would be best to use lined paper that is at least 8" by 10½" in size. Have the students outline their work in a manner similar to that shown on page 276.

2. Reconcile the checkbook balance with the bank balance, using the following information.
Checkbook balance: $467.82   Bank balance: $631.63
Checks written that have not cleared the bank: $62.45, $18.75
Service charge: $.95
Deposit made but never recorded: $83.56   Actual balance: $550.43

3. Reconcile the checkbook balance with the bank balance, using the following information.
Checkbook balance: $762.54   Bank balance: $744.72
Checks written that have not cleared the bank: $12.75, $42.80, $26.18
Service charge: $1.40
Check written but never recorded: $169.40
Deposit made but never recorded: $71.25   Actual balance: $662.99

4. When Mr. Johnson received his bank statement on May 2, he noticed that the balance recorded on it was $513.78. In reconciling his checkbook balance of $647.52 with the bank balance, he discovered that a deposit of $84.50 that he had mailed to the bank on April 30 had not arrived in time to be credited to his account. In addition, his examination of the bank statement revealed the following:
Checks written that had not cleared the bank: $20.75, $12.50
Service charge: $1.25
Check written that had never been recorded: $81.24
Prepare a reconciliation statement showing the actual checkbook balance and the actual bank balance for Mr. Johnson's account.

Actual balance: $565.03

Unit 2:   Borrowing Money from a Bank

Section 1:   Determining the Discount and Proceeds,
Using the Discount Formula

Thus far you have examined the services of a bank from the point of view of a depositor who has either a savings account, or a checking account, or possibly both. There is another service that a bank is only too happy to provide for you, and that is to lend money. As pointed out earlier, if a bank were unable to lend money, it could not remain in business, for this is the only means it has of earning money.

The method for computing the charge for borrowing money is exactly the same as the method used for finding the interest on money deposited in a savings account. This means that once again use is made of the interest formula,

$$I = P \times R \times T$$

Now, however, it is called the discount formula and is written as follows:

$$D = P \times R \times T$$

The earnings that are paid for the use of money are called either interest or discount, depending on when the earnings are given. If they are paid at the end of the period, the amount is called *interest*, while if paid at the beginning of the period, they are called *discount*. Thus, when you deposit your money in a savings account, you do not receive any earnings on this money until the end of either a quarter year, or a half year. At that point, the earnings are added to your account. Since you received it after the time was over, these earnings are called interest. When money is borrowed from a bank, the charge for it is taken out in advance. As an illustration, if $500 is borrowed and the charge for it is $20, then the amount you receive is not $500 but only $480. Since the bank receives its earnings of $20 at the outset, these earnings are called discount.

In the illustration above:

> The $500 is called the *principal* of the debt.
> The $20 is called the *discount*.
> The $480 is called the *proceeds* of the debt.

■ILLUSTRATION 1: Find the discount and proceeds on a $600 loan that was made at a discount rate of 6% for a period of 80 days.

●SOLUTION:

$$D = P \times R \times T$$
$$= \$600 \times 6\% \times 80 \text{ days}$$

$$= \$600 \times \frac{6}{100} \times \frac{80}{360}$$

$$= \$8 \text{ (Discount)}$$
$$\text{Proceeds} = \$600 - \$8$$
$$= \$592$$

Money can be borrowed at either an interest or a discount rate. As stated above, if the charge is paid at the moment the debt obligation is made, then the money is borrowed under a discount rate. If the charge is paid when the debt is terminated, then the money is borrowed under an interest rate.

▼EXPLANATION: There is no difference between the application of the interest formula and the discount formula. The distinction is in name only. Notice that once again 360 days are used as the number of days in a year rather than the exact number of days. It is important to realize that the borrower does not receive the amount of money he has asked to borrow, but only the amount that is left after the discount has been subtracted. Incidentally, the amount that is paid back to the bank at the end of the 80 days is $600, for the charge of $8 had been paid at the outset.

Quite apparently, then, if a person needed the full $600, borrowing $600 would not suit his purpose, for he receives but $592 under the conditions of the illustration above. Would borrowing $608 be enough to receive the $600 that he needs? If your answer is "Yes," then you had better consider the following question: "What will the discount be on $608 at 6% for 80 days?"

■ILLUSTRATION 2: Find the proceeds on a $500 loan that was made at a discount rate of 6½% on May 15 for a period of 3 months.

●SOLUTION:

Three months after May 15 is August 15.

Number of days from May 15 to August 15 = 227 − 135

$$= 92$$

$$D = P \times R \times T$$
$$= \$500 \times 6\tfrac{1}{2}\% \times 92 \text{ days}$$

$$= \$500 \times \frac{13}{200} \times \frac{92}{360}$$

$$= \frac{\$299}{36}$$

$$= \$8.306, \text{ or } \$8.31$$

$$\text{Proceeds} = \$500 - \$8.31$$
$$= \$491.69$$

▼EXPLANATION: People frequently ask to borrow money from a bank for a monthly period of time. In this illustration, the person wanted the money for three months. The bank, however, computes the discount by finding the exact number of days in the period, for, by doing so, the charge is usually slightly higher than if it is computed on a monthly basis. The number of days from May 15 to August 15 is found

For all intents and purposes, this unit is much the same as the one in which the students learned to use the interest formula. Now, however, it is called the discount formula. They are now faced with the one additional step of converting the period of time from months to days.

by referring to the table on page 228. How much would the discount have been had 3 months been used as the "Time" in the formula rather than 92 days? How much extra did the bank make by using the 92 days?

EXERCISES   A

1. By using the table on page 228, find the number of days for which each of the following loans was made.

	Date Money Was Borrowed	Number Of Months	Number Of Days
a.	June 5	3	92
b.	July 7	2	62
c.	March 12	4	122
d.	April 26	5	153
e.	May 18	6	184
f.	August 9	4	122
g.	October 16	3	92
h.	September 5	5	153

2. Find the discount on each of the following loans.

	Principal	Discount Rate	Number Of Days	Discount
a.	$ 700	6%	90	$ 10.50
b.	500	6%	40	3.33
c.	300	5%	72	3.00
d.	600	5%	96	8.00
e.	1,200	7%	48	11.20
f.	1,000	6½%	108	19.50
g.	900	5½%	84	11.55
h.	1,800	5½%	132	36.30
i.	900	6¼%	120	18.75
j.	800	6¾%	144	21.60

3. Find the proceeds on each of the following loans.

	Principal	Discount Rate	Number Of Days	Discount	Proceeds
a.	$ 200	6%	60	$ 2.00	$ 198.00
b.	400	7%	90	7.00	393.00
c.	2,000	9%	100	50.00	1,950.00
d.	600	5½%	30	2.75	597.25
e.	720	6½%	80	10.40	709.60

In the selection of the numbers for Exercises 2 through 4, an effort was made to use those in which the fractions involved in the formula could be reduced quite easily.

4. Find the discount on each of the following loans.

Principal	Discount Rate	Date Borrowed	Number Of Months	Discount
a. $ 700	6%	June 7	1	$ 3.50
b. 1,500	5%	September 12	1	6.25
c. 500	7%	January 23	3	8.75
d. 600	7%	February 16	4	14.00
e. 480	5½%	December 19	3	6.60

B

1. Howard Fleming borrowed $750 from a bank for a period of 80 days at a discount rate of 6%.
   a. How much money did he receive from the bank? $740
   b. How much money did he return to the bank? $750

2. On May 23, Charles Cosgrove borrowed $800 from a bank for a period of four months at a discount rate of 6%.
   a. If the bank computed the charge on a monthly basis, how much would the discount have been? $ 16.00
   b. If the bank computed the charge on a daily basis, how much would the discount have been? $ 16.40
   c. How much would Mr. Cosgrove have saved had the discount been computed on a monthly basis rather than on a daily basis?
                                                       $ .40

3. Mr. Eastman borrowed $10,000 from the Grove Savings Bank at a discount rate of 8% for a period of 90 days.
   a. In computing the discount, the loan clerk used the 360-day year. What was the amount of the discount? $200.00
   b. If the loan clerk had used the 365-day year, what would the amount of the discount have been? $197.26
   c. How much would Mr. Eastman have saved if the 365-day year had been used rather than the 360-day year? $ 2.74

4. Raymond Goodwin borrowed $800 for which he had to pay a charge of $50.
   a. If the $50 was called a discount charge, how much did Mr. Goodwin receive and how much did he have to return?   Received: $750, returned: $800.
   b. If the $50 was called an interest charge, how much did Mr. Goodwin receive and how much did he have to return?
                                     Received: $800; returned: $850.

Students frequently are confused by the answer to Problem 1 b, in that they cannot understand why a person should return only $750 to the bank, when that is the amount he borrowed. Stress the fact that he did not receive $750 at the outset, but rather the $750 less discount.

Section 2:   Determining the Discount and Proceeds, Using Tables

Since the computation for finding discount is exactly the same as that for finding interest, the work of the preceding section could have been greatly simplified if use had been made of the interest table on pages 232–233. Rather than call the answer interest, as was done in the earlier application of this table, now the answer will be called discount. The method of using the table, though, is the same as before.

■ ILLUSTRATION 1: Milton Curtis borrowed $450 at a discount rate of 6% for a period of 35 days. How much was he charged for borrowing the money?

● SOLUTION:

Discount on $1 @ 6% for 35 days = $.0058333
Discount on $450 @ 6% for 35 days = 450 × $.0058333
$$= \$2.6249850, \text{ or } \$2.62$$

▼ EXPLANATION: The discount on $1 at a discount rate of 6% for 35 days is $.0058333. The discount on $450 is 450 times as much. Notice that none of the numbers is rounded off until the discount is found. This is done to avoid either overcharging, or undercharging, the borrower by a small amount.

■ ILLUSTRATION 2: Wilfred Pollard borrowed $625 at a discount rate of 5½% on May 19 for a period of three months. What were the proceeds on this loan?

● SOLUTION:

Three months after May 19 is August 19.
Number of days from May 19 to August 19 = 231 − 139
$$= 92$$

Discount on $1 @ 5½% for 60 days = $.0091667
+ Discount on $1 @ 5½% for 32 days =   .0048889
Discount on $1 @ 5½% for 92 days = $.0140556

Discount on $625 @ 5½% for 92 days = 625 × $.0140556
$$= \$8.7847500, \text{ or } \$8.78$$

Proceeds = $625 − $8.78
$$= \$616.22$$

▼ EXPLANATION: Use the table on page 228 to find the number of days from May 19 to August 19—92. Use the table on pages 232–233 to find the discount first for 60 days on $1 at 5½% and then for 32 days. When these two discounts are added together, their total of $.0140556 represents the discount on $1 at 5½% for 92 days. The discount on $625 is $8.78. When the $8.78 is subtracted from the principal of $625, the difference will be a proceeds of $616.22.

The above is pretty much the same as the material taught earlier with the word "discount" replacing the word "interest." The suggestion made at that time was to round off the numbers in the table to the nearest ten thousandth. This suggestion still applies.

EXERCISES   A

1. Use the table on pages 232–233 to find the discount on each of the
   following loans.

	Loan	Discount Rate	Number Of Days	Discount On $1	Discount
a.	$500	6%	31	$ .0051667	$ 2.58
b.	450	5½%	45	.0068750	3.09
c.	250	5%	50	.0069444	1.74
d.	750	5%	35	.0048611	3.65
e.	625	6%	42	.0070000	4.38
f.	845	5½%	54	.0082500	6.97
g.	925	5%	48	.0066667	6.17
h.	400	6%	62	.0103333	4.13
i.	700	5½%	91	.0139028	9.73
j.	800	5%	92	.0127777	10.22

2. Use the table on pages 232–233 to find the proceeds on each of the
   following loans.

	Loan	Discount Rate	Number Of Days	Discount On $1	Discount	Proceeds
a.	$600	6%	32	$ .0053333	$ 3.20	$ 596.80
b.	550	6%	43	.0071667	3.94	546.06
c.	780	5½%	40	.0061111	4.77	775.23
d.	625	5%	52	.0062222	3.89	621.11
e.	900	5%	61	.0084722	7.62	892.38
f.	500	5½%	75	.0114584	5.73	494.27

3. Use the tables on pages 228 and 232–233 to find the discount on
   each of the following loans.

	Loan	Discount Rate	Date Borrowed	Number Of Months	Discount On $1	Discount
a.	$ 200	6%	May 3	1	$ .0051667	$ 1.03
b.	1,400	5½%	June 6	1	.0045833	6.42
c.	800	5½%	February 7	2	.0090139	7.21
d.	1,600	5%	August 23	2	.0084722	13.56
e.	1,200	5%	September 15	3	.0126389	15.17
f.	1,350	5½%	July 18	3	.0140556	18.98

4. Use the tables on pages 228 and 232–233 to find the proceeds on
   each of the following loans.

	Loan	Discount Rate	Date Borrowed	Number Of Months	Discount On $1	Discount	Proceeds
a.	$ 400	5%	January 5	1	$ .0043056	$ 1.72	$ 398.28
b.	700	5%	March 17	1	.0043056	3.01	696.99
c.	650	5½%	February 14	2	.0090139	5.86	644.14
d.	850	5½%	May 23	2	.0093195	7.92	842.08
e.	1,500	6%	June 24	3	.0153333	23.00	1,477.00
f.	1,650	6%	August 10	3	.0153333	25.30	1,624.70

When the students outline Problems 3 and 4 for computational purposes, you might suggest
that they include an additional column that is not shown above. This column should be
entitled "Number of Days," and should appear immediately after the column entitled
"Number of Months."

B

1. Raymond Leach borrowed $4,000 at 6% on June 7 for a period of three months.
   a. How much would the discount charge have been if it had been computed on the three-month period of the loan? $ 60
   b. How much would the discount charge have been if it had been computed on the actual number of days that the money was borrowed? $ 61.33
   c. How much less would it have cost Mr. Leach if the money could have been borrowed on the monthly period rather than on the daily period? $ 1.33

2. Use the tables on pages 228 and 232–233 to find the cost of borrowing $750 on July 14 for a period of 4 months at an interest rate of 6%. $ 15.38

3. Paul Tully borrowed $575 on May 17 from the Triumph Savings Bank at a discount rate of 5½%. He agreed to return the money on September 1. What were the proceeds of the loan that Mr. Tully received? $565.60

4. On September 23, Mr. Shane borrowed $900 from the Mutual Savings Bank of America at a discount rate of 6%. If he agreed to pay back the loan on January 10 of the following year, how much money did he receive from the bank? $883.65

5. Mr. McCabe has a savings account at the Federal Trust Company where he receives an annual interest rate of 4¾%, compounded quarterly. At the time of an emergency, Mr. McCabe needed $1,600 for 90 days. Rather than withdraw the money from his account, he borrowed the $1,600 from the bank at a discount rate of 6%.
   a. How much interest did he receive on the $1,600 by leaving it in his account? $ 19
   b. How much discount did he have to pay by borrowing the $1,600? $ 24
   c. How much more did Mr. McCabe have to pay the bank for the use of the $1,600 than it was paying him? $ 5

6. Alan Keller purchased a car for which he had to pay $3,200. When he went to the bank to withdraw the money, he found that he was going to receive 3 months' interest at 4½% in just 12 days. However, if he withdrew the money immediately, he would lose the interest for the quarterly period on the $3,200.

   a. How much interest would Mr. Keller receive on the $3,200 for the three-month period? $ 36

b. How much would it cost Mr. Keller to borrow the $3,200 at 6%
for the 12 days until the bank paid the interest? $ 6.40

c. How much would Mr. Keller save by borrowing the $3,200 for
12 days rather than by withdrawing his savings before he received the interest? $29.60

Section 3: Borrowing Money from a Bank to Purchase a Car

PART 1

It has been only within recent years that money could be borrowed
from a bank and repaid on the installment plan. Bankers felt that it was
beneath their dignity to lend money under these conditions. However,
once they discovered that there was much more money to be earned by
installment loans than by their normal loans, they gladly provided this
service. Banks now generally grant this type of loan, either on the
purchase of a car, or for covering the cost of making home improve-
ments.

The interest rate charged for an "Automobile Loan" often appears
to be lower than that charged for a normal loan. However, as you will
learn shortly, the actual rate of interest on an automobile loan turns
out to be just about double the rate that it appears to be. To determine
the cost of borrowing the money, the loan clerk will use the interest
formula as described in the following two illustrations.

■ILLUSTRATION 1: What is the cost of borrowing $3,000 from a
bank for the purchase of a car if the loan is to be repaid over an 18-
month period? The interest rate is quoted at 5½% per year.
●SOLUTION:

$$I = P \times R \times T$$
$$= \$3{,}000 \times 5\tfrac{1}{2}\% \times 18 \text{ months}$$

$$= \$\overset{15}{\cancel{3{,}000}} \times \frac{11}{\underset{1}{\cancel{200}}} \times \frac{\overset{3}{\cancel{18}}}{\underset{2}{\cancel{12}}}$$

$$= \frac{\$495}{2}$$

$$= \$247.50 \ (\text{Cost of borrowing } \$3{,}000)$$

▼EXPLANATION: As in the past, the interest formula is applied to
determine the cost of borrowing the money for 18 months. This,
though, is the first time you have come across a situation where the
period of time is greater than 1 year. The fact that the time happens to

Although the "Truth-in-Lending Law" makes it illegal for banks to advertise automobile
loans in this manner any longer, there are still many banks that are doing it. There may very
well be some flaw in the law as it now stands.

be greater than 1 year has no effect on the application of the formula. Where before the period of 3 months or 4 months was written over the 12 months in a year, now it is the 18-month-period that is written over the 12 months. The fraction 18/12 reduces to 3/2, which can be written as 1½, and this, in turn, means that the money was borrowed for 1½ years. Finding the product of $3,000 with the 5½% gives you the interest for only one year. When this is multiplied by 1½, the interest is found for the 18 months, or 1½ years.

■ILLUSTRATION 2: Bruce Denton borrowed $3,400 from his bank at an interest rate of 6%. He plans to return this money in equal monthly installments over a 24-month period. How large will each monthly installment be?

●SOLUTION:

$$I = P \times R \times T$$
$$= \$3,400 \times 6\% \times 24 \text{ months}$$
$$= \$\overset{34}{\cancel{3,400}} \times \frac{6}{\underset{1}{\cancel{100}}} \times \frac{\overset{2}{\cancel{24}}}{\underset{1}{\cancel{12}}}$$
$$= \$408$$
$$\text{Total debt} = \$3,400 + \$408$$
$$= \$3,808$$
$$\text{Monthly installment} = \$3,808 \div 24$$
$$= \$158.66667, \text{ or } \$158.67$$

▼EXPLANATION: The cost of borrowing the money is found in exactly the same manner as in the first illustration. The loan itself is for $3,400, while the interest charge is $408. Hence the total debt to the bank is $3,808. Since it is being paid back over a 24-month period in equal monthly installments, the size of each installment can be found by dividing $3,808 by 24. The quotient, $158.67, is the monthly installment.

EXERCISES   A

1. Determine the cost of each of the following car loans.

	Amount Borrowed	Number Of Monthly Payments	Rate Of Interest Quoted	Interest
a.	$2,000	24	5½%	$220.00
b.	2,400	18	6%	216.00
c.	1,800	30	6%	270.00
d.	1,500	36	5½%	247.50

Emphasize that the computation here is identical with what they have been doing when finding the interest on a debt. Now, however, they carry the work two steps farther — by first finding the total debt and then the monthly installment.

	Amount Borrowed	Number Of Monthly Payments	Rate Of Interest Quoted	Interest
e.	2,800	40	5%	$ 466.67
f.	3,600	12	4½%	162.00
g.	3,200	15	6%	240.00
h.	3,000	20	5½%	275.00

2. How large will the monthly installment payment be on each of the following car loans?

	Amount Borrowed	Number Of Monthly Payments	Rate Of Interest Quoted	Interest	Total Debt	Monthly Payment
a.	$1,600	24	6%	$ 192	$ 1,792	$ 74.67
b.	1,200	30	6%	180	1,380	46.00
c.	2,100	36	5%	315	2,415	67.08
d.	2,400	18	5%	180	2,580	143.33
e.	3,400	12	5½%	187	3,587	298.92
f.	1,800	36	5½%	297	2,097	58.25
g.	2,600	20	4½%	195	2,795	139.75
h.	2,100	32	4½%	252	2,352	73.50

B

The National Detroit Bank advertised the following new-car loan service. Each of the questions in this section is to be answered in terms of this advertisement.

NATIONAL DETROIT BANK

You'll Like Our Low Bank Rates

Unpaid Balance	12 Months Amount Per Month	18 Months Amount Per Month	36 Months Amount Per Month
$1,500	$130.00	$ 88.34	$46.67
2,000	173.34	117.78	62.23
2,400	208.00	141.34	74.67

1. Answer the following questions in terms of the car loan of $1,500.
   a. If the loan were made for a 12-month period, how much money would be repaid to the bank? $1,560
   b. How much more would have been returned to the bank than was borrowed? $60
2. Answer the following questions in terms of the car loan of $2,000.
   a. If the loan were made for an 18-month period, how much money would be repaid to the bank? $2,120.04
   b. If the loan were made for a 36-month period, how much money would be repaid to the bank? $2,240.28
   c. How much more does a 36-month loan on $2,000 cost than an 18-month loan? $120.24

As a class project, have the students visit their banks to pick up advertisements similar to the one here. These advertisements frequently can be found in local newspapers, too. Hopefully some of the loans may be for the same amounts as those in the advertisement above and can, therefore, be compared with them.

3. a. What is the monthly payment on a $2,400 car loan that is to be repaid over a 12-month period? _____$208_____
 b. What is the monthly payment on a $4,800 car loan that is to be repaid over a 12-month period? _____$416_____
4. a. How much would the monthly payments be on a $1,500 loan for a 12-month period if the interest rate were 5%? _____$131.25_____
 b. Is the bank charging more than a 5% interest rate, or less than a 5% interest rate? _____Less than a 5% rate._____

PART 2

In Part 1 of this section, it was suggested in passing that the banks are charging a much higher rate of interest on car loans than would appear on the surface. The examples that follow go into this point rather thoroughly.

Consider a car loan of $2,400 at a quoted interest rate of 5% that is to be paid off monthly over a 24-month period. The banks will compute the interest charge as follows:

$$
\begin{aligned}
I &= P \times R \times T \\
&= \$2,400 \times 5\% \times 24/12 \\
&= \$240
\end{aligned}
$$

When the $240 is added to the original loan of $2,400, the total debt turns out to be $2,640. After dividing this by 24, the monthly payments of $110 are found. By examining the computation carefully, you will notice that the 5% interest rate is charged on the full $2,400 for 24 months. However, after the first month, the borrower no longer owes $2,400, but only $2,300, for he has just made a payment on the debt of $100. The remaining $10 in the $110 monthly payment went toward paying off the $240 in interest. (Although this statement is not quite correct, it is accurate enough for practical purposes.) Similarly, the following month he made another payment of $100 on the debt, and hence he now owes only $2,200. But, as was noted a moment ago, he is still paying interest on the original debt of $2,400. And so, month after month, his debt keeps decreasing by $100 until, during the 24th month, he owes a mere $100. However, month after month he still pays interest on the original $2,400 that he had owed only during the very first month.

To find the exact rate of interest that a person is paying when he borrows money for a car loan requires a background in mathematics that is somewhat beyond that normally taught in high schools. The

If the class is somewhat above average, you may want to point out that the analysis above is not quite valid for, if the interest each month were the $10 noted, then the principal of the debt would be constant. But this we know is not true, for the debt decreases monthly by virtue of the monthly payment.

following formula, though, gives a rather close approximation of this interest rate.

$$R = \frac{24 \times I}{P \times (n + 1)}$$

where:

I = The interest charged on the debt
P = The original principal of the debt
n = The number of monthly installments

It is important that you keep in mind that this formula can be used only when the following conditions are met:
1. All the installments are exactly the same size.
2. The installments are made in monthly periods.

■ILLUSTRATION 1: A person made a car loan of $2,400, at a quoted interest rate of 5%, that is to be paid off monthly over a 30-month period. What actual rate of interest will he be paying?
●SOLUTION:

$$I = P \times R \times T$$
$$= \$2,400 \times 5\% \times 30 \text{ months}$$
$$= \$2,400 \times \frac{5}{100} \times \frac{30}{12}$$
$$= \$300$$
$$R = \frac{24 \times I}{P \times (n + 1)}$$
$$I = \$300; \ P = \$2,400; \ n = 30$$
$$R = \frac{24 \times \$300}{\$2,400 \times 31}$$
$$= .097, \text{ or } 9.7\%$$

▼EXPLANATION: There are three numbers that you must know before you can apply the formula for finding the rate of interest on an installment loan. These are: the principal of the debt, the amount of interest you will have to pay, and the number of months it will take you to pay back the debt. In this illustration, the amount that was borrowed was $2,400; hence, the principal is $2,400. Also, you know that the debt has to be paid off over a 30-month period; thus, the number of months is 30. What you do not know, however, is the interest that is to be charged on this loan. To determine this, you apply the interest formula and find that the charge is $300. With this information, you simply replace the I, P, and n in the rate of interest formula with $300, $2,400, and 30 respectively. There is only one place in which care

Call the attention of the class to the fact that the actual interest rate of 9.7% in Illustration 1 is approximately double what the quoted rate is. As noted earlier in the text (page 286), the actual interest rate will always be slightly less than double the quoted one.

must be taken. Notice that the formula calls for the fact that 1 must be added to the number of months. Hence, the quantity in the parenthesis must be replaced with a number that is 1 larger than the number of months and not by just the number of months alone. After reducing the fraction and dividing the denominator into the numerator, the answer is found first as the decimal .097. To change this decimal numeral to a percent numeral, you merely move the decimal point two places to the right of its position in the decimal numeral.

Early in the course, you studied about the cost of borrowing money for the purchase of an automobile. At that time, you learned that the loan clerk at the bank would refer to a table such as the section of one here to decide how much would have to be repaid the bank and how

MONTHLY PAYMENT TABLE

	18 Months		24 Months		30 Months	
Amount Of Note	Monthly Payment	Amount To Be Repaid	Monthly Payment	Amount To Be Repaid	Monthly Payment	Amount To Be Repaid
$1,200	$ 73.66	$1,325.88	$ 57.00	$1,368.00	$ 47.00	$1,410.00
1,800	110.50	1,989.00	85.50	2,052.00	70.50	2,115.00
2,800	171.88	3,093.84	133.00	3,192.00	109.66	3,289.80

large the monthly payments would be. Actually, the numbers in this table have been found by exactly the same method you are using. Although the bank clerk does not permit you to see it, somewhere at the bottom of his table in very small print is written the numeral 7%. This tells him that the numbers in this table were computed on the basis of a 7% interest rate. Consider as an example the note for $1,200 that is to be paid off over the 24-month period. To find the interest on this debt, apply the interest formula.

$$I = P \times R \times T$$
$$= \$1,200 \times 7\% \times 24 \text{ months}$$
$$= \$\cancel{1,200}^{12} \times \frac{7}{\cancel{100}^{1}} \times \frac{\cancel{24}^{2}}{\cancel{12}^{1}}$$
$$= \$168$$

When the charge of $168 is added to the original debt of $1,200, the amount to be repaid is found to be $1,368. This number is identical with the one that appears in the table.

Here is how to determine just what rate of interest you really are paying on these loans. You can apply the rate of interest formula, for

If the bank clerk complies with the present law, he must tell the borrower that the interest rate is just under 14% and not the 7% rate. Frequently the borrower is not aware of the law, and just as frequently, the lender may deliberately overlook the requirement of quoting the actual rate.

the situation here complies with the two conditions that must be met before the formula can be used. What are these two conditions?

■ILLUSTRATION 2: Using the table above, determine the rate of interest that a car loan borrower will have to pay on an $1,800 loan for an 18-month period.

●SOLUTION:

$$R = \frac{24 \times I}{P \times (n+1)}$$

$$I = \$1,989 - \$1,800 = \$189; \ P = \$1,800; \ n = 18$$

$$R = \frac{\overset{12}{\cancel{24}} \times \$\cancel{189}^{21}}{\cancel{\$1,800} \times 19}$$

$$= \frac{\overset{100}{\cancel{200}}}{100}$$

$$= \frac{252}{1,900}$$

$$= .132, \text{ or } 13.2\%$$

●SOLUTION:

Finding the interest here is even easier than in the first illustration, for in this case you are told both the amount that had to be repaid and the amount that was borrowed. Hence, by subtracting the $1,800 from $1,989, which is the amount that will be repaid, you find the interest charge to be $189. The remainder of the computation is completed in the same manner as before. Incidentally, when dividing 252 by 1,900, the quotient did not come out even. It is sufficient to carry the division to only the third digit after the decimal point, for this is accurate enough for your work. In fact, as was pointed out earlier, the rate of interest formula you are using does not give an exact interest rate. Hence, carrying out the division further would be pretty much a waste of time, for the extra digits would not be correct anyway.

EXERCISES   A

Do you recall how to do the computation in the following exercises? If not, you will probably want to refer to the pages indicated for additional help.

1. Change each of the following decimal numerals to its equivalent percent numeral (page 583).

a. .34	34%	f. .135	13.5%	k. 1.34	134%
b. .56	56%	g. .423	42.3%	l. 5.86	586%
c. .85	85%	h. .589	58.9%	m. 2.03	203%
d. .03	3%	i. .076	7.6%	n. .004	.4%
e. .04	4%	j. .038	3.8%	o. .0025	.25%

Note that here again in Illustration 2, the actual rate turns out to be just under twice the quoted rate.

2. Change each of the following fraction numerals to its equivalent whole number percent numeral (page 583).

a. 1/4 ___25%___   f. 7/50 ___14%___   k. 12/17 ___71%___
b. 3/4 ___75%___   g. 9/100 ___9%___   l. 9/23 ___39%___
c. 2/5 ___40%___   h. 4/25 ___16%___   m. 16/23 ___70%___
d. 3/5 ___60%___   i. 17/20 ___85%___   n. 165/281 ___59%___
e. 4/5 ___80%___   j. 9/10 ___90%___   o. 327/562 ___58%___

3. Reduce each of the following fractions to its lowest terms (page 573).

a. $\dfrac{5}{7 \times 10} = $ ___1/14___   g. $\dfrac{16 \times 100}{10 \times 32} = $ ___5___

b. $\dfrac{12}{16 \times 27} = $ ___1/36___   h. $\dfrac{60 \times 14}{21 \times 50} = $ ___4/5___

c. $\dfrac{24 \times 2}{16} = $ ___3___   i. $\dfrac{24 \times 100}{500 \times 12} = $ ___2/5___

d. $\dfrac{25 \times 42}{30} = $ ___35___   j. $\dfrac{24 \times 25}{600 \times 13} = $ ___1/13___

e. $\dfrac{2 \times 10}{8 \times 5} = $ ___1/2___   k. $\dfrac{24 \times 60}{1,200 \times 25} = $ ___6/125___

f. $\dfrac{15 \times 9}{6 \times 5} = $ ___9/2___   l. $\dfrac{24 \times 108}{3,600 \times 27} = $ ___2/75___

4. Round off each of the following decimals to the third digit to the right of the decimal point (pages 593–594).

a. .2472 ___.247___   d. .1476 ___.148___   g. .1625 ___.163___
b. .3604 ___.360___   e. .1158 ___.116___   h. .2796 ___.280___
c. .0890 ___.089___   f. .0949 ___.095___   i. .1895 ___.190___

B

When doing the problems in this section, refer to the following.

THE BANKERS' NEW–CAR PAYMENT PLAN

	18 Months		24 Months		30 Months	
Amount Of Note	Finance Charge	Amount To Be Repaid	Finance Charge	Amount To Be Repaid	Finance Charge	Amount To Be Repaid
$1,000	$ 97.50	$1,097.50	$130.00	$1,130.00	$162.50	$1,162.50
2,000	195.00	2,195.00	260.00	2,260.00	325.00	2,325.00

1. For the 18-month plan, how much more did the borrower have to repay than he had received on the $1,000 loan? ___$97.50___
2. For the 24-month plan, how much more did the borrower have to repay than he had received on the $2,000 loan? ___$260.00___
3. For the 24-month plan, how much did the borrower have to repay monthly on the $1,000 loan? ___$47.08___

The exercises in A 3 are designed to give the student practice in simplifying fractions of a nature similar to those he will encounter in computing the rate of interest on the automobile loan.

4. For the 30-month plan, how much did the borrower have to repay monthly on the $2,000 loan? <u>$ 77.50</u>
5. The loans in this table were advertised as 6½% loans.
   a. Find the interest on the $2,000 loan for the period of 24 months at an interest rate of 6½%. <u>$260.00</u>
   b. Find the interest on the $1,000 loan for the period of 18 months at an interest rate of 6½%. <u>$ 97.50</u>
   c. Do the interest charges you found for parts "a" and "b" agree with the finance charges shown in the table? <u>Yes</u>
6. What actual rate of interest is the borrower paying on the loan of $1,000 for the 24-month period? <u>12.5%</u>
7. What actual rate of interest is the borrower paying on the loan of $2,000 for the 24-month period? <u>12.5%</u>
8. What actual rate of interest is the borrower paying on the loan of $2,000 for the 30-month period? <u>12.6%</u>

C

When doing the problems in this section, refer to the following table.

THE BANKERS' USED–CAR PAYMENT PLAN

Amount Of Note	12 Months		24 Months		36 Months	
	Finance Charge	Amount To Be Repaid	Finance Charge	Amount To Be Repaid	Finance Charge	Amount To Be Repaid
$1,000	$130	$1,130	$260	$1,260	$390	$1,390
2,000	260	2,260	520	2,520	780	2,780

1. In terms of the 24-month plan on the loan of $1,000:
   a. How much more interest would a borrower of $1,000 have to pay if he purchased a used car rather than a new car as in Problem Set B? <u>$130.00</u>
   b. How large is the monthly payment in this plan? <u>$ 52.50</u>
   c. How much more would a borrower of $1,000 have to pay each month if he purchased a used car rather than a new car? (See Problem B-3, page 293.) <u>$ 5.42</u>
2. In terms of the $2,000 loan:
   a. How much more would a borrower have to pay if he paid off his debt over a 3-year period rather than a 1-year period? <u>$520.00</u>
   b. How large is each monthly payment if the debt is paid off in two years? <u>$105.00</u>
   c. How large is each monthly payment if the debt is paid off in one year? <u>$188.33</u>

Compare the interest rates in the Used-Car Payment Plan above with those of the New-Car Payment Plan on the preceding page.

3. The numbers in this table were based on a 13% annual interest rate on the original value of the note.
   a. Find the interest on the $2,000 loan for the period of 24 months at an interest rate of 13%. $520.00
   b. Find the interest on the $1,000 loan for the period of 36 months at an interest rate of 13%. $390.00
   c. Do the interest charges you found for parts "a" and "b" agree with the finance charges shown in the table?   Yes
4. What actual rate of interest is a borrower paying on a loan of $1,000 for the 12-month period?   24.0%
5. What actual rate of interest is a borrower paying on a loan of $2,000 for the 36-month period?   25.3%
6. a. What actual rate of interest is a borrower paying on the loan of $1,000 for the 24-month period?   25.0%
   b. How does this rate of interest compare with the rate paid by a new-car purchaser who borrowed $1,000 for 24 months? (See Problem B-6, page 294.)   Double
7. In Problem 3, it was stated that the numbers in the table are based on a 13% annual rate of interest. By examining your answers to Problems 4, 5, and 6a, approximately how many times as large as the quoted rate of 13% is the actual rate?   About twice as large.

D

1. Mr. Greene made a car loan of $3,000 at a quoted rate of 6%. The loan is to be paid off monthly over a 24-month period. What actual rate of interest will Mr. Green be paying? (See Illustration 1 on page 290.)   11.5%
2. Shortly after Ralph Evers was graduated from high school, his father bought him a used car. In order to make the purchase, Mr. Evers had to borrow $1,000, which he agreed to pay off monthly over a period of 18 months. When computing the interest charge, the bank used a 9% rate on the original loan of $1,000.
   a. How much interest did Mr. Evers have to pay on this loan?
                                                                     $135.00
   b. What actual rate of interest was he paying?   17.1%
3. Two months after he started working, Bob Jamieson purchased a new convertible car by making a down payment of $400 on the total price of $2,800. The balance of the money he borrowed from the bank at a quoted rate of 5½%. The loan was to be paid back monthly over a 2-year period.
   a. How much interest did Bob have to pay on the loan? $264.00
   b. What actual rate of interest is he paying?   10.6%

Unit 3:   Chapter Review and Test

1. In terms of the Special-Checking-Account Plan described on page 265, determine the charge for the month that would have to be paid if the following number of checks were issued:
   a. 7 ___$1.20___   b. 15 ___$2.00___   c. 36 ___$4.10___

2. In terms of the Flat-Payment-Checking-Account Plan described on page 265, determine the charge for the month that would have to be paid for the following minimum balances. Do not consider the yearly charge when finding your answer.
   a. $523.17 ___$0___   b. $114.86 ___$2___   c. $295.24 ___$1___

3. In terms of the Analysis-Checking-Account Plan described on page 267, determine the charge for the month that would have to be paid on accounts that had the following activity:
   a. Minimum balance: $456; number of checks issued: 27
                                                              ___$ .35___
   b. Minimum balance: $242; number of checks issued: 19
                                                              ___$ .70___
   c. Minimum balance: $196; number of checks issued: 22; number of deposits: 2   ___$1.20___

4. Draw a checkbook page form similar to the one on page 272. Use the following information to complete this form, including the balance that is to be forwarded to the following page of the checkbook.
   Balance brought forward: $456.32
   Checks issued: June 14, Roger's Motors, $42.70
                    June 14, John Soyden, $14.10
                    June 15, Bednar Door Company, $145.00
   Deposit: June 15, $87.35   Balance: ___$341.87___

5. Use the following information to reconcile the checkbook balance with the bank balance.
   Checkbook balance: $342.80   Bank balance: $458.60
   Checks written that have not cleared the bank: $52, $65
   Service charge: $1.20   Actual balance: ___$341.60___

6. Use the table on page 228 to find the number of days for which each of the following loans was made.
   a. Money was borrowed on April 15 for 4 months.   ___122 days___
   b. Money was borrowed on November 6 for 3 months.   ___92 days___

7. How large is the discount on a loan of $600 at a discount rate of 7% for a period of 90 days?   ___$10.50___

8. William Gans borrowed $400 from a bank at a discount rate of 7½% for a period of 120 days.

By using parts of the above problems for a review, the remaining parts can be used for testing purposes.

a. How much did Mr. Gans actually receive from the bank?

$ 390.00

b. How much did Mr. Gans return to the bank? $ 400.00

9. Use the Simple Interest Table on pages 232–233 to find the discount on each of the following loans.

a. $600 at 5% for 32 days $ 2.67

b. $1,000 at 5½% for 89 days 13.60

10. On May 12, Mr. Hernandez borrowed $800 from his bank for a period of three months at a discount rate of 6%.

a. Use the timetable on page 228 and the Simple Interest Table on pages 232–233 to find the discount that Mr. Hernandez had to pay on this loan. $ 12.27

b. What were the proceeds of this loan? $ 787.73

11. When David Garner purchased his new car, he borrowed $2,500 from the bank at a 6% interest rate, to be paid back monthly over a period of two years.

a. How much interest did Mr. Garner have to pay on this loan?

$ 300.00

b. What was the total amount of money that he paid back to the bank? $2,800.00

c. How large was each of the monthly installments that Mr. Garner paid? $ 116.67

12. If the purchaser of a used car borrows $2,000 from the Second National Bank of Seaside, to be paid back monthly over a period of two years, his monthly payment will be $100.

a. What is the total amount of money that the borrower will return to the bank? $2,400.00

b. What interest is the borrower paying on this loan? $ 400.00

c. What interest rate is the borrower paying on this loan?

19.2%

CHAPTER **8**

INSTALLMENT
PURCHASES
AND SMALL LOANS

In Chapter 7, a formula was given for finding the rate of interest on an automobile loan that was to be paid off in installments. This formula has many other applications. In fact, every time you are faced with a situation where you are repaying money in equal periodic installments, you should start thinking in terms of this formula. This may include paying off a debt to a friend, or paying off a dealer for a motorcycle you bought, or paying off an airline company for last year's vacation trip, and on and on. Some of you will even use the formula to help you decide whether the purchase you are about to make is really worth the high interest rate you have to pay, or whether you should wait until you have the cash to pay for it.

If the "Truth-in-Leading Law" were adhered to strictly by all sellers, the early units in this chapter would prove to be unnecessary, for the buyer would be told the actual rate of interest he had to pay on an installment purchase.

Unit 1:   Interest Rate on an Installment Purchase

Section 1:   Computing the Interest Rate by Formula

Earlier in your work you discussed how to find the additional cost you had to pay whenever you purchased an article on the installment plan. The formula on page 290 now puts you in a position where you are able to find the rate of interest you are being asked to pay. You will find that in general these rates come rather high.

Too often when doing computation for problems in arithmetic you think only in terms of getting an answer rather than what the answer may mean. It might be a good idea to consider the answers to the problems in this chapter in terms of the interest rate you are paid when you keep your own money in the bank. Except for certain special accounts, the maximum rate that a bank can legally pay its depositors is 5%. Hence, when you find that the rate of interest paid by installment purchasers is 25%, 60%, or even 150%, it might be well to say to yourself that this is 5 times, or even 12 times, or, possibly, 30 times the rate you receive when you keep your money in the bank.

Suppose you again take a look at the problem examined on page 290. Now, instead of merely finding the additional cost the installment purchaser has to pay, you will also determine the rate of interest on the purchase.

■ILLUSTRATION 1: A 4-piece living-room suite that regularly sells for $325 can be bought on the installment plan for $20 down and $25 a month for 15 months. What rate of interest will an installment purchaser have to pay?

▼EXPLANATION: Your first task, as in the earlier solution, is to determine the installment charge on this purchase. Actually, an installment purchase can be considered in much the same way as the repayment of an automobile loan to a bank. Before, the additional charge you paid was called the interest on the debt, but now it is called the installment charge. Whatever its name may be, it is still the amount you repay more than you actually borrow. The term "borrow" is deliberately used here, for, in reality, you are borrowing money from the dealer to pay him for the living-room suite, since you, yourself, do not have the money to pay for it. In view of this, you must pay him interest on this loan, and the installment charge is that interest.

Discuss with the students why a dealer may be justified in charging an added amount to the installment purchaser.

●SOLUTION:

$$\text{Total of monthly installments} = 15 \times \$25$$
$$= \$375$$
$$\text{Installment price} = \$20 + \$375$$
$$= \$395$$
$$\text{Installment charge or interest} = \$395 - \$325$$
$$= \$70$$

$$R = \frac{24 \times I}{P \times (n+1)}$$

$$I = \$70; \ P = \$325 - \$20 = \$305; \ n = 15$$

$$R = \frac{\overset{3}{\cancel{24}} \times \overset{\overset{7}{\cancel{14}}}{\cancel{70}}}{\underset{61}{\cancel{305}} \times \underset{2}{\cancel{16}}}$$

$$= \frac{21}{61}$$

$$= .344, \text{ or } 34.4\%$$

▼ EXPLANATION (continued): It is easy to see that the solution is simply a combination of two problems that you are familiar with. The first of these involves finding the installment charge, or interest, and this you investigated on page 289. The second involves determining the rate of interest. This, too, you investigated on page 290. The only questionable step is the one that relates to finding the principal of the debt (P). Notice that the down payment of $20 was subtracted from the cash price of $325, leaving a difference of $305 that is used as the principal. The reasoning behind this goes somewhat as follows: If you had the cash to pay for the living-room suite, it would have cost you only $325. However, you had only $20, so the remaining $305 had to be borrowed. This amount, therefore, represents the principal of your debt.

Before leaving this problem, it might be well to notice that the interest rate the installment purchaser is being asked to pay (34.4%) is probably 7 times as much as he receives for the money deposited in his savings account.

■ ILLUSTRATION 2: Mr. Bamberg purchased a $480 refrigerator-freezer combination by making a 10% down payment and paying off the balance over a three-year period in equal monthly payments of $17.50 each. What interest rate did Mr. Bamberg have to pay by buying the refrigerator-freezer on the installment plan?

As is done in the closing paragraph of the explanation of Illustration 1, always compare the rate of interest the installment purchaser is being asked to pay with the rate of interest offered by banks in the local community. If this is not done, the answers will be meaningless numbers.

●SOLUTION:

$$\text{Total of monthly installments} = 36 \times \$17.50$$
$$= \$630$$

$$\text{Down payment} = 10\% \times \$480$$
$$= .10 \times \$480$$
$$= \$48$$

$$\text{Installment price} = \$630 + \$48$$
$$= \$678$$

$$\text{Installment charge or interest} = \$678 - \$480$$
$$= \$198$$

$$R = \frac{24 \times I}{P \times (n+1)}$$

$$I = \$198; \ P = \$480 - \$48 = \$432; \ n = 36$$

$$R = \frac{\overset{1}{\cancel{24}} \times \overset{11}{\cancel{198}}}{\underset{18}{\cancel{432}} \times \underset{1}{\cancel{37}}}$$

$$= \frac{11}{37}$$

$$= .297, \text{ or } 29.7\%$$

▼EXPLANATION: Except for the fact that you are now finding the interest rate rather than the installment charge, this problem is the same as Illustration 2 on page 292. In view of this, the explanation for finding the installment charge is the same now as it was earlier. Why was 36 used as the total number of months? In finding the principal of the debt, why was $48 subtracted from $480? Why was 37 rather than 36 written in the denominator of the fraction for finding the rate of interest?

In the event you may have forgotten, the formula

$$R = \frac{24 \times I}{P \times (n+1)}$$

can be used for finding the rate of interest on a debt only if two conditions are met. What are these conditions? (See page 290.) Can you explain why it is possible to apply the formula to Illustrations 1 and 2? Can you give an example of a debt where this formula could not be used to solve the problem?

There is no question but that the computation in this section is probably more difficult than any other found in the text, and it should be approached very slowly and carefully.

EXERCISES   **A**

1. Determine the principal of the debt in each of the following installment purchases.

	Down Payment	Cash Price	Principal
a.	$10.00	$120.00	$ 110.00
b.	14.00	134.00	120.00
c.	26.00	358.00	332.00
d.	18.50	98.50	80.00
e.	56.25	425.25	369.00
f.	37.95	549.95	512.00

2. Determine the principal of the debt in each of the following installment purchases.

	Cash Price	Down Payment (Rate)	Down Payment	Principal
a.	$200	10%	$ 20.00	$ 180.00
b.	250	20%	50.00	200.00
c.	350	5%	17.50	332.50
d.	425	15%	63.75	361.25
e.	675	50%	337.50	337.50
f.	595	25%	148.75	446.25

3. Determine the principal of the debt and the interest (installment
   charge) in each of the following installment purchases.

	Down Payment	Monthly Payments	Number Of Months	Installment Price	Cash Price	Interest	Principal
a.	$10	$20	8	$ 170.00	$150	$ 20.00	$ 140.00
b.	30	15	10	180.00	145	35.00	115.00
c.	15	25	12	315.00	275	40.00	260.00
d.	55	18	15	325.00	280	45.00	225.00
e.	64	21	24	568.00	498	70.00	434.00
f.	39	14	36	543.00	409	134.00	370.00

4. Determine the principal of the debt and the interest (installment
   charge) in each of the following installment purchases.

	Cash Price	Down Payment (Rate)	Monthly Payments	Number Of Months	Installment Price	Interest	Principal
a.	$ 50	10%	$ 5	12	$ 65.00	$ 15.00	$ 45.00
b.	200	20%	10	18	220.00	20.00	160.00
c.	120	15%	6	24	162.00	42.00	102.00
d.	900	40%	35	30	1,410.00	510.00	540.00
e.	750	25%	28	36	1,195.00	445.50	562.50
f.	525	35%	37	15	738.75	213.75	341.25

Through the arrangement of these exercises, an effort is made to compute each of the numbers
required in the formula before calling on the student to apply the formula itself.

5. Determine the rate of interest paid by the buyer in each of the following installment purchases.

	Interest (I)	Principal (P)	Number of Months (n)	Interest Rate
a.	$ 6	$ 30	5	_____ 80 %
b.	8	48	7	_____ 50 %
c.	9	24	4	_____ 180 %
d.	50	200	23	_____ 25 %
e.	25	100	11	_____ 50 %
f.	75	300	9	_____ 60 %
g.	20	64	24	_____ 30 %
h.	52	600	12	_____ 16 %

6. Determine the rate of interest paid by the buyer in each of the following installment purchases.

	Down Payment	Monthly Payments	Number Of Months	Installment Price	Cash Price	Interest	Principal	Interest Rate
a.	$10	$ 2	15	$____ 40	$ 30	$___ 10	$___ 20	75 %
b.	20	5	11	75	60	15	40	75 %
c.	16	12	7	100	76	24	60	120 %
d.	21	7	23	182	121	61	100	61 %
e.	25	15	17	280	205	75	180	55.6 %
f.	14	9	12	122	96	26	82	58.5 %
g.	20	7	18	146	116	30	96	39.5 %
h.	16	16	24	400	225	175	209	80.4 %

7. Determine the rate of interest paid by the buyer in each of the following installment purchases.

	Cash Price	Down Payment (Rate)	Monthly Payments	Number Of Months	Installment Price	Interest	Principal	Interest Rate
a.	$ 80	10%	$ 6	17	$___ 110	$___ 30	$___ 72	55.6 %
b.	300	20%	15	23	405	105	240	43.8 %
c.	250	30%	20	11	295	45	175	51.4 %
d.	420	15%	13	36	531	111	357	20.2 %

B

1. Washington Electronics offered to sell its $120 solid-state stereo receiver to installment purchasers under the following terms:

> No down payment
> A credit service charge of $12
> Equal monthly payments spread over a 2-year period

What rate of interest was the buyer being charged?   ___9.6%___

2. After shoveling snow for years, Joe Baker bought a $275 snow blower. He did not have the cash to pay for the blower, so he put $25 down and agreed to pay off the rest in 18 equal monthly install- ments of $17.50 each. What rate of interest did Mr. Baker have to pay by buying the snow blower on the installment plan? _32.8%_

3. The Acme Home Repair Company advertised that it would sell its deluxe, heavy-duty electronic garage door opener for $149.95 cash. The installment buyer could have this same power system by mak- ing a down payment of $19.95 and equal monthly payments of $13.25 each over a period of one year. What rate of interest is the installment purchaser being asked to pay?   _41.2%_

4. When Jim Bailey organized his 4-piece combo, he invested in a $159.50, 70-watt, solid-state, twin-speaker, 2-channel amplifier for the group. Since he didn't have the cash to pay for the amplifier, he arranged to make a 10% down payment and pay off the rest in 9 equal monthly installments of $18.45 each. What rate of interest did Jim pay by buying the instrument on the installment plan?
_37.6%_

C

By making a small change, the rate of interest formula that you have been using for the monthly installment plan can be used for the weekly installment plan. You may recall that you were not shown how this formula was developed. If you had been shown, you would have seen that the 24 in the numerator of the formula came from multiplying 2 by the number of months in a year. Hence, if payments are made weekly, the development of the formula calls for multiplying the num- ber of weeks in one year by 2. Therefore, instead of having 24 in the numerator, the weekly interest rate formula has 104. How is the 104 arrived at? The new formula is:

$$R = \frac{104 \times I}{P \times (n+1)}$$

What number would have replaced the 24 if the payments had been made quarterly, that is, four times a year? What number would have replaced the 24 if the payments had been made semiannually?

1. Determine the rate of interest paid by the buyer in each of the fol- lowing installment purchases that were paid off weekly.

As in the case of the rate of interest formula for monthly installments, the formula above must comply with the requirements that the payments be made monthly and that they be constant. Call the student's attention again to the fact this formula gives only a close approximation of the interest rate.

	Interest (I)	Principal (P)	Number of Weeks (n)	Interest Rate
a.	$30	$100	51	$\dfrac{60}{}$ %
b.	40	320	25	$\dfrac{50}{}$ %
c.	38	832	18	$\dfrac{25}{}$ %
d.	18	120	77	$\dfrac{20}{}$ %
e.	15	350	20	$\dfrac{21.2}{}$ %
f.	38	110	75	$\dfrac{47.3}{}$ %

2. Determine the rate of interest paid by the buyer in each of the following installment purchases that were paid off weekly.

	Down Payment	Weekly Payments	Number Of Weeks	Installment Price	Cash Price	Interest	Principal	Interest Rate
a.	$ 0	$4	25	$ 100	$ 90	$ 10	$ 90	44.4 %
b.	0	2	51	102	80	22	80	55 %
c.	34	7	38	300	250	50	216	61.7 %
d.	6	1	44	50	41	9	35	59.4 %
e.	20	5	52	280	220	60	200	58.9 %
f.	25	3	100	325	285	40	260	15.8 %

Section 2:   Short Method for Computing the Interest Rate

The formula used in Section 1 of this unit for finding the rate of interest on an installment purchase is a good one to know. Its big weakness, though, is that computation takes too long when it is used. If you happen to be in a quiet place, where no one is watching you, that's fine. But all too often you need to apply the formula while you are in a busy, noisy store where a salesman is giving you a rapid-fire sales talk. Hence, it would be much better if you had a faster and easier way than the formula for finding the rate of interest on an installment purchase.

There is, of course, a simpler method but, unfortunately, it does not give quite so accurate an answer as the formula does. Because it is relatively easy to use and the answers are accurate enough for all practical purposes, it is included here. Before examining this method, however, it will be necessary to review a few ideas you learned earlier.

Recall that when you had to find the interest on a debt that was made for a period of one year, it was necessary to multiply the principal of the debt by the annual rate of interest. (See page 220.) In doing this, you used this formula:

$$P \times R = I \qquad ①$$

What you are concerned with now is in finding the annual rate of interest where the principal and interest are known to you. This can easily be accomplished by applying the Product of Two Numbers

Many simple devices have been developed for determining the interest rate on installment purchases. The one presented here is probably as simple and as accurate as any. It would be foolish to let the student think that this method could be applied mentally at the time of purchase. None can!

Principle to equation ①. (See page 36.) When this is done, the formula becomes:

$$R = I \div P$$

When the formula is interpreted as a statement, it will read:

> "The rate of interest is equal to the interest divided by the principal."

As an illustration, if a person borrowed $100 and had to pay $20 interest on this loan, to find the rate of interest you would simply divide the $20 by $100 to get the decimal .20. This, in turn, would be rewritten as the percent numeral 20%. Now, if the loan were for a period of one year, then 20% would be the annual rate of interest. However, if the loan were paid back in 6 months, then 20% would represent the rate of interest for one half year (six months is one half year). To find the interest rate for the entire year, you would have to double the 20% to get 40% for a full year's interest rate.

On the other hand, if the debt were paid back in two years, then the interest rate for one year would be only half the 20%, or 10%. If the debt were paid back in 4 years, what would the annual interest rate be? If the debt were paid back after 3 years, what would the annual interest rate be? If the debt were paid back after 1/3 of a year, what would the annual interest rate be? How many months are there in 1/3 of a year? If the debt were paid back in 4 months, what would the annual interest rate be?

There is only one more point to examine before it is possible to show how to use the new method for finding the rate of interest on an installment purchase. Consider the case where you are paying off a $200 purchase in monthly installments over a two-year period. During the first month, since you have made no payments, you owe the full $200. As each month passes, however, your debt keeps decreasing, for payments are being made. And finally, on that very last month, you owe practically nothing, for most of the debt has been paid off. Hence, you can say that your average debt over the two-year period is about one half of the $200, or $100. For the first 12 months, the debt was more than $100, while for the last 12 months, it was less than $100. Hence, rather than say that you owed $200 the first month, about $192 the second month, about $183 the third month and, finally, only about $8 the last month, you can say that on the average you owed about $100 every month. It is this average debt that you are going to use for finding the rate of interest.

Give the students a number of oral exercises in which they are required to convert a semiannual, or a quarterly, interest rate to an annual rate. Upon completion of these, have them turn to page 308 to check their method against the method shown in the table.

■ILLUSTRATION 1: A radio can be purchased for $50 cash. An installment buyer can buy the same radio for $60 by making no down payment and making equal monthly payments of $5 each for a period of one year. What rate of interest is being paid when this radio is bought on the installment plan?

▼EXPLANATION: Since no down payment has to be made, the original principal of the debt is $50 and, hence, the average principal over the 12-month period is $25. The difference between the installment price and the cash price is $10, which means that the interest on the debt is $10. Therefore, the rate of interest can now be found by dividing the interest by the average principal.

●SOLUTION:

$$\text{Interest} = \$60 - \$50$$
$$= \$10$$
$$\text{Average debt} = \$50 \div 2$$
$$= \$25$$
$$\text{Rate of interest} = \$10 \div \$25$$
$$= .40 \text{ or } 40\%$$

It might be interesting to compare the rate found above with the one you would get by using the formula:

$$R = \frac{24 \times I}{P \times (n+1)}$$
$$I = \$10; \ P = \$50; \ n = 12$$
$$R = \frac{24 \times \overset{1}{\cancel{10}}}{\underset{5}{\cancel{50}} \times 13}$$
$$= \frac{24}{65}$$
$$= .369, \text{ or } 37\%$$

Thus, you can see that there is relatively little difference between the two answers—40% and 37%.

■ILLUSTRATION 2: Freddy Bigelow bought a 15-piece professional drum outfit. Had he had the cash, it would have cost him only $200. But, not having it, he was able to pay for the drums by making a down payment of $20 and paying off the rest in equal monthly installments of $10 each over a two-year period. What rate of interest did Freddy have to pay on his drum outfit?

You might want to point out to the students that the "short" method will always give an interest rate which is greater than that found by the formula. However, the greater the number of payments there are, the closer to each other will the rates become.

●SOLUTION:

$$\text{Principal of debt} = \$200 - \$20$$
$$= \$180$$
$$\text{Average debt} = \$180 \div 2$$
$$= \$90$$
$$\text{Total of monthly installments} = 24 \times \$10$$
$$= \$240$$
$$\text{Installment price} = \$240 + \$20$$
$$= \$260$$
$$\text{Interest} = \$260 - \$200$$
$$= \$60$$
$$\text{Rate of interest for two years} = \$60 \div \$90$$
$$= .667, \text{ or } 66.7\%$$
$$\text{Rate of interest for one year} = 33\%$$

▼EXPLANATION: As in Illustration 1, the rate of interest is found by dividing the interest by the average debt. However, since the debt was paid off over a two-year period, the rate of 66.7% represents a two-year rate. To determine the rate for one year requires dividing the 66.7% by 2. If you wonder why you are finding an annual rate rather than leaving your answer in terms of the two-year rate, it might be well to point out again that all interest rates (unless otherwise noted) are quoted for a period of one year. What would the interest rate have been if the debt had been paid back monthly over a three-year period? What would it have been had it been paid back over a six-month period?

If the debt is paid back over a three-month period (one quarter of a year), then multiply the interest rate found by 4. If it is paid back over a four-month period, then multiply the interest rate found by 3. Why? See if you can determine how the numbers in the table below were arrived at.

If the Number Of Monthly Payments Is:	Then to Find The Annual Interest Rate
3	Multiply by 4
4	Multiply by 3
6	Multiply by 2
12	Multiply by 1
18	Divide by 1.5
24	Divide by 2
30	Divide by 2.5
36	Divide by 3

The table should not be applied without developing how the values in the table were derived.

Should the number of monthly payments be other than those listed above, then it will be just as simple to use the formula for finding the rate of interest on an installment purchase as it would be to use the short method. Don't overlook the fact that the short method can be used only if the equal payments are made monthly. It cannot be applied when payments are made weekly.

EXERCISES   **A**

Whenever the rate of interest is called for in the following exercises, round off each answer to the nearest whole number percent value.
1. What is the average debt on each of the following installment purchases?

	Cash Price	Down Payment	Average Debt
a.	$200	$ 0	$ 100.00
b.	120	0	60.00
c.	80	10	35.00
d.	150	15	67.50
e.	275	25	125.00
f.	463	75	194.00

2. What is the average debt on each of the following installment purchases?

	Cash Price	Down Payment (Rate)	Down Payment	Average Debt
a.	$100	20%	$ 20.00	$ 40.00
b.	400	10%	40.00	180.00
c.	240	50%	120.00	60.00
d.	80	25%	20.00	30.00
e.	75	15%	11.25	31.88
f.	129	5%	6.45	61.28

3. Use the short method to determine the rate of interest paid by the buyer in each of the following installment purchases. The debt was paid off in equal monthly installments over the period of one year.

	Down Payment	Cash Price	Average Debt	Interest	Interest Rate
a.	$ 0	$ 80	$ 40	$10	25 %
b.	0	250	125	25	20 %
c.	20	140	60	15	25 %
d.	60	300	120	60	50 %
e.	15	75	30	12	40 %
f.	9	139	65	26	40 %
g.	17	247	115	45	39 %
h.	26	376	175	58	33 %

The student should find these exercises far easier and, perhaps, for that reason, far more interesting than the earlier ones that involve the rate-of-interest formula on an installment purchase.

4. Use the short method to determine the rate of interest paid by the buyer in each of the following installment purchases. The debt was paid off in equal monthly installments over the period of one year.

	Down Payment (Rate)	Cash Price	Down Payment	Average Debt	Interest	Interest Rate
a.	10%	$ 80	$ 8.00	$ 36.00	$ 9	25 %
b.	20%	140	28.00	56.00	28	50 %
c.	25%	200	50.00	75.00	25	33 %
d.	10%	65	6.50	29.25	10	34 %
e.	15%	250	37.50	106.25	50	47 %
f.	50%	420	210.00	105.00	30	29 %

5. Use the short method to determine the rate of interest paid by the buyer in each of the following installment purchases. The debt was paid off in equal monthly installments over the period of one year.

	Down Payment	Cash Price	Average Debt	Monthly Installments	Interest	Interest Rate
a.	$ 0	$120	$ 60	$12.00	$ 24	40 %
b.	0	150	75	16.00	42	56 %
c.	15	85	35	8.00	26	74 %
d.	5	69	32	6.50	14	44 %
e.	19	179	80	15.50	26	33 %
f.	18	238	110	20.25	23	21 %
g.	25	465	220	42.75	73	33 %

6. Use the short method to determine the rate of interest paid by the buyer in each of the following installment purchases where no down payment was required.

	Cash Price	Average Debt	Monthly Installments	Number Of Months	Interest	Interest Rate
a.	$ 60	$ 30	$12	6	$ 12	80 %
b.	100	50	18	6	8	32 %
c.	120	60	24	6	24	80 %
d.	86	43	16	6	10	46 %
e.	80	40	30	3	10	100 %
f.	150	75	60	3	30	160 %
g.	246	123	90	3	24	78 %
h.	88	44	34	3	14	127 %
i.	50	25	14	4	6	72 %
j.	150	75	42	4	18	72 %
k.	172	86	45	4	8	28 %
l.	348	174	91	4	16	28 %

7. Use the short method to determine the rate of interest paid by the buyer in each of the following installment purchases where no down payment was required.

In Exercises 6, 7, and 8, ask students to include an extra column when outlining the work. The heading of this column should be "Total of Monthly Installments," and it should appear immediately following the column headed "Number of Months." In Exercise 5, it should follow "Monthly Installment" column.

	Cash Price	Average Debt	Monthly Installments	Number Of Months	Interest	Interest Rate
a.	$100	$ 50	$ 5.00	24	$ 20	20 %
b.	170	85	8.00	24	22	13 %
c.	96	48	4.50	24	12	13 %
d.	400	200	14.00	36	104	17 %
e.	500	250	19.50	36	202	27 %
f.	660	330	22.25	36	141	14 %
g.	200	100	13.00	18	34	23 %
h.	150	75	10.50	18	39	35 %
i.	84	42	6.50	18	33	52 %
j.	300	150	15.00	30	150	40 %
k.	440	220	17.50	30	85	15 %
l.	534	267	21.50	30	111	17 %

8. Use the short method to determine the rate of interest paid by the buyer in each of the following installment purchases.

	Down Payment	Cash Price	Average Debt	Monthly Installments	Number Of Months	Interest	Interest Rate
a.	$ 6	$ 36	$ 15	$ 6.00	6	$ 6	80 %
b.	4	44	20	7.50	6	5	50 %
c.	10	60	25	20.00	3	10	160 %
d.	6	58	26	20.00	3	8	123 %
e.	5	75	35	20.00	4	10	86 %
f.	4	36	16	9.25	4	5	94 %
g.	15	165	75	9.00	24	66	44 %
h.	38	298	130	14.25	24	82	32 %
i.	19	519	250	19.00	36	184	25 %
j.	37	687	325	25.75	36	277	28 %
k.	15	215	100	15.00	18	70	47 %
l.	12	462	225	18.50	30	105	19 %

B

Determine the interest rate that Bill Bryon would have to pay if he purchased the amplifier in the following advertisement on the install-ment plan.   33%

In Exercise 8, you might want to include a column headed "Total Debt" just prior to the column headed "Average Debt."

Unit 2:   The Small-Loan Agency

Section 1:   Computing the Cost of Borrowing Money
             From a Small-Loan Agency

Among the many other things the mailman drops into your mailbox each week, you can usually count on advertisements such as the following:

> **"IN DEBT?** We will assist you in getting out of debt. One weekly payment can possibly pay your bills and overdue debts."

> "I'm behind in my house payments . . . bills are coming due . . . the kids need clothes . . . **who'll lend a hand? WE WILL!"**

> "It's time to fix up your home! Get a FIX–UP loan."

> "Don't be bothered by bills. Here's the CASH you need."

> "Exclusive for Engineers! Dear engineer . . . **Borrow $200 to $1,000 or more** in complete confidence by mail! Write us at RST"

As is evident, these companies are most anxious to help you get out of debt. And of course they should be. By lending you the money you supposedly need, they, in turn, reap a profitable reward by charging a high rate of interest. In fact, as you will see, it is much, much higher than your own money can possibly earn by being in the bank.

In all fairness to the small-loan agency, it should be pointed out that there are situations in which it is actually possible to save money by borrowing from these institutions. Notice that three of the advertisements stressed the fact that they wanted to lend you money to clear up bills. When these bills happen to be for articles purchased on the installment plan, you will probably be much better off by borrowing the money from the small-loan agency to get yourself out of debt. The interest rates charged by these agencies are restricted by state laws, while there are no restrictions whatever on the rates that can be charged the buyer on an installment purchase. In view of this, you will find that it is usually cheaper to borrow money and pay cash for an article you need rather than buy it on the installment plan.

Have the students collect as many advertisements similar to those above as they can find. At least one should be required of every student. They add immensely to the interest in the work and the reality of the subject. It is a rare evening newspaper that does not contain one such advertisement.

This is not the case, though, for many other bills that you will have to pay. The gas and electric bill, the water bill, the telephone bill, the doctor's bill, the dentist's bill—all these carry no interest charge with them. If you borrow money to pay them off, you will only be freeing yourself from many small debts on which you pay no interest to get yourself involved in a single large debt that carries with it a substantial interest charge.

Loans made to clear up an accumulation of small debts are called consolidation loans. The theory behind them is that rather than be confused by what seems to be an endless number of small debts, you borrow enough money to pay them off and then have only one large debt to contend with. As was pointed out earlier, the wisdom of investing in a consolidation loan depends on what the small debts happen to be.

The small-loan agency is so called because it deals in small loans. These loans have different meanings in different states. In some, they can be any amount up to $500, while in others the amount might be as high as $2,000. Furthermore, state laws differ on what is considered to be a fair rate of interest that should be charged the borrower. The legal maximum limit (highest rate) in several states happens to be 2½% *per month* on the unpaid balance. Notice that this rate is quoted by the month, not by the year. On a yearly basis it comes to 30%. How was the 30% arrived at from the 2½%?

A number of other states prefer to have a decreasing rate scale as follows:

3% per month on the unpaid balance up to $500
2% per month on the unpaid balance over $500 and under $1,000
1% per month on the unpaid balance over $1,000

Here, again, as is always the case in small loans, the rate is quoted by the month. What would the 3% rate be on an annual basis? What is the maximum annual rate the bank can legally pay you on the money you have in your savings account? How many times as large as the rate you receive is the 3% per month rate?

■ILLUSTRATION 1: The RST Consumer Loan Company mailed the following advertisement to people throughout the country.

SELECT YOUR LOAN HERE ...

Amount Of Loan	24 Months	36 Months	48 Months
$ 200	$10	—	—
400	20	—	—
600	30	$22	$18
800	40	30	24
1,000	50	37	30

As a point of interest for students, mention the likelihood that local small-loan agencies are borrowing money from local banks and lending out this same money at a much higher rate of interest. The irony is that this money may be coming from a bank where the borrower happens to be a depositor!

How much will it cost a person to borrow $800 if he pays it back over a period of 48 months?

▼ EXPLANATION: Run your finger down the column headed by the words "Amount of Loan" until you come to the numeral 800. Then run your finger across the row containing this numeral until it comes to the column headed by "48 Months." Your finger should be pointing to the numeral 24. This numeral implies that you must pay $24 each month over a period of 48 months in order to pay off the debt of $800.

● SOLUTION:

$$\text{Monthly payment} = \$24$$
$$\text{Total of monthly payments} = 48 \times \$24$$
$$= \$1{,}152$$
$$\text{Debt charge or interest} = \$1{,}152 - \$800$$
$$= \$352$$

■ ILLUSTRATION 2: The Economy Credit Corporation placed the following advertisement in a newspaper.

WE'LL LEND YOU A HELPING HAND
$25 to $2,500

If You Owe	Pay As Low As	Time Length
$ 750	$16.50 per week	12 months
1,500	26.00 per week	15 months
2,500	36.90 per week	18 months

How much interest will the borrower be paying if he makes the $1,500 loan?

▼ EXPLANATION: To find the number of weeks in 15 months, consider this time as consisting of two periods. The first of these is 12 months, which is the equivalent of one year, which, in turn, can be thought of as 52 weeks. The second period will be the remaining 3 months. This is equivalent to ¼ of a year, or ¼ of 52 weeks. Thus, 3 months can be rewritten as 13 weeks. Hence, the total number of weeks in 15 months is 65. Chances are that the time length in the advertisement was deliberately stated in months rather than weeks to make it appear much shorter. Since 65 is a much larger number than 15, you tend to associate 65 weeks with a much longer period of time than 15 months. For how many weeks will the borrower have to pay in the 12-month loan? For how many weeks will he have to pay in the 18-month loan?

It would probably be well to point out how much more the borrower is paying in interest in Illustrations 1 and 2 than he would have to pay had he been able to borrow the money at perhaps a 6% or 8% rate.

● SOLUTION:

> Number of weeks in 15 months $= 65$
> Total of weekly payments $= 65 \times \$26$
> $\qquad = \$1,690$
> Interest $= \$1,690 - \$1,500$
> $\qquad = \$190$

EXERCISES   A

1. Use the following table to answer the questions that follow it.

SELECT YOUR LOAN FROM THIS TABLE

(Rates set by law)

Amount Of Loan	24 Monthly Payments	Amount Of Loan	24 Monthly Payments
$100	$ 5.90	$500	$27.81
250	14.43	650	35.73
400	22.49	800	43.83

a. How much interest will the borrower have to pay on the $100 loan? $ 41.60

b. How much interest will the borrower have to pay on the $400 loan? $139.76

c. How much interest will the borrower have to pay on the $800 loan? $251.92

d. Is the interest on the $400 loan 4 times as much as the interest on the $100 loan? If it is not 4 times as much, then is it more than 4 times as much or less than 4 times as much?   No—less

e. Is the interest on the $800 loan 8 times as much as the interest on the $100 loan? If it is not 8 times as much, then is it more than 8 times as much or less than 8 times as much?   No—less

f. Is the interest on the $800 loan 2 times as much as the interest on the $400 loan? If it is not 2 times as much, then is it more than 2 times as much or less than 2 times as much?   No—less

2. Use the advertisement below to answer the following questions.

TERMS TO SUIT YOUR BUDGET				
Cash To You	37 Months	24 Months	18 Months	12 Months
$ 500	—	$ 27.26	$ 34.44	$ 48.33
1,100	$40.72	60.63	72.11	102.66
2,000	70.30	110.24	127.36	182.91

   a. How much interest will the borrower have to pay on the $500 loan for the 18-month period? $119.92

   b. How much interest will the borrower have to pay on the $2,000 loan for the 12-month period? $194.92

   c. How much interest will the borrower have to pay on the $1,100 loan for the 37-month period? $406.64

3. a. How much interest will a person have to pay if he borrows $500 for a 24-month period from the loan company in Exercise 1? $167.44

   b. How much interest will a person have to pay if he borrows $500 for a 24-month period from the loan company in Exercise 2? $154.24

   c. How much money can a person save by borrowing the $500 from the loan company in Exercise 2 rather than the one in Exercise 1? $ 13.20

4. A 16-inch portable television set can be purchased for $100 cash. This set can also be purchased on the installment plan by making no down payment and monthly payments of $6.25 over a period of two years.

   a. How much will the installment purchaser have to pay for the set? $150.00

   b. How much more will a person have to pay for the set if he buys it on the installment plan rather than for cash? $ 50.00

   c. If the installment purchaser had borrowed the $100 for the 24-month period from the loan company in Exercise 1, what would the loan have cost him? $ 41.60

   d. How much could the installment purchaser have saved by borrowing the $100 from the loan company in Exercise 1 and paying cash for the television set? $ 8.40

5. Use the advertisement in Illustration 2, page 314, to answer each of the following questions.

a. How much interest will a borrower have to pay on the $750 loan for the 12-month period? $108.00

b. How much interest will a borrower have to pay on the $2,500 loan for the 18-month period? $378.20

6. The Confidential Cash Loan Corporation mailed advertising circulars to people, urging them to "Consolidate Your Bills." The advertisement read as follows:

CUT YOUR MONTHLY PAYMENTS ⅓ TO ½ AND GET EXTRA CASH BESIDES

Take 24 months to pay

Here's a typical problem that many families face.

Here's how a loan from us **Solved the Problem.**

Accounts	Amount Owed	Monthly Payments
Clothing	$ 48	$ 6
Appliance	100	10
Hospital	110	10
Doctor	24	12
Dentist	105	15
Car Repair	20	5
Home Repair	50	10
Total	$457	$68

Amount of Loan	$500
Amount Needed to Pay Bills	457
Extra Cash for You	43

Monthly Payment For a loan of $500 $27.81

Here's how payments of
$68 ← → $68 were cut to $27.81

---

a. For how many months will the borrower have to make the monthly payments of $27.81?   24

b. If the loan were not made then:

1. In how many months will the clothing bill be paid? _____ 8 _____
2. In how many months will the appliance bill be paid?
                                                        10
3. In how many months will the hospital bill be paid? _____ 11 _____
4. In how many months will the doctor's bill be paid? _____ 2 _____
5. In how many months will the dentist's bill be paid? _____ 7 _____
6. In how many months will the car repair bill be paid?
                                                        4
7. In how many months will the home repair bill be paid?
                                                        5

c. In view of your answers in Part b, how long would it be before the last of the bills is paid?   11 months

d. In what way would you criticize the advertisement?   Answer varies

e. How much interest would the borrower have to pay on the loan of $500? $167.44

Do not bypass Exercise 6. It is an actual advertisement, and it points up how people may be deluded into thinking they can lessen their debts by borrowing money!

Section 2: Computing the Rate of Interest When Borrowing Money From a Small-Loan Agency

The repayment of a loan from a small-loan agency is very much the same as paying for a purchase that was made on the installment plan. In both cases, the payments are exactly the same for each period, and in both cases, the payments are usually made monthly. In view of this, you are able to apply the same interest rate formula used earlier, except that now you will be finding the rate that is paid when borrowing money from a small-loan agency. The computation for this should be even easier than before, for in the repayment of a small loan, you do not have to worry about the down payment.

∎ILLUSTRATION 1 : The Credit Finance Corporation listed a sample of its loans in the following table.

Amount You Receive	Cost of Loan For 12 Months	Amount You Pay Each Month	Cost of Loan For 24 Months	Amount You Pay Each Month
$1,000	$ 80	$ 90	$160.16	$48.34
2,000	160	180	320.32	96.68

What rate of interest will a person be paying on the $1,000 loan for the 24-month period?

▼EXPLANATION : The loan company has made matters relatively simple for you, for it has computed the interest on each of the loans. In the case of the $1,000 loan for the 24-month period, it is $160.16. Should you want to check the computation, you need merely multiply the monthly payment of $48.34 by 24. When the $1,000 is subtracted from this product, the difference should be $160.16. Can you show how the $80 was arrived at for the interest on the $1,000 loan for the 12-month period?

●SOLUTION :

$$R = \frac{24 \times I}{P \times (n+1)}$$

$$I = \$160.16, \text{ or } \$160; \ P = \$1,000; \ n = 24$$

$$R = \frac{\overset{6}{\cancel{24}} \times \overset{16}{\cancel{160}}}{\underset{\underset{25}{\cancel{100}}}{\cancel{1,000}} \times 25}$$

$$= \frac{96}{625}$$

$$= .154, \text{ or } 15\%$$

There is some justification for a small-loan agency to be permitted to charge an interest rate higher than that charged by a bank. Discuss with the students what this justification might be.

▼EXPLANATION (continued): Notice that when you found the value of "I" for the formula, the $160.16 was rounded off to the nearest dollar, making it $160. Whenever either the principal (P) or the interest (I) happens to involve both dollars and cents, it is best to round each off to the nearest dollar. Doing this will not affect the accuracy of your answer to any great degree, and it will certainly make the computation a good deal easier.

■ILLUSTRATION 2: The Friendly Finance Firm displayed a notice in the subways showing the following information.

CHART OF PAYMENTS

Below are some typical personal loan examples.
Other terms can be arranged to suit your individual needs.

Amount of Loan	Monthly Payment
12 Months	
$300	$28.75
500	47.30
700	65.60
18 Months	
$300	$20.42
500	34.03
700	47.64

What rate of interest is being paid on the $500 loan for the 18-month period?

● SOLUTION:

$$\text{Total repaid} = 18 \times \$34.03$$
$$= \$612.54$$
$$\text{Interest} = \$612.54 - \$500$$
$$= \$112.54$$
$$R = \frac{24 \times I}{P \times (n+1)}$$

I = $112.54, or $113; P = $500; n = 18

$$R = \frac{\overset{6}{\cancel{24}} \times 113}{\underset{125}{\cancel{500}} \times 19}$$
$$= \frac{678}{2,375}$$
$$= .285, \text{ or } 29\%$$

▼EXPLANATION: Before you could apply the formula for the interest rate, you had to determine the interest on the debt. Since payments of

Notice that the small-loan tables on these pages all differ from one another in some respect. This was done deliberately to give the students an opportunity to learn how to read and compare small loans no matter how they may be presented.

$34.03 were to be made for 18 months, the total repaid is the product of these two numbers, or $612.54. The interest on the debt, then, is simply the difference between this amount and the $500 you received. To make the computation easier, the interest was rounded off to the nearest dollar, making it $113.

EXERCISES   A

Whenever the rate of interest is called for in the following exercises, round off each answer to the nearest whole number percent value.

1. Use the sample loans of the Credit Finance Corporation shown in Illustration 1, page 318, to answer each of the following questions.
   a. How much interest is charged on the $1,000 loan for the 12-month period? $ 80.00
   b. How much interest is charged on the $2,000 loan for the 24-month period? $ 320.32
   c. How much money will the borrower return on the $2,000 loan over the 12-month period? $2,160.00
   d. How much money will the borrower return on the $2,000 loan over the 24-month period? $2,320.32
   e. How much more does it cost to borrow $2,000 for a 2-year period than for a 1-year period? $ 160.32

2. Use the sample loans of the Friendly Finance Firm, shown in Illustration 2, page 319, to answer each of the following questions.
   a. How much interest is charged on the $300 loan for the 12-month period? $ 45.00
   b. How much interest is charged on the $300 loan for the 18-month period? $ 67.56
   c. How much more will it cost to borrow $300 for the 18-month period than for the 12-month period? $ 22.56

3. Use the sample loans of the Credit Finance Corporation, shown in Illustration 1, page 318, to answer each of the following questions.
   a. What rate of interest is charged on the $1,000 loan borrowed for the 12-month period?   15%
   b. What rate of interest is charged on the $2,000 loan borrowed for the 24-month period?   15%

4. Use the sample loans of the Friendly Finance Firm, shown in Illustration 2, page 319, to answer each of the following questions.
   a. What rate of interest is charged on the $300 loan borrowed for the 12-month period?   28%

   b. What rate of interest is charged on the $300 loan borrowed for
the 18-month period?   29%

   c. What rate of interest is charged on the $700 loan borrowed for
the 12-month period?   23%

5. The advertisement read as follows:

IT'S TIME TO CLEAR UP YOUR DEBTS!

Borrow Quickly!—Take Time to Repay

Amount of Loan	24 Monthly Payments
$150	$ 8.86
200	16.69
550	30.47
600	33.13
750	40.83

---

   a. What rate of interest is charged on the $150 loan?   40%

   b. What rate of interest is charged on the $550 loan?   32%

   c. What rate of interest is charged on the $750 loan?   29%

   d. After examining your answers to the preceding three questions,
what conclusion can you draw? As size of loan increases, rate of interest decreases.

6. When Jack Bradley opened his mail, he found an advertisement
from the Community Financial Service Company, offering him a
choice of loans.

Amount You Borrow	Number of Months To Repay	Cost Of Loan
$200	24	$ 80
200	30	90
600	24	240
600	30	270

   a. What rate of interest will the borrower have to pay on the $200
loan for 24 months?   38%

   b. What rate of interest will the borrower have to pay on the $600
loan for 30 months?   35%

7. The Economy Credit Corporation of Illustration 2, page 314, is one
of the few small-loan agencies that arranges for weekly payments
of debts.

   a. What rate of interest is charged on the $750 loan paid off over the
12-month period? (See formula, page 304.)   28%

   b. What rate of interest is charged on the $1,500 loan paid off
over the 15-month period? (See formula, page 304.) 20%

Unit 3: The Pawnshop Loan

Although a loan from a pawnshop is not usually paid off on the installment plan, it should be investigated at this time, for it is a widely used method of borrowing relatively small amounts of money. Many people prefer the pawnshop to the small-loan agency, since it is much less of a problem to borrow money from a pawnbroker. And, contrary to what most people believe, the cost in most states is not much more—if any more—than that charged by a small-loan agency.

All pawnshop loans are *collateral* loans. This simply means that the borrower turns over to the pawnbroker some article of goods to be held until the debt is paid. The type of goods that is acceptable varies from broker to broker. Some will accept clothing, shoes, window drapes, and the like, while others will not. They reason that people using this merchandise for collateral are probably just trying to get rid of some old, used articles and have no other way of disposing of them. Such things as watches, rings, cameras, musical instruments, radios, and TV sets are accepted by all pawnbrokers. These are items that can be sold quite easily in the event they are not claimed.

Another popular belief about pawnshops is that the bulk of items pawned are never redeemed. This is far from true. The honest, legitimate pawnbroker considers that he has made too many bad loans if even as much as 20% of the articles left in his shop are not eventually redeemed. Actually, it is to the advantage of both the borrower and the pawnbroker to have the article redeemed. Usually, the amount of the loan is so much less than the value of the article that the borrower would be risking too much of a loss to leave it with the pawnbroker as payment for the debt. On the other hand, the pawnbroker may have to turn the article over to an auctioneer to sell it so that he can get his money back. And there is no guarantee that the price at which it is sold will be as much as the amount that was loaned.

The pawnbroker has another reason for wanting the article to be redeemed. A large part of his business consists in selling either new, or pawned, merchandise. Hence, each time a person comes into his shop, either to redeem some item or to make a payment on a debt, the pawnbroker has an opportunity to try to make another sale. Most of the pawnshop sales are made to steady customers who have been borrowing small amounts over the years and not to the infrequent window-shoppers who happen to spot something they would like to have.

There is no legal fixed period by which the pawnshop loan must be paid. Some brokers insist on payment within one month, or they will sell the collateral, while contracts with other brokers permit the bor-

It was suggested much earlier that the narrative material in the text be read and discussed with the student. Much of this material has been class-tested in just this way, and it has been found that the students enjoy doing this. Even just acquiring the informational background is of value to them.

rower to keep the money for an entire year. Usually, though, if the person makes a small payment at the time the loan is due—even the interest is enough—the pawnbroker will extend the period by which the debt must be paid. On the other hand, whenever the borrower is ready and willing to pay off the debt plus interest, he can do so. There is one small point that shouldn't be overlooked, though. Interest always appears to be charged for a full month's time and never for a fractional part of it. Thus, if the debt were paid off after 2 months and 23 days, the borrower would have to pay 3 months' interest on the loan. In fact, even if the period were 2 months and 1 day, the interest would be computed for the period of 3 months.

Just as in the case of the small-loan agency, each state has passed laws governing the rate of interest on pawnshop loans. In most states, the rates are pretty much the same for the two types of loans. There are some states, however, where the interest rate on a pawnshop loan can run as high as 10% per month on the unpaid balance. How high is this rate per year? If the rate were only 100% per year, how much interest would have to be paid on a $50 loan after a period of 1 year?

■ ILLUSTRATION 1: For what period of time will interest have to be paid on a pawnshop loan that was made April 4 and paid off on August 15?

▼ EXPLANATION: In counting the months from April 4 to August 15, you find that May 4 will be one month; June 4, two months; July 4, three months; and August 4, four months. Since any days after August 4 and prior to September 4 have to be considered as a full month, then the time from August 4 to August 15 will bring the interest period to five months.

● SOLUTION:
Interest period from April 4 to August 15 = 5 months

■ ILLUSTRATION 2: Jerry Campbell borrowed $75 from a pawnbroker on March 12 and returned the money with interest on September 9. How much money did Jerry return if state law permitted the pawnbroker to charge the following rates?

On that part of the loan up to and including $50: 2½% per month
On that part of the loan over $50: 2% per month

▼ EXPLANATION: On the first $50 of the loan, Jerry paid an interest rate of 2½% per month. Since he borrowed $75 altogether, then on the remaining $25, he had to pay a rate of 2% per month. The period of time from March 12 to September 9 is considered as 6 months because the fractional part of the last month is counted as an entire month. Hence, in determining the interest on the loan, you first compute it for one month and then multiply this answer by 6 to find the interest for the entire 6 months.

●SOLUTION:

Interest period from March 12 to September 9 = 6 months
Interest on first $50 for 1 month = $50 × 2½%
$$= \$50 \times .025$$
$$= \$1.25$$
Interest on remaining $25 for 1 month = $25 × 2%
$$= \$.50$$
Interest on $75 for 1 month = $1.25 + $.50
$$= \$1.75$$
Interest on $75 for 6 months = 6 × $1.75
$$= \$10.50$$
Total repaid on September 9 = $75 + $10.50
$$= \$85.50$$

In the illustration above, the interest for 1 month is an exact amount of money—$1.75. This will not always be the case. In those situations where it is not, do not round off any answer to the nearest penny until you have found the total interest for the full period of time.

EXERCISES   A

If you do not recall how to find the answers to the following exercises, you will probably want to refer to the pages indicated for help.

1. Change each of the following percent numerals to its equivalent decimal numeral. (See page 583.)

a. 2% .02	g. 4.25% .0425	m. 3¼% .0325
b. 3% .03	h. 3.75% .0375	n. 2¼% .0225
c. 1% .01	i. 2½% .025	o. 4¾% .0475
d. 5% .05	j. 1½% .015	p. 5¾% .0575
e. 2.5% .025	k. 4½% .045	q. 5½% .055
f. 3.5% .035	l. 6½% .065	r. 6¾% .0675

2. Find the product in each of the following. (See page 589.)

a. 30 × 2% = .60	g. 26 × 3.5% = .910
b. 50 × 3% = 1.50	h. 58 × 1.5% = .870
c. 45 × 1% = .45	i. 70 × 2½% = 1.750
d. 18 × 6% = 1.08	j. 32 × 4½% = 1.440
e. 60 × 2.5% = 1.500	k. 46 × 2¼% = 1.0350
f. 40 × 5.5% = 2.200	l. 81 × 5¾% = 4.6575

The pawnshop loan seems to be the only one in which the person is required to pay interest on money during a period after he may have paid off the debt. That is, should he keep the money for only one day into a new month, he is required to pay interest for the entire month.

B

1. Determine the interest period on each of the following pawnshop loans.

	Date Borrowed	Date Returned	Interest Period In Months
a.	March 5	March 17	1
b.	May 18	June 2	1
c.	February 6	April 12	3
d.	September 9	December 20	4
e.	June 16	October 25	5
f.	April 10	June 5	2
g.	July 23	October 11	3
h.	January 9	May 5	4
i.	December 14	February 25	3
j.	October 23	January 29	4
k.	November 6	February 3	3
l.	September 27	March 20	6

2. How much interest will have to be paid on each of the following pawnshop loans in which the interest period is one month?

	Amount Borrowed	Monthly Rate Of Interest	Interest
a.	$50	2%	$ 1.00
b.	40	3%	1.20
c.	15	4%	.60
d.	25	5%	1.25
e.	12	6%	.72
f.	35	2½%	.88
g.	65	3½%	2.28
h.	70	2¾%	1.93
i.	96	4¼%	4.08
j.	47	5¼%	2.47

3. How much interest will have to be paid on each of the following pawnshop loans?

	Amount Borrowed	Monthly Rate Of Interest	Period Of Loan	Interest
a.	$ 80	3%	2 months	$ 4.80
b.	10	4%	3 months	1.20
c.	45	5%	5 months	11.25
d.	26	2½%	4 months	2.60
e.	18	3½%	2 months	1.26
f.	120	2¾%	6 months	19.80

These exercises should cause your students no difficulty. Make a point, though, of reminding them to express the percent numerals as decimal numerals and not as fraction numerals.

4. How much interest will have to be paid on each of the following pawnshop loans?

Amount Borrowed	Monthly Rate Of Interest	Date Borrowed	Date Returned	Period Of Loan (Months)	Interest
a. $ 20	4%	May 3	June 20	2	$ 1.60
b. 60	6%	April 24	July 31	4	14.40
c. 68	3%	February 21	July 10	5	10.20
d. 110	2%	June 14	September 2	3	6.60
e. 75	5%	March 3	August 17	6	22.50
f. 132	3%	December 5	March 15	4	15.84
g. 24	3½%	January 16	June 10	5	4.20
h. 39	2½%	September 21	January 28	5	4.88

5. How much money will have to be repaid on each of the following pawnshop loans?

Amount Borrowed	Monthly Rate	Date Borrowed	Date Returned	Period Of Loan (Months)	Interest	Amount Repaid
a. $ 50	2%	June 12	October 3	4	$ 4.00	$ 54.00
b. 16	4%	February 17	June 14	4	2.56	18.56
c. 41	3%	May 2	October 20	6	7.38	48.38
d. 140	3½%	March 15	July 27	5	24.50	164.50
e. 58	2½%	October 30	January 20	3	4.35	62.35
f. 87	2¼%	November 16	March 21	5	9.79	96.79

C

1. In one of the states, the law permits pawnbrokers to charge the following interest rates:

On first $100   5% per month
On excess above $100   3% per month

How much interest will have to be paid on each of the following loans in which the interest period is one month?

	Amount Borrowed	Interest
a.	$ 80	$ 4.00
b.	120	5.60
c.	160	6.80
d.	135	6.05
e.	108	5.24
f.	175	7.25

2. The following pawnshop loans were made in the state whose rates are quoted in Problem 1, above. How much interest had to be paid?

In Exercises 4 and 5 of Group B, you might prefer to have the students include an additional column in their outline of the work. This column should be headed "Monthly Interest," and should appear immediately after the "Monthly Rate" column.

	Amount Borrowed	Date Borrowed	Date Returned	Period Of Loan (Months)	Interest For 1 Month	Total Interest
a.	$ 75	May 20	July 16	2	$ 3.75	$ 7.50
b.	130	March 6	August 4	5	5.90	29.50
c.	150	June 15	September 25	4	6.50	26.00
d.	142	February 11	February 26	1	6.26	6.26
e.	196	November 24	January 20	2	7.88	15.76
f.	231	October 14	March 23	6	8.93	53.58

3. How much interest will have to be paid on each of the following loans that were made for the period shown? The monthly rate charged by the pawnbroker is:

4½% on any amount up to and including $50
3% on the amount in excess of $50

	Amount Borrowed	Period Of Loan	Interest For 1 Month	Total Interest
a.	$ 30	1 month	$ 1.35	$ 1.35
b.	45	3 months	2.03	6.09
c.	85	1 month	3.30	3.30
d.	90	4 months	3.45	13.80
e.	120	2 months	4.35	8.70
f.	175	5 months	6.00	30.00

4. The following loans were made at the pawnshop whose rates are quoted in Problem 3, above. How much money had to be returned by the borrower? Include interest.

	Amount Borrowed	Date Borrowed	Date Returned	Period Of Loan	Interest For 1 Month	Total Interest	Amount Repaid
a.	$ 40	May 10	June 1	1	$ 1.80	$ 1.80	$ 41.80
b.	26	July 6	September 4	2	1.17	2.34	28.34
c.	80	February 15	March 12	1	3.15	3.15	83.15
d.	100	June 17	August 25	3	3.75	11.25	111.25
e.	130	March 20	September 15	6	4.65	27.90	157.90
f.	150	December 12	January 10	1	5.25	5.25	155.25
g.	185	November 25	February 6	3	6.30	18.90	203.90
h.	225	September 10	March 21	7	7.50	52.50	277.50

Unit 4:   The Credit-Union Loan

Frequently, the cheapest place to borrow money is a *credit union*. The difficulty with this, though, is that in order to borrow from such an organization, you must be a member of the group. Credit unions are formed by people who have some common bond. They may be members of the same church, or employees of the same company, or teach-

Many of the states have laws governing interest rates on small loans, which vary in accordance with the size of the loan. The rates quoted in Exercise 1 of Group C are typical of the manner in which these laws are written.

ers in the same city, or people living in the same apartment house, and so on. One of their purposes in organizing is to give them some place to save their money. More important to them, though, is that it gives them some place where they can borrow money at a cost that is usually a good deal less than at the small-loan agency, or the pawnshop, or the installment house, or, indeed, most places.

To form a credit union, the people must first get permission to do so from either the federal or state government. They do this by obtaining a charter to organize. In addition, the federal or state government sends inspectors around periodically to make certain that no one is illegally helping himself to the funds.

Since most of the work is done by volunteers who are members of the credit union, there are very few expenses involved in running such an agency. What little there are usually involve the rent for a small office, expenses for stationery, and, possibly, the salary of a secretary. Hence, practically all the interest collected from borrowers is distributed among the members of the group as interest on their savings. Thus, if the borrowers are asked to pay an interest rate of 7% or 8%, very likely as much as 5% interest rate is paid to the depositors. Usually the 2% or 3% left over is all that is needed to cover expenses. This is much, much less than is needed by other lending agencies to meet their overhead (expenses).

As was pointed out earlier, the depositors and the borrowers in a credit union are exactly the same people. It is not possible to borrow any money from a credit union unless you belong to the association and have some money on deposit with the group. Furthermore, the amount of money you can borrow is limited by how much you can afford to borrow. Thus, the more you earn, the more you are permitted to borrow—within certain limits. The loans are primarily designed for the payment of small debts, or to help you buy such things as TV sets or washing machines without having to pay the high interest rates asked for on installment purchases. However, you could never borrow the money needed to buy a house or, in some cases, a new car. A credit union just does not have that much money to lend you. And even if it did, it could not afford to lend you so much, for then it would not have any left to lend to someone else in the group.

For many credit unions, finding the cost of borrowing money is exactly the same as the method used for finding the cost of borrowing money from a bank. The following illustrations will show this.

■ILLUSTRATION 1: Bob Aikins borrowed $250 from a credit union of which he was a member. He paid off the debt at the end of four

Have the students check with their parents to see whether the company for which the parents work, or the organizations to which they belong, have organized credit unions where it is possible to save money and to borrow money.

months. If the interest rate charged was 7½%, how much did the loan cost him?

●SOLUTION:

$$I = P \times R \times T$$
$$= \$250 \times 7\tfrac{1}{2}\% \times 4 \text{ months}$$

$$= \$250 \times \frac{15}{200} \times \frac{4}{12}$$

$$= \frac{\$25}{4}$$

$$= \$6.25$$

▼EXPLANATION: There are two things that might cause a little difficulty in applying the interest formula. The first of these involves changing the percent numeral, 7½%, to the fractional numeral, 15/200. If you have forgotten how this is done, refer to page 585 for the explanation. The other point is the need to write the period of time in years rather than months. Remember that an interest rate, unless otherwise noted, is always quoted for the period of one year, and this is the case for the 7½% rate in this problem. Hence, the 4-month period has to be rewritten as 4/12 of a year.

■ILLUSTRATION 2: Joe Becker borrowed $500 from his credit union to purchase a color TV set. At the end of two months, he repaid $200 with interest, and, at the end of five months, he paid off the balance of the debt with interest. If he had to pay an interest rate of 7%, what was the total he returned to the credit union?

●SOLUTION:

Interest on $500 for 2 months $= \$500 \times 7\% \times 2 \text{ months}$

$$= \$500 \times \frac{7}{100} \times \frac{2}{12}$$

$$= \frac{\$35}{6}$$

$$= \$5.833, \text{ or } \$5.83$$

Debt after first 2 months $= \$500 - \$200$
$$= \$300$$

Perhaps the most important piece of information that the student should learn from this chapter is that if he must borrow money some day, it would be best—and cheapest—if he could borrow through a credit union.

Interest on $300 for 3 months $= \$300 \times 7\% \times 3$ months

$$= \$\cancel{300}^{3} \times \frac{7}{\cancel{100}^{1}} \times \frac{\cancel{3}^{1}}{\cancel{12}^{4}}$$

$$= \frac{\$21}{4}$$

$$= \$5.25$$

Total repaid $= \$200 + \$300 + \$5.25 + \$5.83$
$$= \$511.08$$

▼EXPLANATION: Since Joe kept the full $500 for only the first two months, he paid interest on that amount for the 2-month period only. At the end of that time, having paid off $200 with all the interest he owed to that date, Joe still owed $300. He paid interest on the $300 for 3 months, for it was for this period of time only that he owed this money. Where did the 3 months come from?

In the illustrations above, the interest rate was quoted on an annual basis. There are, though, a very large number of credit unions that much prefer to quote the interest rate by the month. When this is done, then the computation for finding the interest is the same as used when finding the interest on a pawnshop loan.

EXERCISES   A

Do you recall how to find the answers in the following exercises? If not, you will probably want to refer to the pages indicated for help.

1. Change each of the following percent numerals to a fraction numeral. (See page 583.)

   a. 1%   __1/100__   e. 1½%   __3/200__
   b. 7%   __7/100__   f. 7½%   __15/200__
   c. 9%   __9/100__   g. 8¼%   __33//400__
   d. 10% __10/100__   h. 7¾%   __31/400__

2. Find the product in each of the following exercises. (See page 573.)

   a. $\$300 \times 4/100 \times 4/12$ = __$ 4.00__
   b. $\$800 \times 5/100 \times 3/12$ = __$10.00__

People who borrow from a credit union will frequently pay back part of the debt at one time and the remainder later, as did Joe Becker of Illustration 2. Call students' attention to the fact that they pay interest only on the part of the debt outstanding and not on the full debt for the entire period.

c. $600 × 6/100 × 5/12 = $15.00

d. $200 × 5/100 × 9/12 = $ 7.50

e. $500 × 9/200 × 4/12 = $ 7.50

f. $700 × 11/200 × 6/12 = $19.25

g. $240 × 17/400 × 3/12 = $ 2.55

h. $150 × 21/400 × 4/12 = $ 2.63

3. Change each of the following percent numerals to decimal numerals. (See page 583.)

a. .75%   .0075   e. ¾%   .0075

b. .5%   .005   f. ½%   .005

c. .8%   .008   g. ⅘%   .008

d. .6%   .006   h. %₁₀%   .009

4. Find the product in each of the following exercises. (See page 589.)

a. $200 × .75% = $1.50   e. $100 × ¾% = $ .75

b. $400 × .5% = $2.00   f. $600 × ¾% = $4.50

c. $450 × .8% = $3.60   g. $700 × ½% = $3.50

d. $180 × .6% = $1.08   h. $300 × ½% = $1.50

B

1. Determine the interest on each of the following loans that were made from a credit union.

	Principal	Interest Rate	Number Of Months	Interest
a.	$400	7%	3	$ 7.00
b.	200	6%	4	4.00
c.	500	7%	6	17.50
d.	210	8%	3	4.20
e.	275	9%	8	16.50
f.	600	7½%	4	15.00
g.	800	6½%	9	39.00
h.	400	8½%	8	22.67
i.	520	8½%	6	22.10
j.	640	7¾%	3	12.40

2. Determine the amount of money that was returned to the credit union on each of the following loans.

	Principal	Interest Rate	Number Of Months	Interest	Amount Returned
a.	$100	7%	6	$ 3.50	$ 103.50
b.	90	8%	1	.60	90.60
c.	140	6%	3	2.10	142.10
d.	80	9%	1	.60	80.60
e.	150	8½%	4	4.25	154.25
f.	240	7½%	3	4.50	244.50

These problems are simply another application of the interest formula.

C

1. In each of the following loans, the borrower returned the money in two payments. Thus, in exercise "a," he made the first payment with interest at the end of 3 months and paid off the balance 6 months after he had borrowed the money. How much interest was paid on each loan?

	Principal	Interest Rate	Amount Of First Payment	First Payment Made At End of:	Balance Paid At End of:	Total Interest
a.	$600	6%	$200	3 months	6 months	$ 15.00
b.	800	8%	400	2 months	5 months	18.67
c.	900	7%	300	4 months	7 months	31.50
d.	700	6%	300	6 months	12 months	33.00
e.	500	9%	100	1 month	5 months	15.75
f.	400	10%	50	1 month	4 months	12.08

2. The payments on the following loans were made in the same manner as those in Problem 1, above. What was the total amount of money that was repaid on each loan?

	Principal	Interest Rate	Amount Of First Payment	First Payment Made At End of:	Balance Paid At End of:	Total Interest	Amount Repaid
a.	$200	8%	$100	3 months	6 months	$ 6.00	$ 206.00
b.	400	6%	300	4 months	7 months	9.50	409.50
c.	900	7%	400	6 months	12 months	49.00	949.00
d.	800	9%	500	2 months	5 months	18.75	818.75

D

The credit unions in each of the following exercises charged their members a monthly interest rate for borrowing money. Determine the interest on each of these loans.

	Principal	Monthly Interest Rate	Number Of Months	Interest
a.	$300	2%	1	$ 6.00
b.	350	2%	1	7.00
c.	200	1½%	1	3.00
d.	400	1½%	1	6.00
e.	100	¾%	1	.75
f.	150	¾%	1	1.13
g.	500	2%	3	30.00
h.	175	2%	5	17.50
i.	240	1½%	4	14.40
j.	325	1½%	6	29.25
k.	160	½%	2	1.60
l.	225	½%	4	4.50
m.	650	¾%	9	43.88
n.	725	¾%	10	54.38

In the exercises of Group C, ask students to include two more columns in their outlines. The first is to be headed "Interest on Original Debt"—to appear as the fifth column in the outline—while the second is to be headed "Interest on Balance" and is to appear before "Total Interest" column.

Unit 5:   Chapter Review and Test

1. a. Mr. Clinton purchased a lawn mower on the installment plan by making a down payment of $5.95. If the cash price of the lawn mower is $89.95, what is the principal of Mr. Clinton's debt? $ 84.00

   b. When Tom Peabody purchased his tractor-mower, he made a down payment of 20% of the cash price. What was the principal of his debt if the cash price was $399.95? $319.96

2. A hand-loomed rug from India was advertised at the sale price of $324.95. An installment purchaser can acquire the rug by making a down payment of $24.95 and 17 monthly payments of $25 each.

   a. How much extra will the installment purchaser have to pay?
                                                                     $125.00

   b. What rate of interest is the installment purchaser paying?
                                                                       56%

3. The cash price of an article is $129.95. However, it can be purchased on the installment plan by making a down payment of $9.95, plus equal monthly installments that can be arranged to suit the buyer. If the short method is used for finding the rate of interest on this installment purchase, what will the average debt be?
                                                                        $60

4. Use the short method for finding the rate of interest on the following installment purchase.

   Cash price: $109.95   Number of monthly installments: 6
   Down payment: $9.95   Amount of each installment: $18
                                                                     32%

5. The Alliance Finance Corporation placed the following advertisement in a local newspaper.

LOANS TO FIT YOUR NEEDS		
Cash Received By You	Amount Of Monthly Payment	Number Of Months
$106	$19	6
147	14	12
387	26	18
638	34	24

   a. How much interest will be paid by the borrower on the $106 loan? $ 8.00

   b. What rate of interest is the borrower paying on the $106 loan?
                                                                       26%

Here again use some sections of the problems for a review and the remaining for a test.

6. If a person borrowed money from a pawnshop on August 17 and paid off the debt on January 5, for how many months would he be charged interest? <u>5 months</u>

7. Steve Billings borrowed $75 from a pawnshop that charged an interest rate of 4% per month on the unpaid balance of the debt. He returned the money with interest at the end of four months.
   a. How much interest did Steve have to pay? <u>$ 12.00</u>
   b. What amount did he return to the pawnbroker? <u>$ 87.00</u>

8. A pawnbroker has his shop in a state where he is permitted to charge the following monthly interest rates:

On the first $50 of the debt	3½%
On the amount over $50	2%

   a. If a person borrows $40 for one month, how much interest will he have to pay? <u>$ 1.40</u>
   b. If a person borrows $85 for one month, how much interest will he have to pay? <u>$ 2.45</u>
   c. If a person borrows $125 for five months, how much interest will he have to pay? <u>$ 16.25</u>

9. Nancy Brookfield belongs to the credit union at her church. In order to buy a used car, she borrowed $400 from the credit union, agreeing to return the money at the end of nine months. If she was charged an annual interest rate of 8%, how much did she have to return? <u>$424.00</u>

10. When Phyllis Riley bought her sewing machine, she borrowed $180 from the credit union to which she belonged. She paid off $80 of the loan at the end of two months and the balance of the debt five months after she had borrowed the money. Her credit union charges an annual rate of 9% on money loaned to its members. How much interest did Phyllis have to pay on her debt? <u>$ 4.95</u>

11. The Clearfield Firemen's Credit Union charges its members an interest rate of 2% per month on the unpaid balance of money borrowed. When Jim Freeman bought an outboard motor for his boat, he borrowed $650 from this credit union. At the end of five months, he paid off his debt.
    a. How much interest did he have to pay on the loan? <u>$ 65.00</u>
    b. How much money did he return to the credit union at the end of the five months? Include interest. <u>$715.00</u>

CHAPTER 9

INVESTMENTS

For several chapters you have been learning what happens when people go into debt, how you can borrow money, and how high the interest rate is when you buy articles on the installment plan. From this you might think that you will always be just one jump ahead of the bill collector. This will just not be so, for the great majority of you will find that you are managing to build up quite a sizable savings account. You will very likely be troubled more by what you should do with your savings than you will be by next month's telephone bill.

The idea of not knowing what to do with the money left over after paying off your bills may strike you as a bit odd at this point. However, jump ahead a few years in your life, and imagine that this will actually happen to you. Even at your age you have no doubt heard of so many people investing their money in stocks and bonds that you begin to wonder whether some day you will do the same. There seems to be little point in talking about investing in stocks and bonds, though, until you find out just what they are.

In this chapter, you are going to take a look at these two ways of having your money work for you. It should give you some thoughts about what you can do with your money other than keep it in a bank.

Unit 1:   The Stock Market

Section 1:   The Stock Market Report

Suppose that five of you get together and form a company for producing a new flavored soda that is to be sold in a pressurized can. You find that you need $600 for the expenses involved in starting the business. One of you contributes $200; a second, only $50; a third, $150; a fourth, $100; and the fifth also $100. In order to be fair to everyone, you decide that each of you will be given sheets of paper on which is stated that every sheet of paper represents $10 in the value of the company. This means that there will be 60 sheets of paper altogether. The person who contributed the $200 will receive 20 of these sheets, while the one who gave $50 will get 5. How many of these sheets will each of the others receive?

Each sheet of paper, called a *stock certificate*, actually indicates that you own 10 shares of stock in the company. It signifies that each of you is a part owner of this company. The person contributing the greater amount will own the greater part of the company.

Imagine that when people once tasted the soda, they just drank more and more of it. In fact, business was so good that the original $600 invested by the five of you jumped to $1,800 in value. Thus, the 60 shares of stock that had originally been worth $10 each were now worth $30 each. Hence, the 20 shares owned by the person who had invested $200 jumped to $600 in value. How was the $600 arrived at? If he wants to sell either some of these shares, or all of them, to anyone else, he can do so at the $30 price per share.

In time business takes a turn for the worse. People find that a good part of the soda spray from the pressurized can wets their clothing. It isn't long before the value of the company drops from a high point of $1,800 to a low point of $300. When this happens, each of the 60 shares of stock that had been worth $30 is now worth only $5. Hence, people buying these shares of stock will now pay no more than $5 each

Do read this material with the students. There are a number of new terms that the students are meeting for the first time. They are woven through the presentation of a story that hopefully may prove interesting to the students.

for them, although when the business was started, each of these pieces of paper was worth twice as much.

Most companies today get started in exactly the same way as the small soda business above. Since a great deal of money is needed to operate a business, a great many people are needed to become part owners. When the company is first organized and shares of stock are sold, it is relatively simple to determine the value of each share, for all shares together represent the value of the company. In the little company you organized, the entire value was only $600, thus making each of the 60 shares worth $10. The original value of each share of stock is called the *par value* of the stock. In time, however, the value of each share fluctuates (varies), depending on how the company prospers.

There are other things, though, that help determine the price of stock at any particular moment. It may be that at the time you are interested in selling your stock, no one is particularly interested in buying the stock you hold. If it happens that you are desperately in need of money, then you may be willing to sell the stock for far less than it is worth. On the other hand, the situation may arise where someone is willing to pay just about any price for the stock that you are lucky enough to own. In that case, it might be possible to get from him far more than the shares are actually worth.

It is also true that, when people buy stocks, they think not in terms of what they are worth at the moment, but rather what they will be worth in the future. Thus, if they believe that over the coming months the company will do a great deal of business and earn a great deal of money, they are willing to pay more for each share than it may be worth at the time of purchase. And, of course, the opposite holds true, too. It may be that they think that business is going to be bad in the months ahead. Then it is more than likely that the only way they can be made to buy shares will be to sell them at much less than the stock is worth at that time.

But, how can you go about buying stock? It is very unlikely that you would personally know someone who happens to own shares in the company in which you wish to invest. Hence, you will probably go to a *stockbroker*—a man who buys and sells stock for other people. He, in turn, will go to a *stock market*—a place where stocks are bought and sold. There he will inquire of other brokers if they know of anyone who would like to sell the stock that you want to purchase. Usually, there will be some such person. In that event, your broker will arrange to buy the stock for you and then bill you not only for the amount he had to pay, but also a small additional fee to cover the cost of his services.

There are frequently brokerage firms in the locality that are more than willing to provide guest speakers to acquaint students with some of the rudiments on stock investments. It is best to invite them toward the close of the unit after the students have some familiarity with the topic.

In the event you want to sell some stocks that you hold, you would follow exactly the same procedure. Now, however, the broker would turn over to you the amount he had received from the buyer, only withholding a small amount to pay for his services. Thus, you have to pay the broker at the time he buys the stock for you and again at the time he sells it for you. This isn't all, though. You may also have to pay a federal tax, a state tax, and a city tax each time you sell stock— and, sometimes, when you buy it. In addition, the owners of the place where the stock is bought or sold may also charge a small fee for the privilege of using their facilities. It appears that if you plan to sell your stock at some gain to yourself, you had better wait until its value increases by at least a few dollars on each share, or you may find that what you thought was a profit for you was actually eaten up by the many fees you had to pay.

The marketplaces where stocks are bought and sold are called *stock exchanges*. The stocks of all companies are not handled at every exchange, but only those stocks that the brokers in that exchange decide they want to handle. The largest of these exchanges is the New York Stock Exchange, which is located in New York City. Another exchange located in New York is the American Stock Exchange. There are a number of other exchanges located throughout the country and throughout the world.

So many people are interested in stock investments that most newspapers publish the daily sales transactions in at least one or more of the stock exchanges. These stock-market reports appear in the form shown on page 339.

Chances are that the first thing that strikes you as you look at this table is the large number of fractions that appear. Actually, there are only seven different fractions that you have to deal with, and these are:

$$\tfrac{1}{8}, \tfrac{1}{4}, \tfrac{3}{8}, \tfrac{1}{2}, \tfrac{5}{8}, \tfrac{3}{4}, \tfrac{7}{8}$$

Each of these fractions represents a fractional part of a dollar, and these are the only fractional parts of a dollar at which stocks are sold. That is, even if you wanted to, you couldn't purchase a share of stock at \$12.57, for it is not sold anywhere at that price. Notice that these fractions are all eighths of a dollar. The fraction $\tfrac{1}{4}$ is really $\tfrac{2}{8}$ that has been reduced to its lowest terms, while the fraction $\tfrac{1}{2}$ was originally the fraction $\tfrac{4}{8}$. How many eighths of a dollar are there in the fraction $\tfrac{3}{4}$ of a dollar?

Since each of the fractions represents a part of a dollar, it might be well if they are written in their decimal form, for this is the way you will be using them. Thus,

Although teachers for many years have been using the device of "giving" students \$10,000 and asking them to purchase stock for this amount, the interest never seems to wane. Try this with your students and have them report their profits or losses periodically during the few weeks this unit is taught.

$\$\frac{1}{8} = 12\frac{1}{2}¢ = \$.125$
$\$\frac{1}{4} = 25¢ = \$.25$
$\$\frac{3}{8} = 37\frac{1}{2}¢ = \$.375$
$\$\frac{1}{2} = 50¢ = \$.50$
$\$\frac{5}{8} = 62\frac{1}{2}¢ = \$.625$
$\$\frac{3}{4} = 75¢ = \$.75$
$\$\frac{7}{8} = 87\frac{1}{2}¢ = \$.875$

Hence, if a share of stock is selling at 14⅞, this would mean that the purchaser had to pay $14⅞, or $14.875 for the share. Similarly, when you say that you can buy a share at 14½, it means that you are willing to pay $14.50 for it.

STOCK MARKET QUOTATIONS

Year To Date High	Year To Date Low	Stocks & Dividend	Sales In 100's	Open	High	Low	Close	Net Change
19½	12	Abacus Corp. 2	16	15½	16	15	15¼	+½
85	72	Abbott Markets 5	4	75	75½	75	75	−1
16¾	12½	Adams Department Store 1	29	15¼	15¾	14⅞	15	+¼
39	25¼	Alabama Electric Co. 2	1	36⅞	36⅞	36⅞	36⅞	+½
16⅝	12⅞	Allen, Inc. 1.20	32	13¼	13⅜	13⅛	13¼	+⅛
78	64	American Bakers pf. 2½	6	64	64¾	64	64¼	−½
96⅞	71½	American Corporation 2	58	84½	85¼	83¼	84½	+1½
12¼	5¾	Atlas Industries	24	8	8¾	8	8½	
48⅝	41⅛	Baldwin Tools 2.50	26	44⅞	45¼	44¾	45	+⅜
58¼	44⅞	Baltimore Credit 1	31	47½	48¼	47⅛	47⅝	−½
65⅜	50¾	Baxter, Inc., pf. 3	7	62⅝	63⅞	62⅜	63¾	+1¼
5⅞	3⅛	Beech Instruments .15	81	4¼	4⅜	4⅛	4⅜	+⅛
17¾	13	Bliss Petroleum 1	9	15¼	15⅝	15¼	15½	+⅞
55½	41½	Bond Foods pf. 2½	14	48½	49	48¼	48¾	−¼
40⅜	23¼	Bullard and Sons 1.70	38	27¾	28	27½	28	+¼
36⅞	29⅝	California Breweries 2	6	30⅝	30⅝	30⅝	30⅝	
46½	37½	Canadian Gas Co. 2	14	38¼	39½	38	38	−1
81⅞	62¼	Carpenter Corp. 1.80	55	78¾	79½	78¼	79	+⅞
43½	35¼	Cenco Chemicals 1.50	26	42	42½	41	42¼	−½
31½	27	Champion Soup Co. 1.06	18	28	28	27	28	
46¾	37⅞	City R. R. Services 1½	16	39⅛	39⅞	38¾	39½	−⅛
82¼	75	Colonial, Inc. 3.25	88	78½	78¾	78	78½	+2
20⅝	14¾	Crane Industries pf. 1½	75	19⅛	19¼	17⅝	18⅜	+¾
33	29⅝	Dana Power and Light Co. 1.60	9	30½	30½	30¼	30½	+⅛
34½	19⅞	Diamond Airlines	68	28⅜	28½	26	28	+1⅛
20¼	13½	Dobbs Productions .37	14	14	14¼	13⅞	13⅞	−⅞
36¾	30¾	Dow Aircraft .84	92	34	35	33	34½	+1
36	25¼	Drexel Mines .70	44	28	28½	28	28	−⅜
23⅜	18¼	Dunhill Limited pf. 1.05	27	23	23⅛	22½	22⅞	+¼
24¼	16½	Dynamics, Inc. 1.20	16	18¼	18½	17½	18	+⅝

In the event that the students do not already know the conversion from eighths of a dollar to their decimal equivalents, they should be required to memorize the table above. Test them on this.

Now you are ready to find out what each of the columns in the stock market report represents. You can do this by examining the quotation for the first company listed.

Year To Date		Stocks & Dividend	Sales In 100's	Open	High	Low	Close	Net Change
High	Low							
19½	12	Abacus Corp. 2	16	15½	16	15	15¼	+½

Year to Date: There are two words that appear under the heading "Year to Date." These are the words "High" and "Low." The numeral 19½ written under the word "High" signifies that the highest price anyone paid for a share of the Abacus Corporation stock thus far that year was $19.50. What does the 12 under the word "Low" represent?

Stocks and Dividend: Obviously, the word "Stocks" refers to the name of the company that is listed in this column, and in this illustration, the company is Abacus Corporation. The explanation for the word "Dividend" is a little more involved. As was pointed out earlier, a stockholder in a company is actually a part owner of the company. He and a great number of other people jointly own the company. Either once or twice a year, or, perhaps, even four times a year, the directors of the company meet to determine how much profit the company had earned for that period of time—assuming that there has been a profit. This profit is then divided among all the shareholders. As you can easily see, it would not be right to give all shareholders the same amount of profit, for some might own as many as 500 shares, while others might own only 5 shares. To distribute the profit fairly, the same amount is allotted for each share of stock. Thus, a person who owns 10 shares of stock will receive 10 times the amount that a person who owns 1 share of stock receives. In the illustration, the numeral "2" to the right of the name of the company tells you that during the previous year, the Abacus Corporation gave its stockholders $2 for each share of stock they held. Thus, a stockholder who owned 400 shares would have received $800 as his part of the company's profit. How was the $800 arrived at? The $2 profit allotted for each share of stock is called a *stock dividend*.

There is another feature about dividends that should be pointed out. Stocks can be divided roughly into two different types—*preferred* and *common*. The owner of preferred stock in a company is usually guaranteed a certain percent of the par value each year as his share of the profit. Remember that the par value of the stock is its original value. Thus, if the par value of the stock is $50, and if he owns "5% pre-

The reporting of stock-market activities varies slightly with different newspapers. Often, the opening price will be deleted in order to save space. Have the students check the format used by the local paper against that shown here.

ferred" stock of the company, it would mean that he will receive 5% of $50, or $2.50 each year on each share he owns. In fact, the preferred stockholders must receive their guaranteed share of the profit before even one penny is distributed among the common stockholders. If no profit is left over, then the common stockholders get nothing. If a great deal of profit remains, then the common stockholders share what remains.

Sales in 100's: Although the stocks in a few companies are sold in groups of 10 shares each—called "lots of 10"—the sales of the great bulk of companies listed on any exchange can be made only in lots of 100. Thus, these sales take place only in what are called round lots, that is, in amounts of 100 shares, or 200 shares, or 300 shares, and so on. This is not to say that you couldn't ask your broker to buy 37 shares of stock of a certain company for you. This can be done, but not in the normal way in which stocks are bought at a stock exchange.

Return now to the numerals under the words "Sales in 100's." The numeral "16" for the Abacus Corporation implies that 16 hundred (1600) shares of this company's stock were sold that day at that stock exchange. How many hundreds of shares of stock of the Abbott Markets company were sold that day?

Open, High, Low, Close: The numerals under these words tell us a little about what happened to the price at which the stocks were sold that day. For instance, on the very first sale that day the purchaser had to pay 15½, or $15.50, for each share of the Abacus Corporation stock. During the day, the highest that anyone had to pay for a share of this company's stock was $16 per share. What was the lowest amount that a person paid that day for a share of the Abacus Corporation stock? The numeral 15¼ under the word "Close" tells you that the last person to buy Abacus Corporation stock that day had to pay $15.25 for each share.

Net Change: One of the things that a person likes to know when he examines the quotations of a particular stock is whether the price that day is higher or lower than it was the day before. It is the numeral that appears under the words "Net Change" that gives him some idea of this. This numeral indicates the amount the closing price per share that day has risen or fallen over the closing price of the previous day. If there is a positive sign (+) in front of the numeral, then the price has risen. If there is a negative (−) sign, then the price has fallen. In the illustration of the Abacus Corporation, the numeral is +½. This means that the closing price of 15¼ is ½ dollar more than the closing price of the day before. Hence, the closing price of the previous day

The only difficulty students may encounter in reading stock quotations is that part of the information pertaining to "net change." Give several oral examples of positive, negative, and zero changes and have students interpret them. At the outset, relate these changes to "closing prices" that are integral values.

must have been 14¾, or $14.75. Is the closing price of the Abbott Markets company higher or lower than it was the previous day? What was the closing price of the previous day? If you go far enough down the list, you will eventually come to the quotations for the Atlas Industries company. Notice that there is no numeral in the "Net Change" column. What do you think this implies? What was the last price paid for each share of this company's stock on the previous day?

■ILLUSTRATION: Joe Manning purchased 400 shares of the Baxter, Inc., preferred stock at the "Low" of the day shown in the stock-market report on page 339. How much did he have to pay for these stocks?

▼EXPLANATION: The price that Joe paid for each share is found in the column under the word "Low." For Baxter, Inc., it is 62⅜ or, $62.375. Since this is the price for 1 share, the price for 400 shares will be 400 times as much as this.

●SOLUTION:

$$\text{"Low" of day} = 62\tfrac{3}{8}$$
$$= \$62.375$$
$$\text{Cost of 400 shares} = 400 \times \$62.375$$
$$= \$24,950$$

▼EXPLANATION (continued): It is important that you realize that Joe had to pay more than the $24,950 for the 400 shares of stock. Not only did he have to pay a broker's commission, but also, possibly, some other small charges in connection with the purchase. None of these fees will be considered in any of this work.

EXERCISES   **A**

1. Rewrite each of these numerals in its equivalent decimal form.

a. $15½ _$15.50_	f. $57⅛ _$57.125_	k. $1⅝ _$ 1.625_
b. $32¼ _32.25_	g. $85⅛ _85.125_	l. $9⅞ _9.875_
c. $49¾ _49.75_	h. $43⅛ _43.125_	m. $14⅞ _14.875_
d. $27¼ _27.25_	i. $7⅝ _7.625_	n. $26⅞ _26.875_
e. $16⅛ _16.125_	j. $2⅝ _2.625_	o. $81⅞ _81.875_

2. Find the product in each of the following exercises. Change each of the numerals to decimal form before multiplying.

a. 10 × $2½ = _$ 25.00_	f. 75 × $8¾ = _$ 656.25_
b. 20 × $5¼ = _105.00_	g. 45 × $12¼ = _551.25_
c. 60 × $7¾ = _465.00_	h. 65 × $15½ = _1,007.50_
d. 25 × $6½ = _162.50_	i. 35 × $32¼ = _1,128.75_
e. 55 × $9¼ = _508.75_	j. 100 × $14⅛ = _1,412.50_

Under no condition should the students be permitted to compute the total cost of the stocks purchased unless they have changed the quotation form of the cost to a decimal numeral expressed in dollars. Experience has shown that too many errors result when the fractional form is used in computations.

k. $100 \times \$26\% = $ __$ 2,637.50__   r. $300 \times \$4\% = $ __$ 1,237.50__
l. $100 \times \$42\% = $ __4,237.50__   s. $400 \times \$5\% = $ __2,150.00__
m. $100 \times \$54\% = $ __5,462.50__   t. $600 \times \$16\% = $ __9,825.00__
n. $100 \times \$18\% = $ __1,862.50__   u. $200 \times \$26\% = $ __5,325.00__
o. $100 \times \$36\% = $ __3,662.50__   v. $500 \times \$12\% = $ __6,312.50__
p. $200 \times \$60\% = $ __12,125.00__   w. $300 \times \$40\% = $ __12,262.50__
q. $200 \times \$17\% = $ __3,425.00__   x. $400 \times \$32\% = $ __13,150.00__

3. Determine the sum in each of the following exercises. Change each of the numerals to decimal form before adding.

a. $\$16 + \$\% \quad = $ __$16.50__   l. $\$18\% + \$\% \ = $ __$18.375__
b. $\$27 + \$\% \quad = $ __27.25__   m. $\$23\% + \$\% \ = $ __23.875__
c. $\$41 + \$\% \quad = $ __41.75__   n. $\$15\% + \$\% \ = $ __16.375__
d. $\$8\% + \$\% \quad = $ __8.75__   o. $\$29\% + \$\% \ = $ __30.125__
e. $\$5\% + \$\% \quad = $ __6.25__   p. $\$76\% + \$\% \ = $ __77.00__
f. $\$14\% + \$\% \ = $ __15.00__   q. $\$41\% + \$\% \ = $ __42.375__
g. $\$62\% + \$1 \ = $ __63.75__   r. $\$59\% + \$1\% = $ __60.375__
h. $\$27\% + \$\% \ = $ __28.25__   s. $\$62\% + \$1\% = $ __64.00__
i. $\$85\% + \$\% \ = $ __85.75__   t. $\$37\% + \$2\% = $ __39.375__
j. $\$27\% + \$\% \ = $ __28.50__   u. $\$94\% + \$1\% = $ __95.875__
k. $\$52\% + \$\% \ = $ __52.50__   v. $\$80\% + \$2\% = $ __82.75__

4. Determine the difference in each of the following exercises. Change each of the numerals to decimal form before finding the difference.

a. $\$12 - \$\% \quad = $ __$11.50__   h. $\$42\% - \$\% \ = $ __$42.125__
b. $\$25 - \$\% \quad = $ __24.25__   i. $\$31\% - \$\% \ = $ __31.125__
c. $\$56 - \$\% \quad = $ __55.375__   j. $\$65\% - \$\% \ = $ __64.75__
d. $\$39 - \$\% \quad = $ __38.625__   k. $\$51\% - \$1\% = $ __50.125__
e. $\$9\% - \$\% \quad = $ __9.25__   l. $\$72\% - \$2\% = $ __69.625__
f. $\$7\% - \$\% \quad = $ __7.25__   m. $\$45\% - \$1\% = $ __43.625__
g. $\$16\% - \$\% \ = $ __16.375__   n. $\$29\% - \$1\% = $ __27.625__

B

The stock quotations that appear on page 339 are to be used in answering each of the questions in the following exercises. Express each answer in decimal form.

1. What was the highest price paid this year prior to the day of this stock table for a share of stock in each of the following companies?

Company	Price per Share
a. Alabama Electric Co.	$ __39.00__
b. Bond Foods pf.	__55.50__
c. Baltimore Credit	__58.25__

All quotations above **must** be changed to decimal form before either addition or subtraction takes place. It is apparent from these exercises why the student must memorize the decimal equivalents of eighths of a dollar.

Company	Price per Share
d. Bliss Petroleum	$ 17.75
e. Baxter, Inc., pf.	65.375
f. California Breweries	36.875

2. What was the first price paid that day for a share of stock in each of the following companies?

Company	Price per Share
a. Abbott Markets	$ 75.00
b. American Corporation	84.50
c. Bullard and Sons	27.75
d. City R.R. Services	39.125
e. Diamond Airlines	28.375
f. Baldwin Tools	44.875

3. What was the lowest price paid that day for a share of stock in each of the following companies?

Company	Price per Share
a. Atlas Industries	$ 8.00
b. Drexel Mines	28.00
c. Dynamics, Inc.	17.50
d. Dana Power and Light Co.	30.25
e. City R.R. Services	38.75
f. Adams Department Store	14.875

4. What was the net change that day for a share of stock in each of the following companies? Indicate whether the price had increased or decreased over the closing price of the previous day.

Company	Net Change	Increase Or Decrease
a. Colonial, Inc.	$ 2.00	I
b. Abbott Markets	1.00	D
c. Alabama Electric Co.	.50	I
d. American Corporation	1.50	I
e. Beech Instruments	.125	I
f. Drexel Mines	.375	D
g. Diamond Airlines	1.125	I
h. Dobbs Productions	.875	D

If the quotations on page 339 can be reproduced in ditto form for the students, a great deal of time in shuffling of pages can be eliminated. If this is not possible, have the students place a marker at page 339 for easy reference.

5. What was the last price paid for a share of stock in each of the following companies on the day prior to the one shown in the quotations on page 339?

Company	Last Price For Day Shown	Net Change	Last Price Of Previous Day
a. Dow Aircraft	$ 34.50	$ + 1.00	$ 33.50
b. Canadian Gas Co.	38.00	−1.00	39.00
c. Champion Soup Co.	28.00	0	28.00
d. Adams Department Store	15.00	+ .25	14.75
e. Bond Foods pf.	48.75	− .25	49.00
f. Cenco Chemicals	42.25	− .50	42.75
g. Baldwin Tools	45.00	+ .375	44.625
h. Bliss Petroleum	15.50	+ .875	14.625
i. Baltimore Credit	47.625	− .50	48.125
j. Crane Industries pf.	18.375	+ .75	17.625

C

1. How much will the buyer have to pay on each of the following stock purchases?

	Price per Share	Number Of Shares	Total Price
a.	42	100	$ 4,200.00
b.	17½	100	1,750.00
c.	15¾	100	1,575.00
d.	52¼	100	5,225.00
e.	31⅜	100	3,137.50
f.	67⅛	200	13,425.00
g.	46⅝	400	18,650.00
h.	25⅞	300	7,762.50

2. How much did the buyer have to pay on each of the following stock purchases that were made on the day of the stock-market quotations on page 339?

Company	Number Of Shares	Price Per Share	Price Per Share In Dollars	Total Price
a. Atlas Industries	100	Open	$ 8.00	$ 800.00
b. Abbott Markets	100	Low	75.00	7,500.00
c. Bullard and Sons	100	Low	27.50	2,750.00

In Exercise 1 of Group B, you may want to ask the students to include an additional column when outlining their work. This column should be headed "Price per Share in Dollars," and should appear directly following the one headed "Price per Share."

Company	Number Of Shares	Price Per Share	Price Per Share In Dollars	Total Price
d. Baldwin Tools	100	High	$ 45.25	$ 4,525.00
e. Baxter, Inc., pf.	200	Close	63.75	12,750.00
f. Allen, Inc.	200	High	13.375	2,675.00
g. Crane Industries pf.	200	Open	19.125	3,825.00
h. Dobbs Productions	300	Low	13.875	4,162.50
i. Dunhill Limited pf.	300	Close	22.875	6,862.50
j. Baltimore Credit	400	Low	47.125	18,850.00

D

1. Timothy Crane purchased 200 shares of Adams Department Store shares at the closing price in the quotations on page 339.
   a. How much did he pay for the stock? $3,000.00
   b. How much would the stock have cost him had he made the purchase at the closing price of the previous day? $2,950.00
   c. How much could he have saved had he been able to make the purchase at the closing price of the previous day? $ 50.00

2. Frank Delman purchased 300 shares of Baxter, Inc., preferred stock at the "Low" of the day in the quotations that appear on page 339.
   a. How much did he save on each share of stock by not having to buy it at the "High" of the day? $ 1.50
   b. How much did he save on the 300 shares by buying them at the "Low" of the day rather than the "High?" $ 450.00

3. Donald Trent was lucky enough to have been able to purchase 100 shares of Bullard and Sons at the "Low" of the year, shown in the quotations on page 339.
   a. How much did these stocks cost him? $2,325.00
   b. Had he been equally lucky and sold them at the "High" of the year, how much would he have received? $4,037.50
   c. How much profit would he have made on the purchase and sale of this stock? $1,712.50

Section 2: Computing Dividends

The common stockholder does not know from year to year how large the dividends on his shares will be. Since the company's profits vary over the years, he has every reason to believe that the dividends he receives will also vary. However, when you examine a large number of

It would be best to point out to the students that the "saving," or "profit" that they found as answers to the problems in Group C is not quite correct, for there are broker's fees and other expenses yet to be considered.

companies, you will find that the dividend distributed on each share remains pretty much the same over the years, although the earnings and the profits of the companies change a great deal. It would seem that if you planned to purchase the stock of a company and wanted to know what you might expect to receive as a dividend on each share, you would be fairly safe in assuming that the dividend for the coming year would be much the same as it had been for the past one. Hence, by examining the quotations on page 339, you can see that the American Corporation paid its shareholders $2 per share in dividends during the previous year. In view of this, it is likely that it will pay $2 in dividends during the coming year. Incidentally, by looking at the quotations, it is not possible to tell whether the $2 was paid in a lump sum, or in two installments during the year (semiannually), or, perhaps, in four installments (quarterly).

■ILLUSTRATION 1: Raymond DaSilva owns 200 shares of Bullard and Sons stock. How much did Mr. DaSilva receive in dividends from the company last year? (Use the quotations on page 339.)

▼EXPLANATION: Next to the words "Bullard and Sons" appears the numeral 1.70. This means that $1.70 was the dividend given for each share of stock last year. Since Mr. DaSilva owns 200 shares, he received 200 times this amount.

●SOLUTION:

$$\text{Dividend per share} = \$1.70$$
$$\text{Dividends on 200 shares} = 200 \times \$1.70$$
$$= \$340$$

The person who owns preferred stock is a little more certain of how much he can expect annually in dividends than the holder of common stock. His stock certificate specifically states that either annually, or semiannually, or quarterly, he will receive a fixed percent of the par value of the stock. What is meant by the par value of a stock?

■ILLUSTRATION 2: Mary Ryan owns 200 shares of the Sunshine Drug Company 6% preferred stock. When she purchased the stock, she paid 46⅛ for each share. However, the par value of the stock is $50. How large was her annual dividend check?

▼EXPLANATION: The amount a person pays for preferred stock has absolutely nothing to do with the dividends he receives. The dividends are computed on the basis of the par value, and, hence, you completely ignore the 46⅛ price that Miss Ryan paid for each share. The dividend on one share is determined by finding 6% of $50, while the dividends on 200 shares are 200 times this amount.

You might want to point out to the students that in the quotations on page 339, the actual amount that the preferred stockholder received the previous year is listed, not the guaranteed percent. (See American Bakers pf, and Baxter, Inc., pf.)

● SOLUTION:

$$\text{Dividend per share} = 6\% \text{ of } \$50$$
$$= .06 \times \$50$$
$$= \$3.00$$
$$\text{Dividends on 200 shares} = 200 \times \$3$$
$$= \$600$$

■ ILLUSTRATION 3: Fred Persing purchased 80 shares of Texas Oil Company's 5½% preferred stock at 104½ per share. If the par value of the stock is $100, how much did Fred receive as his quarterly dividend payment?

▼ EXPLANATION: Here, again, you ignore the purchase price of the stock and use only the par value in computing the dividends. As in Illustration 1, the annual dividends are found for the entire 80 shares. This amount is then divided by 4 in order to determine the quarterly dividend.

● SOLUTION:

$$\text{Annual dividend per share} = 5\tfrac{1}{2}\% \text{ of } \$100$$
$$= .055 \times \$100$$
$$= \$5.50$$
$$\text{Annual dividends on 80 shares} = 80 \times \$5.50$$
$$= \$440.00$$
$$\text{Quarterly dividends on 80 shares} = \tfrac{1}{4} \times \$440$$
$$= \$110$$

EXERCISES   A

1. Use the quotations that appear on page 339 to determine the dividend per share that was paid by each of the following companies during the previous year.

Company	Dividend		Company	Dividend
a. Baltimore Credit	$ 1.00		f. California Breweries	$ 2.00
b. Colonial, Inc.	3.25		g. Dobbs Productions	.37
c. Dunhill Limited pf.	1.05		h. Champion Soup Co.	1.06
d. Crane Industries pf.	1.50		i. Beech Instruments	.15
e. Diamond Airlines	0		j. American Bakers pf.	2.50

2. Determine the annual dividends received by each of the following people who owned the number of shares of stock indicated.

	Number Of Shares	Annual Dividend Per Share	Dividend
a.	100	50¢	$ 50.00
b.	100	75¢	75.00
c.	80	65¢	52.00
d.	40	$1.20	48.00

In finding the total quarterly dividends as in Illustration 3, it is best to follow the solution shown rather than to determine the quarterly dividend for one share from which the total quarterly dividend can be computed. This latter method may lead to difficulties with fractional parts of a cent.

	Number Of Shares	Annual Dividend Per Share	Dividend
e.	75	$2.25	$ 168.75
f.	200	62½¢	125.00
g.	250	18½¢	46.25
h.	300	67½¢	202.50

3. Use the quotations on page 339 to determine the dividends paid the previous year to the holders of stock in each of the following companies.

Company	Number Of Shares	Dividend Per Share	Total Dividends
a. Alabama Electric Co.	100	$ 2.00	$ 200.00
b. Baldwin Tools	100	2.50	250.00
c. Bullard and Sons	200	1.70	340.00
d. Dow Aircraft	800	.84	672.00
e. Bond Foods pf.	75	2.50	187.50
f. City R.R. Services	35	1.50	52.50

4. What annual dividend can each of the following preferred stockholders expect to receive on each share of stock? Do not round off your answers.

	Par Value Per Share	Annual Dividend Rate	Annual Dividend
a.	$ 50	5%	$ 2.50
b.	100	5%	5.00
c.	100	5½%	5.50
d.	50	5½%	2.75
e.	50	6¼%	3.125
f.	100	4¾%	4.75
g.	50	4¾%	2.375
h.	25	5%	1.25
i.	25	4½%	1.125
j.	10	8%	.80
k.	10	6%	.60
l.	10	5½%	.55

5. What annual dividend can each of the following preferred stockholders expect to receive?

	Number Of Shares	Par Value Per Share	Annual Dividend Rate	Annual Dividend Per Share	Total Dividends
a.	100	$ 50	6%	$ 3.00	$ 300.00
b.	100	50	7%	3.50	350.00
c.	100	100	6%	6.00	600.00
d.	50	100	4%	4.00	200.00
e.	75	50	6½%	3.25	243.75
f.	200	100	6½%	6.50	1,300.00
g.	200	100	4½%	4.50	900.00
h.	100	100	4.75%	4.75	475.00
i.	100	50	5.35%	2.675	267.50
j.	40	10	8%	.80	32.00

In Exercises 4, 5, and 6, have the students rewrite all mixed-number percent numerals as decimal-percent numerals before expressing them in final decimal form; that is, write 5½% as 5.5%, and, finally, as .055.

6. What semiannual dividend can each of the following preferred stockholders expect to receive?

	Number Of Shares	Par Value Per Share	Annual Dividend Rate	Annual Dividend Per Share	Total Annual Dividends	Total Semiannual Dividends
a.	100	$100	7%	$ 7.00	$ 700.00	$ 350.00
b.	50	100	3%	3.00	150.00	75.00
c.	40	50	4%	2.00	80.00	40.00
d.	100	50	4½%	2.25	225.00	112.50
e.	70	50	7½%	3.75	262.50	131.25
f.	60	100	6.3%	6.30	378.00	189.00
g.	200	100	5.8%	5.80	1,160.00	580.00
h.	200	50	6.45%	3.225	645.00	322.50

7. What quarterly dividend can each of the following preferred stockholders expect to receive?

	Number Of Shares	Par Value Per Share	Annual Dividend Rate	Annual Dividend Per Share	Total Annual Dividends	Total Quarterly Dividends
a.	200	$100	7%	$ 7.00	$ 1,400.00	$ 350.00
b.	100	50	6%	3.00	300.00	75.00
c.	100	50	4.2%	2.10	210.00	52.50
d.	30	50	5.3%	2.65	79.50	19.88
e.	50	10	6.5%	.65	32.50	8.13
f.	300	10	7.2%	.72	216.00	54.00

B

1. Bill Stanton purchased 65 shares of common stock and 200 shares of 5% preferred stock of the Manhattan Business Corporation.
   a. If the company has been paying an annual dividend of $1.07 per share on its common stock, how much in dividends should Bill expect to receive over the period of one year on his common stock? $ 69.55
   b. If the par value of the preferred stock is $50, how much in dividends should he expect to receive over the period of one year on his preferred stock? $500.00
   c. What total dividends should he expect to receive from the Manhattan Business Corporation over the period of one year?
                                                                                      $569.55

2. For some years now, Jim Feret has owned 200 shares of Dynamics, Inc., stock and 350 shares of Cenco Chemicals stock. The stock of both of these companies is sold at the exchange whose quotations appear on page 339.
   a. How much did he receive in dividends from the Dynamics company last year? $240.00

    b. How much did he receive in dividends from Cenco Chemicals last year? <u>$525.00</u>

    c. What total dividends did he receive from both of these companies last year? <u>$765.00</u>

3. The 5% preferred stock of the Trans-Atlantic Airlines Company is selling for $75 per share, but it has a par value of $100. The 6% preferred stock of the Southern Airlines Company is also selling for $75 per share, but it has a par value of $50.

    a. What is the annual dividend paid per share by the Trans-Atlantic Company? <u>$ 5.00</u>

    b. What is the annual dividend paid per share by the Southern Airlines Company? <u>$ 3.00</u>

    c. When you consider only the dividend and cost of each of these stocks, which is the better buy? <u>Trans-Atlantic Co.</u>

Section 3: Profit or Loss on Stock Investments

You learned earlier that the person who spent his time buying stocks one day and selling them the next after a slight rise in price was probably doing nothing more than supporting his broker. When you consider the broker's fees and the various and sundry taxes on stock transactions, an investor's added costs will run anywhere from a high of 3% to a low of 1% of the price of the stocks each time he buys or sells. The person investing around $300 to $400 will find that his charges are about at the 3% rate. Had he been able to invest $5,000 or more, the added fees would be in the neighborhood of 1%. In general, you can say that the average stock purchaser can count on paying about 1½% of the price in broker's fees and taxes. This is the rate that will be used in the work that follows in this section, since it's a fairly accurate rule of thumb.

■ ILLUSTRATION 1: What was the approximate total amount that Mr. Shanks had to pay when he purchased 100 shares of Hayes Products, Inc., at 23½?

● SOLUTION:

      Cost per share = 23½, or $23.50

      Cost of 100 shares = 100 × $23.50

                  = $2,350

      Approximate amount of additional fees = 1½% of $2,350

                                  = .015 × $2,350

                                  = $35.25

      Approximate total cost of purchase = $2,350 + $35.25

                              = $2,385.25

To add interest to the work, select a committee of volunteers to visit a broker's office to observe how the news of the sales from a stock exchange is reported. (Be sure to call in advance.) While there, students can obtain actual table of fees that members of the exchange can charge on sales.

▼ EXPLANATION: The approximate amount of the additional fees is about 1½% of the cost of the 100 shares. Hence, it is simply a matter of computing 1½% of $2,350 to determine these fees. To do this, you re-write the percent numeral 1½% in its decimal numeral equivalent form as .015. The fees of $35.25, when added to the cost of $2,350, give you the approximate total amount that Mr. Shanks had to pay for the pur-chase.

■ ILLUSTRATION 2: Approximately how much money did Mr. Lar-son receive from his broker at the time he sold his 50 shares of Howard Nickel Company stock at 42⅜?

● SOLUTION:

Selling price per share = 42⅜, or $42.375
Selling price of 50 shares = 50 × $42.375
$$= \$2,118.75$$
Approximate amount of additional fees = 1½% of $2,118.75
$$= .015 \times \$2,118.75$$
$$= \$31.78125, \text{ or } \$31.78$$
Approximate amount received by Mr. Larson = $2,118.75 − $31.78
$$= \$2,086.97$$

▼ EXPLANATION: The computation in this solution is much the same as it is for Illustration 1. They differ, though, in the very last step, for now the fees have to be subtracted from the selling price of the stock. This is much the same as a situation in which you might bring a cam-era to someone and ask him to sell it for you. He agrees to do this on the condition that you pay him $5 for his services. After selling the camera for, say, $70, instead of turning this amount over to you, he gives you only $65. The remaining $5 he keeps as his fee. Similarly, in this illustration, the charges came to approximately $31.78. This is de-ducted from the selling price of $2,118.75, and the balance, $2,086.97, is turned over to Mr. Larson.

The goal in this section is to develop some means of finding the profit (or loss) in the purchase and sale of stock. Consider, for instance, what the total fees might be in buying stock for $1,000 and selling it for $2,000.

Fees paid on purchase of stock = 1½% of $1,000
$$= .015 \times \$1,000$$
$$= \$15$$
Fees paid on sale of stock = 1½% of $2,000
$$= .015 \times \$2,000$$
$$= \$30$$
Total fees paid on purchase and sale = $15 + $30
$$= \$45$$

Using the exact brokerage rates and taxes that must be paid on stock transactions usually requires more time and research than the average person is willing to spend. The "1½%" guide given here seems to be close enough for practical needs.

The cost of the stock, plus the selling price, comes to $3,000. When you take 1½% of this sum, it again equals $45, which is the total of the fees paid on both purchase and sale.

$$1½\% \text{ of } \$3,000$$
$$= .015 \times \$3,000$$
$$= \$45$$

It would appear, therefore, that if you are interested in finding the total fees paid on both the purchase and sale of the same stock, you can save yourself work by adding these two amounts and taking 1½% of the sum. This is much easier than finding 1½% of each number individually and then determining the sum.

■ ILLUSTRATION 3: How much profit or loss did Michael O'Hara have when be bought 100 shares of Reliable Products, Inc., at 37 and sold them at 38½?

● SOLUTION:

Total cost $= 100 \times \$37$
$$= \$3,700$$
Total selling price $= 100 \times \$38.50$
$$= \$3,850$$
Total profit before considering fees $= \$3,850 - \$3,700$
$$= \$150$$
Approximate fees $= 1½\%$ of ($\$3,700 + \$3,850$)
$$= .015 \times \$7,550$$
$$= \$113.25$$
Approximate total profit after considering fees $= \$150 - \$113.25$
$$= \$36.75$$

▼ EXPLANATION: In determining the approximate fees on both the buying and selling of the stock, you first add the purchase price to the selling price, and then you find 1½% of this total. It is interesting to note that the profit of $150 that Michael may have thought he was going to make dwindled to a mere $36.75 after the fees were deducted. In fact, had he sold the stock for 38 rather than 38½, he would probably have had a loss and not a gain.

EXERCISES   A

1. Determine the approximate fees that will have to be paid on each of the following stock orders.

	Total Selling Price	Approximate Fees		Total Selling Price	Approximate Fees
a.	$2,000	$ 30.00	e.	875	$ 13.13
b.	3,000	45.00	f.	618	9.27
c.	1,500	22.50	g.	746	11.19
d.	2,300	34.50	h.	957	14.36

It is important to call the student's attention to the fact that Michael O'Hara of Illustration 3 had better wait until the value of a share of Reliable Products, Inc., has gone up at least a point and quarter before he sells, or else the only person that will profit from his transaction will be the broker.

2. Determine the approximate fees that will have to be paid on each of the following stock sales.

	Number Of Shares	Selling Price Per Share	Total Selling Price	Approximate Fees
a.	100	25	$ 2,500.00	$ 37.50
b.	100	27½	2,750.00	41.25
c.	100	38¾	3,875.00	58.13
d.	100	16⅛	1,612.50	24.19
e.	100	22⅝	2,262.50	33.94
f.	50	45¼	2,262.50	33.94
g.	50	62⅜	3,118.75	46.78
h.	40	71⅞	2,875.00	43.13

3. Use the stock quotations on page 339 to determine the approximate fees that had to be paid on each of the following stock sales.

	Number Of Shares	Name Of Company	Selling at:	Total Selling Price	Approximate Fees
a.	100	Atlas Industries	Open	$ 800.00	$ 12.00
b.	100	Bond Foods pf.	High	4,900.00	73.50
c.	200	Abacus Corp.	Low	3,000.00	45.00
d.	200	Cenco Chemicals	Low	8,200.00	123.00
e.	200	American Bakers pf.	Close	12,850.00	192.75
f.	500	Beech Instruments	High	2,187.50	32.81

4. What is the approximate total cost, including fees, that will have to be paid by the buyer on each of the following stock purchases?

	Total Purchase Price	Approximate Fees	Approximate Total Cost
a.	$1,000	$ 15.00	$ 1,015.00
b.	4,000	60.00	4,060.00
c.	2,500	37.50	2,537.50
d.	3,600	54.00	3,654.00
e.	1,250	18.75	1,268.75
f.	2,375	35.63	2,140.63

5. What is the approximate amount the seller will receive after fees are deducted on each of the following stock sales?

	Total Selling Price	Approximate Fees	Approximate Amount Received
a.	$5,000	$ 75.00	$ 4,925.00
b.	3,500	52.50	3,447.50
c.	2,700	40.50	2,659.50
d.	4,300	64.50	4,235.50
e.	2,450	36.75	2,413.25
f.	1,325	19.88	1,305.12

In Exercises 2 and 3, an additional column headed "Price per Share in Dollars" might prove beneficial in the student's outline of the work.

6. What is the approximate total amount, including fees, that will have to be paid by the buyer on each of the following stock purchases?

	Number Of Shares	Cost Per Share	Purchase Price	Approximate Fees	Approximate Total Purchase Price
a.	100	15	$ 1,500.00	$ 22.50	$ 1,522.50
b.	100	21½	2,150.00	32.25	2,182.25
c.	100	34¼	3,245.00	51.38	3,476.38
d.	200	42¾	8,550.00	128.25	8,678.25
e.	200	26¾	5,350.00	80.25	5,430.25
f.	400	12⅝	5,050.00	75.75	5,125.25

7. What is the approximate total amount, less fees, that will be received by the seller on each of the following stock sales? Use the quotations on page 339.

	Number Of Shares	Name Of Company	Selling at:	Selling Price	Approximate Fees	Approximate Amount Received
a.	100	Bullard and Sons	Close	$ 2,800.00	$ 42.00	$ 2,758.00
b.	100	Abbott Markets	Low	7,500.00	112.50	7,387.50
c.	100	Bliss Petroleum	Close	1,550.00	23.25	1,526.75
d.	200	Dobbs Productions	High	2,850.00	42.75	2,807.25
e.	200	Diamond Airlines	Open	5,675.00	85.13	5,589.87
f.	300	City R.R. Services	High	11,962.50	179.44	11,783.06

B

1. Determine the approximate fees paid on both the purchase and sales in the following stock transactions.

	Purchase Price	Selling Price	Total of Purchase and Selling Prices	Approximate Fees
a.	$2,000	$3,000	$ 5,000.00	$ 75.00
b.	2,400	2,500	4,900.00	73.50
c.	1,900	1,700	3,600.00	54.00
d.	1,450	1,650	3,100.00	46.50
e.	3,240	3,150	6,390.00	95.85
f.	1,025	1,475	2,500.00	37.50

2. Determine the approximate fees paid on both the purchase and sale in the following stock transactions.

	Number Of Shares	Purchase Price Per Share	Purchase Price	Selling Price Per Share	Selling Price	Total of Purchase and Selling Prices	Approximate Fees
a.	100	12	$1,200.00	14	$1,400.00	$2,600.00	$ 39.00
b.	200	18	3,600.00	21	4,200.00	7,800.00	117.00
c.	100	24½	2,450.00	25	2,500.00	4,950.00	74.25
d.	100	36	3,600.00	34½	3,450.00	7,050.00	105.75
e.	200	30¾	6,150.00	36½	7,300.00	13,450.00	201.75
f.	200	25½	5,100.00	20¼	4,050.00	9,150.00	137.25

Inquire of the students why the word "approximate" appears in many of the headings in these exercises.

3. Determine the profit or loss on each of the following stock transactions when the fees for buying and selling are not taken into account.

	Number Of Shares	Purchase Price Per Share	Purchase Price	Selling Price Per Share	Selling Price	Profit Or Loss
a.	100	50	$ 5,000.00	56	$ 5,600.00	$ 600.00 P
b.	40	28	1,120.00	37	1,480.00	360.00 P
c.	100	17½	1,750.00	25¼	2,525.00	775.00 P
d.	100	31¾	3,175.00	47⅝	4,762.50	1,587.50 P
e.	65	12½	812.50	9¾	633.75	178.75 L
f.	30	54⅛	1,623.75	42¼	1,267.50	356.25 L

4. Determine the profit or loss on each of the following stock transactions when the fees for buying and selling are taken into account.

	Number Of Shares	Purchase Price Per Share	Purchase Price	Selling Price Per Share	Selling Price	Profit Or Loss	Fees	Total Profit Or Loss
a.	100	24	$2,400.00	30	$3,000.00	$ 600.00P	$ 81.00	$ 519.00 P
b.	100	32	3,200.00	46	4,600.00	1,400.00P	117.00	1,283.00 P
c.	100	16	1,600.00	17	1,700.00	100.00P	49.50	50.50 P
d.	100	50	5,000.00	51	5,100.00	100.00P	151.50	51.50 L
e.	100	20	2,000.00	16	1,600.00	400.00L	54.00	454.00 L
f.	100	42	4,200.00	37	3,700.00	500.00L	118.50	618.50 L

Section 4: Rate of Return on Stock Investments

There are a great many people who purchase stock simply with the idea of holding it for only a short period. They hope that during this time the stock will rise in value and, therefore, they will be able to sell it at a profit. There are an equally large number of people who purchase stock solely for the purpose of getting a higher rate of interest on their money than they would if they kept it in a bank.

As you know, the rate paid by most banks is somewhere between 4% and 5% per year. Hence, the person who invests in stock for the dividend alone will have to receive a rate higher than the 5%, or it would probably be to his advantage to keep his money in a bank. In order to determine what rate of interest a person does receive on a stock investment, you consider the dividends in exactly the same way as you would the interest that a bank pays its depositors. This is the way it should be, for both dividends and interest represent the money earned by putting your savings to work. In the one case, you are allowing the bank to use your savings, while in the other, you are permitting the management of a company to use your money. In both instances, you are really being paid a rent for the use of this money.

Although this section is interesting from the point of view that it will enable the students to compare the interest rate received on a stock investment against that received on a bank deposit, more important topics follow in the text. Hence, if time is at a premium, delete this unit from the year's work.

Since dividends and interest can be thought of as being interchangeable terms, it is possible for you to use the interest formula in connection with your work on dividends.

$$\text{Interest Formula: Principal} \times \text{Rate} = \text{Interest}$$
$$P \times R = I$$

This is exactly what you did on page 348 at the time you were finding the dividends on preferred stock. Now, however, your problem is somewhat different. Where, before, you knew the interest rate and had to determine the dividends the investor received, at this time you happen to know the dividends that were given to him and you would like to know the rate of interest he received. Expressing this somewhat differently, your object is to find the value of R—the rate of interest—in the formula above. To do this, the Product of Two Numbers Principle is used (see page 36) and the formula is rewritten as follows:

$$R = I \div P$$

Can you explain the Product of Two Numbers Principle in terms of the equation $6 \times 9 = 54$? What numbers in the equation $6 \times 9 = 54$ can be thought of as replacements for the letters P, R, and I?

There is a slight change that you want to make in this formula. In view of the fact that you are dealing with dividends rather than interest, it would be best to use the symbol "D" rather than "I" when writing the formula. Just one more small point—the people involved in stock investments seem to prefer to call the rate of interest by the name *rate of return*. Thus, the formula becomes:

$$\text{Rate of Return} = \text{Dividend} \div \text{Principal Invested}$$
$$\text{or} \quad R = D \div P$$

The application of this formula is relatively simple as you will see in the following illustration:

■ ILLUSTRATION 1: Ralph Tucker purchased 100 shares of Bullard and Sons stock at the "High" of the day shown in the quotations on page 339. What rate of return can he expect from his investment?

▼ EXPLANATION: In examining the quotations on page 339, notice that Bullard and Sons paid $1.70 in dividends on each share of stock during the previous year. In computing the rate of return that Mr. Tucker can expect, assume that the company will pay the same amount this year. Rather than compute the rate of return on the total cost and the total dividends for the 100 shares, you do this for only 1 share. Actually, the rate of return is identical, whether it is based on 100 shares

A review of the "Product of Two Numbers Principle" will probably be necessary before attempting to develop the rate-of-return formula. Use numeral illustrations similar to those at the center of the page.

or 1 share. However, the computation is much easier when 1 share is used. Also, in finding the rate of return, ignore all fees charged in connection with the purchase and sale of the stock. These fees are relatively small when compared to the cost of the stock. Hence they do not affect the rate of return to any extent worth noticing. The number that is to be used as the replacement for the principal in the formula is $28, for this is the amount invested in each share.

●SOLUTION:

$$R = D \div P$$
$$= \$1.70 \div \$28$$
$$= .061, \text{ or } 6.1\%$$

▼EXPLANATION (continued): Assume that the price of each share of Bullard and Sons stock remains the same over the coming year. Would Mr. Tucker have been better off by buying this stock, or by depositing his money in a bank?

■ILLUSTRATION 2: The 4% preferred stock of the Potomac Glass Company is selling at 37½. What rate of return will an investor receive if the par value of the stock is 50?

▼EXPLANATION: Before it is possible to determine the rate of return, it is first necessary to find the dividend the investor receives. This dividend, as you recall, is based on the par value of the stock.

●SOLUTION:

$$\text{Dividend} = 4\% \text{ of } \$50$$
$$= .04 \times \$50$$
$$= \$2.00$$
$$R = D \div P$$
$$= \$2 \div \$37.50$$
$$= .053 \text{ or } 5.3\%$$

▼EXPLANATION (continued): By examining the solution above, can you tell when the rate of return will be exactly the same as the rate paid by the company? When will it be more than the rate paid by the company? When will it be less?

EXERCISES   A

1. Determine the rate of return to the nearest tenth of a percent on each of the following stock purchases.

	Annual Dividends	Cost Per Share	Rate Of Return			Annual Dividends	Cost Per Share	Rate Of Return	
a.	$3.00	$52.00	5.8	%	e.	1.80	30.50	5.9	%
b.	4.00	65.00	6.2	%	f.	2.30	28.25	8.1	%
c.	2.50	46.00	5.4	%	g.	4.75	83.75	5.7	%
d.	1.50	27.00	5.6	%	h.	5.20	96.50	5.4	%

Discuss the rate of return found in the two illustrations by noting whether it might have been to the advantage of the investors to have deposited their money in a bank rather than purchasing these stocks.

2. Determine the rate of return to the nearest tenth of a percent that the purchaser can expect on the following stock. The quotations for these stocks appear on page 339.

	Name Of Company	Purchased at:	Cost Per Share	Dividends	Rate Of Return
a.	Canadian Gas Co.	Close	$ 38.00	$ 2.00	5.3 %
b.	Colonial, Inc.	Low	78.00	3.25	4.2 %
c.	American Bakers pf.	Low	64.00	2.50	3.9 %
d.	Allen, Inc.	Open	13.25	1.20	9.1 %
e.	Abacus Corp.	Close	15.25	2.00	13.1 %
f.	Dobbs Productions	Open	14.00	.37	2.6 %
g.	Dunhill Limited pf.	Low	22.50	1.05	4.7 %
h.	Beech Instruments	Open	4.25	.15	3.5 %

3. What rate of return to the nearest tenth of a percent can the purchaser of the following preferred stock expect to receive?

	Interest Rate	Par Value	Dividend	Purchase Price	Rate Of Return
a.	5%	$100	$ 5.00	$110	4.5 %
b.	6%	100	6.00	112	5.4 %
c.	4%	100	4.00	84	4.8 %
d.	5%	50	2.50	41	6.1 %
e.	4½%	50	2.25	38	5.9 %
f.	5½%	50	2.75	55	5.0 %
g.	4.8%	100	4.80	82	5.9 %
h.	6.1%	100	6.10	95	6.4 %

B

1. Bernard Caswell purchased 100 shares of Drexel Mines at the "High" for the year shown in the quotations on page 339.
   a. To the nearest tenth of a percent, what rate of return can Mr. Caswell expect to receive on his investment? ___1.9%___
   b. If Mr. Caswell had purchased the stock at the "Low" of the year, what rate of return could he have expected to receive? ___2.8%___
   c. Based on the rate of return alone, should Mr. Caswell have invested in this stock, or should he have deposited his money in the bank? ___Bank___

2. a. What rate of return can the purchaser of 100 shares of Atlas Industries expect to receive if he paid the opening price shown in the quotations on page 339? ___0%___
   b. Why would a person want to invest his money in Atlas Industries stock? ___In hopes that the price will go up.___

Section 5: The Mutual Funds

The great difficulty in investing in stocks is in trying to decide which stocks to buy. Some people are interested in getting a fairly high rate of return and do not really care whether the price of the stock goes up, or stays the same—so long as it doesn't go down. Other people are interested in stock as a long-range investment for their money. They hope that, over a long period of time, the stock will increase many times in value and be worth much more than money kept in a bank. Still others are interested in the "fast" dollar. They are looking for stocks whose price will rise rapidly over the coming few months. At the end of this period, they plan to sell their holdings for cash to buy other stocks that, hopefully, will also have a rapid rise.

Whatever a person's objective may be in the purchase of stock, the research he has to do before he can make up his mind as to what the best buy will be for his needs may take endless hours of time. To avoid the problem of making a personal investigation, many an investor will simply purchase shares of stock in a *mutual fund*. A mutual fund is a company that simply owns shares of stock in a great number of other companies. The mutual-fund company does not manufacture anything, nor does it own any buildings, nor does it sell any merchandise. It is simply in the business of investing in other businesses. By buying the stock of many different companies, the mutual fund reduces the risk of any large loss it might suffer by having one company go bankrupt.

Over the past 100 years, the general trend of the value of stocks has very definitely been upward. You, as an individual, cannot possibly buy the stocks of many different companies, for you just don't have that much money to invest. Hence, there is always the possibility that the companies you do invest in may suffer large losses while most other companies are operating at a profit. The mutual-fund company works on the premise that business in the United States is basically sound, and that the general trend of stock prices will continue to rise in the future. Hence, even if a few of their investments turn bad, the bulk of them will be making enough money to outweigh the losses they suffer in a few companies.

To avoid even a small loss by making an unwise investment, the mutual funds employ people who are experts in analyzing stock investments. These men decide what stocks the fund should purchase and which ones they should sell. It is their judgment—good or bad—that determines how successful the fund will be. And when you buy stock in a mutual fund, you really give your savings to these men and ask them to invest it for you.

It is more than likely that should any of the students invest money in stock, the majority of these will be doing it through some mutual-fund service. Hence, this section should not be bypassed but, rather, should be read slowly and carefully with them.

Although the stock of a few of the mutual-fund companies can be purchased at a stock market, the majority of these companies sell their shares only at a stockbroker's office, or through the door-to-door salesmen that the stockbroker hires. This is just where the debate over mutual funds starts. Quite a substantial fee has to be paid to a salesman for making his sale. At the time you investigated the cost of buying and selling stock, you found that the fee plus taxes that had to be paid to the broker ran on the average somewhere around 1½% for buying the stock and another 1½% for selling it, or a total of 3% on both. However, on the purchase of most mutual-fund stocks you have to pay the salesman around 8 to 9 percent for his commission. Some of this money he keeps; some goes to the broker who employs him, and a small amount filters back to the mutual-fund company itself. In spite of the fact that this charge is rather high, most people agree that the small investor who does not have the time to investigate before he invests is a lot better off buying mutual funds than buying stock as a result of, say, a tip from a good friend.

There are two basic ways in which it is possible to purchase mutual funds from a salesman. In the first of these, you make a lump-sum payment and buy whatever number of shares this amount will purchase— that is, after the sales charge is deducted. This method is called the Single-Payment Plan. In the second method, you invest a fixed amount monthly, such as $25, or $50, or $100, and so on. As soon as the total of the monthly payments amounts to enough money to purchase a share of stock, this is done and the stock is mailed to you. This method is called the Monthly-Systematic-Investment Plan.

Many people find fault with the monthly plan because at least half of the first year's payments are deducted for sales charges. Hence, if you should decide, after the first year, not to go on with this program, half of your money would have been used up in fees. On the other hand, the people who run the funds say that this is a good way to force people to save. These monthly plans are designed, usually, to cover a 10-year period. Since the fees drop drastically after the first year, it is only by continuing to make payments over the remaining 9 years that you get the average charges down to the point where they seem reasonable. It is important to point out again that, despite these high charges, most funds have earned more for the investor than he could have earned for himself by keeping his money in a bank.

■ ILLUSTRATION 1: Under the Single-Payment Plan, a person invested $10,000 in shares in a mutual fund. If the sales charge was 8½%, how much of the $10,000 was actually used for the purchase of stock?

For stock investments the students should be made to realize that although the mutual-fund fees do run high, fund investments are by far the safest, for the average person has neither the time nor the ability to do extensive research before making a stock purchase.

● S O L U T I O N :

> Fees = 8½% of $10,000
> = .085 × $10,000
> = $850
> Amount remaining for stock purchase = $10,000 − $850
> = $9,150

▼ E X P L A N A T I O N : Since $850 went for fees, the remainder, which is the difference between the original $10,000 and the $850, is used for buying stock in the mutual fund.

■ I L L U S T R A T I O N 2 : Mr. Thomas enrolled in a $25 Monthly-Systematic-Investment Plan, which consisted of making an initial payment (first payment) of $50 and remaining payments of $25 each over a period of ten years. Sales charges for the first year amounted to half of each payment, while for the remaining nine years, the charge was $12 per year. In addition, he was charged 75¢ per month to pay for the salaries of the experts employed to run the fund. What was the total charge that Mr. Thomas had to pay over the ten-year period?

● S O L U T I O N :

Charge on initial payment of $50 = $25
Monthly charge for first year = $12.50
Total of monthly charges for first year = 12 × $12.50
= $150
Total of annual charges for remaining 9 years = 9 × $12
= $108
Annual charge for salaries of experts = 12 × $.75
= $9
Total charge for salaries of experts = 10 × $9
= $90
Total charges over the ten-year period = $25 + $150 + $108 + $90
= $373

▼ E X P L A N A T I O N : The charges over the ten-year period consisted of the following three parts:

1. The charges for the first year, which amounted to one half of the money he paid in that year; notice that during the first year there is an initial payment, plus 12 additional monthly payments—not 11 payments
2. Annual payments of $12 each over a period of 9 years
3. Monthly charges of 75¢ each for the payment of the salaries of employees to oversee the fund.

The total of each of these charges is $175, $108, and $90 respectively, for a grand total of $373.

Illustration 2 can be taken one step farther where the students are asked to determine the total amount Mr. Thomas invested over the ten-year period. This should then be compared to the amount he had to pay in fees.

EXERCISES   **A**

1. Determine the sales charge that will have to be paid by an investor in mutual funds under each of the following Single-Payment-Plan Investments.

	Amount Invested	Sales Rate Charge	Sales Charge
a.	$ 2,000	8%	$ 160.00
b.	4,000	9%	360.00
c.	6,000	7%	420.00
d.	3,000	8½%	255.00
e.	8,000	7½%	600.00
f.	10,000	9½%	950.00

2. Determine the amount of money that will remain to be invested in mutual funds after the sales charge is deducted in each of the following Single-Payment-Plan Investments.

	Amount Invested	Sales Rate Charge	Sales Charge	Amount Remaining For Investment
a.	$5,000	9%	$ 450.00	$ 4,550.00
b.	1,000	6%	60.00	940.00
c.	7,000	8%	560.00	6,440.00
d.	6,400	7½%	480.00	5,920.00
e.	8,500	8½%	722.50	7,777.50
f.	9,200	9½%	874.00	8,326.00

3. The sales charge that has to be paid to a mutual fund during the first year consists of one half of the initial payment, plus one half of the remaining 12 payments made during the first year. What is the total charge for the first year under each of the following plans?

	Initial Payment	Monthly Payment	Amount Paid During First Year	Sales Charge During First Year
a.	$ 100	$ 50	$ 700.00	$ 350.00
b.	300	50	900.00	450.00
c.	150	75	1,050.00	525.00
d.	200	100	1,400.00	700.00
e.	500	100	1,700.00	850.00
f.	1,400	200	3,800.00	1,900.00

4. James Elroy agreed to make payments into a Monthly-Systematic-Investment Plan. He was told that after the first year, he would have to pay a sales charge of $12 per year on every $25 he contributed on his monthly payments. That is, if he invested $50 per month, the sales charge after the first year would be $24 per year. How much will the annual sales charge be after the first year in each of the following plans?

Compare the sales charges above with the approximate 3% charge that the average investor in stocks has to pay. Emphasize, however, that the mutual-fund investor has achieved diversification which the average investor is unable to do because of lack of funds.

	Monthly Payment	Number of $25's In Monthly Payment	Annual Sales Charge
a.	$ 75	3	$ 36.00
b.	100	4	48.00
c.	150	6	72.00
d.	200	8	96.00
e.	300	12	144.00
f.	500	20	240.00

5. To pay for the salaries of the employees who operate the mutual fund, each invester has to pay a fee of 75¢ per month. How much will an investor in this fund have to pay for this fee if he makes payments for the following periods of time?

	Monthly Payments for:	Total Of Supervisory Fees			Monthly Payments for:	Total Of Supervisory Fees
a.	60 months	$ 45.50	e.	6 years	$ 54.00
b.	80 months	60.00	f.	8 years	72.00
c.	95 months	71.25	g.	9 years	81.00
d.	115 months	86.25	h.	10 years	90.00

6. Many mutual funds charge their investors ½% per month of the monthly payment. How much will this amount to each month on the following plans?

	Monthly Payment	Monthly Fee			Monthly Payment	Monthly Fee
a.	$ 50	$ .25	d.	120	$ .60
b.	100	.50	e.	25	.13
c.	400	2.00	f.	75	.38

B

On page 247, there is a table showing how much money will be worth if placed in a bank and allowed to remain there over a long period of time. Use this table to determine the amount of money each depositor will have in the bank after the period of time shown. Interest is compounded annually in each case. (Review exercises.)

	Amount on Deposit At Beginning of Period	Interest Rate	Period Of Years	Value of $1 At End of Period	Amount on Deposit At End of Period
a.	$ 6,000	5%	10	$ 1.6289	$ 9,773.40
b.	2,000	6%	10	1.7908	3,581.60
c.	10,000	6%	12	2.0122	20,122.00
d.	7,500	5½%	15	2.2325	16,743.75
e.	5,400	4%	8	1.3686	7,390.44
f.	6,800	5%	11	1.7103	11,630.04

The review exercises in Group B are designed to show how much a person would have saved by placing his money in a bank over a period of years rather than by investing it in a mutual fund. The problems in Group C make this comparison directly with the claims of two mutual funds.

C

1. The Seagrave Fund advertised that, over a period of 9 years, an investment of $10,000 in its fund increased in value to a point where, at the end of the period, it was worth $32,500.
   a. If a person had deposited $10,000 in the bank at an interest rate of 5% compounded annually, how much would he have had in the account at the end of 9 years? $15,513.00
   b. How much would a person gain by having invested the $10,000 in the Seagrave Fund rather than by depositing it in the bank?
                                                                          $16,987.00
2. The Midwest Mutual Fund claims that an investment of $5,000 in its fund at the beginning of a particular 10-year period would have been worth $23,600 at the end of the period.
   a. How much would $5,000 have been worth at the end of the 10 years had it been deposited in a bank at an interest rate of 5½% compounded annually? $ 8,540.50
   b. How much more money would a person have if he had purchased $5,000 worth of shares in the Midwest Mutual Fund instead of depositing it in a bank? $15,059.50

Unit 2:   The Bond Market

Section 1:   The Bond Market Report

Somewhere between the extremely cautious fellow who keeps all his money in a bank and the daring young man who enjoys the excitement of playing the stock market falls the person who prefers to invest his money in bonds. An investment of this kind carries with it a greater risk than is involved in a bank deposit. However, it also carries with it the chance of a greater return. On the other hand, a bond investment is a great deal safer than an investment in stocks, and, therefore, as can be expected, there is usually less chance of profiting as much from a bond investment.

At the time you studied the services of a bank, you found that one of these services concerned itself with the lending of money. A bank will not give money to a person unless it receives, in return, a written statement assuring it that the money will be returned. The piece of paper bearing this statement and the signature of the borrower is called a *promissory note*.

A bond is pretty much the same as a promissory note, except that there is much more money involved. When a company starts in busi-

Care should be taken when examining mutual-fund advertisements, for they will frequently use an illustrative period which covers an inflationary cycle during which the values of most stocks have risen markedly.

ness, or, perhaps, when it wants to expand its business, it issues these promissory notes, called *bonds*, to anyone who will lend it money. Usually, these bonds are valued at $1,000 each, and a person buying one is in reality lending the company $1,000. On the bond itself there is a statement to the effect that the company, at some date in the future, will pay back the $1,000. In addition, there is also some statement about the rate of interest the company is going to pay the lender for the use of his money.

The big difference between a stockholder and a bondholder is this:

A stockholder is a part owner of a company. If the company makes a great deal of money, he shares in the profit. If the company goes bankrupt, he stands to lose his entire investment. A bondholder is a person who has lent money to the company. Whether the company does well or does poorly, all he receives is the interest on the money the company owes him. Should the company go bankrupt, then whatever money it may have—such as from the sale of its buildings—must be used to pay off the bondholders first. If any money happens to be left over, it is distributed among the stockholders.

Such a long period of time exists between the day a bond is issued and the day it is redeemed (paid off) that many people want to sell it at some time between these dates. Since the company does not want the bond back before it is due, these people try to sell their bonds at marketplaces that resemble stock markets and are called bond markets. As in the case of stock markets, the only persons permitted into these areas are brokers who are members of that bond-market organization. Hence, in order either to buy or to sell a bond, you must ask a broker to do it for you, and for this service he charges you a small fee There are other fees, too, that you have to pay, which may include federal, state, and city taxes.

Bond-market sales appear daily in newspapers in much the same way that stock-market sales do. On page 367, there is a sample of a section of bond-market quotations as they might appear in a newspaper. In order to explain the meaning of each item, the report of the first company listed follows.

Year to Date		Bonds & Rate	Sales In $1,000	High	Low	Last	Net Change
High	Low						
106½	85	Eastern Mfg. Co. 5s 92	85	89	88¼	88⅜	+ ⅛

Perhaps the most confusing part about bond quotations is the fact that all the decimal points are in the wrong places. To save space— and time, too—the decimal point appears one place farther to the left

Stress the distinction between a bondholder and a stockholder. The bondholder is one of the many persons from whom the company borrowed money, while the stockholder is one of the many persons who own the company. You may have to explain the term "bankrupt" to the students. It appears in the center of the page.

BOND MARKET QUOTATIONS

Year to Date		Bonds & Rate	Sales In $1,000	High	Low	Last	Net Change
High	Low						
106½	85	Eastern Manufacturing Co. 5s 92	85	89	88¼	88⅜	+⅛
155	99¾	Electronic Associates 3½s 87	22	116	115½	116	+1
135	98⅛	Emerson-Brody Corp. 5s 89	17	108	106	107	−½
104½	97	Equitable Light Co. 6s 93	33	103	102½	102½	
96	92	Evans Storage Battery Co. 6s 94	5	94¾	94¾	94½	−1⅛
27	18	Falstaff Finance Corp. 5s 2020	1	20¼	20¼	20¼	+¼
29	20⅛	Family Food Stores 4½s 2015	47	24½	24	24	−1
40	36	Federal Mineral Co. 3⅛s 2000	2	38	38	38	−½
102	71⅜	Florida Products, Inc. 4⅜s 92	17	77½	76⅞	77¼	+1
124	104	Foremost Tire Co. 5½s 87	15	109	108	108½	−1
80¾	74	Franklin Sulphur Co. 3¼s 88	12	80¾	79½	80¾	+1½
97⅞	59⅝	General Department Stores 5½s 2011	58	90	84¼	89⅛	+8⅛
73	68½	Gibraltar Power Co. 5s 2001	2	72¾	72⅜	72⅜	
84½	70	Glenn-Holmes Corp. 4.80s 89	31	78	77	77	+1
163¼	124	Gulf National, Inc. 5½s 90	25	161⅛	159	160⅝	−4⅛
90	82½	Harvey Grace Motors, Inc. 7s 88	137	84¾	83⅜	84	+⅛
129½	109⅜	Hayes Products 5.30s 92	15	120⅞	120⅛	120½	+2⅛
145	112	Hotels International 4¼s 90	13	125	124¼	124⅝	+6
120	98¾	Household Services, Ltd. 6¼s 87	3	105	104½	104½	−½
124	104	Hunt-Portland Engineering Company 4¼s 92	8	116	114	115	−⅛
74	70¼	Idaho Paper Co. 3¼s 86	5	74	72½	73	−1
85½	80	Ideal Powder Co. 5½s 92	16	85¼	84⅜	85	
105	101⅛	Illinois Telephone Co. 4¼s 93	62	103½	102½	102⅝	−⅜
144¾	112	International Sugar Co. 4¾s 91	37	117½	116½	117	−½
103	94⅝	Interstate Transportations 4s 92	36	95½	94¾	95⅜	−2¼
131	109¾	Iowa Refrigerator Co. 5¾s 88	39	125⅞	123¼	124	−⅞
58½	49	Johnson Manufacturing Co. 4s 91	25	54¾	54	54¼	+1¼
106⅝	103⅝	Jonathon and Sons, Inc. 7⅜s 88	54	104½	104	104⅛	−¼
84	74⅞	Jones and Kendall, Inc. 4⅞s 90	10	81⅞	80⅝	81¾	+¼
100¾	93⅞	Joy Steel Corp. 6½s 87	16	98	97¼	97⅝	−1

in the quotation than it should be. For instance, a bond that is selling at a quoted price of "95" actually means that it is being sold for $950. As stated a moment ago, the decimal point in the numeral 95 is one place farther to the left than it should be, as follows:

95.0.

Similarly, a quotation of 94⅜ should first be written in the following form:

94.375

Now, by moving the decimal point one place to the right, you find that the value of the bond is as follows:

$943.75

Strictly speaking, bond quotations are actually percent values of the face value of the bond. However, they are rarely considered in this light, even by bond salesmen. The mechanical approach of converting a quotation to a dollar value is universally used.

From the example above, it would seem best that each time you write a bond quotation, it should be written as a decimal numeral in which three digits fall to the right of the decimal point. If the fraction is ⅜ as it is above, then the three digits will be .375. If the fraction is ¾, then the three digits will be .750. In fact, the fractions that are used in bond quotations are the same as those used in stock quotations. Now, however, you express them with a decimal point followed by three digits.

$$\frac{1}{8} = .125 \qquad \frac{1}{2} = .500$$
$$\frac{1}{4} = .250 \qquad \frac{5}{8} = .625$$
$$\frac{3}{8} = .375 \qquad \frac{3}{4} = .750$$
$$\frac{7}{8} = .875$$

And, of course, if there is no fraction in the quotation, as in 95, then you will write the quotation with a decimal point followed by 3 zeros. Thus:

The quotation of 95 becomes 95.000.
Hence the price of the bond becomes $950.00.

An explanation of the quotations for the Eastern Manufacturing Company follows.

Year to Date: As in the case of the stock quotations, the numerals below the words "High" and "Low" refer to the highest and lowest prices at which a bond of this company has been sold during the year prior to the date of the quotation. You must remember, though, that the "High" quotation of 106½ must be written as 106.500, which, in turn, implies that the price was $1,065.00. Similarly, the "Low" quotation of 85 gives you the low price of $850.00. How was this price arrived at?

Bonds & Rate: As you might guess, the name under the word "Bonds" refers to the company that issued the bond. In this case, it is the Eastern Manufacturing Company. The numeral "5" and letter "s" that appear immediately to the right of the name of the company indicate that the company is paying an interest rate of 5% per year to the holders of these bonds. Had the numeral been 6½s, what would this mean?

After the "5s" is the numeral "92." This numeral tells you that the bonds mature in 1992. This means that the company will pay off the debt owed on these bonds in 1992. If you look down the list of bonds until you come to the Falstaff Finance Corp., you will notice that the numeral 2020 follows the 5% interest rate. What does this numeral mean to you?

The reason for writing these fractional forms of eighths as decimals with three digits to the right of the decimal point is so that, after the decimal point is moved one place, there will still remain two digits to the right of it.

Sales in $1,000: The heading of this column actually omits a word. It should appear as "Sales in $1,000 Bonds" so that for the Eastern Manufacturing Co., you can say that 85 $1,000 bonds were sold that day. Each bond on that day may not have been worth $1,000. That is the value of the bond when issued, and again it is its value at the time the bonds will eventually be paid off. At any time between those dates, the value of the bond may vary, depending on the fortunes of the company. Incidentally, since most bond markets handle only bonds having a face value (original value) of $1,000, it seems almost pointless to head the column "Sales in $1,000 Bonds," since no others are sold.

High, Low, Last: As in the case of stock-market quotations, the numerals found in these columns show the highest, lowest, and last prices paid for bonds of that company during the day of quotation. Again you must keep in mind that the decimal points in the numerals are in the wrong place. The quotation of "89" for the "High" of Eastern Manufacturing Company really means that the highest price paid was $890.00. Similarly, the "Low" quotation of 88¼ indicates that that price was $882.50. How are the prices of $890.00 and $882.50 arrived at?

Net Change: Once again, the meaning of the words "Net Change," as used in bond-market quotations, is the same as the meaning given to it in stock-market quotations. The numerals under these words tell you the amount the closing price that day rose or fell over the closing price of the previous day. Thus, in the case of the Eastern Manufacturing Company, the price rose ⅛. Here, again, the decimal point is in the wrong place. As before, write the net change first as a decimal and then move the decimal point one place to the right to find the price change. In terms of a net change of ⅛, this would mean:

$$⅛ = .125$$
Therefore, the price change is $1.25.

■ ILLUSTRATION 1: Find the amount paid for 5 bonds of Florida Products, Inc., that were purchased at the "Low" of the day shown on page 367.

● SOLUTION:

Quotation for "Low" = 76⅞, or 76.875
Low price per bond = $768.75
Cost of 5 bonds = 5 × $768.75
= $3,843.75

▼ EXPLANATION: Possibly the most difficult part of the solution is in changing the mixed numeral 76⅞ to its equivalent form as the deci-

There seems to be no particular reason why the letter "s" is used in bond quotations to represent the term "percent."

mal numeral 76.875. In the event that you do not recall the decimal
equivalents of the fractions, it is always possible to find them on page
339. However, it would be best to memorize them, since you will be using them so often.

■ ILLUSTRATION 2: What was the closing price paid for a bond of
Evans Storage Battery Co., on the day before the one shown for the
quotations on page 367?

● SOLUTION:

>   Closing quotation on day shown = 94½, or 94.500
>   Closing price on day shown = $945.00
>   Net change = −1⅛, or −1.125
>   Net price change = −$11.25 (down $11.25)
>   Closing price of previous day = $945.00 + $11.25
>   = $956.25

▼ EXPLANATION: The negative sign in front of the 1⅛ shows you that
the price was down 1⅛ from what it had been the previous day. This
means that the closing price was $11.25 more on the previous day.
Hence, by adding $11.25 to the closing price of the day shown, you
can find the closing price of the day before.

EXERCISES   A

1. Change each of the following bond quotations to actual prices.

	Quotation	Price		Quotation	Price
a.	96½	$ 965.00	h.	104¾	$ 1,047.50
b.	85¾	857.50	i.	117½	1,175.00
c.	52¼	522.50	j.	123¼	1,232.50
d.	78⅜	783.75	k.	112⅞	1,128.75
e.	61⅝	616.25	l.	126	1,260.00
f.	76	760.00	m.	110⅜	1,103.75
g.	80⅛	801.25	n.	135⅝	1,356.25

2. Change each of the following net changes for bonds to actual price
   changes.

	Quotation	Price Change		Quotation	Price Change
a.	+¼	$ +2.50	g.	+1½	$ +15.00
b.	+⅜	+3.75	h.	−7	−70.00
c.	−⅝	−6.25	i.	−2¾	−27.50
d.	+¾	+7.50	j.	+4⅛	+41.25
e.	+⅞	+8.75	k.	−5⅜	−53.75
f.	−½	−5.00	l.	+3⅞	+38.75

In the exercises above, it would be best if the students included an additional column headed
"Quotation as a Decimal" in the outline of their work. Be careful, for the students may be
inclined merely to place a dollar sign before the quotation in changing it to the price value.

B

The bond-market quotations that appear on page 367 are to be used in answering each of the questions in the following exercises.

1. During what year will the bonds of each of the following companies mature (have to be paid off)?

	Company	Year
a.	Equitable Light Co.	1993
b.	Hotels International	1990
c.	Iowa Refrigerator Co.	1988
d.	General Department Stores	2011
e.	Federal Mineral Co.	2000

2. What was the lowest price paid that year for a bond in each of the following companies?

	Company	Quotation	Price
a.	Gibraltar Power Co.	68-1/2	$ 685.00
b.	Iowa Refrigerator Co.	109-3/4	1,097.50
c.	Idaho Paper Co.	70-1/4	702.50
d.	Florida Products, Inc.	71-3/8	713.75
e.	General Department Stores	59-5/8	596.25

3. What was the highest price paid that day for a bond in each of the following companies?

	Company	Quotation	Price
a.	Franklin Sulphur Co.	80-3/4	$ 807.50
b.	Ideal Powder Co.	85-1/4	852.50
c.	International Sugar Co.	117-1/2	1,175.00
d.	Household Services, Ltd.	105	1,050.00
e.	Gulf National, Inc.	161-1/8	1,611.25

4. What was the last price paid that day for a bond in each of the following companies?

	Company	Quotation	Price
a.	Evans Storage Battery Co.	94-1/2	$ 945.00
b.	General Department Stores	89-1/8	891.25
c.	Hunt-Portland Eng.	115	1,150.00
d.	Illinois Telephone Co.	102-5/8	1,026.25
e.	Joy Steel Corp.	97-5/8	976.25

5. What was the net price change that day for a bond in each of the following companies? Indicate whether the price had increased or decreased over the closing price of the previous day.

See the suggestion at the bottom of page 370.

Company	Net Change	Net Price Change	Increase Or Decrease
a. Falstaff Finance Corp.	+ ¼	$ 2.50	I
b. Family Food Stores	−1	10.00	D
c. Interstate Transportations	−2¼	22.50	D
d. Hotels International	+6	60.00	I
e. Ideal Powder Co.	0	0	No change

6. What was the last price paid for a bond in each of the following companies on the day prior to the one shown in the quotations on page 367?

Company	Last Price For Day Shown	Net Price Change	Last Price Of Previous Day
a. Emerson-Brody Corp.	$ 1,070.00	$ − 5.00	$ 1,075.00
b. Idaho Paper Co.	730.00	−10.00	740.00
c. Glenn-Holmes Corp.	770.00	+ 10.00	760.00
d. Gibraltar Power Co.	723.75	0	723.75
e. Florida Products, Inc.	772.50	+ 10.00	762.50
f. Federal Mineral Co.	380.00	− 5.00	385.00
g. International Sugar Co.	1,170.00	− 5.00	1,175.00
h. Hayes Products	1,205.00	+ 21.25	1,183.75
i. Franklin Sulphur Co.	807.50	+ 15.00	792.50
j. Jonathon and Sons, Inc.	1,041.25	− 2.50	1,043.75

C

1. How much will the buyer have to pay on each of the following bond purchases?

	Number Of Bonds	Quotation Per Bond	Price Per Bond	Total Price
a.	2	87	$ 870.00	$ 1,740.00
b.	3	96½	965.00	2,895.00
c.	5	75¾	757.50	3,787.50
d.	5	68¼	682.50	3,412.50
e.	4	103⅝	1,036.25	4,145.00
f.	4	107⅛	1,071.25	4,285.00
g.	8	121⅜	1,213.75	9,710.00
h.	6	100⅞	1,008.75	6,052.52
i.	15	91¾	917.50	13,762.50
j.	25	59⅝	596.25	14,906.25

2. How much did the buyer have to pay on each of the following bond purchases that were made on the day of the bond-market quotations appearing on page 367?

Company	Number Of Bonds	Quotation Per Bond	Price Per Bond	Total Price
a. Equitable Light Co.	3	High	$ 1,030.00	$ 3,090.00
b. Family Food Stores	10	High	245.00	2,450.00
c. Franklin Sulphur Co.	5	Low	795.00	3,975.00

Company	Number Of Bonds	Quotation Per Bond	Price Per Bond	Total Price
d. Ideal Powder Co.	4	High	$ 852.50	$ 3,410.00
e. Jones and Kendall, Inc.	6	Last	817.50	4,905.00
f. Interstate Transportations	20	Low	947.50	18,950.00
g. Hayes Products	8	Low	1,201.25	9,610.00
h. Gulf National, Inc.	3	Last	1,606.25	4,818.75
i. Florida Products, Inc.	7	Low	768.75	5,381.25
j. Iowa Refrigerator Co.	16	High	1,258.75	20,140.00

D

1. Robert Perle purchased 5 bonds of Hunt-Portland Engineering Company.
   a. How much would he have had to pay for these bonds had he purchased them at the "High" of the year for the quotations shown on page 367? $6,200.00
   b. How much would he have had to pay for them had he purchased them at the "Low" of the year? $5,200.00
   c. How much money might he have saved had he been able to buy the bonds at the "Low" rather than the "High" of the year? $1,000.00

2. James Turner purchased 10 bonds of Hotels International at the closing price shown in the quotations on page 367. How much more did he have to pay for these bonds than he would have had to pay had be purchased them at the closing price of the previous day? $ 600.00

Section 2: Interest Payments

At the time you were examining the bond quotations in the previous section it was mentioned that symbols such as "6s" or "4⅜s" that are found immediately after the name of the company represent the rate of interest that the company is paying to holders of its bonds. These interest payments are made either annually (once a year), or semi-annually (twice a year), or, possibly, quarterly (four times per year), depending on the arrangements the company made at the time it borrowed the money. The rate of interest shown in the quotations, however, is an annual rate, which is usually the way an interest rate is expressed. Hence, if you have to determine the amount of interest you will receive on a quarterly basis, you must first determine it for an annual period and then divide that answer by 4. By what number should you divide the annual interest if the interest period is semi-annual?

The average investor in bonds is interested in the interest he will receive on his investment rather than on any increase in value the bond may have over the years. Hence the importance of this section.

■ILLUSTRATION: Mr. Shaeffer owns 6 bonds of Florida Products, Inc. (See page 367.) If interest is paid quarterly, how much interest will he receive on these bonds at each interest period?

●SOLUTION:

$$\text{Interest rate} = 4\tfrac{3}{8}\%$$
$$= 4.375\%$$
$$= .04375$$

$$\text{Interest on 1 bond for 1 year} = 4\tfrac{3}{8}\% \text{ of } \$1{,}000$$
$$= .04375 \times \$1{,}000$$
$$= \$43.75$$

$$\text{Interest on 6 bonds for 1 year} = 6 \times \$43.75$$
$$= \$262.50$$

$$\text{Interest on 6 bonds for } \tfrac{1}{4} \text{ year} = \$262.50 \div 4$$
$$= \$65.625, \text{ or } \$65.63$$

▼EXPLANATION: The fractions that appear in the interest rates are the same fractions that appear in the stock and bond quotations. Hence, you have nothing new to learn. After writing the percent numeral 4⅜% in its equivalent form of 4.375%, you can easily change it to its decimal form of .04375 by moving the decimal point two places to the left. From this point on, the solution is quite simple. First you find the interest on 1 bond for 1 year. This answer is then multiplied by 6 to determine the interest on 6 bonds for the 1 year. The solution is completed by dividing the annual interest by 4, since the interest is given in quarterly periods.

EXERCISES   A

1. Change each of the following percent numerals to its equivalent decimal numeral.

a. 4.80% ___.0480___	f. 4½% ___.045___	k. 4⅞% ___.04875___
b. 5.30% ___.0530___	g. 5¼% ___.0525___	l. 6⅜% ___.06375___
c. 6.20% ___.0620___	h. 6¾% ___.0675___	m. 4⅝% ___.04625___
d. 4.60% ___.0460___	i. 7⅛% ___.07125___	n. 3⅞% ___.03875___
e. 5.70% ___.0570___	j. 5⅜% ___.05375___	o. 6⅛% ___.06125___

2. Determine the annual interest payments on each of the following $1,000 bonds.

	Interest Rate	Interest
a.	4%	$ 40.00
b.	5%	50.00
c.	6%	60.00
d.	7%	70.00

The suggestion at the bottom of page 348 is equally as applicable now for bonds as it was for stocks.

	Interest Rate		Interest
e.	4½%	$	45.00
f.	5¼%		52.50
g.	5¾%		57.50
h.	5⅛%		51.25
i.	6⅞%		68.75
j.	4⅜%		43.75
k.	5.80%		58.00
l.	6.30%		63.00
m.	4.70%		47.00
n.	5.40%		54.00

3. Determine the semiannual interest payments on each of the following $1,000 bonds.

	Annual Interest Rate	Annual Interest	Semiannual Interest
a.	5½%	$ 55.00	$ 27.50
b.	6¼%	62.50	31.25
c.	4¾%	47.50	23.75
d.	4⅛%	41.25	20.63
e.	5⅜%	53.75	26.88
f.	6.20%	62.00	31.00

4. Determine the quarterly interest payments on each of the following $1,000 bonds.

	Annual Interest Rate	Annual Interest	Quarterly Interest
a.	6½%	$ 65.00	$ 16.25
b.	6¾%	67.50	16.88
c.	4⅝%	46.25	11.56
d.	5⅞%	58.75	14.69
e.	7.30%	73.00	18.25
f.	5.70%	57.00	14.25

5. Determine the total interest payments made to the owners of the following number of $1,000 bonds for the period of time indicated.

	Number Of Bonds	Annual Interest Rate	Payments Made	Interest per Bond Per Year	Total Interest
a.	2	5%	Annually	$ 50.00	$100.00
b.	4	8%	Annually	80.00	320.00
c.	3	4½%	Semiannually	45.00	67.50
d.	5	7½%	Semiannually	75.00	187.50
e.	4	5¾%	Semiannually	57.50	115.00
f.	7	6⅛%	Semiannually	61.25	214.38
g.	10	4¼%	Quarterly	42.50	106.25
h.	14	7¾%	Quarterly	77.50	271.25
i.	12	6.20%	Quarterly	62.00	186.00
j.	25	5.80%	Quarterly	58.00	362.50

See the suggestion at the bottom of page 348.

B

The bond-market quotations that appear on page 367 are to be used in answering each of the questions in the following exercises.

1. Determine the annual payments made by the following companies on each of their bonds.

Name Of Company	Annual Interest Rate	Interest
a. Emerson-Brody Corp.	5 %	$ 50.00
b. Family Food Stores	4-1/2 %	45.00
c. Hunt-Portland Engineering Company	4-1/4 %	42.50
d. International Sugar Co.	4-3/4 %	47.50
e. Jonathon and Sons, Inc.	7-3/8 %	73.75

2. Determine the semiannual interest payments made by the following companies on each of their bonds.

Name Of Company	Annual Interest Rate	Annual Interest	Semiannual Interest
a. Eastern Manufacturing Co.	5 %	$ 50.00	$ 25.00
b. Equitable Light Co.	6 %	60.00	30.00
c. Foremost Tire Co.	5-1/2 %	55.00	27.50
d. Franklin Sulphur Co.	3-3/4 %	32.50	16.25
e. Hayes Products	5.30 %	53.00	26.50

3. Determine the quarterly interest payments made by the following companies on each of their bonds.

Name Of Company	Annual Interest Rate	Annual Interest	Quarterly Interest
a. Evans Storage Battery Co.	6 %	$ 60.00	$ 15.00
b. Gibraltar Power Co.	5 %	50.00	12.50
c. General Department Stores	5-1/2 %	55.00	13.75
d. Iowa Refrigerator Co.	5-3/4 %	57.50	14.38
e. Jones and Kendall, Inc.	4-7/8 %	48.75	12.19

4. Determine the total interest payments made to the owners of the following number of bonds of the companies shown for the period of time indicated.

Name Of Company	Number Of Bonds	Payments Made	Annual Interest Rate	Total Interest
a. Falstaff Finance Corp.	4	Annually	5 %	$ 200.00
b. Harvey Grace Motors, Inc.	6	Semiannually	7 %	210.00
c. Electronic Associates	10	Semiannually	3-1/2 %	175.00
d. Gulf National, Inc.	5	Semiannually	5-1/2 %	137.50
e. Household Services, Ltd.	3	Semiannually	6-1/4 %	93.75
f. Joy Steel Corp.	12	Quarterly	6-1/2 %	195.00
g. Jones and Kendall, Inc.	16	Quarterly	4-7/8 %	195.00
h. Glenn-Holmes Corp.	8	Quarterly	4.80 %	96.00

It might be helpful to the students if there were two other columns in the outline of their work. These columns should be headed "Annual Interest on One Bond" and "Total Annual Interest." They should be placed before the last column.

Section 3: Rate of Return on Bond Investments

As was pointed out earlier, the person who invests in bonds is hoping to get more for his money than he might if he deposited it in a bank. There is an almost sure way of knowing whether an investor is buying bonds because he thinks the price will rise in the near future and plans to sell them shortly at a profit, or whether he is buying bonds because the interest payments are more than he would receive by keeping his money in a bank. Since the banks pay their depositors 5%, then, if the investor's return on his bonds is more than 5%, he's probably concerned with the interest payments on the bonds. However, if his return is less than 5%, then he probably bought the bonds with plans to sell them as soon as they go up in price.

Finding the interest rate that a bond investor receives on his money is not just the simple process of merely looking at the bond quotations to see what is listed there. This rate of interest is based on the original value of the bond, which was $1,000. As you can see by examining the quotations on page 367, most people are buying bonds at a price other than $1,000. Hence, your problem is to find the rate of interest you will receive on the amount *you* paid for the bond and not the rate of interest paid to the original buyer on the original $1,000 debt.

When the first person bought the $1,000 bond, the company may have agreed to pay him an annual interest rate of 5%. This amounted to $50 a year. Where did the $50 come from? When you buy the bond a few years later, the company continues to pay this interest of $50 each year. However, and this is the important point, you may have paid only $800 for the bond. Thus, you are receiving $50 on an $800 investment rather than on a $1,000 investment and, hence, the rate of interest you are receiving will be more than the rate the original lender received. On the other hand, if you paid more than $1,000 for the bond, say, $1,200, then your rate of interest will be less than 5%. How much interest would you receive each year on your $1,200 investment?

The method for determining the rate of interest you receive on a bond investment is the same as you used earlier for determining the rate of interest received on a stock investment. That rate was called the rate of return on a stock investment, and you found it by using the following formula:

$$\text{Rate of Return} = \text{Dividend} \div \text{Principal Invested}$$

or

$$R = D \div P$$

Since the bond purchaser has a greater interest in the rate he is receiving than on the appreciation of the bond, this unit takes on significance. By computing the rate of return, the investor can compare the potential bond investment with the return on his money if kept in a bank.

The only difference is that now the money you receive from the company is called the interest on the bond rather than the dividend on the stock. Hence, the formula becomes:

$$\text{Rate of Return} = \text{Interest} \div \text{Principal Invested}$$
$$\text{or}$$
$$R = I \div P$$

■ ILLUSTRATION 1: To the nearest tenth of a percent, what rate of return would the purchaser of 5 bonds of General Department Stores receive on his investment if he were able to buy these bonds at the "Low" of the day shown in the quotations on page 367?

● SOLUTION:

$$\text{Rate of interest} = 5\tfrac{1}{2}\%$$
$$= .055$$
$$\text{Annual interest} = 5\tfrac{1}{2}\% \text{ of } \$1,000$$
$$= .055 \times \$1,000$$
$$= \$55$$
$$\text{"Low" of day} = 84\tfrac{1}{4}, \text{ or } \$842.50$$
$$\text{Rate of return} = I \div P$$
$$= \$55 \div \$842.50$$
$$= .065, \text{ or } 6.5\%$$

▼ EXPLANATION: Before you can compute the rate of return, you must know both the cost of the bond and the amount of interest paid on the bond. These turned out to be $842.50 and $55 respectively. Hence, by dividing the interest by the cost to the investor, you find that he is receiving a rate of return of 6.5%. Why did this rate of return turn out to be more than the rate of 5.5% shown in the quotations? Notice that you ignore the fact that he had purchased 5 bonds. The rate of return on 1 bond is the same as that on 5 bonds. Can you explain why this should be so?

■ ILLUSTRATION 2: Mr. Carslaw received a quarterly dividend payment of $27 on a bond that he owned. If he had paid a quoted price of 106⅞ for the bond, what rate of return was he receiving on his investment to the nearest tenth of a percent?

▼ EXPLANATION: Since the rate of return is an annual rate, the first thing you must determine is the amount Mr. Carslaw receives over the period of 1 year. Having received $27 for a quarter of a year, he will receive 4 times this amount for the entire year. The rest of the solution is completed as in Illustration 1.

In order to convince the students that the rate of return for all five bonds of Illustration 1 is the same as when computed for one bond, you may have to do the computation on the basis of the five bonds and compare the answer with the one in the text.

● SOLUTION:

$$\text{Quarterly interest} = \$27$$
$$\text{Annual interest} = 4 \times \$27$$
$$= \$108$$
$$\text{Investment} = 106\%, \text{ or } \$1,063.75$$
$$\text{Rate of return} = \$108 \div \$1,063.75$$
$$= .102, \text{ or } 10.2\%$$

EXERCISES   A

1. Determine the annual rate of return to the nearest tenth of a per-cent on each of the following bond purchases.

	Annual Interest	Price Paid	Rate of Return	
a.	$53	$ 950.00	5.6	%
b.	65	870.00	7.5	%
c.	46	917.50	5.0	%
d.	72	1,075.00	6.7	%
e.	68	1,052.50	6.5	%

2. Determine the annual rate of return to the nearest tenth of a per-cent on each of the following bond purchases.

	Semiannual Interest	Annual Interest	Quotation Paid	Price Paid	Rate Of Return	
a.	$25	$ 50.00	84	$ 840.00	6.0	%
b.	32	64.00	96	960.00	6.7	%
c.	36	72.00	92½	925.00	7.8	%
d.	41	82.00	104½	1,045.00	7.8	%
e.	47	94.00	123¾	1,237.50	7.6	%

3. Determine the annual rate of return to the nearest tenth of a per-cent on each of the following bond purchases.

	Quarterly Interest	Annual Interest	Quotation Paid	Price Paid	Rate Of Return	
a.	$13	$ 52.00	72	$ 720.00	7.2	%
b.	16	64.00	91	910.00	7.0	%
c.	22	88.00	95½	955.00	9.2	%
d.	33	132.00	102⅜	1,023.75	12.9	%
e.	39	156.00	115⅞	1,158.75	13.5	%

B

Use the bond-market quotations on page 367 to determine the rate of return in each of the following exercises.

Examine each of the answers to the exercises by comparing them to the interest rate received by a depositor in a local bank.

Name Of Company	Interest Rate	Annual Interest	Quotation Paid	Price Paid	Rate Of Return
a. Eastern Manufacturing Co.	5 %	$ 50.00	High	$ 890.00	5.6 %
b. Harvey Grace Motors, Inc.	7 %	70.00	Last	840.00	8.3 %
c. Emerson-Brody Corp.	5 %	50.00	Low	1,060.00	4.7 %
d. Family Food Stores	4½ %	45.00	High	245.00	18.4 %
e. Foremost Tire Co.	5½ %	55.00	Last	1,085.00	5.1 %
f. Franklin Sulphur Co.	3¼ %	32.50	High	807.50	4.0 %
g. Gulf National, Inc.	5½ %	55.00	Low	1,590.00	3.5 %
h. Ideal Powder Co.	5½ %	55.00	Low	843.75	6.5 %

Section 4: Federal Government Bonds and Municipal Bonds

There are only two other types of bonds that you might be interested in investigating. These are municipal bonds and federal government bonds. Since the municipal bonds are the easier of the two to examine, this will be done first.

City governments need to raise money to build schools, or roads, or sewerage systems and the like. To get this money as quickly as possible, they usually borrow it by selling bonds. They then pay off the debt over a 20-year period, or a 25-year period, or whatever other period suits them best. In most cases, the bonds are sold directly to banks, or large insurance firms, or large investment companies rather than to individuals. However, these bonds may eventually be resold to individual investors.

Although municipal bonds usually pay a much lower interest rate than the bonds of private corporations, they are sought after by banks, insurance companies, and people who earn a great deal of money. The big advantage these bonds have over other bonds is that no income tax has to be paid on the interest earned by them. In the case of some people, an interest rate of 3% on which no tax has to be paid might be the equivalent of an interest rate of 6% or 7% on which taxes have to be paid. This is a great deal better than the 5% a person would receive from the bank were he to keep his money there. Within recent years, the interest rate on municipal bonds has been somewhere between 3½% and 6%. The better the financial standing of the town, the lower the rate is—although it is a rare case indeed when a town has not paid off its debt.

Federal government bonds carry with them an advantage similar to municipal bonds. However, the advantage here is only a delaying action. In the case of federal government E bonds, the tax on the interest can be delayed until the maturity date of the bond, at which time the government pays off both the debt and all the interest that has accumulated. It is at that time that the tax has to be paid by the owner of the bond.

People who are in the high-income brackets find it to their advantage to invest their money in municipal bonds, for the interest they receive is completely theirs; they do not have to pay any income tax on this return.

People who buy federal bonds may do so for one of two reasons. They hope that by the time they collect the interest, the income tax laws will have been changed so that the tax may be much lower than at the time they bought the bonds. Or they know that by the time the bonds mature, they will have retired. Hence, their income will be a great deal less than when they bought the bonds. As a result, the amount of income tax they will have to pay on the bond interest will be a great deal less than if they received the interest immediately.

The federal government presently issues two types of bonds:

Series E bonds, which are sold in denominations of $25, $50, $75, $100, $200, $500, $1,000, and $10,000.

Series H bonds, which are sold in denominations of $500, $1,000, $5,000, and $10,000.

Holders of the Series H bonds do not have to wait until maturity to receive the interest on their bonds, but receive it semiannually at an average interest rate of 5%. The big advantage of owning these bonds—and the other government bonds, too—is that they are not subject to any state income tax. And since most states do have income taxes, the fact that you do not have to pay this tax on the interest on federal bonds can amount to a substantial savings for some taxpayers. The Series E bonds also pay an *average* annual interest rate of 5%, compounded semiannually over a 5-year, 10-month period. Do you recall the meaning of compound interest? (See pages 241–255.)

When the Series E bond was originally issued, its maturity value was $25, $50, $75, $100, $200, $500, $1,000, or $10,000, depending on what size bond was purchased. Now, however, although they are still called "$25 bonds," or "$50 bonds," and so on, their maturity value is actually slightly higher than these amounts. For instance, the maturity value of a $25 bond is really $25.01; the $50 bond would have a maturity value of twice this amount, while the $75 bond would be three times this amount. Why should the maturity value of the $50 bond be twice the maturity value of the $25 bond?

A Series E bond can be sold back to the federal government at any time beginning within two months after the date of purchase. The amount returned to you includes not only the price you paid, but also the interest that accumulated over the period of time you kept the bond. Should you ask for your money during the first 6 months, you will receive absolutely no interest. In fact, even during the second 6-months' period, you will receive very little interest on your money. However, the interest does begin to increase after that time so that by

The series E bond has the additional advantage wherein no income tax has to be paid on the interest earned until the bond is redeemed. People will often keep these bonds until after retirement when their income is lower than it has been, and, therefore, they pay less tax on the interest accumulated.

the end of the 5-year, 10-month period, when the bond falls due, the average interest rate comes to 5%. The following table shows the redemption value on a $25 bond for which you initially paid $18.75.

REDEMPTION VALUE ON A $25 SERIES E BOND

If Held:	Amount Returned
0 to ½ year	$18.75
½ to 1 year	19.05
1 to 1½ years	19.51
1½ to 2 years	19.95
2 to 2½ years	20.40
2½ to 3 years	20.88
3 to 3½ years	21.39
3½ to 4 years	21.93
4 to 4½ years	22.53
4½ to 5 years	23.16
5 to 5½ years	23.82
5½ to 5 years, 10 months	24.51
5 years and 10 months from issue date	25.01

■ ILLUSTRATION 1: What is the cost of a $200 Series E bond?

▼ EXPLANATION: Since a $200 bond has 8 times the value of a $25 bond, the cost of a $200 bond will be 8 times the cost of the $25 bond. Hence, the computation simply involves multiplying $18.75 by 8. (The cost of a $25 bond is $18.75.)

● SOLUTION:

Cost of a $25 bond = $18.75
Number of $25 amounts in $200 = 200 ÷ 25
= 8
Cost of a $200 bond = 8 × $18.75
= $150.00

■ ILLUSTRATION 2: Bruce Davidson purchased two $500 Series E bonds and kept them until maturity. How much more will he receive for the bonds than he paid for them?

▼ EXPLANATION: The computation involves finding the amount received on the bonds at maturity and the amount paid for the bonds. The difference between these two numbers is the amount that Mr. Davidson received above what he paid for the bonds.

● SOLUTION:

Amount paid for a $25 bond = $18.75
Number of $25 amounts in $500 = 500 ÷ 25
= 20

A person should never redeem a series E bond before maturity date — unless absolutely necessary — for, when this is done, the rate of return is far lower than that yielded by most bonds.

Amount paid for a $500 bond = 20 × $18.75
= $375
Maturity value of a $25 bond = $25.16
Maturity value of a $500 bond = 20 × $25.01
= $500.20
Profit on 1 bond = $500.20 − $375
= $125.20
Profit on 2 bonds = 2 × $125.20
= $250.40

EXERCISES

1. What is the cost of the following Series E bonds?

Bond	Cost	Bond	Cost
a. $50	$ 37.50	c. $100	$ 75.00
b. 75	56.25	d. 500	375.00

2. What is the maturity value of each of the following Series E bonds?

Bond	Maturity Value	Bond	Maturity Value
a. $50	$ 50.02	c. $100	$ 100.04
b. 75	75.03	d. 500	500.20

3. How much money will a person receive if he keeps each of the following Series E bonds for the period of time indicated?

	Bond	Period Held	Amount Returned On $25 Bond	Amount Received
a.	$ 25	1 year 2 months	$ 19.51	$ 19.51
b.	25	3 years 5 months	21.39	21.39
c.	50	4 years 1 month	22.53	45.06
d.	50	5 years 9 months	24.51	49.02
e.	200	2 years 4 months	20.40	163.20
f.	100	5 years 2 months	23.82	95.28
g.	500	3 years 10 months	21.93	438.60
h.	1,000	4 years 7 months	23.16	926.40

4. How much more will a person receive than he pays for the number of Series E bonds shown?

	Bond	Number Of Bonds	Period Held	Cost Per Bond	Amount Returned Per Bond	Profit Per Bond	Total Profit
a.	$ 50	2	3 yrs. 2 mos.	$ 37.50	$ 42.78	$ 5.28	$ 10.56
b.	75	5	4 yrs. 7 mos.	56.25	69.48	13.23	66.15
c.	100	6	5 yrs. 3 mos.	75.00	95.28	20.28	121.68
d.	200	8	2 yrs. 10 mos.	150.00	167.04	17.04	136.32
e.	500	14	1 yr. 1 mo.	375.00	390.20	15.20	212.80

5. How much interest will a person receive annually on each of the following municipal bonds?

	Par Value	Annual Interest Rate	Interest
a.	$ 500	4%	$ 20.00
b.	500	4½%	22.50
c.	1,000	3½%	35.00
d.	5,000	3.8%	190.00
e.	5,000	4.2%	210.00
f.	10,000	3.9%	390.00

6. What will be the semiannual interest payment to the holders of each of the following number of municipal bonds?

	Par Value	Number Of Bonds	Annual Interest Rate	Interest Per Bond	Total Annual Interest	Total Semiannual Interest
a.	$ 500	2	3%	$ 15.00	$ 30.00	$ 15.00
b.	500	4	4¼%	21.25	85.00	42.50
c.	1,000	5	5¼%	52.50	262.50	131.25
d.	1,000	6	4¾%	47.50	285.00	142.50
e.	5,000	3	3¾%	187.50	562.50	281.25
f.	5,000	7	4.7%	235.00	1,645.00	822.50
g.	10,000	8	4.3%	430.00	3,440.00	1,720.00
h.	10,000	3	5.1%	510.00	1,530.00	765.00

Unit 3:   Chapter Review and Test

1. Use the stock-market quotations on page 339 to answer each of the following questions.
   a. What was the lowest price paid that year prior to the day shown for a share of Bullard and Sons stock? $23.25
   b. What was the lowest price paid that day for a share of Carpenter Corp., stock? $78.25
   c. What was the last price paid that day for a share of Dow Aircraft stock? $34.50
   d. How much more did the last buyer of that day have to pay for each share of Colonial, Inc., stock than the last buyer of the previous day? $ 2.00
2. What was the last price paid per share by the buyer of American Bakers preferred stock on the day prior to the one shown in the quotations on page 339? $64.75
3. If the broker's fees and taxes are not considered, how much will each of the following purchases cost?

The odd-numbered problems can be used for review of the chapter's work, while the even-numbered ones can be used for testing purposes.

a. The purchase of 100 shares of stock quoted at 17¾ $1,775.00

b. The purchase of 300 shares of Bliss Petroleum stock purchased at the "High" of the day shown in the stock-market quotations on page 339 $4,687.50

4. If broker's fees and taxes are not considered, how much profit would Mr. Blake have made if he purchased 100 shares of Diamond Airlines at the "Low" of the year and sold them at the "High" of the year shown in the quotations on page 339? $1,462.50

5. Approximately how much would Mr. Sims have to pay in fees when he purchased stock that cost him $2,350? $ 35.25

6. Thomas Paterno owns 300 shares of Allen, Inc., stock. If he owned them the year prior to the quotations shown on page 339, how much would he have received in dividends from the company?
$ 360.00

7. What annual dividend payment will the holder of 200 shares of a 5½% preferred stock receive if the par value of the stock is $100?
$1,100.00

8. Joe Skinner owns 100 shares of 4.40% preferred stock of the Reed Chain Corporation. The par value of the stock is $50, but Joe paid only $34¾ for each share. How much will he receive at each quarterly dividend period? $ 55.00

9. Determine the rate of return to the nearest tenth of a percent on each of the following stock purchases:

a. A stock that is paying an annual dividend of $3.50 and was purchased for $48   7.3%

b. A share of stock of Cenco Chemicals that was purchased at the "High" of the day shown in the quotations on page 339
3.5%

c. A share of 4½% preferred stock that was purchased at 44¾, but has a par value of $50   5.0%

10. Ben Newton invested $4,500 in mutual funds under a Single-Payment-Plan Investment.

a. If the sales charge was 8½% of the investment, how large was this fee? $ 382.50

b. How much money remained to be invested in the mutual fund after the sales charge was deducted? $4,117.50

11. Mr. Wiley invested in mutual funds under a Monthly-Systematic-Investment Plan. During the first year, he made an initial payment of $200, plus 12 monthly payments of $50 each. If the service charge for the first year was one half of the total amount paid to the fund, how much was this in Mr. Wiley's case? $ 400.00

12. Change each of the following bond quotations to actual prices.

	Quotation	Price
a.	87½	$ 875.00
b.	124⅝	1,246.65

13. Use the bond-market quotations on page 367 to answer each of the following questions.
    a. What was the lowest price paid that day for a bond of the Emerson-Brody Corporation?

    Quotation: ___106___   Price: $ 1,060.00

    b. What was the lowest price paid that year to the day shown for a bond of the Gibraltar Power Company?

    Quotation: ___68½___   Price: $ 685.00

    c. How much less did the last buyer of a bond of the Joy Steel Corporation have to pay for it the day shown than he would have had to pay for it had it been purchased the previous day?

    Amount less: $ 10.00

14. Robert Kooms purchased 5 bonds of the Franklin Sulphur Co., at the closing price shown in the quotations on page 367. How much did he have to pay for these bonds? $4,037.50

15. a. What annual interest payment will the holder of two 5¼% bonds receive if the par value of the bonds is $1,000? $ 105.00
    b. What semiannual interest payment will the holder of six Iowa Refrigerator Co., bonds receive? (See the bond-market quotations on page 367.) $ 172.50

16. a. To the nearest tenth of a percent, what rate of return will an investor receive on a bond for which he paid $940, and which gives an annual interest of $62?   6.6%
    b. To the nearest tenth of a percent, what rate of return will the purchaser receive on a bond of the Equitable Light Co., that was purchased at the low price of the day shown in the quotations on page 367?   5.9%

17. a. What is the cost of a $50 Series E bond? $ 37.50
    b. What is the cost of a $200 Series E bond? $150.00

18. a. How much will a person receive if he returns a $200 Series E bond after 4 years and 3 months? $180.24
    b. How much will a person receive if he returns a $100 Series E bond after 11 months? $ 76.20

CHAPTER 10

INSURANCE

At your age, you probably give very little thought to the need for insurance, unless, of course, you are old enough to get your driver's license. And since you may not drive a car without insurance, insurance becomes of utmost importance. Otherwise, the idea of being insured against some possible loss usually does not cross your mind. Not only do you not have anything or anyone to protect, but you probably could not afford to pay the insurance costs. On the other hand, there are occasions when you might worry a little about what might happen to the family if dad lost his job or were killed; or if mother became ill; or if your home were burned down, or if someone in the family were taken seriously ill and had large doctor and hospital bills. These things do happen and happen over and over again to people you know. What will be done in this chapter is to show how people protect themselves financially against these unfortunate experiences.

As recommended earlier, read this material with the students. When the narrative comments were class-tested prior to publication, students found them interesting. In most cases, it is preferable that you, yourself, read the material rather than the students. Pause frequently to ask questions about it.

The idea behind insurance is not a new one at all. Chances are that the colonists had this in mind when many of them would get together to help a neighbor rebuild his house after it had burned down. Who knows but your house might be the next one to burn. Nowadays each person contributes a small amount of money to pay for a large loss that might befall anyone in a group of people. Most people do not contribute this money because they want to lend a helping hand to a neighbor they may not even know. What they are actually worried about is that if they do not join some group to help pay for some common losses, there will be no one who will help to pay for a large loss that might happen to them.

Basically, the principles of insurance rest pretty much on the ideas just described. Here is a practical illustration. Suppose 40 of you owned motorbikes, each of which is valued at approximately $400. Over the years you discovered that every year one of these bikes is completely destroyed. This accident does not happen to the same person every year. Since $400 is a good deal of money for any one of you to put out again in order to buy another motorbike, you decide that every year each of you will contribute $10 to a fund to pay for the replacement of the bike that may be cracked up that year. By doing this, the person involved in the accident suffers a loss of only $10—the cost of his contribution—rather than a $400 loss.

You might say to yourself, "Well, I'm just not going to be involved in an accident, so why should I pay even the small amount of $10 a year?" This would be fine if only you were absolutely sure that this were true. But, unfortunately, you cannot foresee the future, and what you think cannot happen to you may very well happen. And hence, you try to avoid this financial risk by joining with others to help pay off a large loss that is quite certain to happen to some of you in the group.

Through experience, insurance companies know just how many people of a certain age will die each year, or how many automobile accidents there will be in a certain city each year, or how many homes will be destroyed by fire each year. They also know just how much money all of this is going to cost. What they don't know is just who is going to be involved in these mishaps. All of you, therefore, are charged enough money to pay for the loss that will most assuredly happen to a few of you. In addition, you have to pay a little more to cover the expenses needed to operate the company. By doing this, each of you knows that should the worst happen, at least you might not have any financial problems.

Ask for a volunteer to do a report on the origin of Lloyds of London.

Unit 1:   Life Insurance

Section 1:   Life Expectancy and the Mortality Tables

Insurance companies keep records that help them determine what the cost of insurance should be. In the case of life insurance companies, these records are called *mortality tables* and resemble those shown on page 390. These tables were purposely placed side by side so that you could compare the two. The first is based on the total population in the United States over the three-year period 1939–1941, while the second is based on the total population of the United States over the three-year period 1959–1961. Perhaps the most dramatic change that has occurred in the intervening twenty years, as seen in the table, happened in the first year of your life. Back in 1940, approximately 47 babies in every 1,000 died during their first year of life. In 1960, however, that number was just about half, for approximately only 26 of every 1,000 babies died. By now, the number is likely to be down even more. How can you account for this drop in the death rate?

These tables also tell you how long you can expect to live when you are at any given age. Thus, in 1940, a boy of 16 could, under normal circumstances, expect to live another 52.17 years. Hence, he could look forward to reaching the age of 68. In 1960, though, the boy of 16 could plan on another 56.37 years of life, to the age of 72. That 20-year period showed a very definite increase in the number of years you could expect to live.

Actually, there has been an increase in man's life expectancy for sometime now. However, this increase has been most apparent over the last 100 years because of the tremendous growth in medical knowledge. A person born in 1860 could look forward to reaching only 41! As you can see from the table, a baby born 100 years later has a good chance of reaching 70—29 years more than his great-great-grandfather!

■ILLUSTRATION 1: Use the mortality table based on the years 1939–1941 to find to what age a person of 16 can expect to live.

▼EXPLANATION: Follow the "Age" column down until you reach the numeral 16. Then place the edge of a piece of paper along the row containing this numeral. Run your finger along the edge of the paper until it comes to the numeral 52.17 in the column headed "Expectation of Life—Years." Make certain you are using the 1939–1941 part of the table. The numeral 52.17 represents the number of years more that a person of 16 can expect to live. Hence, by adding 52.17 to 16, you can determine the age he should reach.

Life-expectancy tables can be found in the *Life Insurance Fact Book,* distributed by the Institute of Life Insurance at 488 Madison Avenue, New York, N.Y. There is no charge for this book.

MORTALITY TABLES

Age	United States Total Population (1939–1941) Deaths Per 1,000	Expectation of Life (Years)	United States Total Population (1959–1961) Deaths Per 1,000	Expectation of Life (Years)	Age	United States Total Population (1939–1941) Deaths Per 1,000	Expectation of Life (Years)	United States Total Population (1959–1961) Deaths Per 1,000	Expectation of Life (Years)
0	47.10	63.62	25.93	69.89	55	15.64	19.31	11.61	21.37
1	5.21	65.76	1.70	70.75	56	16.84	18.60	12.49	20.62
2	2.67	65.10	1.04	69.87	57	18.12	17.92	13.52	19.87
3	1.88	64.28	.80	68.94	58	19.49	17.24	14.73	19.14
4	1.51	63.40	.67	67.99	59	20.95	16.57	16.11	18.42
5	1.32	62.49	.59	67.04	60	22.51	15.91	17.61	17.71
6	1.17	61.57	.52	66.08	61	24.19	15.27	19.17	17.02
7	1.05	60.65	.47	65.11	62	26.01	14.63	20.82	16.34
8	.96	59.71	.43	64.14	63	27.97	14.01	22.52	15.68
9	.91	58.77	.39	63.17	64	30.12	13.40	24.31	15.03
10	.90	57.82	.37	62.19	65	32.48	12.80	26.22	14.39
11	.92	56.87	.37	61.22	66	35.09	12.21	28.28	13.76
12	.97	55.92	.40	60.24	67	37.98	11.64	30.53	13.15
13	1.07	54.98	.48	59.26	68	41.20	11.08	33.01	12.55
14	1.22	54.04	.59	58.29	69	44.77	10.53	35.73	11.96
15	1.39	53.10	.71	57.33	70	48.73	10.00	38.66	11.38
16	1.57	52.17	.82	56.37	71	53.12	9.49	41.82	10.82
17	1.73	51.26	.93	55.41	72	57.98	9.00	45.30	10.27
18	1.88	50.34	1.02	54.46	73	63.33	8.52	49.15	9.74
19	2.03	49.44	1.08	53.52	74	69.18	8.06	53.42	9.21
20	2.17	48.54	1.15	52.58	75	75.54	7.62	57.99	8.71
21	2.30	47.64	1.22	51.64	76	82.39	7.20	62.96	8.21
22	2.42	46.75	1.27	50.70	77	89.75	6.81	68.67	7.73
23	2.50	45.86	1.28	49.76	78	97.61	6.43	75.35	7.26
24	2.56	44.98	1.27	48.83	79	105.99	6.07	83.02	6.81
25	2.62	44.09	1.26	47.89	80	114.91	5.73	92.08	6.39
26	2.67	43.21	1.25	46.95	81	124.38	5.41	102.19	5.98
27	2.75	42.32	1.26	46.00	82	134.44	5.11	112.44	5.61
28	2.85	41.44	1.30	45.06	83	145.08	4.82	121.95	5.25
29	2.95	40.55	1.36	44.12	84	156.25	4.56	130.67	4.91
30	3.07	39.67	1.43	43.18	85	167.88	4.31	143.80	4.58
31	3.20	38.79	1.51	42.24	86	179.92	4.08	158.16	4.26
32	3.35	37.91	1.60	41.30	87	192.29	3.86	173.55	3.97
33	3.51	37.04	1.70	40.37	88	204.93	3.66	190.32	3.70
34	3.69	36.17	1.81	39.44	89	217.79	3.47	208.35	3.45
35	3.90	35.30	1.94	38.51	90	230.81	3.30	227.09	3.22
36	4.12	34.44	2.09	37.58	91	243.94	3.14	245.98	3.02
37	4.36	33.58	2.28	36.66	92	257.11	2.99	264.77	2.85
38	4.62	32.72	2.49	35.74	93	270.31	2.86	282.84	2.69
39	4.91	31.87	2.73	34.83	94	283.44	2.73	299.52	2.55
40	5.24	31.03	3.00	33.92	95	296.46	2.61	314.16	2.43
41	5.59	30.19	3.30	33.02	96	309.35	2.50	329.15	2.32
42	5.99	29.35	3.62	32.13	97	322.10	2.40	344.50	2.21
43	6.43	28.53	3.97	31.25	98	334.75	2.31	360.18	2.10
44	6.91	27.71	4.35	30.37	99	347.36	2.21	376.16	2.01
45	7.44	26.90	4.76	29.50	100	360.05	2.13	392.42	1.91
46	8.01	26.10	5.21	28.64	101	372.98	2.04	408.91	1.83
47	8.62	25.30	5.73	27.79	102	386.34	1.96	425.62	1.75
48	9.28	24.52	6.33	26.94	103	400.36	1.88	442.50	1.67
49	9.99	23.74	7.00	26.11	104	415.25	1.80	459.51	1.60
50	10.76	22.98	7.74	25.29	105	431.17	1.72	476.62	1.53
51	11.59	22.22	8.52	24.49	106	448.20	1.64	493.78	1.46
52	12.49	21.48	9.29	23.69	107	466.33	1.56	510.95	1.40
53	13.46	20.74	10.05	22.91	108	485.39	1.48	528.10	1.35
54	14.51	20.02	10.82	22.14	109	505.10	1.41	545.19	1.29

It is interesting to compare the figures above with those of the *American Experience Mortality Table.* This is the first of the mortality tables, and was based on the years 1843-1858. This table can be found in the *Life Insurance Fact Book.*

●SOLUTION:

Expectation of life at 16 = 52.17 years

Age a person of 16 should reach = 16 + 52.17

= 68.17

■ILLUSTRATION 2: How many people in a group of 50,000, age 55, will die before they reach 56? Use the mortality table for the years 1959–1961.

▼EXPLANATION: The table shows that 11.61 people in each 1,000 who are alive at 55 will die during that year. Since 50,000 is 50 times as much as 1,000, to find the total number of people who will die you need only multiply 50 by 11.61.

●SOLUTION:

Number per 1,000 who will die = 11.61

Number of 1,000's in 50,000 = 50,000 ÷ 1,000

= 50

Total number who will die in 50,000 = 50 × 11.61

= 580.50, or 581

▼EXPLANATION (continued): Notice that the answer is rounded off to the nearest whole number. Since these are people you are considering, it would not be acceptable to leave an answer in terms of 50 hundredths of a person.

When you talk about the age a person should reach as is done in Illustration 1, you are thinking about the average person. For instance, in that illustration, the average person of 16 should expect to reach 68.17. As you all know, some people will die before this, while others will live well beyond it. The average person is the one who is exactly in the middle of this group, that is to say, he is the one who will die at 68.17. Half the people who started out with him at 16 will die before he does, and half of them will outlive him.

EXERCISES   A

Refer to the mortality tables on page 390 when doing the computations for the following problems.

1. According to the mortality table based on the period 1939–1941, how many years can people at the following ages expect to live?

	Age	Life Expectancy		Age	Life Expectancy
a.	10	57.82	f.	56	18.60
b.	15	53.10	g.	65	12.80
c.	28	41.44	h.	79	6.07
d.	34	36.17	i.	96	2.50
e.	42	29.35	j.	107	1.56

The age 16 was used in Illustration 1 because it is approximately the age of the students who will be taking this course. If the average age in the class differs from this, investigate the "deaths per 1,000" and the "expectations of life" for these years, whatever they may be.

2. According to the mortality table based on the years 1959–1961, until what age can people at the following ages expect to live?

	Age	Age Expectancy			Age	Age Expectancy
a.	1	71.75	f.		61	78.02
b.	5	72.04	g.		69	80.96
c.	18	72.46	h.		82	87.61
d.	25	72.89	i.		95	97.43
e.	43	74.25	j.		104	105.60

3. According to the mortality table based on the years 1939–1941, how many of the following number of persons at each of the ages shown can be expected to die before they reach their next birthday?

	Age	Number Of People	Deaths Per 1,000	Total Number Of Deaths
a.	1	100,000	5.21	521
b.	7	400,000	1.05	420
c.	16	500,000	1.57	785
d.	21	200,000	2.30	460
e.	46	80,000	8.01	641
f.	57	70,000	18.12	1,268
g.	69	60,000	44.77	2,686
h.	86	50,000	179.92	8,996

4. According to the mortality table based on the years 1959–1961, how many of the following number of people, at each of the ages shown, can be expected to live until their next birthday?

	Age	Number Of People	Deaths Per 1,000	Total Number Of Deaths	Total Number Surviving
a.	4	100,000	.67	67	99,933
b.	15	700,000	.71	497	699,503
c.	19	900,000	1.08	972	899,028
d.	37	600,000	2.28	1,368	598,632
e.	54	300,000	10.82	3,246	296,754
f.	65	200,000	26.22	5,244	194,756
g.	78	60,000	75.35	4,521	55,479
h.	95	20,000	314.16	6,283	13,717

B

1. a. Of 200,000 babies born in 1940, how many died during their first year of life?   9,420
   b. Of 200,000 babies born in 1960, how many died during their first year of life?   5,186
   c. How many more died in 1940 than in 1960?   4,234
2. A boy who was 16 in 1960 could expect to live how many more years than a boy who was 16 in 1940?   4.20

Problems similar to those in Group B should be used to show how much greater a person's life expectance has grown over so short a period as from 1940 to 1960.

Section 2:   Life Insurance

PART 1:   TERM INSURANCE

With the information in the mortality tables, life insurance companies are able to predict the number of people of each age who will die each year. On the basis of this, they can determine, in advance, how much money they will need to pay the *beneficiaries* upon the death of the people who are insured. The beneficiary is simply the person who is named in the policy as the one to collect the money when an insured person dies. And the amount that he receives is called the *face value* of the policy.

The cheapest type of life insurance that a person can purchase is *term insurance*. Recall that when you studied about automobile insurance, you learned that after you paid the premium you were insured for one year. At the end of this period, you were no longer insured, nor did you get any money back from the insurance company. If you wanted to continue to protect yourself in the event of an automobile accident, you had to pay the premium again for another year.

This is much the same situation in a *term* policy for life insurance. Now, however, the period for which insurance is purchased is usually 5 or 10 years. At the end of that time, if you are still alive, neither you nor the beneficiary receives anything for the money you paid in. If you want to continue to protect your beneficiaries in the event of your death, you have to purchase another policy for another 5- or 10-year period.

In the following table you can see that the cost of term insurance for a male is exactly the same as the cost for a female who is three years older. Research has shown that women tend to live longer than men. For this reason, a woman who is the same age as a man can buy insurance at a cheaper rate.

ANNUAL PREMIUM PER $1,000 OF TERM INSURANCE

Age		5-Year Term Policy		10-Year Term Policy	
Male	Female	$5,000–$9,999	$10,000–$19,999	$5,000–$9,999	$10,000–$19,999
20	23	$ 6.44	$ 5.69	$ 6.51	$ 5.76
25	28	6.59	5.84	6.72	5.97
30	33	6.88	6.13	7.19	6.44
35	38	7.56	6.81	8.27	7.52
40	43	9.11	8.36	10.24	9.49
45	48	11.60	10.85	13.43	12.68
50	53	15.66	14.91	18.47	17.72
55	58	21.95	21.20	26.28	25.53
60	63	31.80	31.05	38.40	37.65

Term insurance is the cheapest type of life insurance a person can buy. The insured builds up no equity in the policy. Some insurance companies are selling a modified version whereby, for the first few years, the rates are low. Then they jump quite some as the insurance changes to, perhaps, endowment.

Notice, also, that the rates depend on the amount of insurance you purchase. For instance, if at 20 a man were to purchase a 5-year term-insurance policy that had a face value of between $5,000 and $9,999, he would have to pay $6.44 each year for each $1,000 worth of insurance. However, if the face value were between $10,000 and $19,999, then the cost for each $1,000 of insurance would be only $5.69.

It is also possible to purchase less than $5,000 worth of term insurance and more than $20,000 worth. The rates, though, will be different than those shown in the table. Will the rates for a term insurance policy of less than $5,000 be less than the rates for a $5,000 policy, or more? What can be said about the rates for a $25,000 policy relative to the rates for a $15,000 policy?

■ILLUSTRATION 1 : What annual premium will Mr. Jenkins have to pay on a $12,000, 10-year term policy that he took out at age 35?

▼EXPLANATION: Follow down the "Age" column for males until you reach the numeral 35. Run your finger across the row containing this numeral until you reach the two columns headed by the words "10-Year." Since the amount of insurance purchased is $12,000, the rate you want will be in the column headed by the numerals "$10,000–$19,999." The $7.52 that your finger will be pointing to is the cost per $1,000 of insurance. For the $12,000 that Mr. Jenkins purchased, he will have to pay 12 times $7.52.

●SOLUTION:

$$\text{Annual premium per } \$1,000 = \$7.52$$
$$\text{Annual premium for } \$12,000 = 12 \times \$7.52$$
$$= \$90.24$$

There are quite a number of people who feel that they need a great deal of insurance protection early in their married lives. Then, as time goes on and their children get older, their need for this protection becomes smaller. In order to get as much insurance as possible for the least cost, these people buy what is called *decreasing-term insurance*. In most respects, this insurance is the same as normal-term insurance. There is one very important difference, though, and that is that, as the years go by, the amount for which they are insured grows less and less. For instance, in the first year they may be insured for $1,000, while in the second it may be only $925, in the third, $845, and so on.

Since the amount of insurance protection grows smaller each year in decreasing-term insurance, it is cheaper to buy than normal-term insurance. Hence, the same amount of money will purchase more decreasing-term insurance than the normal-term insurance.

The person who wants the most life-insurance protection for his money in the immediate future and less of it as the years go by should best consider the decreasing-term insurance policy. The newly married man with a rather low income should consider this form of insurance.

■ILLUSTRATION 2: Mrs. Pierson is 43 years old. How much will she save annually by purchasing an $8,000 decreasing 10-year term policy rather than an $8,000 normal 10-year term policy?

●SOLUTION:

Annual premium per $1,000 on decreasing-term policy = $4.96
Annual premium per $1,000 on normal-term policy = $10.24
Annual saving per $1,000 insurance = $10.24 − $4.96
$$= \$5.28$$
Annual saving on $8,000 insurance = 8 × $5.28
$$= \$42.24$$

ANNUAL PREMIUM FOR $1,000 INITIAL AMOUNT OF DECREASING–TERM INSURANCE

Age		10-Year	20-Year
Male	Female		
20	23	$ 2.72	$ 2.62
25	28	2.85	2.78
30	33	3.14	3.03
35	38	3.77	3.89
40	43	4.96	5.38
45	48	6.94	7.92
50	53	10.20	11.90
55	58	15.36	18.06
60	63	23.45	

Actually, the preceding problem is a little misleading. There is really no such thing as cheaper insurance. Although Mrs. Pierson would be paying $42.24 per year less on the decreasing-term insurance, she would also be insured for a great deal less. During the first year she would be insured for $8,000 on both policies. After the first year, however, on the normal-term policy, she would still be insured for the $8,000, but on the decreasing-term policy, she would be insured for less than $8,000. Each year thereafter, the amount of protection on the decreasing-term policy would grow less and less. The following table gives you some idea of the amount of protection a person has on a decreasing-term policy as the years go by. It is interesting to notice that although you are paying the same premium every year, in the first year you are insured for $1,000, while in the fifteenth year, you are insured for only $99. That is why decreasing-term insurance is so inexpensive a form of insurance.

See if the students can justify why the rates of a male should be exactly the same as those of a female who is three years older.

AMOUNT OF DECREASING–TERM INSURANCE
FOR EACH $1,000 INITIAL AMOUNT

Year	10-Year Term	15-Year Term
1	$1,000	$1,000
2	925	958
3	845	913
4	760	865
5	670	814
6	575	761
7	473	703
8	365	643
9	251	578
10	129	510
11		437
12		360
13		278
14		191
15		99

■ILLUSTRATION 3: A person originally bought $9,000 worth of decreasing 15-year term insurance. For how much was he insured during the sixth year after the date of purchase?

●SOLUTION:

Value of $1,000 worth of decreasing-
term insurance in the 6th year = $761
Value of $9,000 worth of decreasing-
term insurance in the 6th year = 9 × $761
= $6,849

▼EXPLANATION: Although the person was insured for $9,000 during the first year after buying the insurance, he was insured for only $6,849 during the sixth year.

EXERCISES   A

In doing the following exercises, you will have to refer to the tables in this section.

1. Determine the annual premium on each of the following term-insurance policies.

	Age	Sex	Face Value	Term	Rate per $1,000	Premium
a.	30	M	$ 6,000	5-Year	$ 6.88	$ 41.28
b.	45	M	8,000	5-Year	11.60	92.80
c.	50	M	7,000	10-Year	18.47	129.29
d.	23	F	9,000	5-Year	6.44	57.96
e.	38	F	15,000	10-Year	7.52	112.80
f.	55	M	7,500	10-Year	26.28	197.10
g.	53	F	6,500	5-Year	15.66	101.79
h.	60	M	18,500	5-Year	31.05	574.43
i.	28	F	15,500	10-Year	5.97	92.54
j.	23	F	9,500	5-Year	6.44	61.18

Call the attention of the students to the fact that in a 15-year decreasing-term insurance policy, the person is insured on the 15th year for only 1/10 of the coverage he had on the 1st year. Inquire, also, on the amount of coverage the person had on the 16th year.

2. Determine the annual premium on each of the following decreasing-term insurance policies.

	Age	Sex	Face Value	Term	Rate per $1,000	Premium
a.	35	M	$ 4,000	10-Year	$ 3.77	$ 15.08
b.	50	M	6,000	20-Year	11.90	71.40
c.	38	F	3,000	10-Year	3.77	11.31
d.	23	F	7,000	10-Year	2.72	19.04
e.	30	M	15,000	20-Year	3.03	45.45
f.	25	M	25,000	20-Year	2.78	69.50

3. For what amount will a person be insured during the year shown on each of the following decreasing-term policies?

	Year	Term	Initial Value	Amount per $1,000	Total Insurance
a.	1st	10-Year	$ 8,000	$ 1,000.00	$ 8,000.00
b.	3rd	10-Year	6,000	845.00	5,070.00
c.	7th	10-Year	9,000	473.00	4,257.00
d.	10th	10-Year	10,000	129.00	1,290.00
e.	3rd	15-Year	8,000	913.00	7,304.00
f.	9th	15-Year	20,000	578.00	11,560.00
g.	14th	15-Year	75,000	191.00	14,325.00
h.	12th	15-Year	25,000	360.00	9,000.00
i.	1st	15-Year	30,000	1,000.00	30,000.00
j.	15th	15-Year	30,000	99.00	2,970.00

B

1. Mr. Baker purchased a $10,000 5-year term policy.
   a. How much will his beneficiary receive if he dies two years after he purchased the policy?   **$10,000.00**
   b. How much will his beneficiary receive if he dies one day after he pays his first premium?   **$10,000.00**
   c. How much will his beneficiary receive if he dies six years after he pays his first premium?   Nothing
2. Mrs. Bigelow purchased a decreasing-term policy, the initial value of which was $15,000.
   a. For how much will she be insured in the third year if it is a 10-year policy?   **$12,675.00**
   b. For how much will she be insured in the third year if it is a 15-year policy?   **$13,695.00**
   c. For how much more will she be insured under the 15-year policy than under the 10-year policy during the third year? **$ 1,020.00**
3. At age 30, William Kent purchased a $15,000 10-year term policy. He lived the entire 10-year period.
   a. If he had purchased a normal-term policy, what would his total premium have been for the 10-year period?   **$ 966.00**

b. If he had purchased a decreasing-term policy, what would his total premiums have been for the 10-year period? <u>$471.00</u>

c. How much less would he have to pay under the decreasing-term policy over the 10-year period? <u>$495.00</u>

PART 2: ORDINARY–LIFE, LIMITED–PAYMENT LIFE, AND ENDOWMENT INSURANCE

There are three basic types of life insurance other than the term insurance you just investigated. In the case of term insurance, if the insured does not die during the period that the policy is in effect, then neither he, nor his beneficiary, receives any money from the insurance company. In the case of each of the other three types of insurance, someone, at sometime, must get some money back from the company. Because of this, the cost of any one of these policies is greater than the cost of a term policy having the same face value.

The three types of policies are: the ordinary, or whole-life, policy, the limited-payment life policy, and the endowment policy. Just as you found that there were variations of term insurance, such as decreasing-term insurance, so, too, are there variations of each of these three. The following explanations will try to point out not only the manner in which you are protected under each of these policies, but also what variations of them exist.

Ordinary-Life or Whole-Life Insurance

If you buy this type of insurance, you agree to pay premiums for your entire life. The company agrees that, at the time of your death, they will pay your beneficiary the face value of the policy. Thus, according to the mortality tables, if you take out insurance at 18 and happen to be the one and only person in 1,000 who dies the first year, then the insurance company will pay the full face value of the policy to the beneficiary you named. On the other hand, if you live for the 54 years beyond age 18 that the insurance company expects you to live, you will have to pay the premium for the entire period, but the company will still pay your beneficiary only the face value of the policy. In fact, even if you live until 109—the mortality tables end at that point—you must still continue to pay the premiums every year.

A variation of this policy is one involving an ordinary-life policy paid up at a certain age. For instance, if you felt you did not want to pay for insurance after 65, you could agree to pay the company slightly higher premiums each year than you would under the ordinary-life

The Institute of Life Insurance referred to at the bottom of page 389 makes available to teachers at no charge a unit on life insurance. They will furnish you with sufficient pamphlets for each member of the class.

policy. Then, at 65 you would no longer have to make any further payments. However, after that age you would still be insured, that is, at the time of your death your beneficiary would receive the face value of the policy. Of course, should you die before 65, your beneficiary would get the face value of the policy at that time.

Limited-Payment Life Policy

This type of insurance is much the same as the ordinary-life policy, except that you agree to pay the premiums for a limited period only. This period may be 20 years, or 25 years, or 30 years. At the end of that period, although you no longer make any payments, you are insured for the rest of your life as in the ordinary-life policy paid up at age 65. Hence, from the day you pay the first premium until the day you die, you are fully insured. A limited-payment life policy, in which you pay premiums for 20 years, is called a 20-payment life insurance policy. What would the policy be called if you paid the premiums for 30 years?

Endowment Policy

In each of the life-insurance policies already examined, you never receive one penny of the amount you pay in premiums. In the endowment policy, however, you get your money back—in fact, you get back the face value of the policy. Here, as in the limited-payment life policy, premiums are paid for a fixed number of years. If you do not die during that period, the company agrees to give you the face value of the policy at the end of the period, and then you are no longer insured. Should you die during that period, the face value of the policy will go to your beneficiary. For instance, on a $5,000, 20-year endowment policy, if you die at any time during the 20-year period, your beneficiary will receive the $5,000. In the event you live to make the 20 annual payments, then, at the end of the 20 years, the insurance company will give you the $5,000. Once you receive the money, though, you are no longer insured.

A variation of the endowment policy is a policy that is similar to the ordinary-life policy paid up at age 65. In the latter policy, you pay premiums until 65 and then make no further payments. Then, at the time of your death, and not before, your beneficiary receives the face value of the policy. In the case of the endowment policy paid up at 65, you yourself get the face value of the policy at that age and then you are no longer insured. What would an endowment policy paid up at 60 be? A person buying this type of insurance is usually interested in using this money as part of his retirement fund if he manages to live to

Several variations of the policies listed above have been noted. Actually, for the person willing to pay for it, practically any type of protection he may want can be written into the policy. The policies listed above are those most commonly purchased by the great majority of people.

ANNUAL LIFE-INSURANCE PREMIUM RATES PER $1,000

Age		Ordinary-Life		Life-Paid-Up-At-Age-65 (Male Only)		20-Payment-Life		Endowment-At-Age-65 (Male Only)		20-Year-Endowment	
Male	Female	$5,000–$9,999	$10,000–$19,999	$5,000–$9,999	$10,000–$19,999	$5,000–$9,999	$10,000–$19,999	$5,000–$9,999	$10,000–$19,999	$5,000–$9,999	$10,000–$19,999
20	23	$ 15.07	$ 14.32	$15.98	$15.23	$ 22.90	$ 22.15	$ 18.74	$ 17.99	$ 46.70	$ 45.95
25	28	17.08	16.33	18.41	17.66	25.43	24.68	21.85	21.10	46.93	46.18
30	33	19.63	18.88	21.65	20.90	28.42	27.67	26.00	25.25	47.36	46.61
35	38	22.94	22.19	26.09	25.34	32.02	31.27	31.71	30.96	48.19	47.44
40	43	27.25	26.50	32.39	31.64	36.40	35.65	39.88	39.13	49.66	48.91
45	48	32.85	32.10	41.72	40.97	41.72	40.97	52.01	51.26	52.01	51.26
50	53	40.23	39.48	57.21	56.46	48.33	47.58	70.72	69.97	55.76	55.01
55	58	49.93	49.18	86.46	85.71	56.64	55.89	109.55	108.80	61.64	60.89
60	63	62.47	61.72			67.60	66.85			70.59	69.84
65	68	79.43	78.68			82.77	82.02			84.27	83.52
70	73	102.25	101.50			103.94	103.19			104.53	103.78

As oral exercises, have the students compare the costs of various insurance coverage at the same age and the same insurance coverage at various ages.

65. Before looking at the table on page 400, which of the various types of insurance do you think would be the most expensive to buy?

■ ILLUSTRATION 1: Use the table on page 400 to find the annual premium Mr. Ellis would have to pay on a $6,000, 20-year-endowment policy that he purchased at age 35.
▼ EXPLANATION: The method for finding the annual premium is exactly the same here as it was in the case of term insurance.
● SOLUTION:

Annual premium per $1,000 = $48.19
Annual premium for $6,000 = 6 × $48.19
= $289.14

Although at one time most people paid their life-insurance premiums on a weekly, or monthly, basis, they no longer do so, for they found this to be much too expensive. The more frequently premiums are paid, the higher the cost of insurance. On the other hand, some people might find it difficult to make a single lump-sum payment of $289.14 once each year, as Mr. Ellis had to do in Illustration 1, above. Hence, for a small additional cost arrangements can be made to make payments semiannually (twice each year) or quarterly. (How often is that?) The following table shows the percent of the annual premium that will have to be paid at each period.

Period	Percent of Annual Premium
Semiannually	52%
Quarterly	26.5%

If you were charged nothing extra, the semiannual premium should be one half, or 50%, of the annual premium. However, you are being asked to pay 52% of the annual premium, or 2% more than you should on each payment. What percent extra are you being asked to pay on each quarterly payment?

■ ILLUSTRATION 2: Gracie Hammond purchased a $12,000 ordinary-life-insurance policy at age 28.
  a. If she pays her premiums quarterly, how much will each payment be?
  b. How much can she save each year by making annual payments rather than quarterly payments?
▼ EXPLANATION: The annual payment is found in exactly the same manner as in the first illustration. By computing 26.5% of the annual premium, you determine the quarterly premium.

Question students on such points as, "What percent more per year will a person be charged if he pays his premiums semiannually rather than annually?" "What percent more if premiums are paid quarterly?" and "Can you justify why a company would need to charge more for semiannual than annual premiums?

●SOLUTION:

    (a) Annual premium per $1,000 = $16.33

         Annual premium for $12,000 = 12 × $16.33

$$= \$195.96$$

        Quarterly premium for $12,000 = 26.5% of $195.96

$$= .265 \times \$195.96$$

$$= \$51.9294, \text{ or } \$51.93$$

    (b) Annual cost when premiums are paid quarterly = 4 × $51.93

$$= \$207.72$$

        Annual cost when premiums are paid once each year

        = $195.96 (See above for annual premium on $12,000).

        Saving per year = $207.72 − $195.96

$$= \$11.76$$

EXERCISES   A

1. Determine the annual premium on each of the following policies purchased at the age indicated.

	Sex	Age	Policy	Face Value	Premium Per $1,000	Total Premium
a.	M	40	20-Year-Endowment	$ 8,000	$ 49.66	$ 397.28
b.	M	25	Ordinary-Life	6,000	17.08	102.48
c.	M	50	Life-Paid-Up-at-65	7,000	57.21	400.47
d.	F	38	20-Payment-Life	12,000	31.27	375.24
e.	M	55	Endowment-at-65	15,000	108.80	1,632.00
f.	M	20	Ordinary-Life	16,000	14.32	229.12
g.	M	45	20-Year-Endowment	7,500	52.01	390.08
h.	M	20	Life-Paid-Up-at-65	12,500	15.23	190.38
i.	M	35	Endowment-at-65	17,500	30.96	541.80
j.	F	28	20-Payment-Life	18,500	24.68	456.58

2. Determine the semiannual premium for each of the annual premiums shown.

	Annual Premium	Semiannual Premium
a.	$200	$ 104.00
b.	168	87.36
c.	175	91.00
d.	209	108.68
e.	257	133.64
f.	125.50	65.26
g.	146.50	76.18
h.	185.46	96.44
i.	238.57	124.06
j.	269.85	140.32

In Exercise 1, parts g through j, you will need to spend some time showing the students how to determine the number of thousands in the face value of a policy.

3. Determine the quarterly premium for each of the annual premiums shown.

	Annual Premium	Quarterly Premium			Annual Premium	Quarterly Premium
a.	$300	$ 79.50	f.		$240.04	$ 63.61
b.	240	63.60	g.		123.50	32.73
c.	180	47.70	h.		184.30	48.84
d.	164	43.46	i.		237.62	62.97
e.	235	62.28	j.		268.16	71.06

4. Determine the semiannual premium on each of the following policies purchased at the age indicated.

	Sex	Age	Policy	Face Value	Premium Per $1,000	Annual Premium	Semiannual Premium
a.	M	20	Ordinary-Life	$ 5,000	$ 15.07	$ 75.35	$ 39.18
b.	M	35	Life-Paid-Up-at-65	7,000	26.09	182.63	94.97
c.	F	43	20-Year-Endowment	10,000	48.91	489.10	254.33
d.	M	50	Endowment-at-65	8,000	70.72	565.76	294.20
e.	F	28	20-Payment-Life	11,000	24.68	271.48	141.17
f.	M	40	Life-Paid-Up-at-65	16,000	31.64	506.24	263.24

5. Determine the quarterly premium on each of the following policies purchased at the age indicated.

	Sex	Age	Policy	Face Value	Premium Per $1,000	Annual Premium	Quarterly Premium
a.	M	35	20-Payment-Life	$ 6,000	$ 32.02	$ 192.12	$ 50.91
b.	M	70	20-Year-Endowment	8,000	104.53	836.24	221.60
c.	F	63	Ordinary-Life	10,000	61.72	617.20	163.56
d.	M	55	Endowment-at-65	5,000	109.55	547.75	145.15
e.	M	45	Life-Paid-Up-at-65	14,000	40.97	573.58	152.00
f.	F	23	20-Year-Endowment	16,500	45.95	758.18	200.92

B

1. Mr. Hayden purchased a $15,000 20-payment life-insurance policy at age 25.
   a. If he paid his premiums annually, what would each payment be?
   $ 370.20
   b. If he paid his premiums quarterly, what would each payment be?
   $ 98.10
   c. How much could he save each year by making annual payments rather than quarterly payments? $ 22.20
2. At age 23, Mary Parker purchased a $10,000 20-year-endowment policy.
   a. What annual premium will she have to pay? $ 459.50
   b. If she lives the entire 20 years, what will be the total of the premiums she will have paid? $9,190.00

The problems in Group B bring out some comparisons that you will want to discuss with the class.

   c. How much will she receive from the company at the end of the
20-year period?   **$10,000.00**

   d. How much more will she receive from the company than she
paid in premiums?   **$ 810.00**

3. George Chapman purchased a $5,000 ordinary-life policy at age 50.

   a. What annual premium will he have to pay?   **$ 201.15**

   b. According to the mortality table for the years 1959–1961 on page
390, indicate, to the nearest year, how many years the insurance
company expects George to live.   **25**

   c. If he should live exactly the number of years he is supposed to,
what will be the total of the premiums he will have paid the insurance company?   **$ 5,028.75**

   d. How much more (or less) will he have paid the company than
his beneficiary will receive at the time of his death?   **$ 28.75**

C

Refer to the table on page 400 in order to answer each of the following
questions.

1. Why should the rates at 45 be exactly the same for a 20-payment
life policy as they are for a life-paid-up-at-65 policy?   Same policy

2. a. Why should the rates for an endowment-at-65 policy be less than
the rates for a 20-year-endowment when a person is under 45?
He will pay premiums for more than 20 years.

   b. Why should the rates for an endowment-at-65 policy be more
than the rates for a 20-year-endowment when a person is over 45?
He will pay premiums for less than 20 years.

3. a. Why should the rates for a life-paid-up-at-65 policy be less than
the rates for a 20-payment life policy when the person is under
45?   He will pay premiums for more than 20 years.

   b. Why should the rates for a life-paid-up-at-65 policy be more than
the rates for a 20-payment-life policy when a person is over 45?
He will pay premiums for less than 20 years.

4. Why should the rates on a 20-year-endowment policy be more than
the rates on a 20-payment-life policy taken out at the same age?
At age 40 the policyholder of the 20-year endowment policy receives the face
value of the policy, while the other policyholder receives nothing till death.

Unit 2: Disability Insurance

In the previous unit you learned how a person could continue to
provide for his family in the event his income was cut off by his death.
However, a person does not have to die in order to lose his income. He

may be involved in a serious accident, or have a long siege of illness. Either of these will prevent him from working and thus lead to a loss of salary.

People who are concerned that this will happen to them, and thus leave them with no money to support either themselves or their families, usually protect themselves by buying *disability insurance*, that is, insurance in the event of sickness or accident. This insurance can be purchased in a variety of forms, and, as might be expected, the more you pay, the more protection you receive. For instance, under this insurance, if you are unable to work because of either illness or accident, the insurance company will send you monthly checks to replace, in some way, the income you may no longer be receiving from your employer. The greater the premium you pay, the greater will be your monthly allotment.

There are two other factors that determine how large the premiums will be. The first of these concerns itself with when you want the insurance company to begin sending you monthly checks. If this income is to start the very first day that you can no longer work, then the rates are going to be quite high. Most people who become ill or are injured in an accident are often back at work within a few days. Hence, if you arrange so that payments do not begin until the second week of your illness, the rates will be a great deal lower than if payments include the very first day of illness. Similarly, the rates are even lower if payments begin only after you have been out of work for at least two weeks. The longer the delay in your receiving money from the insurance company, the lower the premiums will be. The usual time, though, is about a two-week delay.

The last factor contributing to the cost of disability insurance concerns itself with just how long you want the insurance company to send you monthly payments. If you want the payments to last for only the first year you are disabled, your premiums will be less than if you want them to last for two years, or, perhaps, even for life. It is always possible that you can be so injured, or become so ill—such as with a heart ailment—that you may never be able to return to work. To cover such an eventuality, you may want to think in terms of having the insurance payments continue for life. If you do, though, the cost will be a great deal more than if the payments were to last for only one year.

Incidentally, insurance companies will not permit everyone to protect himself with disability coverage. If you happen to be an airline pilot, or an author, or a tunnel worker, or a window cleaner, or a miner, or an aerial photographer, to name a few occupations, the insurance companies will not give you disability insurance. All other people are

Experience has shown that students are more than willing to discuss accidents that have disabled parents, relatives, or friends. This may be one of the few times that some students can participate in class discussion. You may find you are forced to terminate discussion in order to continue the work.

separated into four occupation classifications: AAA, AA, A, and B, with the people in the AAA occupations paying the lowest rates and the B people paying the highest. Some of the occupations that fall into the AAA ratings are: accountants, office workers, cashiers, clerks, executives, physicians, studio photographers, and classroom teachers. The B occupations include farmhands, bartenders, boiler makers, road laborers, elevator repairmen, firemen, motorcycle policemen (but not foot patrolmen, who get an A rating), and welders. Why should the people in the B occupations have to pay more for disability insurance than the people in the AAA occupations?

DISABILITY INSURANCE

Annual Premium per $100 of Monthly Income—Male

14-Day Elimination Period

Age	AAA			AA			A		
	1-Year	2-Year	Lifetime	1-Year	2-Year	Lifetime	1-Year	2-Year	Lifetime *
20	$23.10	$27.90	$ 66.30	$29.10	$33.90	$ 83.50	$37.10	$41.90	$107.50
25	25.00	30.40	73.10	31.00	36.40	89.90	39.00	44.40	114.10
30	27.80	33.80	81.20	33.80	39.80	98.10	41.80	47.80	122.50
35	31.50	38.50	90.80	37.50	44.50	107.80	45.50	52.50	132.30
40	36.30	44.50	101.80	42.30	50.50	118.80	50.30	58.50	143.40
45	42.00	51.90	117.60	48.00	57.90	134.70	56.00	65.90	159.30
50	50.40	62.40	139.80	56.40	68.40	157.00	64.40	76.40	131.70
55	60.30	75.10	156.80	66.30	81.10	173.30	74.30	89.10	196.90

* Not used for a monthly income of more than $300.

The table above shows a sampling of what the rates are for people in the AAA, AA, and A occupations if they purchase disability insurance. The "1-Year," "2-year," and "Lifetime" columns refer to the period of time monthly payments are to be received. Notice, also, that this table can be used only if no disability payments are sent covering the first 14 days of illness. Other tables will have to be used in the event that only the first 7 days are to be eliminated from payments or, actually, any other period but 14 days. It is interesting to notice that this company feels that the A occupations are so dangerous they will not permit anyone in these occupations to insure himself for more than $300 of monthly payments to last over a lifetime.

■ILLUSTRATION 1: Use the disability insurance table to determine how much it would cost Mr. Evans annually if he wanted to be covered by a monthly disability insurance income of $400 that would be paid for two years. Mr. Evans is employed in a AA occupation, and he is 40 years of age.

▼EXPLANATION: Place the edge of a piece of paper along the row containing the age "40." Run your finger along the paper to the three

The occupational classifications outlined here are not necessarily the same for all companies. All, however, do use some form of classification and establish premium rates for each classification.

columns in the AA occupations. Since Mr. Evans wants to be paid for a 2-year period in the event he is disabled, the rate per $100 of monthly income is $50.50. To find the cost for a monthly income of $400, multiply $50.50 by 4.

● SOLUTION:

Premium per $100 of monthly income = $50.50
Number of 100's in 400 = 400 ÷ 100
$$= 4$$
Premium for $400 of monthly income = 4 × $50.50
$$= \$202.00$$

The heading in the disability insurance table tells you that it can be used only for men. If you want to determine the cost of this insurance for a woman, you must first find the cost for a man in the same occupation and at the same age and then determine 150% of that premium. What decimal is the equivalent of 150%? Thus, women have to pay 50% more for disability insurance than do men. It would appear, then, that although women, on the average, live longer than men, they tend to be away from work for either sickness or accident many more days than men.

Just as in the case of life insurance, it is possible to pay disability insurance premiums either semiannually or quarterly at the same rates used earlier. That is:

Semiannual premium = 52% of annual premium
Quarterly premium = 26.5% of annual premium

■ ILLUSTRATION 2: Mrs. McAdams works in a AAA occupation. At 25, she purchased an insurance policy to pay her a $250 monthly income for one year in the event she became disabled. What semiannual premium will she have to pay?

● SOLUTION:

Annual premium per $100 of monthly income (male) = $25.00
Number of 100's in 250 = 250 ÷ 100
$$= 2.5$$
Annual premium for $250 of monthly income (male) = 2.5 × $25
$$= \$62.50$$
Annual premium for $250 of monthly income (female)
$$= 150\% \text{ of } \$62.50$$
$$= 1.50 \times \$62.50$$
$$= \$93.75$$
Semiannual premium = 52% of $93.75
$$= .52 \times \$93.75$$
$$= \$48.75$$

This is one of the few times the students have encountered a percent value greater than 100%— in this case, it is 150%. Make certain that, when changing from the percent numeral to the equivalent decimal numeral they do not automatically place a decimal point to the left of the 1, but move it only two places.

EXERCISES   **A**

1. Determine the annual premium per $100 of monthly income that a man will have to pay on each of the following disability policies.

	Age	Occupation Rating	Years For Monthly Income	Annual Premium Per $100
a.	30	AAA	1	$ 27.80
b.	45	AA	2	57.90
c.	20	A	1	37.10
d.	25	AA	Lifetime	89.90
e.	50	AAA	2	62.40
f.	35	AA	1	37.50
g.	40	AAA	Lifetime	101.80
h.	40	AA	Lifetime	118.80

2. Determine the annual premium a man will have to pay on each of the following disability policies.

	Age	Occupation Rating	Monthly Income	Years Of Monthly Income	Annual Premium Per $100	Total Annual Premium
a.	25	AAA	$300	2	$ 30.40	$ 91.20
b.	40	A	400	1	50.30	201.20
c.	30	AA	200	Lifetime	98.10	196.20
d.	45	A	500	1	56.00	280.00
e.	50	AAA	350	2	62.40	218.40
f.	20	AA	450	1	29.10	130.95
g.	35	AAA	150	Lifetime	90.80	136.20
h.	55	A	250	Lifetime	196.90	492.25

3. What annual premium will a woman have to pay if the male at the same age and in the same occupation has to pay the following annual premiums?

	Male Premium	Female Premium
a.	$ 60	$ 90.00
b.	80	120.00
c.	126	189.00
d.	137	205.50
e.	159	238.50
f.	48.20	72.30
g.	67.30	100.95
h.	97.62	146.43
i.	109.65	164.48
j.	134.87	202.31

4. Determine the annual premium a woman will have to pay on each of the following disability insurance policies.

	Age	Occupation Rating	Monthly Income	Years Of Monthly Income	Annual Premium Per $100	Male Premium	Female Premium
a.	20	AAA	$200	1	$ 23.10	$ 46.20	$ 69.30
b.	30	AA	300	2	39.80	119.40	179.10
c.	45	A	100	Lifetime	159.30	159.30	238.95
d.	25	AA	400	2	36.40	145.60	218.40
e.	40	A	250	1	50.30	125.75	188.63
f.	50	AAA	350	2	62.40	218.40	327.60

5. Determine the semiannual premium a man will have to pay on each of the following disability insurance policies.

	Age	Occupation Rating	Monthly Income	Years Of Monthly Income	Annual Premium Per $100	Annual Premium	Semiannual Premium
a.	30	AA	$100	1	$ 33.80	$ 33.80	$ 17.58
b.	40	AAA	200	Lifetime	101.80	203.60	105.87
c.	25	A	500	2	44.40	222.00	115.44
d.	50	AAA	400	1	50.40	201.60	104.83
e.	45	AA	150	Lifetime	134.70	202.05	105.07
f.	35	AAA	450	2	38.50	173.25	90.09

6. Determine the quarterly premium a man will have to pay on each of the following disability insurance policies.

	Age	Occupation Rating	Monthly Income	Years Of Monthly Income	Annual Premium Per $100	Annual Premium	Quarterly Premium
a.	25	AAA	$100	2	$ 30.40	$ 30.40	$ 8.06
b.	35	A	200	1	45.50	91.00	24.12
c.	45	AA	500	Lifetime	134.70	673.50	178.48
d.	40	A	250	2	58.50	146.25	38.76

B

1. At 35, Mr. Fleming purchased a disability-insurance policy that would pay him $300 per month over a period of two years in the event that he was disabled. His occupation was classified as an AA risk.

a. How much were his annual premiums? $ 133.50

b. By renewing the policy year after year, he continued to pay the same rate that he paid at age 35. If he did this for a period of 8 years, what did this insurance cost him? $1,068.00

c. During the eighth year, he received disability payments from the insurance company for a period of nine months because of a serious illness. What was the total of these payments? $2,700.00

d. How much more did he receive from the company than he had paid them in premiums? $1,632.00

2. An insurance company wrote a policy for a 20-year-old cashier—
   AAA rating—that would pay $200 monthly for life in the event the
   person was permanently disabled.
   a. If the person were a male, what annual premium would he have
      to pay?   <u>$132.60</u>
   b. If the person were a female, what annual premium would she
      have to pay?   <u>$198.90</u>
   c. How much less does a male have to pay annually than a female?
                                                                 <u>$ 66.30</u>

Unit 3:   Hospital, Surgical, and Medical Insurance

In recent years, the increased cost of operating a hospital has so
skyrocketed the price of hospital care that very few people can truly
afford to spend any time in one. Fortunately, for most people, many
employers have taken on the task of paying hospitalization insurance
as part of their employee benefits. No matter who pays for it, though,
the cost is high.

Some insurance companies will write two different policies. One of
these will cover just hospital expenses, while the other will cover only
the fees that have to be paid to the surgeon for an operation. In this
way, you can purchase one policy or the other, or, if you prefer, both.
Other insurance companies include both hospital and surgical expenses in a single policy, as is done in the table of premiums shown.
Notice that this company offers two different plans. In the first, the
maximum amount the company pays for the use of a hospital bed is
$20 per day. In the event the charge is $23 per day, then you, yourself,
will have to pay the additional $3 for each day you spend in the hospi-
tal. Similarly, the company will pay the surgeon no more than $300 for
the operation he performs. If the operation is relatively minor, then
the $300 will probably cover his fees. But if it is not, then any amount
over the $300 will have to come out of your pocket. The second of the
plans available to you through this insurance company has a $25 maxi-
mum daily hospital benefit and a $400 maximum surgical benefit.

In the particular policies that are shown here, the insured has to pay
annual premiums until 65. At that time, social security benefits cover
most of these same costs, so people do not continue purchasing this insurance. Notice that there are three rates: the first one for the individual male, the second for the individual female, and the last for a
wife. A family consisting of a husband and wife pays the sum of the
individual male's premium and the wife's premium. That isn't all,

Have the students make a survey to determine how many of their families are covered by
hospital benefits, surgical benefits, or both. In addition, have them check as to whether the
premiums are being paid by the family, or by the employer, as part of fringe benefits.

HOSPITAL EXPENSE PREMIUMS

Age	$20 Maximum Daily Hospital Benefit $300 Maximum Surgical Expense Benefit $4 Maximum Daily Medical Expense Benefit			$25 Maximum Daily Hospital Benefit $400 Maximum Surgical Expense Benefit $5 Maximum Daily Medical Expense Benefit		
	Individual Male	Individual Female	Wife	Individual Male	Individual Female	Wife
20	$ 80.20	$106.78	$122.00	$ 99.26	$132.52	$151.00
25	86.53	114.73	122.00	106.97	142.27	151.00
30	95.18	125.12	122.00	117.72	159.98	151.00
35	107.22	136.97	125.00	132.48	169.53	154.90
40	123.88	149.28	131.46	153.02	184.62	162.84
45	145.54	164.84	145.13	179.66	203.76	179.67
50	177.56	193.12	170.08	219.24	238.58	210.42
55	231.85	245.84	219.38	286.45	303.74	271.42
60	382.50	386.48	345.44	471.90	476.82	426.66

For 1 child, add $42.40 annually   For 1 child, add $52.70 annually

For 2 or more children, add $84.80   For 2 or more children, add $105.40

Semiannual premiums = 52% of annual premiums

Quarterly premiums = 26.5% of annual premiums

See if the students can ascertain why the premium for the "individual female" should be less than that of the "wife" until age 30, and then greater after that age.

though. If there are children in the family, and if they are to be covered, too, the cost is still more.

■ILLUSTRATION 1 : Joe Boswell is 30 years old, while his wife is only 25. They have three children—1, 2, and 4. If Mr. Boswell insured the entire family under the less expensive of the two hospital-expense plans, how much would his semiannual premium be?

●SOLUTION:

Mr. Boswell's premium = $95.18
Mrs. Boswell's premium = $122.00
Premium for the three children = $84.80
Total annual premium = $95.18 + $122.00 + $84.80
= $301.98
Semiannual premium = 52% of $301.98
= .52 × $301.98
= $157.0296, or $157.03

As mentioned earlier, a surgeon's fees will rarely run under the $300 or $400 maximum you are allowed under the hospital-expense insurance of this company. Similarly, the costs of drugs, operating-room fees, oxygen-tent fees, private nurses, and on and on tend to run the extra charges well beyond the means of most people. Hence, within recent years, a new type of policy, called the *major-medical insurance plan*, has been designed to protect you against any large hospital or surgical bills that you might incur. Under this type of policy, you have to pay the first $500 of these expenses, after which the company pays the rest of the costs, that is, the rest of the costs within certain limits. In the case of the policy whose premiums are shown here, this limit is $10,000. With other policies for other companies, the maximum benefit may run as high as $20,000 or $25,000. Similarly, the amount deductible may be $750, or even $1,000 rather than the $500.

People will frequently purchase both major-medical and hospital-expense insurance. By doing this, they can cover the first $500 of their expenses by the second policy and the remainder of their costs by the first. This usually leaves them with little or nothing that they, themselves, have to pay—except the premiums, of course.

■ILLUSTRATION 2: At 35, Miss Atwell insured herself under both the major-medical and the $25-per-day hospital plan. How much will her total insurance premium be if she pays it on a quarterly basis?

When discussing the major-medical insurance above, you should point out that there is rarely an an operation costing less than the $300 or $400 covered in the hospital-surgical insurance policy shown on page 411. Hence, a person who purchased the policy on that page would also want to purchase major-medical insurance.

● SOLUTION:

Hospital-expense premium = $169.53
Major-medical premium = $61.21
Total annual premium = $169.53 + $61.21
= $230.74
Quarterly premium = 26.5% of $230.74
= .265 × $230.74
= $61.14610, or $61.15

MAJOR–MEDICAL PREMIUMS

$500 Deductible Amount
$10,000 Maximum Benefit

Age At Issue	Individual Male	Individual Female	Wife
25	$ 33.45	$ 49.38	$ 39.80
30	37.66	54.99	45.39
35	43.11	61.21	51.58
40	50.35	68.42	58.76
45	59.62	77.22	67.50
50	71.26	88.67	78.88
55	86.63	108.42	94.55
60	108.22	127.01	117.02

For 1 or more children, add $20 annually.

EXERCISES   A

In doing the following exercises, refer to the tables in this unit.
1. Determine the annual premium on each of the following hospital-expense insurance policies.

	Age	Person	Maximum Daily Benefit	Annual Premium
a.	25	Male	$20	$ 86.53
b.	40	Female	20	149.28
c.	55	Male	25	286.45
d.	35	Wife	25	154.90
e.	20	Female	25	132.52
f.	45	Male	20	145.54

2. Determine the annual premium on each of the following major-medical insurance policies.

	Age	Person	Annual Premium
a.	30	Male	$ 37.66
b.	45	Female	77.22
c.	60	Wife	117.02
d.	55	Male	86.63

See if the students can account for the fact that rates on major-medical insurance are so much less than on the the hospital-expense insurance at the same age. Also, have them make a survey similar to the one described at the bottom of page 410.

3. How much of the medical costs in column 1 will each of the following medical policies pay?

	Medical Cost	Amount Deductible	Maximum Limit	Cost Covered
a.	$ 600	$500	$10,000	$ 100.00
b.	450	500	10,000	0
c.	1,200	500	10,000	700.00
d.	1,200	750	10,000	450.00
e.	659	750	10,000	0
f.	7,460	500	10,000	6,960.00
g.	12,500	500	10,000	10,000.00
h.	12,500	500	20,000	12,000.00

4. Determine the total annual family premium on each of the following hospital-expense insurance policies.

	Husband's Age	Wife's Age	Number Of Children	Maximum Daily Benefit	Husband's Premium	Wife's Premium	Children's Premium	Total Premium
a.	40	Deceased	1	$20	$ 123.88	$ —	$ 42.40	$ 166.28
b.	50	Deceased	2	20	177.56	—	84.80	262.36
c.	Deceased	35	4	20	—	136.97	84.80	221.77
d.	Deceased	40	3	25	—	184.62	105.40	290.02
e.	30	30	2	25	117.72	151.00	105.40	374.12
f.	45	40	1	25	179.66	162.84	52.70	395.20
g.	25	20	1	20	86.53	122.00	42.40	250.93
h.	35	25	3	25	132.48	151.00	105.40	388.88

5. Determine the total annual premium that has to be paid by the following individuals who purchase both a hospital-expense policy and a major-medical policy.

	Sex	Age	Maximum Daily Hospital Benefit	Hospital-Expense Premium	Major-Medical Premium	Total Premium
a.	M	30	$25	$ 117.72	$ 37.66	$ 155.38
b.	F	40	20	149.28	68.42	217.70
c.	F	45	25	203.76	77.22	280.98
d.	M	35	20	107.22	43.11	150.33
e.	M	55	25	286.45	86.63	373.08
f.	F	55	25	303.74	108.42	412.16

6. Determine the semiannual premium on each of the following hospital-expense insurance policies.

	Age	Person	Maximum Daily Benefit	Annual Premium	Semiannual Premium
a.	30	Male	$20	$ 95.18	$ 49.49
b.	40	Male	25	153.02	79.57
c.	35	Female	20	136.97	71.22
d.	55	Female	25	303.74	157.94

7. Determine the quarterly premium on each of the following major-medical policies.

	Age	Person	Annual Premium	Quarterly Premium
a.	40	Female	$ 68.42	$ 18.13
b.	35	Male	43.11	11.42
c.	60	Male	108.22	28.68
d.	50	Female	88.67	23.50

B

1. Stephen Barnard is a bachelor. At 30, he purchased both the $25 hospital-expense insurance policy and the major-medical insurance policy.
   a. If he paid the premiums annually, what was the total amount he had to pay each year? $155.38
   b. If he paid the premiums quarterly, what was the total amount he had to pay each quarter? $ 41.18
   c. If he paid the premiums quarterly, how much did this amount to on an annual basis? $164.72
   d. How much can he save each year by paying the premiums annually rather than quarterly? $ 9.34
2. Mr. Ellis, 40, and Mrs. Ellis, 35, have four children—16, 12, 10, and 9.
   a. What annual premium will Mr. Ellis have to pay for the family under the major-medical plan? $121.93
   b. What annual premium will Mr. Ellis have to pay for the family under the $25-maximum-daily-hospital-expense plan? $413.32
   c. What total annual premium will Mr. Ellis have to pay for the family under both plans? $535.25
   d. If Mr. Ellis preferred to pay his premiums semiannually, what would his payments be? $278.33

Unit 4: Unemployment Insurance

You have learned how a person can protect himself against loss of income in the event of death, sickness, or accident. You have also examined how he can help make certain that his hospital and doctor bills can be paid should he require the services of either. Usually, though, the greatest concern about loss of income is not from any one of these, but, rather, from loss of job. There is nothing that distresses a man more than the thought of being unemployed for a long period with no income to support his family.

To soften the blow of unemployment, every state in the union now has some form of unemployment insurance. The laws governing the amount you will receive differ so from state to state that it is rather difficult to show any uniform method by which benefits are paid. In only three states—Alabama, Alaska, and New Jersey—is the employee required to make any contributions to the unemployment fund. In all funds, including those of these three states, the employer pays for the unemployment insurance that protects you in the event that you lose your job.

Although there is no uniformity in state unemployment laws, there are a few generalizations about all of them. For instance, every state has a minimum number of weeks that you have to work or a minimum amount you have to earn before you are eligible to receive unemployment insurance. The minimum earnings required range from as little as $300 per year to as much as $800 per year, while the number of weeks of employment required range all the way from 14 to 46. Practically all states require a waiting period of 1 week before you can start collecting weekly benefits. A few states will even give you the benefits lost during that first week if you are unemployed for a long enough period. No state pays unemployment benefits indefinitely. The majority seem to favor a maximum period of 26 weeks after you have become unemployed. On the other hand, although you might use up all your benefits in less than 9 weeks, no state will pay you benefits for less than this period—if you remain unemployed. There appears to be only a handful of states that base their unemployment benefits on the number of dependents you have. All other states base benefits solely on a certain fraction of what your wages were at the time you were employed. Incidentally, you must show that you are willing to accept reasonable employment if it can be found for you, or you will not be given the weekly benefits.

Here are a few situations that arise most often in the payment of state unemployment insurance.

■ILLUSTRATION 1: In a number of states, the maximum amount that a person can collect in unemployment insurance during any one year is ⅓ of the amount he has earned the previous year. If Fred Barclay's earnings this year are $8,400, how much might he be able to collect in unemployment compensation next year in one of these states?

●SOLUTION:

Previous year's earnings = $8,400

Maximum Fred can receive in unemployment compensation
$$= \tfrac{1}{3} \times \$8,400$$
$$= \$2,600$$

It was during the depression in the middle 1930's that many states enacted laws covering individuals from loss of income during unemployment. Have a committee of students check to determine what the unemployment benefits are for the state in which you live, and, also, when the law came into being.

■ ILLUSTRATION 2: In a certain state, the weekly benefit a person can receive is 1/26 of the amount he earned during the best 3-month period of the previous year. If, during the previous year, Robert's best quarterly earnings were $2,680, how much might he receive as his weekly benefit if he is unemployed?

● SOLUTION:

$$\text{Best quarterly earnings} = \$2,680$$
$$\text{Weekly benefit} = 1/26 \times \$2,680$$
$$= \$2,680/26$$
$$= \$103.08$$

▼ EXPLANATION: The only trouble with the answer above is the fact that no state will pay an unemployed person that large a weekly benefit. For most states, the largest amount he can be paid will be somewhere between $40 and $65 weekly. Hence, Robert would receive whatever the maximum happened to be in the state where he lived.

■ ILLUSTRATION 3: In the state where Allen Jamieson lives, it is possible to receive unemployment benefits for a total of ⅖ of his annual earnings, which are $5,650. His weekly unemployment benefit is $46. For how many weeks will he be entitled to receive this benefit?

● SOLUTION:

$$\text{Total unemployment benefits Allen can receive} = \tfrac{2}{5} \times \$5,650$$
$$= \$2,260$$
$$\text{Number of weeks he can receive these benefits} = \$2,260 \div \$46$$
$$= 49 \text{ full weeks}$$

($6 will remain for the 50th week)

▼ EXPLANATION: No state will pay Allen $46 for 49 consecutive weeks. As explained earlier, most states would pay him $46 for the maximum number of weeks permitted by their state laws. Let us say that in the state where Allen lives, this maximum happens to be 26 weeks in the year. If Allen is still unemployed the following year, they will continue to pay him for another 23 weeks (Where did this number come from?), and in the 26th week of that year he will receive only $6.

EXERCISES

1. In the following exercises, the state gave each of these people a certain percent of their average weekly wage. However, they could not receive less than the minimum, nor more than the maximum shown. How large was each of the weekly unemployment benefits?

An examination of the maximum benefits that a person can receive under unemployment compensation would seem to belie the impression that people quit working solely to collect unemployment benefits. In addition, should they, themselves, leave their jobs without good cause, they are not eligible for these benefits.

	Average Weekly Wage	Minimum Possible	Maximum Possible	Percent Given	Weekly Benefit
a.	$ 84	$10	$45	50%	$ 42.00
b.	76	10	45	50%	38.00
c.	35	10	45	50%	17.50
d.	106	10	45	50%	45.00
e.	18	10	45	50%	10.00
f.	75	10	55	67%	50.25
g.	63	10	55	67%	42.21
h.	95	10	55	67%	55.00
i.	82	12	76	63%	51.66
j.	15	12	76	63%	12.00
k.	67	10	46	54%	36.18
l.	126	10	46	54%	46.00

2. In the following exercises, the state gave each of these people weekly a certain percent of their annual wages. However, they could not receive less than the minimum, nor more than the maximum shown. How large was each of the weekly unemployment benefits?

	Annual Wages	Weekly Minimum Possible	Weekly Maximum Possible	Percent Given	Weekly Benefit
a.	$3,325	$12	$42	1.0%	$ 33.25
b.	5,650	12	42	1.0%	42.00
c.	927	12	42	1.0%	12.00
d.	2,640	17	42	1.1%	29.04
e.	1,250	17	42	1.1%	17.00
f.	3,940	17	42	1.1%	42.00
g.	3,720	12	45	1.6%	45.00
h.	2,460	12	45	1.6%	39.36
i.	4,250	15	80	1.8%	76.50
j.	5,340	15	80	1.8%	80.00
k.	1,020	15	80	1.8%	18.36
l.	3,780	12	45	.9%	34.02
m.	4,540	12	45	.9%	40.86
n.	1,130	12	45	.9%	12.00

3. In the following exercises, the state gave each of these people weekly a certain fraction of their quarterly wages. However, they could not receive less than the minimum, nor more than the maximum, shown. How large was each of the weekly unemployment benefits?

	Quarterly Wages	Minimum Possible	Maximum Possible	Fraction Given	Weekly Benefit
a.	$ 860	$ 9	$53	$\frac{1}{22}$	$ 39.09
b.	950	9	53	$\frac{1}{22}$	43.18
c.	180	9	53	$\frac{1}{22}$	9.00
d.	740	10	53	$\frac{1}{25}$	29.60
e.	930	10	53	$\frac{1}{25}$	37.20
f.	1,150	10	53	$\frac{1}{25}$	46.00
g.	690	15	48	$\frac{1}{26}$	26.54

Notice that the incomes given in these exercises are quite low under current wage scales, and that even these yield weekly unemployment benefits in excess of the maximum permitted in most states.

		Quarterly Wages	Minimum Possible	Maximum Possible	Fraction Given	Weekly Benefit
h.	$	820	$15	$48	$\frac{1}{26}$	$ 31.54
i.		210	15	48	$\frac{1}{26}$	15.00
j.		560	12	44	$\frac{1}{23}$	24.35
k.		680	12	44	$\frac{1}{23}$	29.57
l.		270	7	31	$\frac{1}{15}$	18.00
m.		316	7	31	$\frac{1}{15}$	21.07
n.		1,265	17	54	$\frac{1}{19}$	54.00

4. Each of the following fractions shows the fractional amount of their annual wages that unemployed persons in these states can receive in total unemployment benefits if they are without work for a long enough period of time. How much will this amount be for each of the following persons?

	Annual Wages	Fraction of Annual Wages They Can Receive	Amount Possible
a.	$4,620	$\frac{1}{3}$	$1,540.00
b.	3,750	$\frac{1}{3}$	1,250.00
c.	8,600	$\frac{1}{4}$	2,150.00
d.	7,540	$\frac{1}{4}$	1,885.00
e.	5,390	$\frac{2}{5}$	2,156.00
f.	4,265	$\frac{2}{5}$	1,706.00
g.	6,270	$\frac{3}{5}$	3,762.00
h.	4,135	$\frac{3}{5}$	2,481.00
i.	9,420	$\frac{3}{10}$	2,826.00
j.	8,950	$\frac{3}{10}$	2,685.00
k.	7,280	$\frac{3}{4}$	5,460.00
l.	5,396	$\frac{3}{4}$	4,047.00

5. The weekly unemployment benefit and the total amount that a person can receive are shown. If he is totally unemployed, what is the maximum number of weeks in one year that a person will receive these benefits? Consider any fractional part of a week as an entire week.

	Weekly Benefit	Total Benefit	Minimum Number of Weeks If Totally Unemployed	Maximum Number of Weeks If Totally Unemployed	Number Of Weeks
a.	$40	$ 800	10	26	20
b.	32	576	10	26	18
c.	53	1,113	15	28	21
d.	38	1,026	17	34	27
e.	41	492	17	34	17
f.	27	702	18	30	26
g.	35	615	12	26	18
h.	44	1,150	10	22	22
i.	39	1,262	14	34	33
j.	51	1,085	22	36	22

Unit 5: Homeowner's and Fire Insurance

Section 1: The Cost of Homeowner's and Fire Insurance

Actually, there is no loss against which you cannot insure yourself. If you were cautious enough to do so, however, you would soon find that your entire income went toward the payment of insurance premiums. Anyone who found himself in this position would be far too over-insured. This might easily happen at a time when you are buying a number of relatively expensive new appliances, such as a dishwasher, washing machine, clothes drier, television set, electric oven, and so on. On each of these, the appliance company is only too happy to sell you a customer's service policy. These policies are designed to cover the cost of any repairs that might be needed on the appliances during the period in which you are insured.

In many instances, the premiums are far higher than the value of the protection you receive from a service policy. To protect yourself in the event that a black and white picture tube went bad on your TV set might cost you as much as $35 per year. The likelihood that this tube will have to be replaced within 8 or 10 years is quite small. Hence, the cost of this insurance will soon exceed the amount you would have to pay for a brand-new set. This is not an isolated illustration. Before purchasing or renewing a service insurance policy, a great deal of thought should go into deciding whether you are really getting your money's worth.

There is, though, one variety of insurance that you should not be without—and this is fire insurance. If you are the owner of a house, you should have this insurance on both the house and its contents. If you rent an apartment, then you should buy fire insurance to cover your personal property in your apartment. These policies cover not only the damage caused by fire, but also the damage caused by lightning or smoke. For an additional fee, and this cost is a little high, it is possible to buy protection called *extended coverage*. This will protect you from any loss caused by windstorm, hail, explosion, riot, civil commotion, aircraft, and vehicles. The person buying this, however, would be a lot better off purchasing the homeowner's policy. In the homeowner's policy he would get a lot more protection for just a little more money.

By examining the table of rates on page 421, you can see that the cost of fire insurance depends on two things. One of these is the fire protection available in the community in which the house is located. This is shown in the column headed by the words "Town Class." The better the fire department, the lower are the fire insurance rates. Notice that

Insurance on home appliances seems to be ridiculously overpriced. As far as can be ascertained, the rates charged are not based on any experience similar to those established in the mortality tables by the life-insurance companies.

the rate takes a big jump between town class G and town class H. In the first of these towns, there are fire hydrants, but they are not necessarily near the house. In the second, there are not even fire hydrants available. For class H, the fire department is within 5 miles of the house. Town class K not only does not have fire hydrants, but the fire department is more than 5 miles from the house. The insurance company really does not expect any part of the house to be saved by the time the fire engines arrive. That's why the rates for this town class are so high.

The other factor that determines how high the rates will be is whether the house is made of wood or brick. Why should the cost of insurance on a brick house be less than the cost of insurance on a frame (wood) house?

There are three different ways in which you can buy fire insurance. In the first of these, you can buy a new policy each year. In the second, you can buy a policy that will last for three years and pay for it in one lump-sum. The third way, called the deferred-payment plan, is pretty much like the second, except that instead of making one payment to cover the three years, you make three payments—one each year. In what way is this last method any different from the first?

FIRE INSURANCE

Rate per $100

Brick Homes

Town Class	One Year		Three Years		Deferred Payments (Annual Rates)	
	House	Contents	House	Contents	House	Contents
A	$.066	$.128	$.178	$.346	$.062	$.121
B	.071	.133	.192	.359	.067	.126
C	.076	.138	.205	.373	.072	.130
D	.081	.143	.219	.386	.077	.135
E	.086	.148	.232	.400	.081	.140
F	.096	.158	.259	.427	.091	.149
G	.136	.198	.367	.535	.129	.187
H	.250	.288	.675	.778	.236	.272
K	.300	.348	.810	.940	.284	.329

Frame Homes

A	.102	.165	.275	.446	.096	.156
B	.107	.170	.289	.459	.101	.161
C	.112	.175	.302	.473	.106	.165
D	.117	.180	.316	.486	.111	.170
E	.122	.185	.329	.500	.115	.175
F	.132	.195	.356	.527	.125	.184
G	.172	.235	.464	.635	.163	.222
H	.270	.310	.729	.837	.255	.293
K	.320	.360	.864	.972	.302	.340

You may want to discuss with your students why fire insurance is almost impossible to obtain for homes in some urban communities, while in others the rates have skyrocketed.

■ILLUSTRATION 1: A brick house in a town class D community was insured for $18,000 against damage by fire.

    a. If the owner purchased a 3-year policy and paid for it in a lump-sum, how much would this cost him?   _____

    b. If the owner purchased a 3-year policy and paid for it under the deferred-payment plan, how much would this cost him over the 3-year period?

    c. How much can he save by paying for the insurance in a lump-sum?   _____

▼EXPLANATION: Place the edge of a piece of paper along the row for town class D community. Run your finger along this row until it reaches the two columns headed by the words "Three Years." Since the house was insured, and not the contents, it is the rate of $.219 per $100 that you use to obtain the answer to Part (a) of this problem. For Part (b), you continue to move your finger along the row for town class D until it reaches the two columns for the "Deferred-Payments" rates. Here, again, you want the rate for the house—not the contents—and this time it is $.077 per $100.

●SOLUTION:

    (a) Rate per $100 = $.219
        Number of 100's in 18,000 = 180
        Cost of $18,000 insurance = 180 × $.219
                           = $39.42

    (b) Deferred payment plan:
        Rate per $100 annually = $.077
        Cost of $18,000 insurance annually = 180 × $.077
                                 = $13.86
        Cost of $18,000 insurance for 3 years = 3 × $13.86
                                   = $41.58

    (c) Saving = $41.58 − $39.42
              = $2.16

With the *homeowner's policy,* you are protected not only against loss caused by fire and the extended coverage items—windstorm, hail, and so on—but also against theft, medical payments for people injured on your property, bodily injury that you might inflict on anyone through an accident, and damage that you might cause to someone else's property.

The table on page 423 gives a sample of the cost of this insurance in three different communities. These communities are not necessarily the same as the town class A, B, and C communities of the fire-insurance table. The cost in this table is for three years of insurance. In fact, this insurance can be purchased only for three-year periods. You can,

Not mentioned above is the fact that under certain homeowner's policies you are also covered to a limited extent for loss by theft or fire of personal items that are damaged elsewhere than in the home.

HOMEOWNER'S POLICY

3-Year Premiums

Face Value	A Community		B Community		C Community	
	Frame	Brick	Frame	Brick	Frame	Brick
$15,000	$144	$133	$178	$174	$214	$202
20,000	180	166	226	214	274	258
25,000	217	199	274	234	334	314
30,000	252	231	321	292	393	369
35,000	288	263	368	331	451	424
40,000	322	294	414	370	510	478
45,000	358	326	461	389	569	533
50,000	393	358	508	428	628	588

Deferred-Payment Plan

Annual cost = 35% of 3-year plan

(All premiums rounded off to the nearest dollar)

though, pay for it annually under a deferred-payment plan by paying 35% of the three-year premium each year. When premiums are computed on this basis, they are always rounded off to the nearest dollar.

■ ILLUSTRATION 2: Mr. Yerby purchased a $25,000 homeowner's policy which he paid off by making annual payments. He owns a frame house in a "B" community. How much did he pay for this insurance over the three-year period?

● SOLUTION:

$$\text{Three-year premium} = \$274$$
$$\text{Annual premium} = 35\% \text{ of } \$274$$
$$= .35 \times \$274$$
$$= \$95.90, \text{ or } \$96$$
$$\text{Cost for 3 years} = 3 \times \$96$$
$$= \$288$$

EXERCISES   A

In doing the following exercises, refer to the tables in this unit.

1. Find the three-year premium on each of the following homeowner's policies.

	Community	Type Of Structure	Amount Of Insurance	3-Year Premium
a.	A	Brick	$20,000	$ 166.00
b.	C	Frame	35,000	451.00
c.	B	Frame	25,000	274.00
d.	C	Brick	40,000	478.00
e.	A	Brick	30,000	231.00
f.	B	Brick	30,000	292.00
g.	C	Brick	30,000	369.00
h.	B	Frame	50,000	508.00

Notice that on the homeowner's policy, as was the case in the cost of automobile insurance, the premiums are rounded off to the nearest dollar.

2. Find the annual cost of each of the following 3-year homeowner's policies that were purchased under the deferred-payment plan.

	Community	Type Of Structure	Amount Of Insurance	3-Year Premium	Annual Premium
a.	A	Brick	$30,000	$ 231.00	$ 81.00
b.	B	Frame	40,000	414.00	145.00
c.	A	Frame	50,000	393.00	138.00
d.	C	Brick	20,000	258.00	90.00
e.	A	Brick	35,000	263.00	92.00
f.	B	Frame	25,000	274.00	96.00
g.	A	Frame	40,000	322.00	113.00
h.	C	Frame	45,000	569.00	199.00

3. Find the cost of each of the following one-year fire-insurance policies.

	Town Class	Type Of Structure	Insured For:	Amount Of Insurance	Rate	Total Cost
a.	C	Brick	House	$10,000	$ .076	$ 7.60
b.	F	Brick	House	12,000	.096	11.52
c.	D	Brick	Contents	4,000	.143	5.72
d.	E	Frame	Contents	5,000	.185	9.25
e.	E	Brick	Contents	5,000	.148	7.40
f.	B	Frame	House	20,000	.107	21.40
g.	H	Frame	House	23,000	.270	62.10
h.	K	Brick	House	27,000	.300	81.00

4. Find the cost of each of the following three-year fire-insurance policies, each of which is paid for in a lump-sum.

	Town Class	Type Of Structure	Insured For:	Amount Of Insurance	Rate	Total Cost
a.	E	Frame	House	$ 9,000	$ .329	$ 29.61
b.	C	Frame	House	14,000	.302	42.28
c.	A	Frame	Contents	6,000	.446	26.76
d.	G	Brick	Contents	23,000	.535	123.05
e.	B	Brick	House	17,000	.192	32.64
f.	H	Frame	Contents	2,500	.837	20.93
g.	D	Brick	Contents	3,500	.386	13.51
h.	F	Brick	House	16,500	.259	42.74

5. Find the annual cost of each of the following three-year deferred-payment fire-insurance policies.

	Town Class	Type Of Structure	Insured For:	Amount Of Insurance	Rate	Annual Cost
a.	D	Frame	Contents	$ 5,000	$ .170	$ 8.50
b.	B	Frame	House	30,000	.101	30.30
c.	G	Brick	House	32,000	.129	41.28
d.	A	Brick	House	27,500	.062	17.05
e.	C	Frame	Contents	7,500	.165	12.38
f.	H	Brick	Contents	6,800	.272	18.50

B

1. A brick home was insured under a 3-year homeowner's policy for $25,000 and paid for in a lump-sum.
   a. If the house is located in an A community, how much will the cost of the insurance be? $199.00
   b. If the house is located in a C community, how much will the cost of the insurance be? $314.00
   c. How much less is the cost of the insurance in the A community than in the C community? $115.00
2. A 3-year $20,000 fire-insurance policy was purchased on a frame house in an F community.
   a. What will the three-year policy cost be if paid for in a lump-sum? $ 71.20
   b. What will the three-year policy cost be if paid for in annual installments on the deferred-payment plan? $ 75.00
   c. How much more will the owner pay under the deferred-payment plan than under the lump-sum plan? $ 3.80
3. A frame house in an H community was insured against fire for one year for $45,000, while its contents were insured for $12,000. What was the total cost of the insurance? $158.70
4. A person living in a B community purchased a $40,000 homeowner's policy on a brick house for a three-year period.
   a. What was the cost of this insurance if paid for in a lump-sum?
                                                                       $370.00
   b. What was the annual cost of this insurance if paid for under the deferred-payment plan? $130.00
   c. What was the total three-year cost of the insurance if paid for under the deferred-payment plan? $390.00
   d. How much can a person save by paying for this policy in a lump-sum rather than on the deferred-payment plan? $ 20.00

Section 2:   The 80% Clause

Practically all homeowner's policies contain an important statement in them that should not be overlooked. This statement is called the "80% clause." Through it, the owner agrees to insure his property for at least 80% of its value. If it is insured for less than that, he further agrees that he will share part of the loss caused by the fire. Thus, if he insures the property for ½ of 80% of its value, the company will pay for ½ of the fire damage and he will have to pay for the other half. Or, if he insures it for ¾ of 80% of its value, the company will pay for ¾ of any fire dam-

The problems in Group B are designed to compare the cost of insurance in different communities, or for different purchase-plans. Discuss these comparisons.

age and he will have to pay for the remaining ¼. The following few illustrations should help clear up this point.

■ILLUSTRATION 1: A house is valued at $25,000, but insured against fire for only $22,000. If fire destroys the property to the extent of $6,000, how much of this will the fire insurance company have to pay?
●SOLUTION:

$$80\% \text{ of the value} = 80\% \text{ of } \$25,000$$
$$= .80 \times \$25,000$$
$$= \$20,000$$
$$\text{Amount of insurance} = \$22,000$$
$$\text{Amount paid by company} = \$6,000$$

▼EXPLANATION: Since 80% of the value of the house is $20,000, and since the house is insured for more than that amount, the insurance company must pay the full cost of the damage of $6,000.

■ILLUSTRATION 2: A house is valued at $25,000, but insured against fire for only $15,000. If fire destroys the property to the extent of $6,000, how much of this will the fire insurance company have to pay?
●SOLUTION:

$$80\% \text{ of the value} = 80\% \text{ of } \$25,000$$
$$= .80 \times \$25,000$$
$$= \$20,000$$
$$\text{Amount of insurance} = \$15,000$$

Fraction of loss the insurance company will have to pay
$$= \$15,000/\$20,000$$
$$= ¾$$

Amount of loss the insurance company will have to pay
$$= ¾ \text{ of } \$6,000$$
$$= ¾ \times \$6,000$$
$$= \$4,500$$

▼EXPLANATION: The house is insured for only $15,000, while 80% of the value of the house is $20,000. Hence, the insurance company will pay for only $15,000/$20,000, or ¾ of any loss. And ¾ of the $6,000 loss, in this case, is $4,500. How much of the $6,000 loss will the owner have to pay?

EXERCISES

1. For at least what amount of money will each of the following properties have to be insured under the 80% clause if the insurance company is to pay the entire fire loss?

The premium saving on a policy that contains an 80% clause is usually quite substantial, so that the homeowner would be well advised to consider the inclusion of this clause. He must realize, however, that if face value of the policy is less than 80% of property value, he becomes a coinsurer of his own property.

	Property Value	Amount Of Insurance			Property Value	Amount Of Insurance
a.	$20,000	$ 16,000	e.		$35,000	$ 28,000
b.	30,000	24,000	f.		29,000	23,200
c.	24,000	19,200	g.		37,000	29,600
d.	18,000	14,400	h.		46,000	36,800

2. What fraction of the fire damage will the insurance company have to pay in each of the following exercises if the policies contain an 80% clause?

	80% Of the Property Value	Amount Of Insurance	Fraction of Loss Paid By Insurance Company
a.	$20,000	$10,000	1/2
b.	16,000	12,000	3/4
c.	25,000	15,000	3/5
d.	30,000	20,000	2/3
e.	28,000	24,000	6/7

3. In each of the following exercises, the policies contain an 80% clause. How much of the loss will the insurance company have to pay?

	80% Of the Property Value	Amount Of Insurance	Fraction of Loss Paid By Insurance Company	Fire Loss	Amount Paid By Insurance Company
a.	$15,000	$10,000	2/3	$6,000	$ 4,000
b.	12,000	10,000	5/6	1,800	1,500
c.	24,000	18,000	3/4	1,500	1,125
d.	27,000	24,000	8/9	3,600	3,200
e.	25,000	15,000	3/5	1,300	780
f.	30,000	32,000	1/1	1,700	1,700
g.	30,000	27,000	9/10	2,100	1,890
h.	32,000	30,000	15/16	6,400	6,000

4. What fraction of the fire damage will the insurance company have to pay in each of the following exercises if the policies contain an 80% clause?

	Property Value	80% Of the Property Value	Amount Of Insurance	Fraction of Loss Paid By Insurance Company
a.	$20,000	$ 16,000	$12,000	3/4
b.	30,000	24,000	20,000	5/6
c.	25,000	20,000	18,000	9/10
d.	40,000	32,000	28,000	7/8
e.	35,000	28,000	20,000	5/7
f.	24,000	19,200	19,200	1/1

Students usually find the computations related to the 80% clause a bit difficult for them. An effort was made to set up these exercises so that the work would develop step-by-step in a very slow fashion.

5. In each of the following exercises, the policies contain an 80% clause. How much of the loss will the insurance company have to pay?

	Property Value	80% Of the Property Value	Amount Of Insurance	Fire Loss	Amount Paid By Insurance Company
a.	$20,000	$ 16,000	$ 8,000	$6,000	$ 3,000
b.	30,000	24,000	18,000	8,000	6,000
c.	40,000	32,000	24,000	1,600	1,200
d.	50,000	40,000	36,000	2,500	2,250
e.	15,000	12,000	10,000	2,400	2,000
f.	25,000	20,000	16,000	1,200	960
g.	35,000	28,000	24,000	3,500	3,000
h.	32,000	25,600	29,000	4,200	4,200

Unit 6:   Chapter Review and Test

Refer to the tables in this chapter when doing the computation for the problems below.

1. a. According to the mortality table for the years 1959–1961, until what age can a person of 15 expect to live? $ 72.33
   b. According to the mortality table for the years 1959–1961, how many people per 1,000 at age 60 will die before they reach the age of 61? $ 17.61

2. According to the mortality table for the years 1959–1961, in a group of 400,000 of age 50, how many will not live to age 51? $ 3,096.00

3. a. Mr. Sandford purchased a $10,000 20-year-term policy. If he lived the entire 20 years, how much would he receive from the insurance company at the end of that time?   Nothing
   b. If the policy had been a 20-year-endowment policy, how much would he have received? $10,000.00

4. What is the annual premium on a $9,000 decreasing 10-year-term policy? It was purchased by a man when he was 45. $ 62.46

5. Mr. Simpson purchased a $25,000 15-year decreasing-term policy. For how much was he insured during the sixth year after he made the purchase? $19,025.00

6. At 33, Betty Higgins purchased a $14,000 20-payment life-insurance policy.
   a. If she paid the premiums annually, how large would each payment be? $ 387.38
   b. If she paid the premiums semiannually, how large would each payment be? $ 201.44
   c. In one year, how much could she save by paying the premiums annually rather than semiannually? $ 15.50
   d. In twenty years, how much could she save by paying the premiums annually rather than semiannually? $ 310.00

As in earlier chapter review and test units, parts of some of the problems can be used for review purposes, while the remainder can be used for testing.

e. Will Betty receive the $14,000 from the company at the end of the 20 years? **No**

7. Mr. Porter, who is employed in an AA risk occupation, purchased a disability-insurance policy to cover him for two years in the event he was ill and could not work. Were this to happen, he would receive $300 per month in benefits. Mr. Porter is 45.

a. How much was his annual premium for this coverage? **$ 173.70**

b. If Mrs. Porter had had the same job as her husband and purchased the same insurance, what would her annual premium have been? Mrs. Porter is 45. **$ 260.53**

8. The cost of Bruce Mallon's surgical and hospital bills totaled $4,726 when he was injured in an accident. If he carried major-medical insurance that had a $500 deductible clause and a $10,000 maximum limit and no other insurance, how much of the surgical and hospital bill did Bruce have to pay? **$ 500.00**

9. Thomas Johnson insured both himself and his wife under a $25 maximum-daily-hospital-expense-insurance policy. Mr. Johnson is 30 years of age and his wife is 25.

a. What total annual premium would he have to pay for the two of them? **$ 268.72**

b. What total quarterly premium would he have to pay for the two of them? **$ 71.21**

10. Grace Bigelow lives in a state where the weekly unemployment compensation payments are 63% of the average weekly wage that the person has been earning. However, these payments cannot be less than $12, nor more than $76. If Grace's average weekly salary before she became unemployed was $94.50, how much did she receive each week in unemployment benefits? **$ 59.54**

11. Mr. Palmer lives in a C community and owns a brick home which he insured under a homeowner's policy for $25,000. If he pays his premium under the deferred-payment plan, how much will each of his annual payments be? **$ 110.00**

12. What is the annual premium on a $20,000 fire-insurance policy on a frame house in a class D community? **$ 23.40**

13. Mr. Farrington owns a $30,000 home which he insured under a homeowner's policy that contains an 80% clause. Fire damaged his property to the extent of $6,000.

a. If he had insured the house for $25,000, how much of the loss would the insurance company have had to pay? **$6,000.00**

b. If he had insured the house for $20,000, how much of the loss would the insurance company have had to pay? **$5,000.00**

CHAPTER 11

RETIREMENT
INCOME

It may seem a bit odd that you should be studying about retirement benefits when you have not even completed high school. As pointed out in an earlier chapter on personal income, however, you have little to say about whether you want to save for retirement or not. From the very first salary check you get—at least in most jobs—deductions are made to provide an income for you when you retire. Earlier you investigated how these deductions were computed. Now you are going to find out what you get for the money that is sent to the federal government for your retirement benefits.

Unit 1:   Social Security Benefits

Section 1:   The Primary Benefit

It is not possible to understand social security insurance without knowing what is meant by a *quarter of coverage*. This term refers to the fact that during any one of the following four quarterly periods,

QUARTERLY PERIODS

January	April
February	May
March	June
July	October
August	November
September	December

you earned at least $50 at a job where social security deductions were taken from your pay. There are still a few occupations in which people are not covered by the social security law. In all of those occupations which come under this law, the moment you earn at least $50 during any one of the four periods above, you are said to have earned a quarter of coverage. In fact, if you earned $7,800 or more during one year—even if this were earned in a single day—you would immediately have four quarters of coverage. On the other hand, suppose that you earned only $7,000 during the year, and that $4,000 of this was earned during the months of January and February, while the remaining $3,000 was earned during May. Then you would be credited with only two quarters of coverage. This is because you earned more than $50 during only two of the quarters listed. Had the same $7,000 been spread evenly through the year, it would have meant that you had earned more than $50 in each quarter. And this, in turn, would have meant that you had been able to earn four quarters of coverage rather than two.

Now you are ready for the next step. There are two ways in which you can be insured under the social security laws. In the first of these, you are covered under a program that is called being *currently insured*. This means that, during the previous 12 quarters—three years—you were employed in occupations where you earned at least 6 quarters of coverage. What is the shortest period of time in which it is possible to earn 6 quarters of coverage? The advantage of being currently insured falls not to yourself but rather to your family—if you happen to have a family—in the event that you die. At that time, survivors, that is, the widow and children, receive monthly benefits. In addition, they receive a lump-sum payment at the time of your death.

Many adolescents think that social-security benefits are only for "old people." Experience has shown, though, that there is rarely a class in this subject area in which at least one of the students is not receiving social-security benefits. Ask for a show of hands of those who are.

The second way in which you can be insured under the social security laws is to be *fully insured*. To get this type of coverage you will have to earn 40 quarters of coverage. What is the least number of years it will take to earn 40 quarters of coverage? When this happens, even if you do not earn another penny, you will be insured under the social security law for the rest of your life. Exactly what it means to be insured under this law is what you will investigate at this time.

The amount you receive depends entirely on an amount called the *average monthly earnings*. This number is determined by adding up all the money you earn from the time you reach 22 until you retire at 65 (for women, 62). To make this number as large as possible, the five years of lowest earnings are dropped off before the sum is computed. For instance, in the case of a college student, he may not start working until 24. Hence, the years in which he was 23 and 24 will be eliminated, for he earned nothing at that time. In addition, three other years will also be eliminated. This sum is then divided by the number of months in that period of years to give the average monthly earnings.

Under the present law, there will never be a year in which your income as used in this averaging process can be greater than $7,800, for this is the largest annual income from which social security deductions are taken. (See page 173.) Because of this, it is unlikely that most people will receive the greatest benefits possible under the social security law. One other point is that people born before 1927 do not need as many as 40 quarters of coverage to be fully insured. Since none of you are that old, this won't concern you.

At the time you or your family begins to receive benefits, the social security agency computes your average monthly earnings. On the basis of this amount, the monthly allotment that you, personally, are to be given is determined. This allotment is called the *primary benefit*. All other benefits—those to your wife and children and also the death payment—are based on this amount. The table on page 433, which shows the primary benefits for various monthly earnings, is not complete. What it shows are some average monthly earnings that are the smallest that can be received; some that are in the middle of the group; and, finally, some that are the highest that can be earned.

■ ILLUSTRATION : What primary benefit will a person receive whose average monthly earnings are $86?

▼ EXPLANATION : Run your finger down the "Average Monthly Earnings" column until it comes to the numeral 86. There are actually two numerals that you will be looking at—86 and 87. The primary benefit

Of those terms that appear on this page, the most important is "primary benefits." It is on this benefit that all other benefits are based. Since the maximum taxable earnings under social security keep changing with each change in the law, it is never possible for a person to receive the maximum primary benefit.

SOCIAL SECURITY MONTHLY BENEFITS

Average Monthly Earnings	Primary Benefit	Family Maximum
$74 or less	$55.00	$ 82.50
75–76	55.40	83.10
77–78	56.50	84.80
79–80	57.70	86.60
81	58.80	88.20
82–83	59.90	89.90
84–85	61.10	91.70
86–87	62.20	93.30
88–89	63.30	95.00
90	64.50	96.80
91–92	65.60	98.40
93–94	66.70	100.10
95–96	67.80	101.70
97	69.00	103.50
98–99	70.20	105.30
100–101	71.50	107.30
102	72.60	108.90
103–104	73.80	110.70
105–106	75.10	112.70

Average Monthly Earnings	Primary Benefit	Family Maximum
$310–314	$130.70	$251.20
315–319	131.90	255.20
320–323	133.00	258.40
324–328	134.30	262.40
329–333	135.50	266.40
334–337	136.80	269.60
338–342	137.90	273.60
343–347	139.10	277.60
348–351	140.40	280.80
352–356	141.50	284.80
357–361	142.80	288.80
362–365	144.00	292.00
366–370	145.10	296.00
371–375	146.40	300.00
376–379	147.60	303.20
380–384	148.90	307.20
385–389	150.00	311.20
390–393	151.20	314.40

Average Monthly Earnings	Primary Benefit	Family Maximum
$589–591	$201.00	$410.80
592–595	202.00	412.40
596–598	203.00	413.60
599–602	204.00	415.20
603–605	205.00	416.40
606–609	206.00	418.00
610–612	207.00	419.20
613–616	208.00	420.80
617–620	209.00	422.40
621–623	210.00	423.60
624–627	211.00	425.20
628–630	212.00	426.40
631–634	213.00	428.00
635–637	214.00	429.20
638–641	215.00	430.80
642–644	216.00	432.00
645–648	217.00	433.60
649–650	218.00	434.40

Although the social-security law may have changed since the publication of this text, as it has changed many times before, basically the method of applying this table for determining benefits has remained pretty much the same over a number of years.

for an average monthly earning of either $86 or $87 is exactly the same. It is the amount that appears immediately to their right—$62.20. The numeral that appears immediately to the right of $62.20 is $93.30. This is in the column headed by the words "Family Maximum." The $93.30 represents the largest amount of money that will be given to a family where the primary benefit is $62.20. As pointed out earlier, the $62.20 is the monthly benefit the husband receives. However, the wife and children may also be entitled to monthly benefits. If the total of all these benefits is more than $93.30 per month in this case, then only $93.30 will be sent to the family.

●SOLUTION:

Primary benefit on $86 = $62.20

EXERCISES   **A**

1. Determine the primary benefit on each of the following average monthly earnings.

a. $77 _$56.50_	g. $329 _$135.50_	m. $603 _$205.00_
b. $91 _65.60_	h. $352 _141.50_	n. $650 _218.00_
c. $99 _70.20_	i. $347 _139.10_	o. $629 _212.00_
d. $79 _57.70_	j. $354 _141.50_	p. $618 _209.00_
e. $81 _58.80_	k. $377 _147.60_	q. $600 _204.00_
f. $56 _55.00_	l. $325 _134.30_	r. $646 _217.00_

2. Determine the maximum family benefit on each of the following average monthly earnings.

a. $92 _$98.40_	e. $334 _$269.60_	i. $598 _$413.60_
b. $83 _89.90_	f. $356 _284.80_	j. $634 _428.00_
c. $46 _82.50_	g. $374 _300.00_	k. $615 _420.80_
d. $90 _96.80_	h. $382 _307.20_	l. $594 _412.40_

B

1. What is the smallest primary benefit a person can receive under the social security law?   _$ 55.00_
2. What is the largest primary benefit a person can receive under the social security law?   _$218.00_
3. What is the largest benefit a family can receive under the social security law?   _$434.40_
4. If a person earns $75 in February and $46 in May and no other money for the rest of the year, how many quarters of coverage will he have earned that year?   _1_

As has been suggested in the case of other tables throughout the text, if dittoed copies of the primary-benefit table can be placed in the hands of the students, it would eliminate the need for flipping pages and reduce the possibility of transpositional errors.

5. What is the greatest number of quarters of coverage a person can earn during one year? ___4___

6. How is it possible for a person to earn four quarters of coverage during a year in which he worked for only one week? ___By___ earning $7,800 or more during that week.

Section 2:   Retirement Benefits

In this section you will now examine how the social security agency computes the benefits for the entire family at the time the husband retires. In all of the discussions from this point on you will assume that it was the husband who was covered by social security and not the wife.

As you have already learned, the amount the husband receives each month is the primary benefit. Both the wife and each child under the age of 18 will receive 50% of the primary benefit. However, if the child is not going to school, as soon as he reaches 18, his benefits are cut off. Should he be in school, whether high school or college, his benefits will continue until he reaches 22, and then they are stopped. On the other hand, his mother can receive benefits only if he is under 18. Once he is beyond that age, she will no longer receive anything until she, herself, reaches the retirement age.

If the husband is retired, then the wife's retirement age can be as early as 62. Should she begin taking her benefits at that time, though, they will not be as great as they will be if she waits until 65. In the table below, you can see that if the wife begins to take her payments at 62, then she receives only 37½% of the primary benefit. If she waits, though, until she is 65, she receives 50% of the primary benefit. As long as she is taking care of a child under 18, though—no matter what her own age may be—the wife will receive 50% of the primary benefit.

RETIREMENT BENEFITS

Person	Percent Of Primary Benefit
Husband 65 or older	100%
Wife 65 or older	50%
Wife with child under 18	50%
Child under 18	50%
Child under 22 attending school	50%
Husband at 62	80%
Wife at 62	37½%

Notice, also, that the husband does not have to wait until 65 to start receiving his benefits. If he so elects, he can retire at 62 and ask the

Although the percent numerals in this table are simple enough to recall, the students should not be asked to memorize them, for it would serve little purpose.

social security office to start sending him his monthly allotments at that time. He, too, will be penalized for taking an early retirement by receiving only 80% of the primary benefit at that age rather than the entire primary benefit.

Regardless of the percents listed in the table, no family can receive more than the maximum family benefit allotted for the primary benefit the husband is supposed to receive.

■ ILLUSTRATION 1: Mr. Swensen retired at 66, at which time his wife was 65. If his average monthly income was $344, how much will both he and his wife receive in social security benefits each month?

● SOLUTION:

Mr. Swensen's benefit = $139.10
Mrs. Swensen's benefit = 50% of $139.10
= $69.55, or $69.60
Total benefit of both husband and wife = $139.10 + $69.60
= $208.70

▼ EXPLANATION: Mr. Swensen will receive the primary benefit. According to the table on page 435, this will amount to $139.10 on an average monthly earning of $344. Since Mrs. Swensen is at least 65, she will receive 50% of the primary benefit, or $69.55. However, the amount sent to her will be $69.60. Social security checks are always in 10¢ amounts. Whenever the computation indicates that the monthly benefit will fall between two 10¢ values, the check will be written for the larger of the two. In this illustration, the benefit should have been $69.55. However, it was rounded off to the first 10¢ amount higher than that, or $69.60. Had the benefit turned out to be $69.51, it would still have been rounded off to $69.60.

■ ILLUSTRATION 2: When Mr. Williams reached 62, he retired and asked the social security agency to begin sending him his monthly benefits. Mrs. Williams was only 45 at the time, and they had two children under the age of 18. What is the total family benefit if Mr. Williams' average monthly earnings were $597?

● SOLUTION:

Primary benefit = $203
Mr. Williams' benefit = 80% of $203
= $162.40
Mrs. Williams' benefit = 50% of $203
= $101.50

This is the first time students have come across the situation where they have to round off a number to the next higher 10¢ value. They will be inclined to round off numbers to the nearest 10¢ amount; caution them against this.

First child's benefit = 50% of $203
= $101.50
Second child's benefit = 50% of $203
= $101.50
Total family benefit = $162.40 + $101.50 + $101.50 + $101.50
= $466.90
Maximum family benefit received = $413.60

▼EXPLANATION: The interesting feature of this problem is that the family benefit is not the total of the four benefits received by Mr. Williams, his wife, and his two children. That sum comes to more than the amount given to any single family where the average monthly income is $597. The maximum for this income is only $413.60, and that is all the Williams family will receive. When the oldest child reaches 18, his benefit of $101.50 will be subtracted from $466.90—not $413.60 —and the family will receive the balance of $365.40. What will happen when the second boy reaches 18?

The social security law provides for disability payments in exactly the same manner as retirement payments. A disabled person will receive the primary benefit, while his wife and children will receive the same percents of the primary benefit as if the husband had retired. To be covered for disability payments, a person must have earned 5 years of social security credits in the 10 years prior to the time he became disabled. This statement isn't quite true for everybody, though. If the person happens to be under 31, he will need fewer than 5 years of credits to qualify for disability payments. And if he happens to be under 24, he will need fewer still. In any event, he can receive these payments only if his disability is expected to last for at least 12 months. Also of interest is the fact that the payments do not begin until after the sixth month of disability.

EXERCISES   **A**

1. Round off each of the following to the next 10¢ amount.

a.	$123.67	$123.70	g. $238.92	$239.00
b.	156.89	156.90	h. 341.97	342.00
c.	137.52	137.60	i. 456.94	457.00
d.	243.76	243.80	j. 129.98	130.00
e.	205.21	205.30	k. 249.93	250.00
f.	317.02	317.10	l. 199.91	200.00

Students who are receiving social-security benefits frequently do not think in terms of education beyond their high-school years, for they believe that these benefits terminate at age 18. Advise them that the benefits do continue until age 22 so long as they are attending an accredited school.

2. Use the following average monthly earnings to determine how much a wife will receive monthly if she is over 65.

		Primary Benefit	Wife's Benefit
a.	$363	$ 144.00	$ 72.00
b.	98	70.20	35.10
c.	321	133.00	66.50
d.	600	204.00	102.00
e.	625	211.00	105.50
f.	378	147.60	73.80
g.	339	137.90	69.00
h.	90	64.50	32.30
i.	355	141.50	70.80

3. Use the following average monthly earnings to determine how much the husband will receive monthly if he retires at 62 and begins to collect at that time.

		Primary Benefit	Husband's Benefit
a.	$590	$ 201.00	$ 160.80
b.	97	69.00	55.20
c.	611	207.00	165.60
d.	391	151.20	121.00
e.	83	59.90	48.00
f.	98	70.20	56.20
g.	383	148.90	119.20
h.	335	136.80	109.50
i.	368	145.10	116.10

4. Use the following average monthly earnings to determine how much the wife will receive if she elects to take her benefits at 62.

		Primary Benefit	Wife's Benefit
a.	$615	$ 208.00	$ 78.00
b.	644	216.00	81.00
c.	600	204.00	76.50
d.	336	136.80	51.30
e.	364	144.00	54.00
f.	372	146.40	54.90
g.	105	75.10	28.20
h.	98	70.20	26.40
i.	82	59.90	22.50

5. In the following exercises, the ages of both the husband and wife are shown, and there are no children in the family. What are the total family benefits in each exercise?

In these exercises you may find that you have to caution the students to round off each of the benefits to the next higher 10¢ amount.

Average Monthly Earnings	Husband's Age	Wife's Age	Primary Benefit	Husband's Benefit	Wife's Benefit	Family Benefit
a. $348	65	57	$ 140.40	$ 140.40	$ 0	$ 140.40
b. 601	66	60	204.00	204.00	0	204.00
c. 102	67	66	72.60	72.60	36.30	108.90
d. 391	68	65	151.20	151.20	75.60	226.80
e. 625	62	65	211.00	168.80	105.50	274.30
f. 369	62	66	145.10	116.10	72.60	188.70
g. 327	62	67	134.30	107.50	67.20	174.70
h. 351	65	62	140.40	140.40	52.70	193.10
i. 373	67	62	146.40	146.40	54.90	201.30
j. 99	70	62	70.20	70.20	26.40	96.60
k. 386	62	62	150.00	120.00	56.30	176.30
l. 632	62	62	213.00	170.40	79.90	250.30

6. In the following exercises, the ages of the husband, wife, and children are shown. If the child is 18 or over, assume that he is no longer attending school. What are the total family benefits in each exercise? (Check family maximum benefits.)

Average Monthly Earnings	Husband's Age	Wife's Age	Children's Ages	Family Benefit
a. $594	65	57	24	$ 202.00
b. 642	65	65	31	324.00
c. 360	65	52	16	285.60
d. 387	69	55	17	300.00
e. 650	66	50	17	434.40 (436.00)*
f. 335	67	59	14, 16	269.60 (342.00)
g. 100	68	53	13, 16	107.30 (178.90)
h. 622	70	51	9, 15	423.60 (525.00)
i. 383	62	48	21	119.20
j. 311	62	50	14	235.40

B

1. Mr. Burns is collecting disability insurance under the social security law. His average monthly earnings are $325. He has a wife of 32 and three children—9, 14, and 16.

   a. What is the total monthly benefit the family will receive?

   $262.40

   b. What is the total monthly benefit the family will receive when the oldest child reaches 18? $262.40

2. Mr. Campara retired at 65 and began receiving his social security benefits based on an average monthly earning of $601.

   a. How much did he receive each month? $204.00

   b. How much would he have received each month had he retired at 62 at the same average monthly earnings? $163.20

*This is the actual amount. However, the family can receive no more than the maximum amount given in the answer column.

   c. How much more does he receive monthly by having retired at
      65 rather than at 62? $ 40.80
3. The social security agency found that Mr. Flanagan's average
   monthly earnings were $340 at the time he retired at 66.
   a. How much will Mr. Flanagan's monthly benefit be? $ 137.90
   b. According to the mortality table for the years 1959–1961 on page
      390, how many years, to the nearest year, can Mr. Flanagan ex-
      pect to live?   14
   c. How much should the social security agency plan on paying Mr.
      Flanagan over his expected lifetime? $23,167.20

Section 3: Survivor's Benefits

    Whenever you hear of someone receiving social security benefits,
your immediate reaction is that the person must be old and retired. As
you learned in the preceding section, this could be quite far from the
truth, for some of you, although under 18, might be receiving these
benefits, based on your father's retirement payments. In addition to
this, there are a great many more of you who may be receiving monthly
social security payments because either your dad or mother died and
you are under 18, or perhaps still attending school and under 22. In this
section, you will learn how large these payments will be in the event
of the death of the father of the family. Remember, of course, that
the father has to be fully insured or, at least, currently insured for the
family to collect any benefits. What do these terms mean?

SURVIVOR'S BENEFITS

Person	Percent Of Primary Benefit
Widow 62 or older	82.5%
Widow under 62, but caring for a child under 18	75%
Widow under 62, but caring for a disabled child	75%
Child under 18	75%
Child under 22 while attending school	75%
Child disabled before 18	75%
Widow 60	71.5%

Lump-sum death payment is 3 times the
primary benefit, but never more than $255.

    Notice that, in the table above, provision is made for making pay-
ments to a widow caring for a disabled child, no matter what the age

As in the case of the earlier table on retirement benefits (page 435), do not have the students
memorize these percent values, for this serves little purpose.

of the child, or the age of the mother. Actually, these same benefits can be received if the husband is retired rather than deceased. In both cases, though, the child would have had to have been disabled before reaching 18.

■ILLUSTRATION 1: Mrs. Bailey was 63 at the time her husband died. His average monthly earnings were $322.
   a. How large will the lump-sum death payment be?
   b. How much will Mrs. Bailey's monthly benefits be?
●SOLUTION:
   (a) Primary benefit = $133
       Lump-sum death payment = 3 × $133
                              = $399
       Actual lump-sum death payment = $255
   (b) Mrs. Bailey's monthly benefit = 82.5% of $133
                              = .825 × $133
                              = $109.725, or $109.80

▼EXPLANATION: To find the lump-sum death payment, you would normally multiply the primary benefit by 3. In this illustration, however, the product is greater than $255. Since this payment can be no more than $255, this is all that Mrs. Bailey receives. Her monthly benefit is computed by determining 82.5% of the primary benefit. Had she been only 60, you would have found 71.5% of the primary benefit.

■ILLUSTRATION 2: Mr. Newman died, leaving a wife aged 40 and two children of 12 and 14. The social security agency computed his average monthly earnings at $615.
   a. What total monthly benefit will the family receive?
   b. What total monthly benefit will the family receive after the oldest child reaches 18, assuming he is no longer attending school?
●SOLUTION:
  (a) Primary benefit = $208
      Mrs. Newman's benefit = 75% of $208
                           = $156
      Benefit of child, 12 = 75% of $208
                           = $156
      Benefit of child, 14 = 75% of $208
                           = $156
      Total monthly benefit = $156 + $156 + $156
                           = $468
      Actual monthly benefit = $420.80
  (b) Total monthly benefit after oldest child reaches 18 = $468 − $156
                           = $312

It is interesting to note that whereas every other benefit under social security increased over the years with each change in the law, the lump-sum death payment has remained at $255. At one time, the $255 was 3 times the maximum benefit ($85) a person could receive. Now it is far from this.

EXERCISES   **A**

1. Determine the lump-sum death payment for each of the following average monthly earnings.

a. $77 _$231.00_   d. $93 _$255.00_   g. $322 _$255.00_
b. 82 _246.00_   e. 98 _255.00_   h. 360 _255.00_
c. 87 _255.00_   f. 104 _255.00_   i. 615 _255.00_

2. Determine the widow's monthly payment if she begins to receive her monthly benefits at the age shown:

	Average Monthly Earnings Of Husband	Age Of Widow	Primary Benefit	Widow's Benefit
a.	$ 97	62	$ 69.00	$ 57.00
b.	70	63	55.00	45.40
c.	98	63	70.20	58.00
d.	350	64	140.40	115.90
e.	364	65	144.00	118.80
f.	393	60	151.20	108.20
g.	604	60	205.00	146.60
h.	632	60	213.00	152.30

3. Determine the widow's monthly benefit if she is under 62, but caring for a child who is under 18.

	Average Monthly Earnings Of Husband	Primary Benefit	Widow's Benefit
a.	$387	$ 150.00	$ 112.50
b.	81	58.80	44.10
c.	105	75.10	56.40
d.	369	145.10	108.90
e.	607	206.00	154.50
f.	645	217.00	162.80

4. The father in each of the following exercises has died. Determine the monthly benefit his family will receive.

	Average Monthly Earnings Of.Husband	Age Of Widow	Ages Of Children	Primary Benefit	Family Benefit
a.	$358	37	10	$ 142.80	$ 214.20
b.	95	29	6	67.80	101.70 (101.80)*
c.	390	56	32	151.20	0
d.	593	64	40	202.00	166.70
e.	632	25	2	213.00	319.60
f.	335	32	12	136.80	205.20
g.	98	24	5, 1	70.20	105.30 (158.10)
h.	618	43	17, 14, 11	209.00	422.40 (627.20)

See annotation at the bottom of page 439.

B

1. When Mr. Pitt died, the social security agency found his monthly earnings to be $372. At the time of his death his wife was 48. Mrs. Pitt was left with the care of a disabled son, who was 25 years old. The young man had been permanently disabled at 14.
   a. What monthly benefit did Mrs. Pitt receive? <u>$109.80</u>
   b. What monthly benefit did the son receive? <u>$109.80</u>
2. When Mr. Waring died, his wife was 42 and his daughter, who was attending college, was 20. Mr. Waring's average monthly earnings were computed at $360.
   a. What lump-sum death payment did the family receive?
   <u>$225.00</u>
   b. What monthly benefit did Mrs. Waring receive? <u>$107.10</u>
   c. What monthly benefit did the daughter receive? <u>$107.10</u>

Section 4:   The Medicare Program

It has just been within recent years that medicare has been added to the social security program. Medicare consists of two different types of insurance, for neither of which you are eligible until you reach 65. The cost of the first of these—hospital insurance—is tacked on to the social security deductions that are taken from your weekly salary checks. You really have no choice as to whether you want to buy this insurance or not, for deductions are made before you receive your earnings.

The cost of the second insurance coverage—medical insurance—is voluntary. At the time you reach 65, you simply notify the social security agency that you want this coverage. To pay for it, deductions of $4 per month will be made from your social security monthly benefits. This cost will change periodically, depending on how much it costs to run the program. Incidentally, the federal government contributes an amount equal to what you have paid so that, in reality, you are getting relatively cheap insurance, for you are paying only half the cost.

Actually, the medicare program has been a real aid to the elderly. Before this law was passed, many aged people feared to become so ill that they would have to be taken to a hospital. They knew that the extremely high cost of hospital care would soon devour the small savings that had taken them a lifetime to accumulate. All too frequently they would deliberately avoid going to a hospital, although this might be the best place for them to go. The passage of the medicare bill has changed this. Although there are a few people who take advantage of

Problem 2 of Group B is designed to show the students that although the daughter of 20 is collecting social security benefits by virtue of the fact that she attends college, her mother, who is only 42, cannot collect these benefits since there is no child under 18.

this law by getting themselves admitted to a hospital or nursing home more often than they should be and by staying perhaps longer than they should, the majority of people are not doing this.

Here is how you will be covered under the hospital insurance program when you reach 65.

Hospital care for a single period of illness:

For first 60 days ...... Total payment less $52
For next 30 days ...... Total payment less $13 per day

Nursing-home care following hospital care:

For first 20 days ...... Total payment
For next 80 days ...... Total payment less $6.50 per day

In addition to the above, the hospital insurance provides for a *lifetime-reserve* of 60 days, during which all but $26 per day of your hospital bill will be paid. For instance, if, during a single period of illness you had to be in the hospital 100 days, this would be 10 days more than the total of 90 days in the table. For those last 10 days the insurance company will pay all but $26 of each day's cost. This will leave you, however, with only 50 more days in the lifetime-reserve. Once you use up the full 60 days in this reserve, you can never use them again.

The 90 days in the single period of illness are quite different from the lifetime-reserve days. These 90 days can be used over and over again each time you have to be taken to the hospital. If you go to the hospital for 35 days, for example, the insurance company will pay all but the first $52 of the bill. If it then becomes necessary for you to go to the hospital for another 50 days, the insurance company will again pay for all but the first $52 of the bill. The first stay of 35 days has no effect on the second stay of 50 days. This can be repeated as often as required. So long as 60 days elapse between the first hospital stay and the second hospital stay, then they are considered as two separate periods of illness.

Should it be necessary for you to have to go to a nursing home for care after you have been released from the hospital, then you must be admitted within 14 days after leaving the hospital. If you are admitted after the 14 days are over, then you, yourself, will have to pay the bill. Just one other point pertaining to this. Unless you have been in a hospital for at least 3 days before entering the nursing home, you will not be covered by the insurance program.

There is one more costly item whose expense is covered by this insurance. If you have been in the hospital for at least 3 days, then you

During recent years, the monetary coverage of the medicare program has changed quite frequently. The number of days of coverage, however, has not changed, nor the method for finding the cost to the injured.

are entitled to 100 visits to your home, if needed, by nurses and physical therapists—but not doctors. Here, again, the insurance company
will not pay the cost of the treatment unless your doctor sets up a plan
for this within 14 days after you leave the hospital. Also, the treatments have to be completed within one year.

■ ILLUSTRATION 1 : Mr. Sherman, who is covered by medicare, spent
75 days in the hospital. The total bill amounted to $2,625. How much
of this did the insurance company have to pay?

● SOLUTION :

> Amount deducted for first 60 days = $52
> Amount deducted for remaining 15 days = $15 \times 13
> $$= \$195$$
>
> Total deducted = $52 + $195
> $$= \$247$$
> Amount paid by the insurance company = $2,625 − $247
> $$= \$2,378$$

▼ EXPLANATION : Mr. Sherman had to pay the first $52 of whatever
the cost had been during the first 60 days. In addition, he had to pay
$13 of the cost for each of the 15 days he stayed in the hospital beyond
the 60 days. The cost to Mr. Sherman for the 15 days was $195. Hence,
the total he had to pay for the 75 days was $247. Therefore, the insur-
ance company paid the difference between $2,625 and $247, or $2,378.

■ ILLUSTRATION 2 : Mr. Williamson is 66 and covered by the medicare program. Because of a serious illness, he was hospitalized for 96
days. How much will this cost him?

● SOLUTION :

> Cost for first 60 days = $52
> Cost for next 30 days = $30 \times 13
> $$= \$390$$
> Cost for remaining 6 days = $6 \times 26
> $$= \$156$$
> Total cost = $52 + $390 + $156
> $$= \$598$$

▼ EXPLANATION : The computation here is much the same as in the
early part of the previous illustration, except that in this case, 6 days
of the lifetime-reserve must be used. For each of these days, Mr. Williamson has to pay $26 of the hospital cost, or a total of $156.

The second part of the medicare program, that is, the part you help
to pay for after you reach 65, covers almost all doctor's and medical
bills. During any single year, if these bills amount to more than $50,

The computation connected with the cost of hospital care or nursing-home care under the
medicare program is quite straightforward and relatively simple. Permit the students to refer
to the table on page 444 when doing exercises in this connection.

then you pay only the first $50, in addition to 20% of the remaining amount. The insurance company pays the rest. Among the costs that are covered are:

Physician's services, up to 100 visits by either a nurse or a physical therapist; x-ray treatments, surgical dressings, casts, artificial limbs, wheelchairs, hospital beds, and drugs.

■ILLUSTRATION 3: Last year, Mr. Harper, who is covered by medical insurance under the medicare program, had a total cost of $856 for doctor's bills and medical bills. How much of this amount did the insurance company have to pay?

●SOLUTION:

Amount Mr. Harper paid:
Deductible amount = $50
20% of balance = 20% of ($856 − $50)
$$= .20 \times \$806$$
$$= \$161.20$$
Total = $50 + $161.20
$$= \$211.20$$
Amount paid by insurance company = $856 − $211.20
$$= \$644.80$$

▼EXPLANATION: Mr. Harper had to pay the first $50 of the cost. In addition, he paid 20% of the balance of $806, and this amounted to $161.20. Hence, the total he paid was $211.20. Therefore, the amount remaining for the insurance company to pay was the difference between $856 and $211.20, or $644.80.

EXERCISES   A

1. In each of the following exercises, the person was covered by the medicare program. How much will his part of the bill be if he was in the hospital the number of days shown?

   a. 15 days _$ 52.00_   e. 69 days _$169.00_
   b. 27 days _$ 52.00_   f. 85 days _$377.00_
   c. 53 days _$ 52.00_   g. 78 days _$286.00_
   d. 65 days _$117.00_   h. 87 days _$403.00_

2. Each of the people in the following exercises was admitted into a nursing home under the medicare program. How much of the bill will each person have to pay if he remains in the home for the number of days shown?

By this time the students should be familiar with deductible clauses on insurance policies. There is, however, one additional feature in the payment of physician's services, and that is that the insured must pay 20% of the cost over and above the first $50. This part of the computaion will be new to them.

a. 8 days $0   e. 25 days $ 32.50
b. 14 days $0   f. 78 days $377.00
c. 17 days $0   g. 84 days $416.00
d. 47 days $175.50   h. 95 days $487.50

3. Each of the people in the following exercises was admitted into a hospital under the medicare program. If no one used up his lifetime-reserve days, how much of the bill will each person have to pay if he remains in the hospital for the number of days shown?

a. 100 days $ 702.00   d. 126 days $1,378.00
b. 107 days $ 884.00   e. 135 days $1,612.00
c. 120 days $1,222.00   f. 148 days $1,950.00

4. How much of each of the following hospital bills will have to be paid by the insurance company if the person is covered by the medicare program?

	Hospital Cost	Number Of Days Hospitalized	Amount Paid By Insured	Amount Paid By Insurance Company
a.	$ 378	10	$ 52.00	$ 326.00
b.	759	22	52.00	707.00
c.	1,510	45	52.00	1,458.00
d.	2,014	53	52.00	1,962.00
e.	2,653	65	117.00	2,536.00
f.	2,912	74	234.00	2,678.00
g.	2,714	82	338.00	2,376.00
h.	3,158	88	416.00	2,742.00

5. How much of each of the following nursing-home bills will have to be paid by the insurance company if the person is covered by the medicare program?

	Nursing-Home Cost	Number Of Days In Nursing Home	Amount Paid By Insured	Amount Paid By Insurance Company
a.	$ 154	7	$ 0	$ 154.00
b.	225	10	0	225.00
c.	341	14	0	341.00
d.	456	20	0	456.00
e.	678	30	65.00	613.00
f.	783	35	97.50	685.50
g.	1,237	56	234.00	1,003.00
h.	1,978	84	416.00	1,562.00

When discussing Exercise 3, it would be well to emphasize that a person can use the lifetime-reserve days but once in his life. Once these days have been used, they are lost forever.

6. The following are medical costs that persons had over the period of one year. If each of them was covered by the medicare program, how much of these bills did each person have to pay himself?

	Medical Cost	Deductible Amount	Remainder	20% Of Remainder	Insured's Cost
a.	$ 150	$ 50.00	$ 100.00	$ 20.00	$ 70.00
b.	200	50.00	150.00	30.00	80.00
c.	280	50.00	230.00	46.00	96.00
d.	575	50.00	525.00	105.00	155.00
e.	40	40.00	0	0	40.00
f.	37	37.00	0	0	37.00
g.	856	50.00	806.00	161.20	211.20
h.	1,050	50.00	1,000.00	200.00	250.00
i.	1,762	50.00	1,712.00	342.40	392.40
j.	4,374	50.00	4,324.00	864.80	914.80

7. The following are medical costs that persons had over the period of one year. If each of them was covered by the medicare program, how much of the bill did the insurance company have to pay?

	Medical Cost	Deductible Amount	Remainder	20% Of Remainder	Amount Paid By Insured	Amount Paid By Insurance Company
a.	$ 170	$ 50.00	$ 120.00	$ 24.00	$ 74.00	$ 96.00
b.	260	50.00	210.00	42.00	92.00	168.0
c.	45	45.00	0	0	45.00	0
d.	640	50.00	590.00	118.00	168.00	472.00
e.	782	50.00	732.00	146.40	196.40	585.60
f.	2,390	50.00	2,340.00	468.00	518.00	1,872.00

B

1. Mrs. Yarby was covered by the medicare program at the time she was taken ill and had to go to the hospital. She spent 27 days there, for which the cost ran to $837, and another 16 days in a nursing home at a cost of $358.

   a. How much of the hospital bill did Mrs. Yarby have to pay?

   $52.00

   b. How much of the nursing-home bill did she have to pay?

   $0

   c. What is the total amount that Mrs. Yarby had to pay to both institutions?

   $52.00

2. Mr. Darden, who is covered by medicare for both hospital and medical insurance, had a serious operation for which the surgeon's charge was $1,400. He spent 70 days in the hospital and another 38 days in a nursing home before returning to his own home. The

hospital costs came to $2,945, while the nursing home charged him $954.

a. How much of the hospital bill did Mr. Darden have to pay?

$182.00

b. How much of the nursing-home bill did Mr. Darden have to pay?

$117.00

c. How much of the surgeon's fee did Mr. Darden have to pay?

$320.00

d. How much of the entire bill did the insurance company have to pay? $4,680.00

Unit 2:   Private Retirement Plans

There are a great many companies that offer their employees a retirement plan in addition to the one they will receive under the social security program. Most of these plans operate as a joint responsibility —that is, part of the cost is paid for by the employer and the rest is paid for by the employee. Unfortunately, every private retirement plan is different from every other one. However, the one described below is somewhat typical of a great number of them.

PRICE–DAVIS CORPORATION
Employee Contribution Rate

Entrance Age	Percent of Contribution		Entrance Age	Percent of Contribution	
	Men	Women		Men	Women
20	4.80	5.27	40	6.04	6.81
21	4.80	5.31	41	6.14	6.92
22	4.81	5.36	42	6.23	7.04
23	4.83	5.40	43	6.34	7.15
24	4.87	5.45	44	6.44	7.27
25	4.91	5.51	45	6.55	7.39
26	4.96	5.57	46	6.65	7.50
27	5.01	5.64	47	6.77	7.62
28	5.06	5.71	48	6.88	7.75
29	5.12	5.78	49	7.00	7.88
30	5.19	5.85	50	7.12	8.02
31	5.26	5.93	51	7.25	8.18
32	5.34	6.02	52	7.39	8.34
33	5.43	6.11	53	7.54	8.51
34	5.51	6.21	54	7.69	8.67
35	5.59	6.30	55	7.84	8.83
36	5.67	6.39	56	7.99	9.00
37	5.76	6.50	57	8.14	9.16
38	5.86	6.60	58	8.30	9.33
39	5.95	6.71	59	8.45	9.51

Before turning the page to where this is explained, you might ask the students why women at the same age as men are asked to pay a higher contribution rate.

In this retirement program, the amount contributed depends upon whether the employee is a man or a woman, and also upon the age at which the person began working for the firm. The rates for women are higher than those for men at the same age, since women, in general, are expected to live longer than men. And, therefore, since women will be collecting retirement benefits for a greater period of time, they have to contribute a greater amount into the fund. Notice, also, that the older you are at the time you begin to work for this company, the higher your contribution rate will be.

■ILLUSTRATION 1: Ben Nelson began working for the Price-Davis Corporation when he was 24. His annual income now is $7,356. How large will his contribution to the fund be this year?

▼EXPLANATION: Ben's contribution rate will be 4.87%, as he entered the company at age 24. To determine his contribution, you will have to determine 4.87% of $7,356. What decimal numeral is equivalent to the percent numeral 4.87%?

●SOLUTION:

$$\text{Contribution rate} = 4.87\%$$
$$= .0487$$
$$\text{Contribution that year} = 4.87\% \text{ of } \$7,356$$
$$= .0487 \times \$7,356$$
$$= \$358.2372, \text{ or } \$358.24$$

Usually, company retirement plans carry with them the condition that the person must be an employee of the firm for some minimum period of time. In the case of the Price-Davis Corporation, this minimum period is 10 years.

As an employee, equally important to you as the amount you contribute is the question of how much you will get back in benefits at the time you retire. The method used for finding the monthly benefits received by the Price-Davis employees is one that involves their average annual earnings over the last five years of employment and also the number of years they have been employed by the company. A fraction is found, made up of the numerator, which represents the number of years of employment, and the denominator, which is always 60. This fraction is then multiplied by the average annual earnings of the last five years. Their product equals the annual benefit the employee receives.

$$\text{Annual Benefit} = \frac{\text{Number of Years of Employment}}{60}$$
$$\times \text{Average Annual Salary of Last Five Years}$$

Ask the students to justify why the retirement benefits should be based on the average earnings of the last five years rather than those of the first five years. Have the students check with their parents for other private retirement programs.

■ILLUSTRATION 2: For the last five years before retirement, Clarence Lee had an average annual income with the Price-Davis Corporation of $8,450. If he worked for the company for 28 years, how large was his annual retirement benefit?

●SOLUTION:

$$\text{Annual benefit} = 28/60 \times \$8,450$$
$$= \$236,000/60$$
$$= \$3,943.33$$

EXERCISES   A

The following exercises are based on the retirement plan of the Price-Davis Corporation.

1. Change each of the following percent numerals to its equivalent decimal numeral.

a. 4.93% __.0493__   c. 5.40% __.0540__   e. 7.03% __.0703__
b. 5.02% __.0502__   d. 6.39% __.0639__   f. 8.00% __.0800__

2. How much will each of the following employees have to contribute to the fund during the year shown?

	Annual Earnings	Entrance Age	Sex	Contribution Rate		Contribution
a.	$ 8,000	49	Male	7.00	%	$ 560.00
b.	6,400	35	Female	6.30	%	403.20
c.	7,500	41	Male	6.14	%	460.50
d.	9,300	46	Female	7.50	%	697.50
e.	5,420	21	Male	4.80	%	260.16
f.	5,420	21	Female	5.31	%	287.80
g.	7,370	28	Male	5.06	%	372.92
h.	10,450	52	Male	7.39	%	772.26
i.	12,360	49	Female	7.88	%	973.97
j.	14,630	44	Male	6.44	%	942.17

3. Determine the annual benefit received by each of the following retired employees of the Price-Davis Corporation.

	Number of Years Of Employment	Average Annual Earnings Of Last 5 Years	Annual Benefit
a.	30	$ 7,000	$ 3,500.00
b.	20	9,000	3,000.00
c.	15	8,400	2,100.00
d.	10	9,600	1,600.00
e.	40	7,800	5,200.00
f.	45	7,900	5,925.00
g.	35	10,200	5,950.00
h.	25	11,700	4,875.00
i.	32	9,300	4,960.00
j.	36	10,500	6,300.00

In Exercises 2 e and 2 f, the annual earnings and entrance ages are the same. However, the first pertains to a male, while the second pertains to a female. Use two exercises to compare the annual contributions for the different sexes.

B

1. Mary Travis began working for the Price-Davis Corporation at 22 and retired at 64. Her average annual salary during the last five years before retirement was $9,450.
   a. What was her annual retirement benefit? $6,615.00
   b. If she was paid this benefit on a monthly basis, how much was her check each month? $551.25
2. Jack Freeman retired from the Price-Davis Corporation at 65. He had begun working for the corporation at age 31. His average annual earnings during the last five years of employment were $12,360.
   a. What was his annual retirement benefit? $7,004.00
   b. According to the mortality table for the years 1959–1961 on page 390, how many years, to the nearest whole number of years, is Mr. Freeman expected to live after retirement?   14
   c. If he lives the number of years predicted, what total amount of money will he collect under the retirement plan? $98,056.00

Unit 3:   Retirement Income from Annuities

Many people feel that social security benefits at the time of retirement will not give them nearly enough income to live on in the manner they would like. Some of you will be covered by company retirement plans, too, and yet you will feel the same way. If you can afford it, you will probably purchase for yourself your own private retirement program called an *annuity*. A retirement plan of this type consists simply of a contract drawn up between you and, usually, an insurance company whereby you agree to pay the insurance company a certain amount of money. The company, in turn, agrees that, starting at a certain age, it will pay you a fixed amount of money for the rest of your life.

It would not be quite right if, after the insurance company sent you the first payment, you happened to die. Were this to occur, you would have received far too little in return for the amount you had contributed. Hence, the contract freqently states that the company guarantees to pay someone, either yourself—if you are alive—or someone you name —if you die—for at least a 10-year period. As mentioned before, should you happen to live more than 10 years, the company will continue to pay you this monthly income for the duration of your life.

The payments you make to the insurance company can be in one of two forms. Either you give the company a lump-sum payment and never make any other payments, or you pay it a certain amount

Frequently retirement plans drawn up between employees and employer consist of two parts — an employee contributory part, which is an annuity, and a pension part paid for by the employer. Should the employee quit his job before retirement, he can withdraw payments he has made, but usually not his employer's payments.

SINGLE–PREMIUM ANNUITY

Monthly Life Income Purchased by $1,000 Single Premium

MALE Age at Date Of Maturity			Age	FEMALE Age at Date Of Maturity		
60	65	70		60	65	70
$15.11	$19.43	$24.98	20	$13.49	$17.31	$22.26
14.71	18.91	24.31	21	13.13	16.84	21.66
14.31	18.41	23.66	22	12.78	16.39	21.08
13.93	17.92	23.03	23	12.44	15.95	20.52
13.56	17.44	22.41	24	12.11	15.53	19.97
13.19	16.97	21.81	25	11.78	15.11	19.43
12.84	16.51	21.23	26	11.47	14.71	18.91
12.50	16.07	20.66	27	11.16	14.31	18.41
12.16	15.64	20.10	28	10.86	13.93	17.92
11.84	15.22	19.57	29	10.57	13.56	17.44
11.52	14.82	19.04	30	10.29	13.19	16.97
11.21	14.42	18.53	31	10.01	12.84	16.51
10.91	14.03	18.04	32	9.74	12.50	16.07
10.62	13.66	17.55	33	9.48	12.16	15.64
10.34	13.29	17.08	34	9.23	11.84	15.22
10.06	12.94	16.63	35	8.98	11.52	14.82
9.79	12.59	16.18	36	8.74	11.21	14.42
9.53	12.25	15.75	37	8.51	10.91	14.03
9.27	11.93	15.33	38	8.28	10.62	13.66
9.02	11.61	14.92	39	8.06	10.34	13.29
8.78	11.30	14.52	40	7.84	10.06	12.94
8.55	10.99	14.13	41	7.63	9.79	12.59
8.32	10.70	13.75	42	7.43	9.53	12.25
8.10	10.41	13.38	43	7.23	9.27	11.93
7.88	10.13	13.03	44	7.04	9.02	11.61
7.67	9.86	12.68	45	6.85	8.78	11.30
7.46	9.60	12.34	46	6.67	8.55	10.99
7.26	9.34	12.01	47	6.49	8.32	10.70
7.07	9.09	11.69	48	6.31	8.10	10.41
6.88	8.85	11.37	49	6.14	7.88	10.13
6.70	8.61	11.07	50	5.98	7.67	9.86
6.52	8.38	10.77	51	5.82	7.46	9.60
6.34	8.16	10.48	52	5.66	7.26	9.34
6.17	7.94	10.20	53	5.51	7.07	9.09
6.01	7.73	9.93	54	5.37	6.88	8.85
5.85	7.52	9.66	55	5.22	6.70	8.61
	7.32	9.41	56		6.52	8.38
	7.12	9.15	57		6.34	8.16
	6.93	8.91	58		6.17	7.94
	6.75	8.67	59		6.01	7.73
	6.57	8.44	60		5.85	7.52
		8.21	61			7.32
		7.99	62			7.12
		7.57	63			6.93
		7.37	64			6.75
			65			6.57

ANNUAL–PREMIUM ANNUITY

MALE Monthly Life Income (10 Year Certain) Purchased by $100 Annual Premium — Age at Date Of Maturity			Age	FEMALE Monthly Life Income (10 Year Certain) Purchased by $100 Annual Premium — Age at Date Of Maturity		
60	65	70		60	65	70
$35.74	$48.98	$66.33	20	$31.92	$43.62	$59.11
34.29	47.12	63.93	21	30.63	41.96	56.97
32.88	45.30	61.60	22	29.37	40.34	54.89
31.51	43.53	59.33	23	28.14	38.77	52.87
30.17	41.81	57.12	24	26.94	37.23	50.90
28.87	40.14	54.97	25	25.78	35.74	48.98
27.60	38.51	52.87	26	24.65	34.29	47.12
26.37	36.93	50.84	27	23.55	32.88	45.30
25.17	35.38	48.85	28	22.48	31.51	43.53
24.00	33.88	46.92	29	21.44	30.17	41.81
22.87	32.42	45.05	30	20.42	28.87	40.14
21.76	31.00	43.22	31	19.44	27.60	38.51
20.69	29.62	41.44	32	18.47	26.37	36.93
19.64	28.27	39.71	33	17.54	25.17	35.38
18.62	26.96	38.02	34	16.63	24.00	33.88
17.63	25.68	36.38	35	15.74	22.87	32.42
16.66	24.44	34.79	36	14.88	21.76	31.00
15.72	23.23	33.23	37	14.04	20.69	29.62
14.81	22.06	31.72	38	13.22	19.64	28.27
13.92	20.91	30.25	39	12.43	18.62	26.96
13.05	19.80	28.82	40	11.66	17.63	25.68
12.21	18.71	27.43	41	10.90	16.66	24.44
11.39	17.66	26.07	42	10.17	15.72	23.23
10.59	16.63	24.75	43	9.46	14.81	22.06
9.81	15.63	23.47	44	8.76	13.92	20.91
9.06	14.66	22.22	45	8.09	13.05	19.80
8.32	13.71	21.00	46	7.43	12.21	18.71
7.60	12.79	19.81	47	6.79	11.39	17.66
6.91	11.89	18.66	48	6.17	10.59	16.63
6.23	11.02	17.54	49	5.56	9.81	15.63
5.57	10.17	16.45	50	4.97	9.06	14.66
4.93	9.34	15.39	51	4.40	8.32	13.71
4.30	8.54	14.35	52	3.84	7.60	12.79
3.69	7.76	13.35	53	3.30	6.91	11.89
3.10	6.99	12.37	54	2.77	6.23	11.02
2.52	6.25	11.41	55	2.25	5.57	10.17
	5.53	10.49	56		4.93	9.34
	4.83	9.58	57		4.30	8.54
	4.15	8.70	58		3.69	7.76
	3.48	7.85	59		3.10	6.99
	2.83	7.02	60		2.52	6.25
		6.21	61			5.53
		5.42	62			4.83
		4.65	63			4.15
		3.91	64			3.48
		3.18	65			2.83

Call the attention of the students to the fact that the male at age 60 will always receive more than the female at that age, although both had purchased the annuity at the same age. Ask them to account for that.

each year until you reach the age when the company begins to pay you back. The first of these is called the *single-premium annuity*, while the second is an *annual-premium annuity*. As an illustration, in the single-premium annuity, you might pay the company $1,000 at 20 and then make no further payments. When you reach 60, the company will begin to send you $15.11 every single month as long as you live. In the annual-premium annuity, you might arrange to pay the insurance company $100 every year, starting at 20. When you reach 60, you will stop making payments to the company, and at that time, it will begin making payments to you of $35.74 every month until the day you die.

Notice in the Single-Premium Annuity Table on page 453 that a male who pays $1,000 at age 20 will get back $15.11 each month starting at 60, while a female will receive only $13.49 monthly for the same $1,000. Do you know why this is so?

■ILLUSTRATION 1 : When George Turner was 23, he made a $6,000 payment on a single-premium annuity from which he would begin to receive a monthly income starting at 65. How large will these benefits be?

▼EXPLANATION : Use the Single-Premium Annuity Table on page 453. Run your finger down the "Age" column until you reach the numeral 23. Place the edge of a piece of paper along this row and then run your finger to the left into that part of the table headed by the word "Male." Stop at the column headed by the numeral 65. Your finger should be pointing at $17.92. This is the amount that Mr. Turner will receive monthly, starting at 65, for each $1,000 in the lump-sum payment he made at 23. Since the total payment was $6,000, he will receive 6 times $17.92, or $107.52 monthly.

●SOLUTION :

Monthly payment at age 65 per $1,000 = $17.92
Monthly payment at age 65 for $6,000 = 6 × $17.92
= $107.52

■ILLUSTRATION 2 : At 33, Grace Becker purchased an annual premium annuity by agreeing to pay $500 each year until she reached 60. How large will the monthly payments be that Miss Becker will receive from the insurance company beginning at 60?

▼EXPLANATION : In this illustration, use the Annual-Premium Annuity Table and look at the "Female" section. For an entrance age of 33, a woman will receive $17.54 each month when she reaches the age of 60. This $17.54 is for each $100 that Miss Becker paid annually.

As a point of interest, you might want to show the students how much Mr. Turner's $6,000 would amount to if he had deposited it in the bank at 5% interest compounded annually over the 42-year period. (See table on page 247.)

Since her total annual payment is $500, she will be sent 5 times $17.54, or $87.70 monthly.

●SOLUTION:

Monthly payment at age 60 per $100 premium = $17.54
Monthly payment at age 60 for $500 premium = 5 × $17.54
= $87.70

EXERCISES   **A**

1. Determine the monthly income that can be purchased for $1,000 on each of the following single-premium annuities.

	Entrance Age	Age At Maturity	Sex	Monthly Income
a.	25	60	Male	$ 13.19
b.	27	60	Female	11.16
c.	34	65	Female	11.84
d.	41	65	Male	10.99
e.	23	70	Male	23.03
f.	48	60	Female	6.31
g.	54	65	Female	6.88
h.	49	65	Male	8.85
i.	36	70	Female	14.42
j.	58	65	Male	6.93
k.	21	60	Female	13.13

2. Determine the monthly income that can be purchased for $100 annually on each of the following annual-premium annuities.

	Entrance Age	Age At Maturity	Sex	Monthly Income
a.	22	60	Male	$ 32.88
b.	32	60	Female	18.47
c.	27	65	Male	36.93
d.	31	70	Male	43.22
e.	29	65	Female	30.17
f.	43	70	Female	22.06
g.	48	65	Female	10.59
h.	57	70	Male	9.58

3. Determine the monthly income that can be purchased on each of the single-premium annuities.

Use the "Growth" table on page 257 to determine with the students how much money Mrs. Becker of Illustration 2 would have in the bank had she deposited the $500 annually over the 27-year period. Both this suggestion and the one at the bottom of page 454 give you an opportunity to review earlier work.

	Lump-Sum Payment	Entrance Age	Age At Maturity	Sex	Monthly Income Per $1,000	Monthly Income
a.	$ 5,000	27	60	Male	$ 12.50	$ 62.50
b.	4,000	21	65	Male	18.91	75.64
c.	6,000	34	65	Male	13.29	79.74
d.	12,000	36	60	Female	8.74	104.88
e.	10,000	48	70	Female	10.41	104.10
f.	15,000	50	65	Male	8.61	129.15
g.	18,000	31	60	Female	10.01	180.18
h.	25,000	35	70	Male	16.63	415.75

4. Determine the monthly income that can be purchased on each of the following annual-premium annuities.

	Annual Premium	Entrance Age	Age At Maturity	Sex	Monthly Income Per $100	Monthly Income
a.	$200	20	60	Male	$ 35.74	$ 71.48
b.	300	29	60	Male	24.00	72.00
c.	300	29	60	Female	21.44	64.32
d.	200	45	65	Male	14.66	29.32
e.	400	32	65	Female	26.37	105.48
f.	400	47	70	Male	19.81	79.24
g.	600	30	65	Male	32.42	194.52
h.	800	34	60	Female	16.63	133.04

5. As in the case of the life-insurance premiums, semiannual payments can be made instead of yearly payments on annual-premium annuities. When this is done, the semiannual premium is 52% of the annual premium. Determine the semiannual premium that will have to be paid for each of the following annual premiums.

	Annual Premium	Semiannual Premium		Annual Premium	Semiannual Premium
a.	$100	$ 52.00	d.	250	$ 130.00
b.	200	104.00	e.	450	234.00
c.	500	260.00	f.	750	390.00

6. If quarterly premiums are paid on an annuity, they are 26.5% of the annual premium. Determine the quarterly premiums that would have to be paid for each of the following annual premiums.

	Annual Premium	Quarterly Premium		Annual Premium	Quarterly Premium
a.	$100	$ 26.50	d.	350	$ 92.75
b.	300	79.50	e.	550	145.75
c.	800	212.00	f.	850	225.25

Discuss with the students whether the monthly incomes found in Exercises 3 and 4 would be large enough to meet the financial needs of two people. Be careful to point out that these needs are much less for people of 65 than for people of 25.

B

1. Mr. Charles Samuels purchased a single-premium annuity for $15,-000. He is to begin receiving payments at 60.
   a. How large will the payments be if Mr. Samuels purchased the annuity at 20? $ 226.25
   b. How large will the payments be if Mr. Samuels purchased the annuity at 40? $ 131.70
   c. How much more will he receive each month if the purchase is made at 20 rather than at 40? $ 94.95

2. Mrs. Evelyn Noyes purchased a $20,000 single-premium annuity at 36.
   a. How much will she receive monthly if the payments are to start at 60? $ 174.80
   b. How much will she receive monthly if the payments are to start at 70? $ 288.40
   c. How much more will she receive monthly if the payments are to begin at 70 rather than at 60? $ 113.60

3. Mr. John Blanchard purchased a $10,000 single-premium annuity at 34. He is to begin receiving monthly payments at 60.
   a. How large will each monthly payment be? $ 103.40
   b. How much will he receive over the period of 1 year? $1,240.80
   c. According to the Mortality Table for the years 1959–1961 on page 390, how many years, to the nearest year, can a man of 60 expect to live? 18
   d. If Mr. Blanchard lives exactly the expected number of years shown in the table, how much money will he receive on his annuity? $22,334.40
   e. How much more—or less—will he receive from the insurance company than he gave in his lump-sum payment? $12,334.40

4. Mr. Hawkins purchased a $600 annual-premium annuity at 30 for which payments are to begin at 65.
   a. How large will each of his monthly benefits be? $ 194.52
   b. If Mrs. Hawkins had purchased the same annuity at the same age, how large would her monthly benefits be, beginning at 65? $ 173.22
   c. How much more would Mr. Hawkins receive during a year than Mrs. Hawkins? $ 255.60
   d. How much more would Mr. Hawkins receive over a 15-year period than Mrs. Hawkins? $3,834.00

There are interesting comparisons made in these problems that you may want to expand upon.

Unit 4: Chapter Review and Test

Refer to the tables in this chapter when doing the computation for the following problems.

1. Determine the social security primary benefit on each of the following average monthly earnings.

   a. $87 __$ 62.20__   c. $321 __$133.00__   e. $597 __$203.00__
   b. $98 __70.20__   d. $384 __148.90__   f. $623 __210.00__

2. Determine the maximum social security benefit a family can receive on each of the following average monthly earnings.

   a. $81 __$ 88.20__   c. $345 __$277.60__   e. $590 __$410.80__
   b. $95 __101.70__   d. $378 __303.20__   f. $622 __423.60__

3. A husband's average monthly earnings are computed by the social security agency to be $369.
   a. What will his monthly benefit be if he begins to receive it at 65?
      __$145.10__
   b. If his wife is also 65 at the time she begins receiving her monthly allotment, how much will she receive?   __$ 72.60__

4. Mr. Campbell's average monthly income under social security was $604. How much will his monthly benefit be if he begins to receive it at 62?   __$164.00__

5. Mr. Perkins was 66 at the time he began to collect his monthly social security benefits on an average monthly earning of $317. His wife was 59 at the time, and they have no children.
   a. How much did Mr. Perkins receive?   __$131.90__
   b. How much did Mrs. Perkins receive?   __Nothing__

6. How large will the lump-sum death payment be on each of the following average monthly earnings under social security?
   a. $94 __$200.10__   b. $81 __$176.40__   c. $353 __$255.00__

7. Mr. Alkorn died, leaving a wife, 27, and a daughter, 5. His average monthly earnings under social security were $321.
   a. How much did Mrs. Alkorn receive each month in social security benefits?   __$ 99.80__
   b. How much did the daughter receive each month in social security benefits?   __$ 99.80__
   c. If there had been a second young child in the family, how much would the family have received each month in social security benefits?   __$258.40__

As usual, parts of these problems can be for review purposes and other parts for testing.

8. The following persons are covered by medicare. How much will their hospital stay cost them if they are there the following number of days?

a. 48 days ___$52.00___   b. 72 days ___$208.00___

9. The following persons are covered by medicare. How much will their nursing-home stay cost them if they are there the following number of days?

a. 18 days ___0___   b. 64 days ___$286.00___

10. Mr. Merkin spent 105 days in the hospital as a result of a serious operation. He was covered by medicare and had never used any of his lifetime-reserve days. The total hospital bill for this stay was $3,892.
    a. How much of this bill did Mr. Merkin have to pay? ___$ 832.00___
    b. How much of this bill did the insurance company have to pay?
    ___$3,060.00___

11. During the past year, Mrs. Chester had medical bills amounting to $570. If she was covered for medical costs under the medicare program, how much of this bill did she, herself, have to pay?
    ___$ 154.00___

12. Under the Price-Davis Corporation retirement plan described in this chapter, how much will Robert Riley have to contribute during a year in which he earned $9,370? He started to work for the company at 26.   ___$ 464.75___

13. Frank Daley had been working for the Price-Davis Corporation for 28 years at the time he retired. His average annual earnings during the last five years of this period were $8,490. How much did Mr. Daley receive from the company each year in retirement benefits?   ___$3,962.00___

14. When Mr. Johnson was 27, he purchased a single-premium annuity for $8,000. If he begins to collect monthly payments at 65, how large will these payments be?   ___$ 128.56___

15. Mrs. Jorgeson purchased an annuity by electing to make annual payments of $700. Her first payment was made at 35, and her last at 60. How large were the monthly benefits sent to her from age 60 on?   ___$ 110.18___

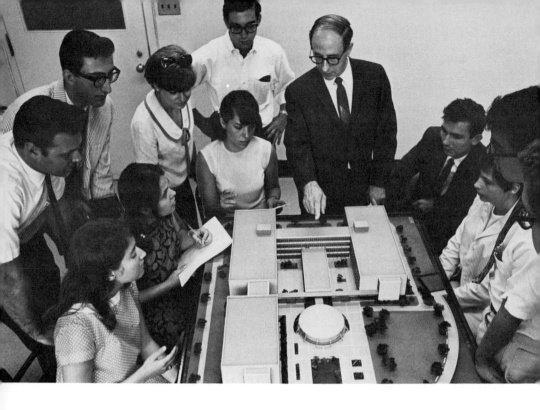

CHAPTER 12

THE COST
OF HOUSING

It is quite likely that sometime in your life you will purchase a home or rent an apartment. Both of these ways of living have their advantages and disadvantages. Which way of living you select depends largely on your way of life, or, perhaps, the area in which you want to live.

The person who rents an apartment often does so because it frees him from mortgage payments, real estate taxes, lawn problems, unsatisfactory plumbing, faulty electric wiring, water seepage in the cellar, a leaking roof, peeling paint inside and out, and so on. To him, there is something satisfying about being able to leave his apartment for a vacation and simply close the door with no worries about what will happen to the house or the garden.

The homeowner, on the other hand, looks at things quite differently. Usually he has a very definite pride in both his home and the condi-

In recent years, much time and effort have been spent in trying to develop a sense of pride in people for the environment in which they live, whether it be an apartment house or a one-family home. The design of this program is excellent, and it would be well to introduce this chapter on that note.

tion in which it is kept. He knows that he can look forward to the day —even though it may be twenty years off—when the property will be his. The payments that he makes over the years do not lead to a pile of rent receipts, but rather to the ownership of a home for him and his family.

The question of which is a better way to live is purely a personal one. What one person views as a constant battle, another one sees as an opportunity to display his skill as a do-it-yourselfer. Similarly, the question of which is cheaper is meaningless. It is usually possible to find an apartment where the rent is less than the cost of maintaining a particular home. Equally true is the fact that there is usually a house somewhere for which the cost of upkeep will be less than the monthly rental payments you may be making. However, there is one very important factor that prevents many people from buying a home—the down payment. All too often it is difficult for many people to save enough money to make the initial deposit required.

In this chapter, you will consider the expenses—other than rent—of a person renting an apartment. In addition, you will also examine the major bills of a homeowner.

Unit 1: Renting an Apartment

Section 1: The Cost of Electricity

PART 1

No doubt you, along with other teen-agers, have had your parents speak to you about leaving the lights on in one room while you went off to study in another. Or you fall asleep late at night while the radio continues to blare. The cause for your parents' concern is the money you are wasting, for the electricity used by these appliances costs money.

The company from which electricity is bought charges for its services in terms of the number of kilowatt-hours of electricity used during a monthly period. Perhaps the simplest way of explaining the meaning of a kilowatt-hour is in terms of the electric light bulbs in your home. These bulbs can be purchased in various sizes, depending on the intensity of light that you want. Usually, for household needs the size will range from small night lights that are labeled 6 watts to the 300-watt bulbs for three-way lights. Should a 100-watt bulb burn 1 hour, then you have used 100 watt-hours of electricity. This is found by multiplying the 100 watts by the 1 hour to get a product that is called 100 watt-hours. Similarly, if a 300-watt bulb burns for 2 hours,

Contact your area electrical utility company to get rates for comparison with those in this unit. Before the student can understand how the cost of electricity is computed, he must be taught the meaning of kilowatt-hour. For this understanding, read the material on these few pages with the students.

then the consumption of electricity is 600 watt-hours. Here, again, the 600 represents the product of 300 and 2.

If you were asked to give the distance from Chicago to London, you would certainly not state the answer in terms of inches, for this is far too small a unit for measuring long distances. Similarly, the watt-hour is also far too small a unit for measuring the cost of electricity. For this reason, the *kilowatt-hour* was devised. The kilowatt-hour is the equivalent of 1,000 watt-hours. Thus, 3,000 watt-hours is the same as 3 kilowatt-hours and 8,000 watt-hours is the same as 8 kilowatt-hours.

> If the number of watt-hours of electricity is divided by 1,000, you will find the number of kilowatt-hours of electricity.

■ILLUSTRATION 1: How many kilowatt-hours of electricity are there in 8,350 watt-hours of electricity?

▼EXPLANATION: Since there are 1,000 watt-hours in each kilowatt-hour, dividing 8,350 watt-hours by 1,000 will determine the number of kilowatt-hours. The quickest way to divide 8,350 by 1,000 is simply to move the decimal point 3 places to the left of its present position in 8,350. Can you show that this is so?

●SOLUTION:

$$\text{Number of kilowatt-hours} = 8{,}350 \div 1{,}000$$
$$= 8.35$$

If you look at the bottom—or, possibly, the back—of any household appliance, you will find that each one has marked on it the number of watts of electricity needed to operate it. Examples of this are the steam iron at one extreme, which may use as many as 1,100 watts of electricity. At the other extreme is the electric clock, which uses as few as 2 watts.

■ILLUSTRATION 2: Mrs. Turner spent 3½ hours ironing her clothes last Tuesday. If her iron operates on 1,050 watts of electricity, how many kilowatt-hours of electricity did she consume during this period of ironing?

▼EXPLANATION: By finding the product of 1,050 and 3½, you will determine the number of watt-hours of electricity consumed. Dividing this answer by 1,000 will give you the number of kilowatt-hours consumed.

●SOLUTION:

$$\text{Number of watt-hours} = 1{,}050 \times 3\frac{1}{2}$$
$$= 3{,}675$$
$$\text{Number of kilowatt-hours} = 3{,}675 \div 1{,}000$$
$$= 3.675$$

Take time to verify for the students that the quotient, when a number is divided by 1,000, will be that same number with the decimal point moved 3 places to the left. In Illustration 2, make certain that the mixed numeral, 3-1/2, is changed to its equivalent decimal form, 3.5, before multiplying.

EXERCISES   A

1. How many kilowatt-hours are there in each of the following number of watt-hours?

	Watt-Hours	Kilowatt-Hours			Watt-Hours	Kilowatt-Hours
a.	4,000	4	f.		6,750	6.75
b.	7,000	7	g.		29,324	29.324
c.	12,000	12	h.		346,815	346.815
d.	56,000	56	i.		700	.7
e.	124,000	124	j.		225	.225

2. Each of the following appliances is used for the number of hours indicated. How many watt-hours of electricity are consumed?

	Number Of Watts	Number Of Hours	Watt-Hours
a.	2	24	48
b.	345	3	1,035
c.	1,100	4	4,400
d.	240	5	1,200
e.	180	7	1,260
f.	2,500	5½	13,750
g.	645	4⅓	2,795
h.	30	2¼	67.5
i.	150	3¾	562.5
j.	225	6⅔	1,500

3. How many kilowatt-hours of electricity are consumed by each of the following appliances?

	Number Of Watts	Number Of Hours	Watt-Hours	Kilowatt-Hours
a.	400	15	6,000	6
b.	800	9	7,200	7.2
c.	350	6	2,100	2.1
d.	190	4	760	.76
e.	2,400	7	16,800	16.8
f.	6	24	144	.144

B

1. The markings on the motor of Fred Evans' electric table saw show that it operates on 1,150 watts of electricity. When Mr. Evans remodeled his home, he used the saw for a period of 75 hours. How many kilowatt-hours of electricity were consumed by the operation of the saw?   86.25

In Exercises 2 f, 2 h, and 2 i, the mixed numerals should be rewritten as equivalent decimals. However, the mixed numerals in 2 g, and 2 j should be expressed in their equivalent improper fraction numeral form.

2. To cool off his bedroom during the summer evenings before going to bed, William Carlton ran a portable fan for a period of 2½ hours. The fan operates on 395 watts of electricity. If William found it necessary to operate the fan for 60 days, how many kilowatt-hours of electricity did he use?   <u>59.25</u>

3. Mrs. Templer's electric coffeepot runs for approximately 40 minutes each time she makes coffee. If the information on the appliance shows that it uses 600 watts of electricity, how many kilowatt-hours are used each time Mrs. Templer brews coffee?   <u>.4</u>

4. During a recent evening, Mr. Speer watched television for 4½ hours. During the same evening, Mrs. Speer ironed for 2 hours and 20 minutes and listened to their stero set at the same time. Each used light bulbs of 30 and 150 watts respectively. In addition, the TV set operated on 180 watts, the stereo on 150 watts, and the iron on 1,200 watts. What was the total number of kilowatt-hours of electricity used that evening?   <u>4.445</u>

PART 2

As mentioned earlier, the company that supplies the electric current to your home charges for it in accordance with the number of kilowatt-hours used. Each month a company representative will read a meter such as the one shown and record the information in a book. From the meter reading for this month, he subtracts the amount shown on the meter last month to find out how many kilowatt-hours of electricity were used during the month.

■ ILLUSTRATION 1: The electric meter reading on June 28 was 34,726. The previous reading, taken on May 27, was 34,631. How many kilowatt-hours of electricity were used during the month?

▼ EXPLANATION: The numeral 34,726 represents the number of kilowatt-hours of electricity that had been used in this house from the time the meter was installed until June 28. Similarly, the numeral 34,631 gives the number of kilowatt-hours of electricity used from the time the meter was installed until May 27 of the preceding month. Hence, the difference between these numbers will tell you how many kilowatt-hours of electricity were used during the month.

● SOLUTION:

$$\text{Number of kilowatt-hours used} = 34,726 - 34,631$$
$$= 95$$

Stress with students the fact that no utility meters are designed so that they give a reading directly of the number of kilowatt-hours of electricity consumed that month. They work like a car mileage indicator. To determine the number of miles covered on a trip, you must know the beginning and end readings for the trip.

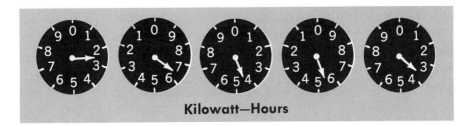

Kilowatt—Hours

Here is how the meter, shown above, is read. Notice that the numerals on each dial appear in the reverse direction from those on the dial following it. Thus, for the one farthest to the right, the numerals are written in a clockwise direction, while for the one immediately to its left, the numerals are written in a counterclockwise direction. For the next dial, they are clockwise again, and so on. This is done deliberately, for the turning of the hand on the dial farthest to the right activates a wheel that starts the hand on the second dial turning in the opposite direction. And the same is true for each of the other clock hands.

When reading an electric meter, look first at the dial farthest to the left. In this case, notice that the hand is between the numerals 2 and 3. Since there are four numerals yet to follow, this would imply that the number of kilowatt-hours had to be between 20,000 and 30,000. Therefore, you know that the first numeral in the reading must be a 2, making the reading a number such as, perhaps, 27,394. Were you to make the first numeral a 3, then the reading would be a number such as 37,394. This you know cannot be, for the reading must be between 20,000 and 30,000. In the same way, whenever the arrow points between two numerals, always write down the smaller of the two. Of course, if it points directly at a numeral, then it will be that numeral that must be written down.

In examining the second dial from the left, notice that the arrow falls between 6 and 7. Hence the numeral 6 will appear as the second digit. For the third dial, the arrow, being between 4 and 5, makes the third digit a 4. When all five dials are recorded, the reading will be 26,453. This means that 26,453 kilowatt-hours of electricity were used in this house since the meter was installed.

A rate table used by the Cape Electric and Gas Company is on page 466. It is on the basis of tables such as this that a monthly electric bill is computed.

■ILLUSTRATION 2: On August 25, Mr. Muir's electric meter was read and recorded at 35,682. On September 24, when it was read again,

Experience has shown that meters are occasionally read inaccurately by employees of utility companies. If, at no other time, it would certainly be important for a person to be able to check the readings at these times to verify for themselves the accuracy of the company readings.

CAPE ELECTRIC AND GAS COMPANY Residential Rate per Month—Electric	
For the first 8 kilowatt-hours or less	$1.65
For the next 62 kilowatt-hours, per kilowatt-hour	6.5¢
For the next 70 kilowatt-hours, per kilowatt-hour	4.5¢
For all over 140 kilowatt-hours, per kilowatt-hour	3¢

it registered 35,796. If Mr. Muir's apartment was in the area serviced by the Cape Electric and Gas Company, how large was his electric bill for this month?

●SOLUTION:

$$
\begin{array}{lll}
\text{Number of KWH}^* \text{ used} = 35,796 - 35,682 = & 114 \\
\text{Cost for first} \quad 8 \text{ KWH} \qquad\qquad = \$1.65 & \underline{-\quad 8} \\
& \qquad 106 \\
\text{Cost for next } 62 \text{ KWH} = 62 \times .065 = \;\; 4.03 & \underline{-\; 62} \\
& \qquad\;\; 44 \\
\text{Cost for next } 44 \text{ KWH} = 44 \times .045 = \;\; 1.98 & \underline{-\; 44} \\
\overline{\text{Cost for} \qquad 114 \text{ KWH}} \qquad\quad = \$7.66 & \qquad\;\; 0
\end{array}
$$

* The abbreviation KWH means kilowatt-hours

▼EXPLANATION: On the left is the total number of KWH used. On the far right, beyond the vertical line, is a running tally of how many KWH remained to be paid for. Thus, after paying for the first 8, there were still 106 KWH to be paid for. Then, after paying for the next 62 KWH, this number was subtracted from 106 to leave a balance of 44 KWH to be paid for.

EXERCISES   **A**

1. Record the readings on each of the following electric meters.

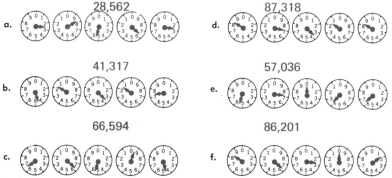

The format of the solution above may appear cumbersome. It is designed, however, to give a running tally of the number of kilowatt-hours of electricity paid for in the process of computation. If you prefer not to use this outline, then whatever format you do devise should include a running tally.

2. For each of the following, determine the number of kilowatt-hours of electricity used during the month.

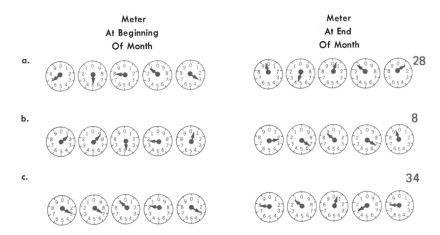

	Meter At Beginning Of Month	Meter At End Of Month	
a.			28
b.			8
c.			34

3. Determine the bill for each of the following customers. Use the rate table of the Cape Electric and Gas Company.

	Number of KWH Used During Month	Cost			Number of KWH Used During Month	Cost
a.	20	$ 2.43		d.	137	$ 8.70
b.	75	5.91		e.	156	9.31
c.	6	1.65		f.	384	16.15

4. Determine the bill for each of the following customers. Use the rate table of the Cape Electric and Gas Company.

	Reading At Beginning Of Month	Reading At End Of Month	Number Of KWH	Cost
a.	25,674	25,680	6	$ 1.65
b.	37,065	37,113	48	4.25
c.	46,381	46,493	112	7.57
d.	21,576	21,725	149	9.10
e.	16,974	17,341	367	15.64
f.	60,284	60,952	668	24.67

B

1. The information on the back of an electric clock shows that it operates on 2 watts of electricity. What is the total cost of operating this clock for an entire month of 31 days if the cost of each kilowatt-hour is 6.5¢?

10¢

Ask the students, if they can, to bring in electric bills. Check the accuracy of these bills, based on their learning experience in this unit. It may not be possible for all of them to obtain these bills, since the cost of electricity may be included in the apartment rent.

2. A 65-gallon hot-water heater requires 2,500 watts of electricity to operate. In order to heat the water, electric current must flow through the appliance approximately 6 hours per day. During a 30-day month, what will be the cost of heating water for this home if the price of each kilowatt-hour is 1.6¢? $7.20

3. An electric clothes drier operates on 4,200 watts of electricity. Mrs. Armond uses the drier for approximately 2 hours and 30 minutes every Monday. How much will it cost Mrs. Armond to dry her clothes during a month in which there are four Mondays if the cost of each kilowatt-hour is 2.75¢? $1.16

4. Each weekday evening after dinner, Mr. and Mrs. Riker sit down to a routine of 4½ hours with their TV set. Their son, George, goes to his room to study and to listen to the radio for approximately 3 hours before going to bed. The lamp he uses requires a 150-watt bulb, while the light burning in the room where his parents sit is only 50 watts. The TV set operates on 210 watts, and the radio on 32 watts. During a month of 22 weekdays, what will the cost of electricity be for just this use alone? Use the Cape Electric and Gas Company rate table. $3.60

Section 2:   The Cost of Gas

The only need that an apartment dweller would have for gas would be for his gas range and oven. The meters that register the flow of gas are very much the same in appearance as electric meters. But there is one major difference, for electric meters measure the quantity of electricity used in kilowatt-hours, while gas is measured in cubic feet.

One way of picturing the flow of gas is to think of a box that is 1 foot long, 1 foot wide, and 1 foot deep. Were this box filled with water, then you would say that the amount of water it held was 1 cubic foot. You could pour this same amount of water into a long plastic hose and then close off both ends. Although the water would not have the same shape that it did when it was in the box, the quantity of water—which was 1 cubic foot—would be the same.

Similarly, you can think of this same box as containing gas rather than water and that, in some way, you are able to pour the cubic foot of gas from the box into the hose. This is about what takes place in the purchase of gas. The company that services your apartment pumps the gas out of large storage tanks through pipes into your apartment. In this process, it passes through a gas meter which registers the number of cubic feet of gas used.

Problems such as 2 and 3 above are not entirely accurate. As is evident from the Cape Electric and Gas Company table, rates vary in accordance with total use of electricity over the month. Hence, it is unlikely that the rate would be constant as quoted. It might have been better to express an average rate.

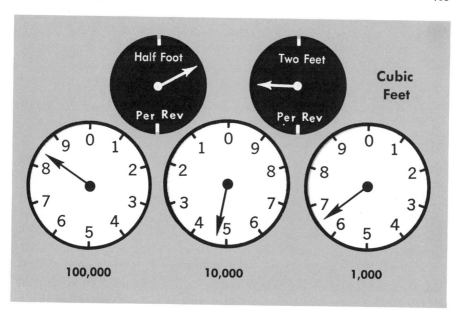

In getting a reading from the meter, the two small dials are completely ignored. Now, if the hand on the dial farthest to the right is rotated completely around and returned to the 0, then 1,000 cubic feet of gas would have flowed through the meter. Since the arrow points between the 6 and the 7, this implies that somewhat more than 600 cubic feet of gas have been consumed. Notice that, as in the case of the electric meter, when the arrow falls between two numerals, it is always the smaller one that is recorded. Hence, when the 8 and the 4, which are the readings of the first two dials, are written in front of the 600, then the entire reading becomes 84,600. Thus, 84,600 cubic feet of gas have passed through the meter since it was installed in this apartment.

Earlier you learned that the watt-hour was too small a unit for measuring the cost of electricity. Because of this, the much larger kilowatt-hour had to be used. The cubic foot, too, is much, much too small a unit for billing purposes and, therefore, gas is sold by the 100 cubic-foot units. As a result, meter readings are rarely, if ever, recorded as above, namely, 84,600, but simply as 846. This number is interpreted as follows:

> 846 hundreds of cubic feet of gas have passed
> through the meter since its installation.

The table on page 470 gives the rates charged by the Cape Electric and Gas Company for the use of gas.

There is always the possibility that a student may raise the point that a cubic foot of gas will vary with the amount of pressure used to force the gas into that space. Should this arise, and only if this occurs, answer the question by saying that the utility company decides in advance what the pressure will be.

CAPE ELECTRIC AND GAS COMPANY
Residential Rate per Month—Gas

For the first 2 hundred cubic feet or less	$1.05
For the next 7 hundred cubic feet, per hundred cubic feet	21.4¢
For the next 17 hundred cubic feet, per hundred cubic feet	18.5¢
For the next 24 hundred cubic feet, per hundred cubic feet	14.5¢
For all over 50 hundred cubic feet, per hundred cubic feet	11.4¢

■ ILLUSTRATION: On March 17, the gas meter for Mr. Link's apartment was read as 628. On April 18, when it was again checked, it showed a reading of 732. If Mr. Link lives in the area serviced by the Cape Electric and Gas Company, determine his gas bill for this period.

▼ EXPLANATION: Neither the meter readings nor the rate table include the two zeros that should be at the end of each number. Therefore, to simplify computation, you do not need to use them. Notice, also, that in the following computation, a running account is kept at the far right of the number of hundreds of cubic feet of gas that has been paid for at each step of the work.

● SOLUTION:

Number of hundreds of cubic ft. used $= 732 - 628 \qquad = \quad 104$

Cost of first 2 hundred cubic ft. $= \$1.05 \qquad \underline{- \quad 2}$

102

Cost of next 7 hundred cubic ft. $= 7 \times 21.4¢ = 1.498 \qquad \underline{- \quad 7}$

95

Cost of next 17 hundred cubic ft. $= 17 \times 18.5¢ = 3.145 \qquad \underline{- \quad 17}$

78

Cost of next 24 hundred cubic ft. $= 24 \times 14.5¢ = 3.480 \qquad \underline{- \quad 24}$

54

Cost of next 54 hundred cubic ft. $= 54 \times 11.4¢ = 6.156 \qquad \underline{- \quad 54}$

Cost for 104 hundred cubic ft. $= \qquad \$15.329,$ $\qquad 0$

or $15.33

Incidentally, if the reading for one month was 986, while the reading the following month turned out to be 017, it would merely indicate that, at some time during the month, the dials on the meter had recorded 1,000 hundred cubic feet, which is the largest number the meter can record. When this occurs, the meter begins to register the number of cubic feet from 0 again. Thus, for the readings just described, you would first subtract 986 from 1,000, for a difference of 14. This number is then added to 17 for a total of 31 hundred cubic feet of gas used during that month.

In the solution here, as in computing the cost of electricity, a running tally was kept of the number of cubic feet of gas paid for. Should you prefer a less cumbersome outline, do include in some way a comparable running tally.

EXERCISES

1. Record the readings on each of the following gas meters in terms of the actual number of cubic feet—not hundreds of cubic feet.

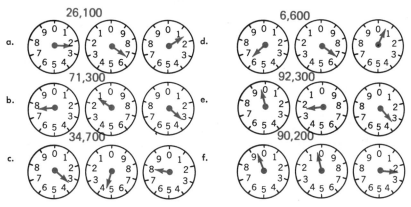

2. For each of the following, determine the number of hundreds of cubic feet of gas used during the month.

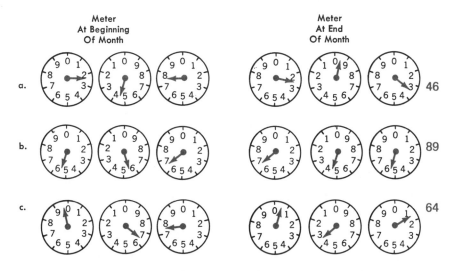

3. Determine the cost of gas for each of the following customers. Use the rate table of the Cape Electric and Gas Company.

Number of Hundreds Of Cubic Feet Used During Month		Cost		Number of Hundreds Of Cubic Feet Used During Month		Cost
a.	6	$ 1.91	d.	57	$ 9.97
b.	18	4.21	e.	98	14.65
c.	35	7.00	f.	134	18.75

4. Determine the cost of gas for each of the following customers. Use the rate table of the Cape Electric and Gas Company.

	Reading At Beginning Of Month	Reading At End Of Month	Number Of Hundreds Of Cubic Feet	Cost
a.	385	398	13	$ 3.29
b.	714	740	26	5.69
c.	888	957	69	11.34
d.	643	801	158	21.49
e.	993	014	21	4.77
f.	954	131	177	23.65

5. The Great Western Electric and Gas Company charges for gas consumption in accordance with the following monthly rate table.

$1.15 for the first..........................	300 cubic feet or less
22.3¢ per 100 cubic feet for the next..........	2400 cubic feet
18.1¢ per 100 cubic feet for the next..........	5300 cubic feet
12.6¢ per 100 cubic feet in excess of..........	8000 cubic feet

Determine the cost of gas for each of the following customers of the Great Western Electric and Gas Company.

	Reading At Beginning Of Month	Reading At End Of Month	Number Of Hundreds Of Cubic Feet	Cost
a.	257	271	14	$ 3.60
b.	193	235	42	9.22
c.	814	843	29	6.87
d.	873	942	69	14.10
e.	961	094	133	22.77
f.	879	021	142	23.91

6. The bills of the Cape Electric and Gas Company resemble the following form. Use the rate tables of this company to compute the total cost for electricity and gas for each of the following customers.

a.

CAPE ELECTRIC AND GAS COMPANY
Servant of a Great State

Next Meter
Reading Date
September 6

Service Period
July 7   August 5

Service	Meter Readings From	To			Amount
Electricity	6842	6878	36	KWH	$ 3.47
Gas	165	193	28	Hundred cubic feet	$ 5.98
				Total	$ 9.45

The suggestions made at the bottom of page 467 for electric bills apply equally well for gas bills.

b.

		Next Meter
	Service Period	Reading Date
	May 15 June 16	July 15

	Meter Readings					Amount
Service	From	To				
Electricity	3591	3725	134		$	8.56
Gas	847	889	42		$	8.01
				Total	$	16.57

c.

		Next Meter
	Service Period	Reading Date
	October 22 November 24	December 21

	Meter Readings					Amount
Service	From	To				
Electric	23684	23859	175		$	9.88
Gas	913	024	111		$	16.13
				Total	$	26.01

d.

		Next Meter
	Service Period	Reading Date
	February 16 March 15	April 16

	Meter Readings					Amount
Service	From	To				
Electric	61652	61982	330		$	14.53
Gas	416	604	188		$	24.91
				Total	$	39.44

Section 3:   The Telephone Bill

One of the large monthly bills of an apartment dweller is the telephone bill. The basic rate he has to pay depends entirely on the area in which he lives. In one state the monthly charges have the following range:

$3.35 for a private line   or $3.05 for a two-party line
$6.55 for a private line   or $5.20 for a two-party line

For this fee, the telephone user can make as many calls as he wants to certain neighboring towns at no cost. However, should he call someone outside of this limited area, there is an additional charge that he must pay in accordance with the table on page 474.

Notice that the table is separated into two parts. In the first part is shown the cost of those calls that are outside of the free-call zone, but are less than 20 miles from this zone. The second section of the table lists charges that are made if calls are to points that fall somewhere between 20 and 172 miles from the free-call zone.

Telephone rates vary quite drastically around the country. Those shown here are probably typical of the manner in which they are set up, if perhaps not typical of the fee itself. Obtaining a rate table from the telephone company is not quite so simple as obtaining one from the utility company.

RATE SCHEDULE						
	Station-to-Station				Person-to-Person	
Airline Miles	Paid			Collect	Paid & Collect	
Over	Up to and Including	Initial Period	Overtime	Amount Added To Charges On a Paid Basis	Initial 3 Minutes	Each Additional Minute
0	10	$.10—5 Minutes	$.05—3 Minutes	$.15	$.25	$.05
10	15	.15—5 Minutes	.05—2 Minutes	.10	.30	.05
15	20	.20—5 Minutes	.05—2 Minutes	.05	.35	.05

PAID OR COLLECT CALLS										
Airline Miles		Station-to-Station						Person-to-Person		
		Day		Evening		Night		Day		Night	
Over	Up to and Including	Initial 3 Minutes	Each Additional Minute	Initial 3 Minutes	Each Additional Minute	Initial 3 Minutes	Each Additional Minute	Initial 3 Minutes	Each Additional Minute	Initial 3 Minutes	Each Additional Minute
20	25	$.25	$.05	$.25	$.05	$.25	$.05	$.40	$.05	$.40	$.05
25	32	.30	.10	.30	.10	.30	.10	.45	.10	.45	.10
32	48	.35	.10	.35	.10	.30	.10	.50	.10	.50	.10
48	64	.40	.10	.35	.10	.30	.10	.65	.10	.60	.10
64	80	.45	.15	.40	.10	.30	.10	.75	.15	.65	.10
80	96	.50	.15	.40	.10	.30	.10	.85	.15	.75	.10
96	112	.55	.15	.40	.10	.30	.10	.90	.15	.75	.10
112	128	.60	.15	.45	.15	.35	.10	1.00	.15	.85	.15
128	150	.65	.20	.50	.15	.35	.10	1.05	.20	.90	.15
150	172	.70	.20	.55	.15	.35	.10	1.10	.20	.95	.15

There are certain words in the table that need clarification.

1. **Station-to-Station Call:** In a call of this nature, you want anyone at the other end of the phone to answer it. Even though he may not be the person you want to speak to, you will still have to pay for the call.

2. **Person-to-Person Call:** In this call, you tell the operator that you wish to speak only to a certain individual. If this person is not at home, you are not charged for the call. Notice that "Person-to-Person" calls cost more than "Station-to-Station" calls. As an example, a "Station-to-Station" call 8 miles from home would cost 10¢ for the first 5 minutes, while a "Person-to-Person" call to the same point would cost 25¢ for only 3 minutes.

3. **Paid Call:** In this call, the person who makes the call pays for it.

4. **Collect Call:** In this type of call, the person who receives the call agrees to pay for it. According to the table, there is no additional

The students should be required to know the difference between the various types of telephone calls that can be made. They should also discuss under what conditions it would be best to make certain calls.

charge for this service if the call is made to a point that is more than 20 miles from the free-call zone. Businessmen who are away on trips sometimes use this service to call their offices and have their firms pay the cost.

Examine the second part of the table carefully. Notice that on calls that are more than 48 miles from the free-zone, the charge during evenings or during nights is quite a good deal less than during the day hours. The telephone company designates "Day," "Evening," and "Night" rates as follows:

MONDAY THROUGH FRIDAY

Day Rates——4:30 A.M. to 6:00 P.M.
Evening Rates——6:00 P.M. to 8:00 P.M.
Night Rates——8:00 P.M. to 4:30 A.M.

For the remaining two days of the week, the hours for these rates are different.

SATURDAY AND SUNDAY

Sunday Rates——Night rates apply throughout the entire day.

Saturday Rates ⟨ Day rates from 4:30 A.M. to 8:00 P.M.
Night rates from 8:00 P.M. to 4:30 A.M.

Person-to-person calls in the evening are not listed in the table. This is because the rates are the same as day rates.

■ ILLUSTRATION 1: A phone call was made on Thursday at 7:05 P.M. over a distance of 84 miles. If the conversation lasted 15 minutes, what was the charge for this call?

● SOLUTION:

Cost for first 3 minutes	= $ .40
Cost for remaining 12 minutes = 12 × $.10 =	1.20
Total cost	= $1.60

▼ EXPLANATION: The call was made at 7:05 P.M. on Thursday. Hence, the evening rates applied. Since 84 miles is between 80 and 96 miles, you place a piece of paper along this row in the table and run your finger over to the column headed by the word "Evening." There are two sections in this column. The left one tells you the cost for the initial, or first, 3 minutes—$.40. From the right column, you learn that each additional minute costs $.10. Since there were 12 additional minutes, the charge for this was 12 × $.10, or $1.20. Hence, the total phone call cost $1.60.

Periodically, the telephone company changes hours which are classified as "day," "evening," or "night." Have a committee of students check to determine what the current definition of these terms may be.

■ILLUSTRATION 2: Mrs. Ervin has a private line for which there is a basic charge of $5.20 per month. During the past month, in addition to the calls made within the free-call zone, she made the following calls:

> a. 1 12-minute call to a distance of 14 miles
> b. 1 18-minute call to a distance of 17 miles
> c. 2 7-minute calls to a distance of 8 miles

If all the calls were station-to-station, and Mrs. Ervin, herself, paid for them, what was her bill for the month?

●SOLUTION:

> a. 1 12-minute call of 14 miles
>   First 5 minutes: $ .15
>   Remaining 7 minutes: 4 × $.05 =   .20
> b. 1 18-minute call of 17 miles
>   First 5 minutes: .20
>   Remaining 13 minutes: 7 × $.05 =   .35
> c. 1 7-minute call of 8 miles
>   First 5 minutes: .10
>   Remaining 2 minutes: 1 × $.05 =   .05
>   1 7-minute call of 8 miles: .15
>   Basic Charge: 5.20
>   Total: $6.40
>   Federal Tax (10%):   .64
>   Total Charge: $7.04

▼EXPLANATION: For the 12-minute call of 14 miles, the first 5 minutes cost $.15; for each 2 minutes of the 7 minutes that remained, the charge was $.05. By dividing 7 by 2, we find that there are 3½ 2-minute periods in 7 minutes. However, you are charged for any fraction of a period at the same rate that you would be charged for the full period. Hence, in the problem solution, the computation shows a charge of $.05 for each of 4 periods, or a total of $.20. Similarly, for the 18-minute call, a payment of $.20 was made for the first 5 minutes. To compute the cost for the remaining 13 minutes, you divide 13 by 2 to get 6½ 2-minute periods, which are changed to 7 periods. When you multiply 7 by $.05, you get the $.35 charge.

One method the federal government uses to raise money is to tax phone bills at a rate of 10%. After computing the telephone company bill, an additional 10% is added for tax. Ten percent of $6.40 is $.64. Hence, the total charge for the month is $7.04.

The computational aspects connected with finding the cost of telephone service is quite simple. However, students will very likely make a great number of careless errors in reading the table on page 474. It is important that a card be used as a guide when reading the table. Too many errors result without one.

EXERCISES   **A**

In each of the following problems, "S–S" will mean station-to-station and "P–P" will mean person-to-person.
1. Find the cost for each of the following calls that were made out of the free-call zone.

	Miles	Type of Call	Collect or Paid	Time in Minutes	Cost
a.	7	S–S	Paid	3	$ .10
b.	12	S–S	Paid	4	.15
c.	18	S–S	Paid	2	.20
d.	6	P–P	Paid	2	.25
e.	11	P–P	Paid	3	.30
f.	17	S–S	Collect	4	.25
g.	15	S–S	Collect	5	.25
h.	8	S–S	Collect	3	.25
i.	16	P–P	Collect	2	.35
j.	9	P–P	Collect	3	.25

2. Find the cost for each of the following calls that were made out of the free-call zone during a weekday.

	Miles	Type of Call	Time in Minutes	Hour of Call	Cost
a.	46	S–S	2	Day	$ .35
b.	58	S–S	1	Night	.30
c.	137	S–S	3	Evening	.50
d.	154	P–P	3	Night	.95
e.	85	P–P	2	Day	.85
f.	117	P–P	3	Evening	1.00

3. Find the cost for each of the following calls that were made out of the free-call zone.

	Miles	Type of Call	Time in Minutes	Hour of Call	Cost
a.	29	S–S	7	Monday—2:00 P.M.	$ .70
b.	52	S–S	9	Thursday—10:00 P.M.	.90
c.	106	S–S	6	Tuesday—8:10 P.M.	.60
d.	89	S–S	14	Friday—8:00 A.M.	2.15
e.	68	S–S	23	Wednesday—4:30 P.M.	3.45
f.	151	P–P	12	Monday—6:30 P.M.	2.90
g.	98	P–P	17	Sunday—1:30 P.M.	2.15
h.	74	S–S	8	Saturday—9:20 A.M.	1.20

4. Find the cost of each of the following calls that were made out of the free-call zone.

Do not include the federal tax of 10% when computing the answers for the exercises in either Group A or Group B, except where it is called for in Problem 6 of Group B.

	Miles	Type of Call	Collect or Paid	Time in Minutes	Cost
a.	11	S–S	Paid	13	$ .35
b.	18	S–S	Paid	8	.30
c.	17	S–S	Paid	19	.55
d.	12	S–S	Collect	12	.45
e.	19	S–S	Collect	15	.50
f.	7	S–S	Paid	16	.30
g.	9	P–P	Paid	7	.45
h.	16	P–P	Paid	14	.40

B

1. The Princess phone is a special small telephone that is offered at an additional charge of 65¢ per month—that is, if there is no other phone in the house. The basic charge in Mr. Alden's area is $6.55 for a private line, or $5.20 for a two-party line.
   a. How much extra will Mr. Alden have to pay each month if he chooses to have a Princess phone and a private line rather than a regular phone and a two-party line? $ 2.00
   b. How much extra will he have to pay over the period of a year? $24.00

2. Dorothy called her mother person-to-person from college, which is 143 miles from her home. The call was made at 2:30 in the afternoon on Wednesday. The conversation lasted five minutes.
   a. What was the cost of the call? $ 1.45
   b. What would the cost have been had it been made station-to-station? $ 1.05
   c. How much would Dorothy have saved by making it station-to-station? $ .40
   d. What would the cost have been if made person-to-person at 8:30 that same evening? $ 1.20
   e. How much would Dorothy have saved had she made the call at 8:30 in the evening rather than at 2.30 in the afternoon? $ .25

3. The day rate station-to-station calls from New York to Los Angeles are $2.00 for the first 3 minutes and $.50 for each minute thereafter. The night rate is $1.00 for the first 3 minutes and $.25 for each minute thereafter. How much would Mr. Shanks save if he made a 25-minute call from New York to Los Angeles at 9:00 P.M. on Monday rather than at 9:00 A.M. on Tuesday? $ 6.50

4. Mrs. Carlton is now married and lives in a town that is 125 miles from her parents' home. Each week she phones her parents. The calls are made on a station-to-station basis, and they usually last about 15 minutes.

a. How much would Mrs. Carlton save on these calls by making them on Sundays at 2:00 P.M. rather than Saturdays at 2:00 P.M.?

$ .85

b. Would there be any saving if the calls were made on Sunday at 9:00 P.M. rather than on Sunday at 2:00 P.M.?   No

5. What additional total charge over the basic fee will Mr. Denton have to pay for the following calls that were made out of the free-call zone? All of the calls were made station-to-station and none was collect.

   12   7-mile calls for less than 5 minutes
    9   12-mile calls for less than 5 minutes
    3   8-mile calls for 9 minutes each $ 3.15

6. The basic charge for Mr. Clemen's private line is $5.85 per month. He also has two extra phones in the house for which he has to pay 90¢ per month each. During the past month, he made the following calls to points that were not within the free-call zone.

    6   9-mile calls for less than 5 minutes
  14   17-mile calls for less than 5 minutes
    1   14-mile call for 26 minutes
    1   8-mile call for 15 minutes
    1   162-mile call for 12 minutes at 3:15 P.M. on a Thursday

All calls were made station-to-station and none was collect. How large was Mr. Clemen's telephone bill that month? Include federal tax. $16.01

Unit 2: Home Ownership

Section 1: The Mortgage

PART 1

The homeowner, like the apartment dweller, must pay gas, electric, and telephone bills. He must also meet monthly mortgage payments. There is little likelihood that many people would, or could, buy a house if it were necessary to pay the entire cost at the time of purchase. The price of the average house in this country is somewhere between $15,000 and $45,000. It is a rare family, indeed, that has that much cash to lay out for a house. Normally, the purchaser gives a down payment that may be as small as 10% of the selling price of the house. The

Have the students outline Problems 5 and 6 above in exactly the same manner as the solution to Illustration 2 on page 476 is outlined.

rest of the money is often borrowed from either a bank or a savings and loan association.

When a person borrows money, he signs a piece of paper called a note, to show that at some specified date in the future he intends to pay back that money. In the present situation, where money is borrowed to pay for a home, the piece of paper that is signed is called a *mortgage*. Payments are made on the debt in monthly periods and may extend over a period of 20, 25, 30 or, even, in some rare instances, 40 years. Should the borrower fail to meet these payments, then, by an agreement written in the mortgage, the bank—or whoever may be the lender—is permitted to sell the house to get back the money still owed to it.

The rate of interest charged for mortgage money varies widely around the country. It ranges from a low of 6% to a high of 11% or 12%. To determine what the monthly payments will be, the banker examines a table such as the following. This table is based on each $1,000 in the value of the mortgage—that is, the amount of money borrowed.

LOAN PAYMENT SCHEDULE								
Monthly Payment Necessary on a $1,000 Loan								
Years	6%	6½%	7%	7½%	8%	8½%	9%	9½%	10%
15	$8.44	$8.71	$8.99	$9.27	$9.56	$9.85	$10.15	$10.45	$10.76
20	7.16	7.46	7.75	8.06	8.37	8.69	9.01	9.34	9.67
25	6.44	6.75	7.07	7.39	7.72	8.05	8.39	8.73	9.08
30	6.00	6.32	6.65	6.99	7.34	7.69	8.05	8.41	8.78
35	5.70	6.04	6.39	6.74	7.11	7.47	7.83	8.20	8.57
40	5.50	5.85	6.21	6.58	6.96	7.34	7.72	8.10	8.48

■ILLUSTRATION 1: Mr. Temple was granted a 6½% mortgage of $18,500 on his home. If the debt is to be paid off over a 20-year period, what will the monthly payments have to be?

▼EXPLANATION: Run your finger down the column headed by the word "Years" until you come to the numeral 20. Place a piece of paper across this row. Then run your finger along this row until you reach the column headed "6½%." Your finger will come to rest on the numeral "$7.46." This is the amount of money that Mr. Temple will have to pay monthly for each $1,000 in the $18,500 that he borrowed. Since there are 18.5 thousands in 18,500, then the total monthly payment will be 18.5 times $7.46, or $138.01.

Someone has facetiously referred to the term "mortgage" as being derived from the terms "mort" and gage," — meaning "a grip of death." And this is how some homeowners often feel about their mortgages.

● SOLUTION:

$$\text{Number of thousands in } 18,500 = 18,500 \div 1,000$$
$$= 18.5$$

Monthly payment per \$1,000 at $6\frac{1}{2}\%$ = \$7.46

Monthly payment for \$18,500 = $18.5 \times \$7.46$
$$= \$138.01$$

There are some states in which the legal maximum interest rate that can be charged is 7%. To get around this law, many lending agencies have begun to charge the mortgage borrower *points* just for the privilege of borrowing money from them. A point is another name for 1 percent. As an example, if a person is charged 2 points for being granted a mortgage, this simply means that he has to pay a fee of 2% of the amount borrowed merely for having been granted the loan. If the borrower is unwilling to pay this additional amount, he will not receive the loan.

There is some justification for charging these points, for there are times when the interest rate that a bank pays its depositors may be very close to the legal limit that it can charge its borrowers. When this is so, there would be no way in which this institution could pay the salaries of its employees, or make a profit, unless it used this point system. Many institutions, however, employ this as a device for getting around the law.

■ ILLUSTRATION 2: Mr. Spencer purchased a \$23,000 home by making a down payment of 10%. For the balance of the debt, he took out a mortgage for which the bank charged him 4 points. To help him with the legal problems involved in buying the home, Mr. Spencer hired a lawyer who charged him \$325. What was the total amount of money that Mr. Spencer had to have in cash on the day he took over possession of the house?

● SOLUTION:

$$\text{Down payment} = \$23,000 \times 10\%$$
$$= \$2,300$$

$$\text{Size of mortgage} = \$23,000 - \$2,300$$
$$= \$20,700$$

$$\text{Charge for receiving mortgage} = \$20,700 \times 4\%$$
$$= \$828$$

$$\text{Legal expenses} = \$325$$
$$\text{Total cash needed} = \$2,300 + \$828 + \$325$$
$$= \$3,453$$

▼ EXPLANATION: Since the points are charged only on the size of the mortgage, the down payment of \$2,300 was subtracted from the cost

Although it has been only recently that the students were taught a short method for dividing a number by 1,000, it is best to review this process for them at this time. (See the suggestion on page 462.)

of the house of $23,000. This left a mortgage of $20,700. The 4 points were written as 4%, and 4% of $20,700 is $828.

EXERCISES   A

1. Points were charged in obtaining each of the following mortgages. How much extra did the purchaser have to pay?

	Size of Mortgage	Number of Points	Cost For Obtaining Mortgage
a.	$16,000	1	$ 160.00
b.	12,000	3	360.00
c.	9,400	2	188.00
d.	23,500	4½	1,057.50

2. After making the down payment shown, each of the following purchasers had to pay points for being granted a mortgage for the remainder of the money he needed. How much was this charge in each case?

	Price Of Property	Down Payment (Percent)	Down Payment	Mortgage	Points	Additional Charge
a.	$18,000	10%	$ 1,800.00	$ 16,200.00	2	$ 324.00
b.	16,000	5%	800.00	15,200.00	4	608.00
c.	28,000	40%	11,200.00	16,800.00	1	168.00
d.	21,800	60%	13,080.00	8,720.00	2½	218.00
e.	34,500	50%	17,250.00	17,250.00	3½	603.75

3. How large will the monthly payments be on each of the following mortgages?

	Size of Mortgage	Interest Rate	Period of Debt	Monthly Payment
a.	$12,000	9%	20 Years	$ 108.12
b.	14,000	8½%	25 Years	112.70
c.	9,200	7%	30 Years	61.18
d.	16,400	7½%	25 Years	121.20
e.	15,900	10%	20 Years	153.75
f.	23,600	8%	15 Years	225.62

B

1. A mortgage company requires that the borrower purchase *title insurance* to the extent of the mortgage at the time he receives the money. The purpose of this insurance is to make certain that the mortgage company gets its money from the insurance firm in case someone, at some future time, can legally show that the person who sold the property really had no right to do so. If the cost

The reason for the use of the term "points" rather than "percent" relative to the extra fee for borrowing mortgage money appears to be rather obscure. It may very well be that the lending agency may feel that this word will carry with it the impression of a smaller cost than the use of the word "percent."

of title insurance is at the rate of $5.00 per $1,000, how much will a person have to pay for this if the size of his mortgage is $12,000?

$60.00

2. Henry Stevens purchased a house for $28,700. He made a down payment of 45% and was granted a mortgage for the remainder. The title insurance he purchased at $5.50 per $1,000 covered only the amount of the mortgage. How much did this cost him? $86.82

3. Mr. Clarke received a 9% mortgage for $10,500 when he purchased his house. He agreed to pay off this debt over a 20-year period.
   a. What were his monthly payments? $94.61
   b. How much did this amount to annually? $1,135.32
   c. What was the total amount that he paid back over the 20-year period? $22,706.40

4. When purchasing his house, Mr. Denton put down a 20% deposit on the $24,000 that he had to pay. The remainder he borrowed at 7%, to be paid off over a period of 25 years.
   a. What were his monthly payments? $135.74
   b. What was the total he paid back over the 25-year period? $40,722.00
   c. How much more did he pay back than he borrowed? $21,522.00

5. At the time that Charles Martin purchased his house, he obtained an $18,000 mortgage from his bank at a 9½% interest rate.
   a. If he agrees to amortize—that is, to pay off—the debt in monthly payments over 20 years, what will be the total amount that he will return to the bank? $40,348.80
   b. If he agrees to amortize the debt over a 30-year period, what will be the total amount he will return to the bank? $54,496.80
   c. How much will Mr. Martin save by amortizing the mortgage over a 20-year period rather than a 30-year period? $14,148.00

6. Fred Huck was granted a mortgage of $14,000 for his house. He arranged to amortize the loan over a 25-year period.
   a. What will be the total amount he will return if the interest rate is 7½%? $31,038.00
   b. What will be the total amount he will return if the interest rate is 8%? $32,424.00
   c. How much will Mr. Huck save by being able to borrow the money at 7½% rather than 8%? $1,386.00

7. Mr. Kempton purchased a house for $28,300, for which he planned to give a 40% down payment. The rest of the money he borrowed from a savings and loan association, which charged him 2 points for obtaining the mortgage.

The students may find the problems above somewhat difficult. However, they are important, for they emphasize certain comparisons that a person contemplating the purchase of a home should consider. The problems were purposely broken up into small segments in order to simplify them.

a. How much did Mr. Kempton have to pay just for the privilege of borrowing the money? $339.60

b. The savings and loan association charged Mr. Kempton $23 for expenses it incurred in checking to see if he should receive the mortgage. In addition, Mr. Kempton had to pay George Stacey, his lawyer, $285 for legal fees connected with Mr. Stacey's work relative to the purchase of this house. What was the total of these fees? $308.00

c. Mr. Kempton was required to take out title insurance to the extent of the mortgage. How much did this cost him if the rate was $5.25 per $1,000? $89.15

d. What was the total amount of money that Mr. Kempton had to have in cash on the day he took possession of the house? Exclude the down payment. $736.75

PART 2

Each monthly payment on a mortgage consists of two parts. Part of the payment is used to decrease the debt, while the remainder is the interest for one month on the balance of the debt that is still owed. As an example, consider a mortgage of $15,000 that is to be paid off monthly over a 20-year period. If you use the table on page 480, you will find that the monthly payments will be $107.40. When the very first payment is made, the debt is still $15,000, for nothing has been paid prior to this point. Hence, the interest for that month is as follows:

$$I = \$15,000 \times 6\% \times 1 \text{ month}$$
or, $$I = \$15,000 \times 6/100 \times 1/12$$
therefore $$I = \$75$$

The monthly payment of $107.40 included $75 in interest. The remainder of $32.40 is part payment on the debt. For the second month, the debt will be $15,000 less $32.40, or $14,967.60. In the same way, the interest for the second month is as follows

$$I = \$14,967.60 \times 6/100 \times 1/12$$
or, $$I = \$74.84$$

Since the monthly payment is still $107.40, and $74.84 of this was used for the interest payment, then the balance of $32.56 went toward reducing the debt.

Use the opportunity provided here to point out that a very large part of the early mortgage payments is needed to pay the interest on the debt. On the other hand, the last few mortgage payments are devoted almost entirely to paying off the debt, for the interest then is very small.

ORIGINAL DEBT: $15,000				
Payment Number	Monthly Payment	Amount For Interest	Amount Toward Decreasing Debt	Balance Of Debt
1	$107.40	$75.00	$32.40	$14,967.60
2	107.40	74.84	32.56	14,935.04

When we arrange this in the form of a table, it becomes apparent that, although the monthly payments remain the same, the interest charge decreases each month, while the amount that goes toward paying off the debt increases. In fact, in this problem, the amount will increase by approximately 16¢ each month. For the very last payment of $107.40, almost all of it will go toward paying off the debt and very little will be used for interest.

■ILLUSTRATION 1: Mr. Jenkins had reduced his 8% mortgage to the point where he owed the bank only $5,775.93. His monthly payments were $109.39. How much of the very next payment would be interest and how much would be used to reduce the balance of his debt?

● SOLUTION:

$$\text{Interest} = P \times R \times T$$
$$= \$5,775.93 \times 8\% \times 1 \text{ month}$$
$$= \$5,775.93 \times 8/100 \times 1/12$$
$$= \$38.51$$
$$\text{Amount used to reduce debt} = \$109.39 - \$38.51$$
$$= \$70.88$$

▼EXPLANATION: Since the debt at this point was only $5,775.93, you compute the interest for the one month on that amount. By subtracting the interest from the monthly payment of $109.39, you find that the amount used toward reducing the debt is $70.88. Had you wished, you could have gone one step farther and found the balance of the debt by subtracting the $70.88 from $5,775.93.

Banks and savings and loan associations, just as other business enterprises, operate for the purpose of making money. For this reason, they do not like to have the person who borrowed money on a mortgage pay off his debt before it is due. When this happens, they lose the interest they had planned on receiving. To discourage an early repayment of the mortgage, a penalty is charged. The rate charged by a number of banks is similar to the one on page 486.

The statement above about banks being unhappy when a mortgage is paid off before it is due is not quite accurate. At present, banks would be only too happy to have mortgages made 15 or 20 years ago paid off immediately, for the interest rate they can now charge is far higher than the rate at which the loan was then made.

THE GIBRALTER SAVINGS BANK			
If Debt Is Paid Off During	Penalty Charged	If Debt Is Paid Off During	Penalty Charged
1st Year	Not Permitted	6th Year	1¼% of Original Debt
2nd Year	Not Permitted	7th Year	1% of Original Debt
3rd Year	2% of Original Debt	8th Year	¾% of Original Debt
4th Year	1¾% of Original Debt	9th Year	½% of Original Debt
5th Year	1½% of Original Debt	10th Year	¼% of Original Debt

■ ILLUSTRATION 2: After making payments on his $11,500 mortgage for 5 years and 2 months, Mr. Thorn found that he was in a financial position to pay off the balance of his debt. How much would The Gibralter Savings Bank charge him if he did this?

● SOLUTION:

$$\text{Penalty} = \$11,500 \times 1\tfrac{1}{4}\%$$
$$= \$11,500 \times .0125$$
$$= \$143.75$$

▼ EXPLANATION: The penalty is determined on the original mortgage of $11,500. The computation is made slightly easier by changing the 1¼% to the decimal .0125 rather than to a fraction.

EXERCISES   **A**

1. How much would each of the following people be charged if they paid off their mortgages held by The Gibralter Savings Bank during the year shown?

	Original Mortgage	Paid Off During	Penalty Charge
a.	$ 7,000	3rd Year	$ 140.00
b.	8,500	7th Year	85.00
c.	12,400	5th Year	186.00
d.	15,300	4th Year	267.75
e.	21,600	6th Year	270.00
f.	25,750	8th Year	193.13
g.	26,250	10th Year	65.63

2. The balance of the debt still owed on their mortgages and the monthly payments for each of the following borrowers are given on page 487. Determine what part of the next payment represents the interest and what part will be used to pay off the balance of the debt of each.

Some time will have to be spent in reviewing how to rewrite the percent numerals for the 4th year through the 10th year as decimal numerals. For example, for the 8th year, the change should be made as follows:

$$3/4\% = .75\% = .0075$$

	Unpaid Balance Of Mortgage	Monthly Payment	Interest Rate	Interest	Payment On Debt
a.	$12,000.00	$107.47	6%	$ 60.00	$ 47.47
b.	9,200.00	128.25	9%	69.00	59.25
c.	6,450.00	83.70	8%	43.00	40.70
d.	4,600.00	77.75	7%	26.83	50.92
e.	7,846.80	83.96	10%	65.39	18.57
f.	14,351.68	123.09	9%	107.64	15.45
g.	2,424.45	77.20	8%	16.16	61.04
h.	5,946.23	120.18	7%	34.69	85.49
i.	8,000.00	93.20	6½%	43.33	49.87
j.	12,000.00	104.85	7½%	75.00	29.85

3. To make certain that the real estate tax is paid, the mortgage company requires that the borrower pay the company each month 1/12 of the annual tax bill. This is in addition to the monthly payment on the mortgage. The mortgage company then pays the real estate tax. How much will the monthly tax payments be for each of the following?

	Annual Tax Bill	Monthly Payment
a.	$300.00	$ 25.00
b.	420.00	35.00
c.	570.00	47.50
d.	375.00	31.25
e.	824.56	68.71
f.	928.23	77.35

4. A mortgage company frequently requires that the borrower pay it monthly 1/36 of the insurance premium on the house. This money is then sent to the insurance agent. The mortgage company does this to make certain that in the event the house is destroyed, it will be paid the balance of its debt by the insurance company. The numeral 1/36 comes from the fact that insurance is purchased for a three-year period, and that there are 36 months in 3 years. How much will the monthly insurance payment be for each of the following?

	Three-Year Insurance Cost	Monthly Payment
a.	$180	$ 5.00
b.	450	12.50
c.	265	7.36
d.	317	8.81

In Exercises 3 and 4, the mortgage company will try to anticipate what the tax or the cost of the insurance will be for the coming year. Should the monthly payments be too small, then the borrower will be billed for an additional amount at the close of the year.

B

1. Mr. Tracey currently has a balance of $4,374.24 on his mortgage, for which he is making monthly payments of $114.63. The interest rate on the debt is 8%.
   a. How much of the next payment will be interest? $29.16
   b. How much of the next payment will be used to reduce the mortgage? $85.47
   c. What will be the balance of Mr. Tracey's debt after the next payment? $4,288.77

2. After having made his monthly payment of $79.84 on his 7% mortgage for a number of years, Mr. Dorman found that he still had a balance of $6,200. How much will the balance be after the next payment? $6,156.33

3. Arthur Jefferson was given a $12,000 mortgage for a period of 25 years at an interest rate of 6%.
   a. Determine Mr. Jefferson's monthly payments. Use the table on page 480. $77.28
   b. Set up a table similar to the one on page 485, which shows the monthly payment, the interest paid each month, the amount of the monthly payment that goes toward decreasing the debt, and the balance of the debt for the first two payments on Mr. Jefferson's mortgage.

Payment Number	Monthly Payment	Amount For Interest	Amount Toward Decreasing Debt	Balance Of Debt
1	$77.28	$60.00	$17.28	$11,982.72
2	77.28	59.91	17.37	11,965.35

4. Mr. Corbley's mortgage on his house was for $14,000 at 8% for a 20-year period.
   a. Determine the monthly payments on the mortgage. Use the table on page 480. $117.18
   b. The estimated real estate tax on the house for the year was $495. How large were the monthly tax payments to the mortgage company? $41.25
   c. The cost of insurance on the house for the three-year period was $246. How large were the monthly insurance payments to the mortgage company? $6.83
   d. What was the total amount of money that Mr. Corbley paid the mortgage company each month? $165.26

Section 2:   Real Estate Tax

PART 1

It is the local government that takes care of the schools, the roads, the police and fire departments, the library, the sanitation department, and many other service areas in a city or town. The burden of supplying money needed for these operations falls on the property owner. The share that he has to pay is called a real estate tax.

Everyone does not, and should not, pay the same amount of tax. Consider as a very simple example a community in which there are only two residents—Mr. Evans and Mr. Harper. The value of Mr. Evans' property is $1,000, while that of Mr. Harper's is $2,000. In the course of a conversation between them they decide that they would like to have a service for which the cost is $600. They soon realize that Mr. Harper should pay more than Mr. Evans, because his property is the more valuable of the two. Since the Harper property is twice as valuable, Mr. Harper agrees to pay twice as much as Mr. Evans. Hence, Mr. Harper will pay $400, while Mr. Evans will pay only $200.

If the two men had had any trouble deciding what each would have to contribute, they could have solved their problem by finding the total value of both their properties—$3,000. Thus, the cost of the service they desire represents $600 in comparison to the total property value of $3,000. This is exactly one of the interpretations that was given to a fraction earlier in your work. Therefore, $600 compared to $3,000 can be written as the following fraction:

$$\$600/\$3,000$$

When this is reduced to the fraction where the denominator is 1, it becomes:

$$\$.20/\$1 \qquad \text{①}$$

This fraction is interpreted as follows: For each $1 in the total value of both properties, $.20 will have to be spent for the service both men want. Since the value of Mr. Evans' property is $1,000, then he will have to pay:

$$1,000 \times \$.20, \text{ or } \$200$$

Similarly, the value of Mr. Harper's property is $2,000. Hence, he will have to pay:

$$2,000 \times \$.20, \text{ or } \$400$$

These, of course, are the numbers arrived at earlier.

Read the illustration above with the students. It has been found simple enough for them to understand. Using the typical expenses that face a community would involve figures that only tend to confuse the students.

Before leaving this problem, it should be pointed out that the $.20 in the fraction labeled ① above was found by dividing $600 by the denominator of $3,000.

The real estate tax that each property owner must pay is computed in exactly the same way as that just described. At the outset, the sum of all the expenses that a town will have for the year is found. This number is then divided by the total value of all the property of the entire town. The quotient represents the amount of money that will be needed for each dollar in the value of the property.

■ILLUSTRATION 1: The town of Triton needs $840,000 to meet expenses for the coming year. If the total value of all the property in the town is $24,000,000, how much money will have to be received for each dollar in the value of the property?

▼EXPLANATION: As in the case of Mr. Harper and Mr. Evans, you divide the total amount of money needed by the total value of the property. In this way you will determine the amount of money needed per dollar of the total value. In the following solution, it is found that 3.5¢ per dollar of property value is needed.

●SOLUTION:

Amount needed per $1 of property value = $840,000 ÷ 24,000,000
= $.035, or 3.5¢

It was not quite correct to say that the total value of the property in Triton was $24,000,000. What normally happens is that a person, called an *assessor*, is employed by the governing body of a community to visit every piece of property in that community and record what he believes the value of it should be. The price that he attaches to it is called the *assessed value* of the property. This amount varies widely from town to town and from state to state. In fact, the assessed value ranges from as low as 10% of the actual value of the property in some communities to as high as 100% of the actual value in other communities.

In Illustration 1, the $24,000,000 should have been properly called the total assessed value of the property in Triton rather than merely the total value of the property. One other point has to be made concerning this problem—the 3.5¢ per $1 in the solution is called the tax rate. Although there are many towns that quote the rate in this form, there are many, many more that prefer to quote the rate either as a percent value, or in dollars per $100, or in dollars per $1,000, or even in mills per $1!

■ILLUSTRATION 2: Change the tax rate of 3.5¢ per $1 to one quoted in dollars per $100.

In the solution of Illustration 1, have the students express the quotient of 840,000 and 24,000,000 as a fraction from which they eliminate as many zeros as possible from the numerator and denominator before dividing.

▼EXPLANATION: It would be best if at the outset the numeral 3.5¢ was written with a dollar sign. This, of course, is done by moving the decimal point two places to the left and rewriting the numeral as $.035. To change the $1 in the rate to $100, it is necessary to multiply $1 by 100. Hence, the same must be done to the $.035, making it $3.50. Recall that the fastest way to multiply a number by 100 is to move the decimal point two places to the right in the number.

●SOLUTION:

> 3.5¢ per $1
> is rewritten as
> $.035 per $1
> Then both $.035 and $1 are multiplied by 100, giving
> $3.50 per $100

■ILLUSTRATION 3: Change the tax rate of $4.76 per $100 to one quoted in mills per $1.

▼EXPLANATION: Your first objective should be to change the $4.76 to mills. Although there is no coin in the United States that represents a mill, there are a number of items whose costs are quoted in mills, and one of these is a tax rate. The value of a cent is 1 hundredth of a dollar. The value of a mill is 1 thousandth of a dollar. For your purposes, it would be best to reverse this and think in terms of the fact that each dollar is the equivalent of 1,000 mills. Hence, $2 is the equivalent of 2,000 mills, and $8 is the equivalent of 8,000 mills. Or, in general, dollars can be changed to mills simply by multiplying the number of dollars by 1,000. Thus, $4.76 is the equivalent of 4,760 mills, for when 4.76 is multiplied by 1,000, the decimal point is moved 3 places to the right. Therefore, the rate of

> $4.76 per $100

can be written as

> 4,760 mills per $100

Then, if both the 4,760 mills and the $100 are divided by 100, the rate will be quoted in terms of mills per $1: 47.60 mills per $100.

●SOLUTION:

> $4.76 per $100
> is rewritten as
> 4,760 mills per $100
> Then both 4,760 mills and $100 are divided by 100, giving
> 47.60 mills per $1

■ILLUSTRATION 4: Change the tax rate of $54.20 per $1,000 to one quoted in dollars per $100.

Since the students are not familiar with the "mill" as a monetary unit, some time should be spent converting from dollars to mills and vice versa. This will involve either multiplication or division by 1,000, and this can be done by movement of the decimal point.

● S O L U T I O N :

$54.20 per $1,000
When both $54.20 and $1,000 are divided by 10, you obtain
$5.42 per $100.

EXERCISES   A

1. Change each of the tax rates below from its present form to the one
quoted at its right.

    a. $2.50 per $100 = $_25.00____ per $1,000

    b. $5.46 per $100 = $_54.60____ per $1,000

    c. $43.80 per $1,000 = $_4.38____ per $100

    d. $36 per $1,000 = $_3.60____ per $100

    e. 4¢ per $1 = $_4.00____ per $100

    f. 6.1¢ per $1 = $_6.10____ per $100

    g. $3.40 per $100 = _3.4____¢ per $1

    h. $6.27 per $100 = _6.27____¢ per $1

    i. 5.2¢ per $1 = $_52.00____ per $1,000

    j. 3.95¢ per $1 = $_39.50____ per $1,000

    k. $72.20 per $1,000 = _7.22____¢ per $1

    l. $12.46 per $1,000 = _1.246____¢ per $1

    m. $3.72 per $100 = _37.2____ mills per $1

    n. $6.30 per $100 = _63____ mills per $1

    o. $35.40 per $1,000 = _35.4____ mills per $1

    p. $29.81 per $1,000 = _29.81____ mills per $1

2. For each of the following problems, find the tax rate in the form
quoted in the last column. Carry out the division until the remainder is zero.

	Total Expenses For the Year	Total Assessed Value	Tax Rate	
a.	$ 450,000	$ 9,000,000	$_.05____	per $1
b.	1,380,000	23,000,000	_6____¢	per $1
c.	1,035,000	45,000,000	$_2.30____	per $100
d.	2,315,500	84,200,000	$_2.75____	per $100
e.	1,938,000	57,000,000	_34____	mills per $1
f.	5,803,976	125,600,000	$_46.21____	per $1,000

In doing Exercise 1, the student should be advised to compare the base at the left with the one
he is asked to use at the right to determine how the one at the right can be found from the one
at the left. That is, if the present one is $100, and the one sought at the right is $1,000,
multiplication will have to be by 10.

B

1. Brighton Township is one of four communities that contribute to the support of a regional high school. Brighton's share of this cost amounted to $492,000 last year. If the total assessed value of the property in the township was $41,000,000, what was the tax rate in dollars per $100 that was needed for the high school alone?

    $1.20

2. In its budget for the coming year, the town of Lakeside listed its contribution to the cost of maintaining the county government as $801,920. What is the tax rate per $1,000 that is needed for this expenditure if the total assessed valuation in Lakeside is $64,000,000?

    $12.53

3. In order to meet its expenses for the coming year, the town of West Camden will have to raise $1,040,000 in taxes. Through fines collected for traffic and building violations, the town will collect $20,100. If the assessed valuation of property in the town is $16,450,000, what will the tax rate have to be in mills per $1?   62 mills

4. During the present year, Lansing Township paid $430,000 to support its school system. For the coming year, it will have to pay $483,749.99 to meet this cost. The total assessment of property in the town is $38,392,850. How much more will the school tax rate be in dollars per $100 for the coming year than it was for the past year?

    $.14 per $100.00

PART 2

Although there are some homeowners who are concerned with the cost of running their local government, the majority are much more interested in what their share of this cost will be. All too frequently their attention seems to be centered on the tax rate, for they wrongly consider a high tax rate to mean high taxes and a low tax rate to mean low taxes. They have overlooked the fact that the tax they pay depends not only on the tax rate, but, also, on the assessed value of their property. The following illustration should help clear up this point.

■ILLUSTRATION 1: In the town of West Millford, the tax rate is $4.12 per $100, while property is assessed at approximately 80% of its actual value. In the adjacent town of East Millford, the tax rate is $6.18 per $100, while the property here is assessed for only 50% of its actual value. How much more tax will Mr. Thompson have to pay if he decides to purchase a $22,000 home in one of these communities rather than the other?

A great deal of emphasis should be placed on the fact that real estate tax depends on two factors –the assessed value and the tax rate. Knowing the size of the one alone, without a knowledge of the other, will not in any way indicate whether the tax will be high or low.

●SOLUTION:

Assessed value in West Millford = $22,000 × 80%
$$= \$17,600$$
Number of 100's in 17,600 = 17,600 ÷ 100
$$= 176$$
Tax in West Millford = 176 × $4.12
$$= \$725.12$$
Assessed value in East Millford = $22,000 × 50%
$$= \$11,000$$
Number of 100's in 11,000 = 11,000 ÷ 100
$$= 110$$
Tax in East Millford = 110 × $6.18
$$= \$679.80$$
Amount of tax more in West Millford than in East Millford
$$= \$725.12 - \$679.80$$
$$= \$45.32$$

▼EXPLANATION: Although the tax rate in East Millford is more than $2 per $100 greater than in West Millford, Mr. Thompson's tax for a $22,000 home will be $45.32 less if he purchases it in East Millford. The cause for this is the fact that property in East Millford is assessed at a smaller percent of the actual value than it is in West Millford. Before deciding whether the taxes in a community are high or low, the homeowner should compute the actual tax he will have to pay. His decision should not be made by examining only the assessed value, or only the tax rate.

Notice that in computing the tax to be paid in the town of West Millford you first had to divide the assessed value of $17,600 by 100 to find the number of 100's in 17,600. This was necessary, since for each $100 in the assessed value, the owner of the property had to pay $4.12. As there are 176 100's in 17,600, the tax was computed by finding the product of 176 and $4.12. The same method was used for finding the tax in East Millford. If the tax rate had been quoted in dollars per $1,000, then it would have been necessary to find the number of thousands in 17,600. This is done by dividing 17,600 by 1,000, that is, by moving the decimal point 3 places to the left in 17,600. This results in a quotient of 17.6 thousands.

■ILLUSTRATION 2: The assessed value of Mr. Sanford's home and land is $21,600. If the tax rate is 37.2 mills per $1, how much tax will he have to pay?

▼EXPLANATION: Your first objective is to rewrite the 37.2 mills in terms of dollars. Since 1 mill is 1 thousandth of 1 dollar, then 37.2 mills

Certain state laws insist that the assessed value of property throughout the state be consistent. Hence, they legislate that real estate be assessed at 100% of its actual value. Check to see at what percent of actual value property is assessed in your local community.

are 37.2 thousandths of 1 dollar. When 37.2 thousandths is expressed as a numeral, it becomes 37.2/1000. After dividing by 1,000, it will be .0372. Thus, the tax rate of 37.2 mills per dollar equals $.0372 per dollar. Hence, for each dollar in the assessed value, the taxpayer will have to pay $.0372.

● SOLUTION:

$$\text{Tax rate} = 37.2 \text{ mills per } \$1$$
$$= \$.0372 \text{ per } \$1$$
$$\text{Number of dollars in } \$21,600 = 21,600 \div 1$$
$$= 21,600$$
$$\text{Tax} = 21,600 \times \$.0372$$
$$= \$803.52$$

EXERCISES   A

1. Compute the tax for each of the following properties.

	Assessed Value	Tax Rate	Tax
a.	$12,400	$2.30 per $100	$ 285.20
b.	18,200	$4.56 per $100	829.92
c.	23,000	$34.27 per $1,000	788.21
d.	19,600	$42.85 per $1,000	839.86
e.	21,300	$.041 per $1	873.30
f.	29,800	$.067 per $1	1,996.60
g.	27,500	5.3¢ per $1	1,457.50
h.	12,900	3.94¢ per $1	508.26
i.	26,800	48 mills per $1	1,286.40
j.	35,200	39.4 mills per $1	1,386.88

2. Each of the following properties is assessed at the percent of its actual value that is shown. Compute the tax that will have to be paid.

	Actual Value	Assessed At the Following Percent	Assessed Value	Tax Rate	Tax
a.	$18,400	50%	$ 9,200.00	$2.59 per $100	$ 238.28
b.	19,600	75%	14,700.00	$7.82 per $100	1,149.54
c.	25,000	60%	15,000.00	$43.76 per $1,000	656.40
d.	21,400	20%	4,280.00	$12.93 per $1,000	55.34
e.	27,300	90%	24,570.00	3.6¢ per $1	884.52
f.	32,100	80%	25,680.00	5.92¢ per $1	1,520.26
g.	37,600	70%	26,320.00	53 mills per $1	1,394.96
h.	68,200	55%	37,510.00	64.2 mills per $1	2,408.14

B

1. Last year, the borough of Moorestown had a tax rate of 2.57%. How much tax did the owner of a property assessed at $8,400 have to pay?
$215.88

2. The tax rate in Orangeburg is 89¢ per $10. How much tax will have to be paid on a property whose actual value is $28,000, but is assessed at 40% of this value?
$996.80

3. Which of the following tax rates is the greater?
   a. $5.37 per $100   or $48.26 per $1,000 $5.37 per $100.00
   b. 5.4¢ per $1   or $6.27 per $100 $6.27 per $100.00
   c. 46 mills per $1   or   6¢ per $1   6¢ per $1.00

4. The budget for Elmsport showed that its tax rate of $3.52 per $100 was to be spent as follows:

Borough Tax	$ .19
School Tax	1.18
Regional School Tax	1.20
County Tax	.95
Total	$3.52

Mr. Armstrong owns a home in Elmsport that is valued at $40,000 but is assessed at 9/10 of its value.
   a. What is the total tax that Mr. Armstrong will have to pay?
$1,267.20

   b. How much of Mr. Armstrong's tax will go to each of the expenses listed in the budget? B.T.: $68.40; S.T.: $424.80; R.S.T.: $432; C.T.: $342.

5. When Mr. Cramer built an addition to his home, his assessed value was increased from $26,400 to $28,600. If the tax rate last year was $4.81 per $100, how much extra in tax did Mr. Cramer have to pay because of the enlargement of his home?
$105.82

6. Mr. Shearing owns a house worth $21,500 in Great Meadow and another one valued at $26,300 in Cedarville. In the first town, property is assessed at 100% of its value, while in the second, it is assessed at only 65% of its value. The tax rate in Great Meadow is $4.23 per $100, and in Cedarville it is $38.64 per $1,000. What is the total real-estate tax that Mr. Shearing has to pay for these two houses?
$1,570.00

Section 3:   The Cost of Water

One of the public utility costs that the person who rents an apartment does not have to pay for is water. Although there are cities where

Usually, somewhere on a real estate tax bill will appear the information shown in Problem 4 of Group B. Have the students whose parents own property investigate this. If it does not appear there, have a committee visit the town hall to obtain this information.

the feeling is that water should be free, unfortunately for the home-owner, their number is extremely small. Hence, in addition to paying for gas and electricity, the homeowner must pay for the water that is piped into his house.

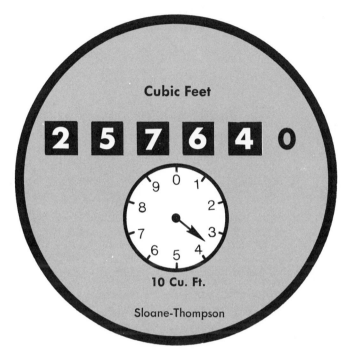

Although water meters vary in appearance, most look like the one shown. This meter is far easier to read than the gas and electric meters, for here the numerals in the small squares record the reading. The reading of 257,640 indicates the number of cubic feet of water that have passed through the meter since it was installed. To be exact, the last digit should have been a 3 rather than a 0. (The numeral 3 comes from the dial in the center.) However, the cost of 3 cubic feet of water is so small that it will not affect the total bill. Further, although it is dropped off now, it will be included as part of the total water consumption at the next reading.

It is evident from the meter that water is purchased by the cubic foot. The rates, though, are quoted per 1,000 cubic feet, for they would be far too small and too clumsy to use if they were quoted per cubic foot. Some communities prefer to sell water by the gallon rather than the cubic foot. Their meters are the same as the one on page 469. The only difference is that these meters are geared to record consumption in gallons instead of cubic feet.

If this was not done at the time of the earlier unit on the purchase of gas, you might want to point out exactly what a cubic foot resembles. We all too often find that, although students can talk about this unit and compute the cost of water based on it, they have only vague ideas about its size.

The way in which the water rates are quoted by the town of Bloomington, Rhode Island, is very much the way you would find for most communities. Notice that the homeowner is billed for water quarterly. Every three months an inspector from the water department records the reading on the meter. By computing the difference between this reading and the previous reading, the number of cubic feet of water consumed is determined.

BLOOMINGTON, RHODE ISLAND

Water Rates—Quarterly

For the first 700 cubic feet or less	$2.00 minimum charge
For the next 2,000 cubic feet	$2.60 per 1,000 cubic feet
For the next 17,000 cubic feet	$2.40 per 1,000 cubic feet
For the next 20,300 cubic feet	$2.10 per 1,000 cubic feet
For in excess of 40,000 cubic feet	$1.30 per 1,000 cubic feet

---

■ILLUSTRATION: On March 27, the reading on the water meter at Mr. Taylor's home was 136,240. When it was read again on June 29, it was recorded as 142,670. If Mr. Taylor lived in Bloomington, how large was his water bill for this 3-month period?

●SOLUTION:

Number of cubic feet used $= 142,670 - 136,240 \qquad = 6,430$

Cost of first   700 cubic feet $= \$2.00 \quad | - \quad 700$

$\qquad\qquad\qquad\qquad\qquad\qquad\qquad\qquad\qquad\qquad\qquad\qquad 5,730$

Cost of next 2,000 cubic feet $= 2 \times \$2.60 \quad = 5.20 \quad | - 2,000$

$\qquad\qquad\qquad\qquad\qquad\qquad\qquad\qquad\qquad\qquad\qquad\qquad 3,730$

Cost of next 3,730 cubic feet $= 3.73 \times \$2.40 = 8.95 \quad | - 3,730$

$\qquad\qquad$ Cost for 6,430 cubic feet $\qquad\qquad = \$16.15 \qquad\qquad\qquad 0$

▼EXPLANATION: The method for finding the cost of water is exactly the same as that used for finding the cost of either gas or electricity. Care, however, must be taken when determining the cost of the 2,000 cubic feet, for the rate is in terms of $2.60 per 1,000 cubic feet. Hence, 2,000 is divided by 1,000 in order to determine the number of thousands in 2,000. The same is true when finding the cost of 3,730 cubic feet of water. The quotient of 3,730 with 1,000 is 3.73, which is the number of thousands in 3,730.

See the comment at the bottom of page 470.

EXERCISES   A

1. Determine the quarterly charge for each of the following customers. Use the water-rate table of the town of Bloomington, Rhode Island.

	Number Of Cubic Feet Used During Quarter	Cost			Number Of Cubic Feet Used During Quarter	Cost
a.	340	$ 2.00		e.	14,390	$ 35.26
b.	1,460	3.98		f.	18,150	44.28
c.	5,670	14.33		g.	26,940	63.20
d.	8,280	20.59		h.	43,510	95.19

2. Determine the quarterly charge for each of the following customers. Use the water-rate table of the town of Bloomington, Rhode Island.

	Reading At Beginning Of Quarter	Reading At End Of Quarter	Number Of Cubic Feet	Cost
a.	005820	007510	1,690	$ 4.57
b.	024370	024980	610	2.00
c.	069510	074370	4,860	12.38
d.	023840	031620	7,780	19.39
e.	369570	382430	12,860	31.58
f.	997650	016790	19,140	46.66

3. In Livingston Township, water is sold by the gallon, and its rates are quoted as follows:

LIVINGSTON TOWNSHIP

Quarterly Water Rates

Minimum Charge $4.20

60¢ per 1,000 gallons for first 4,000 gallons
45¢ per 1,000 gallons for next 6,000 gallons
40¢ per 1,000 gallons for next 20,000 gallons
33¢ per 1,000 gallons in excess of 30,000 gallons

Determine the quarterly charge to each of the following customers.

	Reading in Gallons At Beginning of Quarter	Reading in Gallons At End of Quarter	Number Of Gallons	Cost
a.	036750	049360	12,610	$ 6.14
b.	058470	064230	5,760	4.20
c.	249360	268410	19,050	8.72
d.	573540	596290	22,750	10.20
e.	628480	671360	42,880	17.35
f.	998640	014280	15,640	7.36
g.	981370	024830	43,460	17.54

As an extra-credit project, have the students investigate what the water rates are in their community. In particular, have them note whether water is sold by the cubic foot or by the gallon. You might also have them investigate as to where the community reservoir is.

B

1. How many gallons of water will have to be consumed by a resident of Livingston Township in order to cover his minimum charge? (See the table for Problem 3 of Group A.)   8,000

2. Mr. Clark has a water softener that requires regenerating twice a week. During each of these periods, 90 gallons of water are used at a cost of 65¢ per 1,000 gallons. How much will Mr. Clark have to pay for water during one year for regenerating his water softener?
$6.08

3. During a particularly dry summer, Mrs. Kern had to water her lawn an average of 6 hours per day for 47 days. If water flowed through her garden hose at the rate of 2½ gallons per minute, how much did Mr. Kern have to pay to keep the lawn green? The cost of water is 75¢ per 1,000 gallons. $31.73

4. A cubic foot of water is the equivalent of approximately 7.5 gallons of water. Approximately how many gallons of water are there in 7,000 cubic feet of water?   52,500

5. Mr. Bates has a home in Bloomington, Rhode Island. During a quarterly period he used 6,000 cubic feet of water.
    a. Determine the cost of the water. Use the table on page 498.
$15.12

    b. How many gallons of water did Mr. Bates consume during this quarterly period?   45,000

    c. If Mr. Bates had lived in Livingston Township whose water-rate table appears on page 499, what would his water bill have been?
$18.05

    d. How much more, or less, did he have to pay for water by living in Bloomington rather than in Livingston Township? $2.93 less

Section 4:   The Cost of Repairs and Maintenance

The apartment dweller out for a Sunday drive rarely is aware of the hidden costs that account for the beauty he sees. He may know vaguely of the taxes and mortgage payments of a homeowner, but somehow he thinks such small things as the grass and shrubs have been there forever. Little does he realize that the grass that resembles the putting green of a golf course may have cost the homeowner $3,000 to plant, while the shrubs that look as if they were there long before the house was built were probably brought in at the cost of another $1,800. But this is only the beginning—for someone must fertilize the grass, cut the lawn, trim the shrubs, cut dead branches from trees and so on.

The design of the problem in this section is to point up the "hidden" costs in owning a home, which the apartment dweller rarely sees.

It is these small things that build up to a large part of the expense of owning and maintaining a house. The problems in this section are designed to present an overall picture of the financial obligations that the homeowner will have to face, other than those discussed earlier in this chapter.

■ILLUSTRATION: Mr. Sheldon designed a free-form patio that was surfaced with bricks laid flat side up in a bed of soft sand. For this he needed 4,480 bricks at 6¢ per brick and 11 tons of sand at $4.35 per ton. Since his son volunteered to do the work, there was no charge for labor. How much did the material for the patio cost Mr. Sheldon?

●SOLUTION:

$$\text{Cost for bricks} = 4{,}480 \times \$.06 = \$268.80$$
$$\text{Cost for sand} = 11 \times \$4.35 \quad = \quad 47.85$$
$$\text{Total} \quad \$316.65$$

EXERCISES

1. Mr. Pollard lives in a community where the water is very hard. For this reason, he rents a water softener that requires servicing once every 4 weeks at a cost of $5.85. How much does Mr. Pollard pay over the period of a year in order to have soft water in his home?
   $76.05

2. Mr. Norton lives in the same community as Mr. Pollard of Problem 1. However, Mr. Norton preferred to purchase a water softener. The cost and installation for this device was $374. To service the water softener himself, Mr. Norton uses salt which he purchases in a 100-pound bag four times each year. The cost of the salt is $2.75 per bag.
   a. How much does the salt cost Mr. Norton each year? $11.00
   b. How much less does Mr. Norton pay each year for servicing his water softener than does Mr. Pollard? $65.05
   c. In terms of saving alone, to the nearest year, how many years will it take Mr. Norton to pay off the cost of his investment in the water softener? 6 years

3. The driveway of the Moreland home is 60 feet long. Parallel to one edge of the driveway Mrs. Moreland planted small spruce trees 3 feet apart at a cost of $3.75 for each tree. How much did she have to pay for the trees? (Be careful in counting the trees, for one is needed at both the beginning and end of the driveway.) $78.75

4. After walking 5 miles while mowing his lawn on a hot summer day, Mr. Leach decided that this exercise was no longer to his liking.

Although each problem is different from every other one, an effort has been made to break down each particular problem so that the small segments that the student has to digest will be relatively simple.

The following day he bought a riding mower for $510. His neighbor, whose property is approximately the same size as Mr. Leach's employs a gardener, who charges $12 each time he mows the lawn.

a. If the lawn needs to be cut an average of 16 times during the spring, summer, and fall, how much does Mr. Leach save by not using his neighbor's gardener? $192.00

b. As the mower is very sturdy, Mr. Leach attaches a plow to the front of it during the winter and uses to it push the snow from his driveway. His neighbor, on the other hand, hires someone to do this at a cost of $8 for each snowplowing. During a normal winter, the driveway needs plowing five times. How much does Mr. Leach save by plowing his driveway himself? $ 40.00

c. In terms of Mr. Leach's annual saving, how many years will it take him to pay for the cost of the mower? (The upkeep of the machine has been disregarded in this problem.)   2.2 years

5. Mr. Ryan's lawn covers 15,000 square feet. Insects have been chewing the roots of his grass.

a. He can buy a liquid insecticide—insect killer—at $18.90 a gallon, that will cover 30,000 square feet. How much will this cost him for one application? $ 9.45

b. If he prefers, he can buy a powder insecticide at $5.75 that will cover 5,000 square feet. How much will this cost him for one application? $ 17.25

c. How much will he save by using the liquid rather than the powder? $ 7.80

6. The lawn around the Walter's home covers 14,000 square feet. Twice each year Mr. Walter fertilizes the lawn with a fertilizer that costs him $3.85 a 50-pound bag. Each bag will cover 2,000 square feet. What is the cost of fertilizing this lawn each year? $ 53.90

7. Both Mr. and Mrs. Skinner love roses. Hence they have set aside a large area of their garden, where they have planted more than 250 bushes. Each year they find it necessary to replace approximately 6 dozen bushes that have either died or are diseased. This year they made the following purchase of roses:

>1 dozen Betty Uprichard at $1.75 per bush
>2 dozen Good News at $2.25 per bush
>2 dozen Saratoga at $2.85 per bush
>1 dozen Summer Rainbow at $3.45 per bush

What was the total cost? $184.80

If the students in your class are primarily apartment dwellers, then it might be best not to teach this set of problems.

8. Along both sides of his driveway, Mr. Nash laid curved cement blocks at a cost of 37¢ per block. The driveway is 60 feet long, while each block is 15 inches long.
   a. How many cement blocks did Mr. Nash need? (Do not consider the space between the blocks.)   96
   b. What was the total cost of the cement blocks? $35.52
   c. Had Mr. Nash purchased Belgium blocks, each of which is 9 inches long, how many would he have needed?   160
   d. If each Belgium block costs 42¢, what would have been the cost to edge the driveway with these blocks? $67.20
   e. How much did Mr. Nash save by using cement blocks rather than Belgium blocks? $31.68

9. Mr. Merkle built a paneled family room in the basement of his home with 4- by 8-foot sheets of finished plywood that cost $5.35 per sheet. The dimensions of the room are 18 feet long, 12 feet wide, and 7 feet, 8 inches high. In determining how many plywood sheets he would need, Mr. Merkle disregarded the two small windows and the door, for it is impossible to buy a fraction of a sheet.
   a. How many sheets of plywood did he have to purchase?
      15
   b. What was the total cost of the plywood? $80.25

10. Being somewhat short of money and having plenty of time on his hands, Mr. Libby decided to paint the outside of his house himself. His estimate of the number of square feet that would have to be covered by paint was 4,800. He planned to buy a latex paint at $6.35 per gallon. Each gallon was said to cover 450 square feet.
    a. How many full gallons of paint will he need?   11
    b. What will the cost of the paint be? $69.85

11. The Forsyth home is heated by oil at a cost of 17.3¢ per gallon. From November through May inclusive, Mr. Forsyth finds that he averages about 365 gallons per month. During the remaining months, he uses only 350 gallons all told.
    a. How many gallons of oil does Mr. Forsyth purchase during the year?   2,905
    b. What is the total annual cost for oil to heat the Forsyth home?
       $502.57
    c. What is the average monthly cost for oil? $ 41.88

12. Mrs. Lodge wanted the open porch of her home to be enclosed with louvered windows and knotty pine paneling. The lowest estimate of the cost of this project came to $1,850. Feeling that this price was prohibitive, Mr. Lodge decided to do the work himself.

After completing the room, he found that his expenses had been as follows:

> 8 louvered windows at $32.50 each
> 1 louvered door at $84.75
> Cost of lumber—$67.54
> 286 vinyl floor tiles at 48¢ each
> 172 asbestos ceiling tiles at 17¢ each
> Incidental supplies—$40

a. What was the total of all of his expenses? $ 618.81

b. How much did Mr. Lodge save by doing the work himself?
                                                  $1,231.19

c. Mr. Lodge kept a tally of the number of hours he spent working on the porch. If the record shows that he required 204 hours to complete the job, how much can Mr. Lodge consider his hourly earnings to be? $ 6.04

Unit 3:   Chapter Review and Test

1. How many kilowatt-hours are there in each of the following number of watt-hours?
   a. 6,000 ___6___   b. 19,000 ___19___   c. 4,650 ___4.65___

2. How many kilowatt-hours of electricity are consumed by the use of each of the following appliances?

	Number Of Watts	Number Of Hours	Watt-Hours	Kilowatt-Hours
a.	500	14	7,000	7
b.	2,100	2½	5,250	5.25

3. How many kilowatt-hours of electricity were used during a month in which the meter readings at the beginning and end of the month appeared as below?

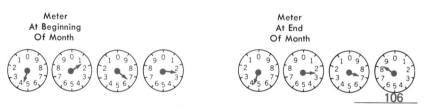

Meter At Beginning Of Month   Meter At End Of Month

106

4. Determine the cost of electricity for a month in which 142 kilowatt-hours of electricity were used. Use the electric rate table of the Cape Electric and Gas Company on page 466. $ 8.89

As usual, by selecting carefully, some of these problems can be used for review purposes, while the remaining problems can be used for testing.

5. Mrs. Shanley roasted a turkey in an electric oven for 4 hours and 15 minutes. The oven operated on 2,200 watts of current. If the cost of each kilowatt-hour is 5.8¢, what was the total cost for roasting the turkey? $ .54

6. Determine the cost of consuming 89 hundred cubic feet of gas during the period of one month. Use the rate table of the Cape Electric and Gas Company. $13.62

7. The gas meter readings on two successive months were 623 and 691 respectively. How much would the Great Western Electric and Gas Company, whose rates appear in Problem 5, page 472, charge this customer? $13.92

8. Use the telephone company table on page 474 to determine the cost of each of the following calls that were made out of the free-call zone.

Miles	Type Of Call	Time In Minutes	Hour Of Call	Paid Or Collect	Cost
a. 16	Station-to-Station	8	Wednesday—3 P.M.	Paid	$ .30
b. 126	Person-to-Person	14	Monday—11 P.M.	Paid	2.50
c. 8	Station-to-Station	9	Saturday—9 A.M.	Collect	.35
d. 93	Station-to-Station	17	Sunday—4 P.M.	Paid	1.70
e. 158	Station-to-Station	12	Saturday—4 P.M.	Paid	2.50

9. Mr. Green was granted a $14,300 mortgage by his savings and loan association, but he had to pay 3½ points to obtain the loan. How much money did this amount to? $ 500.50

10. When the Rymers purchased their home, they were granted a $17,400 mortgage at 7½%, to be paid off over a period of 20 years in monthly installments.
  a. How large was each payment? $ 140.24
  b. How much money did the Rymers pay to the mortgage company over the 20-year period? $33,657.60
  c. How much more did they have to pay back than they had borrowed? $16,257.60

11. After having made payments on his 6% mortgage for some time, Mr. Engels still owed $8,320. His monthly payments were $107.02. How much of the next payment was interest and how much would be used to decrease the debt?   Int.: $41.60; payment on debt: $65.42

12. Change each of the following tax rates from its present form to the one quoted at its right.
  a. $4.75 per $100 = $__47.50__ per $1,000
  b. $5.40 per $100 = ____54____ mills per $1
  c. $35.20 per $1,000 = $_3.52_ per $100

13. Mr. Durkee's property is worth $40,000, but it is assessed at 80% of its value. If the tax rate in his community is $2.95 per $100, how much real estate tax will he have to pay? $944.00

14. Compute the cost of water to the consumer whose meter read 468,470 at the beginning of the quarterly period and 471,630 at the end of the period. Use the Bloomington Water Rate Table on page 498. $ 8.30

15. Water flows through a garden water sprinkler at the rate of 3½ gallons per minute. This sprinkler was run an average of 8 hours per day for a period of 35 days. At a cost of 55¢ per 1,000 gallons, what was the cost of using the sprinkler for this period? $ 32.34

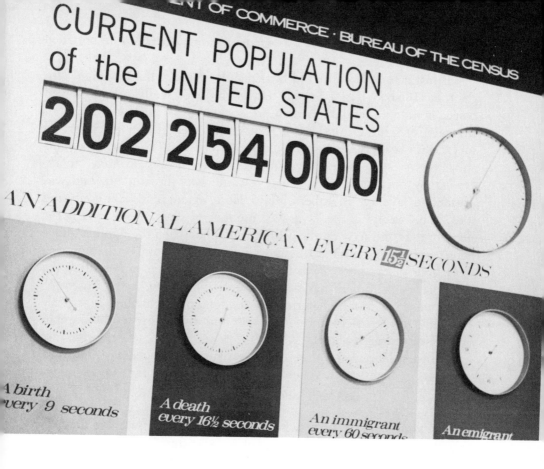

A birth
every 9 seconds

A death
every 16½ seconds

An immigrant
every 60 seconds

An emigrant

CHAPTER 13

UNDERSTANDING
STATISTICAL
INFORMATION

Unit 1: Averages

Early in your work this year, you discussed something called the average cost per mile of driving a car. At that time, it was assumed that everyone had the same idea of what is meant by an average. Unfortunately, though, all people do not think of the same thing when considering an average. In fact, this term is probably the most misused and the least understood word that is part of the daily language.

It may very well be that Mark Twain had in mind the confusion about the term "average" when he made the remark, "There are lies, damn lines, and statistics."

For instance, it is normal to hear people speak of the "average" student at Hillsboro High School. Have you ever really taken time to consider, though, of whom they are speaking? Is this the student of "average" height? Or perhaps it is "average" weight they are referring to. Or this may actually be the boy who is receiving "C" marks in all his subjects, for a "C" mark is usually considered as an "average" mark. Or it may be that who they had in mind was the student who was present an "average" number of days. Here, again, is another confusing idea. What really is the "average" number of days present? Is it the number that is exactly on the center of the line when the numbers have been arranged from highest to lowest? Or is it the number that appears most frequently when you write down all the numbers representing the days that each student has been present? Or, finally, is the "average" the number you find by determining the total of all the days that every student is in the school during the year and dividing it by the number of students in the school?

Confusion more often than not is the key word whenever the word "average" is mentioned. When a person talks about the "average student," or the "average farm girl," or the "average working mother," or the "average city-dweller," or the "average suburbanite," it is almost impossible to understand to whom he is referring. In fact, it is unlikely that the speaker, himself, could explain who this "average" person is supposed to be. Terms such as these are so vague that they are meaningless. The person using these terms is usually doing so to create some kind of impression in the mind of the listener. He knows that he probably will never be called on to point out, or explain, who the "average" person is that he is talking about.

Misunderstandings about averages can be somewhat eliminated through the use of numbers. To illustrate, if someone were to refer to the "average" number of points made by a player in a basketball league during a particular season, you might ask him the same three questions asked earlier of the "average" days a student was present. Each of these "averages" is called by a different name, and each of these will be explained in terms of basketball points.

1. The mode. This "average" represents the number that appears most frequently in the group of numbers being considered. Thus, if you examine the number of points made by each player in the league over the entire season, and you notice that more players scored 46 points that season than any other number of points, then 46 is called the mode of this set of numbers.

The design of the analysis above is not to confuse the student, although it may seem that way, but rather to get him to realize that the term "average" is an extremely vague term. Even when it is not used by a speaker as a catchall term, it is still difficult to interpret.

Similarly, in the following set of 10 test marks,

4, 6, 6, 6, 7, 8, 8, 8, 8, 10,

the mark of 8 is the mode, for it is the score that occurs most frequently.

2. The median. This "average" represents the number that is midway in the group of numbers being considered—that is, it is the midway number if the numbers are arranged in order running from high to low, or in the reverse direction. Thus, in the case of the number of points made by each player in the basketball league, you would first arrange the scores in an order where the lowest score appeared first, then the next higher, and so on until the very highest appeared last. The score appearing exactly in the middle of all the scores is called the median.

In the following set of 11 test marks, the sixth score is the one that is exactly in the middle. There are 5 test marks that are lower than this one and there are 5 higher than it is. Therefore, this one is called the median.

3, 4, 4, 4, 6, (7,) 8, 8, 9, 10, 10

Notice that the mark of 7 is not the mode in this set of marks. Which mark is the mode?

If there is an odd number of scores in a set, then the middle score can be found by adding 1 to the number of scores and dividing this sum by 2. Thus, in the case just examined, there were 11 scores. By adding 1 to 11, you get a total of 12. This number, divided by 2, gives you the quotient of 6, and it was the 6th score that turned out to be the median score. Five were below it and five were above it.

What happens, though, in the case where there are an even number of scores? Should this occur, you may end up with a median score that is not even a member of the set. For instance, if there are 14 scores, then you still add 1 to the 14 and divide the sum by 2 to give you a quotient of 7½. This tells you that midway between the 7th and 8th scores is the median of this set. In the following set of the 14 scores:

2, 3, 3, 4, 5, 6, 6, ↑ 11, 11, 12, 12, 14, 15, 15

the median score falls halfway between the score of 6 and the score of 11. To find it, you add 6 and 11, and then divide this sum by 2. This will give you a median score of 8½ which, as you see, is not one of the scores above.

Emphasize that the term "average" should be synonymous with the word "typical." The member of the set that is most typical of the set is the "average." In some cases, this may be the mode; in others, it is the median; while in still others, it is the mean.

Had the 14 scores been

2, 3, 3, 4, 5, 6, 6, 6, 9, 10, 10, 12, 14, 15
$\uparrow$

then the score that is midway between the 7th score and the 8th score would be the score of 6, for both the 7th and 8th scores are the number 6. What score is the mode of this set?

3. The mean. This is the number that most people think of as being the "average." It is the number you find by adding all the scores in the set and then dividing this sum by the number of scores. Thus, considering the basketball players again, you would add all the points that each of them scored during the season and then divide that sum by the number of players in the league in order to find the mean.

Consider the set of 10 test marks:

4, 6, 6, 6, 7, 8, 8, 8, 8, 10.

The mean of this set is found by first adding the 10 scores.

$$4 + 6 + 6 + 6 + 7 + 8 + 8 + 8 + 8 + 10 = 71$$

The quotient of 71 and 10, which is 7.1, is the mean of the 10 test marks. Notice that the mean in this case is not a single one of the test scores.

The explanations above should have pointed up the fact that the mode, median, and mean, although they are all called "averages," are not necessarily the same for any given set of numbers. All of them, however, are supposed to represent a number that is typical of the set of numbers under consideration. Which one will prove to be the most representative of a particular group is hard to say, for this depends entirely on the numbers in the group. For instance, in a team of 5 basketball players whose heights are

5′9″, 5′9″, 5′9″, 5′9″, and 6′10″

you would not want to find the mean of this group and consider that height to be the average. Were you to do this, the mean would be,

$$\begin{aligned}
\text{Mean} &= (5′9″ + 5′9″ + 5′9″ + 5′9″ + 6′10″) \div 5 \\
&= (26′46″) \div 5 \\
&= 358″ \div 5 \\
&= 71\tfrac{3}{5}″ \\
&= 5′11\tfrac{3}{5}″
\end{aligned}$$

This height is certainly not typical of the group, since this is a height that is greater than the height of 4 of the 5 players! In a case such as

In computing the median of a set of scores, it is imperative that they be arranged in rank order. Although this is helpful in the case of the mode, it is not absolutely necessary. In finding the mean, this is not required at all.

this, you would use the mode as the typical height and say that the average height of the players is 5′9″.

In fact, whenever one of the numbers in a set is far out of line with the others, as it was with the heights of the basketball players, it is best not to use the mean as an average of the numbers. On the other hand, if the set of numbers were

$$2, 4, 4, 4, 5, 6, 8, 10, 15, 17, 23$$

then the mode, which is 4, would certainly not be typical of this group, for it does not represent the majority of the numbers. A better average in this case would be either the median or the mean.

■ILLUSTRATION: Use the following set of numbers:

$$5, 7, 7, 8, 9, 11, 11, 12, 14, 15, 15, 15, 15, 17, 17, 18$$

Find: a. The mode. b. The median. c. The mean.

●SOLUTION:

(a) The mode is the score that occurs most frequently: 15.
(b) The median is the midway score. There are 16 scores. Therefore, the midway score will be halfway between the 8th and 9th scores. Halfway between 12 and 14 is

$$(12 + 14)/2 = 13, \text{ median score.}$$

(c) The mean score is the sum of the scores divided by the number of scores.

$$(5 + 7 + 7 + 8 + 9 + 11 + 11 + 12 + 14 + 15 + 15 + 15 + 15 + 17$$
$$+ 17 + 18) \div 16$$
$$= 196 \div 16$$
$$= 12\tfrac{1}{4}$$

EXERCISES   **A**

1. Determine the mode in each of the following sets of scores. If necessary, rearrange the scores.

a. 2, 4, 4, 5, 6, 6, 6, 7, 8   6
b. 1, 3, 3, 3, 3, 4, 5, 5, 5, 7, 7, 7, 8, 9, 9   3
c. 5, 8, 8, 8, 9, 9, 10, 11, 12, 12, 12, 14, 14, 14, 14, 14, 15
                                                                                  14
d. 3, 2, 4, 7, 6, 9, 5, 2, 5, 8, 3, 4, 5, 4, 3, 7, 2, 9, 2   _____2
e. 1, 7, 6, 9, 12, 8, 5, 4, 7, 6, 11, 10, 7, 8, 14, 7, 6, 7_____7

In the discussion of the illustration above, inquire as to which of the averages found they would consider as typical of the group.

2. Determine the median in each of the following sets of scores. If necessary, rearrange the scores.

a. 3, 5, 7, 12, 14   7

b. 2, 8, 9, 10, 12, 17, 23, 25, 27   12

c. 3, 4, 4, 7, 8, 9, 9, 10, 10, 10, 11   9

d. 4, 5, 5, 7, 7, 12   6

e. 3, 3, 4, 5, 6, 6, 7, 8, 8, 8, 9, 10   6½

f. 4, 4, 4, 5, 5, 7, 8, 10, 15, 15, 16, 16, 16, 17, 17, 20

                                                                                12½

g. 1, 7, 4, 2, 1, 8, 5, 9, 3, 6, 12   5

h. 10, 3, 7, 7, 12, 1, 6, 9, 4, 8, 5, 2, 3, 1, 6   6

i. 3, 9, 5, 4, 2, 7, 6, 12, 9, 2, 8, 4, 6, 7   6

j. 12, 2, 3, 9, 7, 4, 1, 11, 16, 3, 8, 14, 15, 2, 6, 9, 5, 10

                                                                                7½

3. The sum of the scores and the number of scores are given in each of the following exercises. Find the mean of the scores in each exercise.

	Sum Of the Scores	Number Of Scores	Mean
a.	72	8	9
b.	108	9	12
c.	156	12	13
d.	238	14	17
e.	468	26	18
f.	374	15	24.9
g.	695	27	25.7
h.	784	32	24.5

4. Determine the mean of each of the following sets of scores.

a. 5, 6, 6, 6, 7, 8, 8, 8, 9, 11   7.4

b. 2, 3, 3, 4, 6, 7, 7, 7, 8, 9, 9, 13   6.5

c. 3, 4, 8, 7, 6, 9, 4, 10, 2, 1, 8, 5, 9, 12, 17   7.0

d. 72, 75, 75, 78, 83, 85, 92   80.0

e. 64, 73, 73, 74, 77, 78, 78, 79, 80, 80, 80, 84, 85   77.3

f. 65, 93, 72, 84, 91, 85, 87, 76, 70, 85, 81, 76, 84, 91

                                                                                81.4

B

1. Twelve boys ran the 100-yard dash. The time of each in seconds was as follows:

        12, 13, 15, 13, 14, 17, 20, 14, 13, 28, 16, 13

a. What was the mode time of the group?   13

b. What was the median time of the group?   14

c. What was the mean score of the group?   15 7

2. Six boys formed a partnership to purchase a motorboat. Each of the boys contributed one of the following amounts:

$50, $75, $75, $75, $75, $250

a. What is the mode contribution? $ 75.00
b. What is the median contribution?   75.00
c. What is the mean contribution?   100.00
d. Which average should not be used as being typical of the contributions?   mean

3. On a test containing 10 possible points, the scores of the students in a class turned out to be the following:

4 scored 5 points
7 scored 6 points
5 scored 7 points
10 scored 8 points
3 scored 9 points
1 scored 10 points

a. What is the mode number of points scored?   9
b. What is the median number of points scored?   9
c. What is the mean number of points scored?   8.1

Unit 2: The Graph

The average of a set of numbers is just one of several ways for examining these numbers. As you have just learned, an "average," which may be either the mean, the mode, or the median of the group, is simply the number that is supposed to be typical of all the numbers in the group. There are times, though, when you are interested in all the numbers themselves rather than in just the single typical representative. To examine all of them, however, even when there are so few as 10, is very difficult for most people. And when the number of scores runs into the hundreds, as may often happen, then there are very few people who can look at all the scores and try to see if there are any general comments or predictions that can be made from them.

To try to achieve some order out of a mass of numbers collected—for instance, the heights of all the students in the school—pictures are drawn to make the reading of these numbers as easy as possible. These pictures are called *graphs*, and they come in a variety of forms. Some resemble rectangles, others are circles, while still others are bars or straight lines. Some are even drawings of houses, or people, or animals, or, in fact, anything the data (numbers) happen to be about.

As an outgrowth of Problem 3 of Group B, the students should be taught that in finding the mean, it is not necessary that each of the scores appears individually. Thus, the total of the 4 scores at 5 points each is 20, and this is found as the product of 4 and 5 and not as the sum of the four 5's.

In the remainder of this chapter you are going to examine a few of the most frequently used types of graphs. The major purpose will be to learn how to read and interpret a graph rather than actually to construct one.

Section 1: The Bar Graph

The bar graph consists of a series of bars in which all of them are exactly the same width. By looking at the bars, it becomes quite simple to compare one quantity in the graph against another. To do this, you merely compare the lengths of the various bars. Even without reading the numbers in the column at the left (vertical axis) you can see that Joe earned twice as much as Fred since the length of his bar is twice that of Fred's. Similarly, Joe earned exactly the same as Bill, for the lengths of both bars representing the earnings of the two boys are the same. What can be said of Dave's earnings relative to Fred's? How do Sam's earnings compare to Dave's?

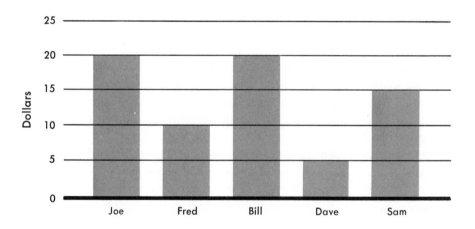

Earnings of Five Boys

■ ILLUSTRATION 1: Use the graph above to determine the mean earnings of the five boys.

▼ EXPLANATION: The numbers along the vertical axis will help you determine the earnings of each of the boys. To find Joe's earnings, place the edge of a piece of paper along the top of the bar over the word "Joe." Then run your finger along the edge of the paper until it comes to the vertical axis. The numeral that your finger should be

The design of this unit on graphing is completely to exclude graphic construction by the student. The consumer will never, at any time, be called upon to construct a graph, yet if he reads either a newspaper or magazine, he will often have to interpret graphic data. It is to this goal that the work is geared.

pointing to is $20. This is the number of dollars earned by Joe. Then repeat the same process with Fred and you find that the edge of your guide paper meets the vertical axis at $10. This is again repeated for each of the other three boys. Thus you find their earnings to be respectively $20, $5, and $15.

● SOLUTION:

$$\text{Mean earnings} = (\$20 + \$10 + \$20 + \$5 + \$15) \div 5$$
$$= \$70 \div 5$$
$$= \$14$$

■ ILLUSTRATION 2: Use the graph above to determine what percent of Bill's earnings Fred's earnings happen to be.

▼ EXPLANATION: To do the computation for this problem, you must first rewrite the question as follows:

"Fred's earnings compare to Bill's earnings as what number compares to 100?" (See pages 587–588 for review.)

This is then rewritten with symbols as follows:

$$\$10/\$20 = n/100$$

From this point on, by using the Equal Fractions Principle and the Product of Two Numbers Principle, you can determine the value of n. Once you know this number, you will also know the percent you are asked to find.

● SOLUTION:

$$\$10/\$20 = n/100$$
$$20 \times n = 10 \times 100$$
$$20 \times n = 1,000$$
$$n = 1,000 \div 20$$
$$n = 50$$

Therefore, Fred's earings are 50% of Bill's earnings.

Occasionally, bar graphs are drawn in such a way as to distort the information being presented. For instance, the bar graph page 516 was drawn to show earnings of Mr. Allen and Mr. Carr during the past year. If you do not take time to read the numbers in the vertical column, your immediate reaction would be that Mr. Allen earned twice as much money as Mr. Carr, because the length of the bar showing Mr. Allen's earnings is twice that of Mr. Carr's. This distortion is caused by the fact that the lowest numeral on the vertical axis is $8,000, while it should be $0. In fact, in every bar graph the bottom numeral should always be 0.

If you find that the majority of students in your class has been exposed to the "Percentage Formula," then you may want to teach them the solution of Illustration 2 through this method rather than through the two principles used above

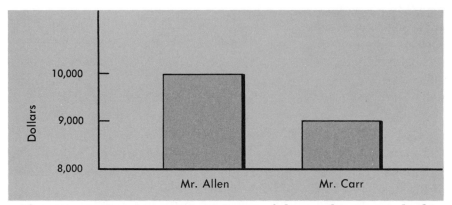

If, to save space, you want to omit part of the graph, you can do this by drawing a jagged line across the page such as shown. This tells you that you should be careful and not try to compare the lengths of the bars, for part of the picture has been cut away.

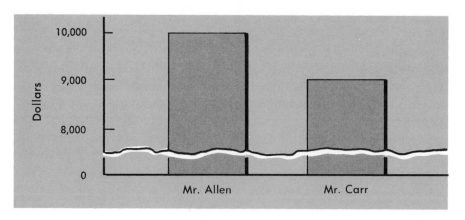

EXERCISES

1. The graph on page 517 shows the daily distance traveled by Joe Clark on a five-day trip. Use the graph to answer each of the questions that follow it.

   a. On which day did Joe travel the least distance?   Monday

   b. How far did Joe travel on the day he rode the greatest distance?
                                                           300 miles

   c. How much farther did Joe travel on Wednesday than he traveled on Monday?
                                                           60 miles

   d. What percent more did he travel on Wednesday than he traveled on Monday?
                                                           50%

Take time to point to the students that data presented through a bar graph cannot only be distorted, as indicated above, but also can be distorted by varying the widths of the rectangles. When this is done, the reader does not know whether to compare merely the lengths, or to compare the areas of the rectangles.

Daily Distance Traveled by Joe Clark

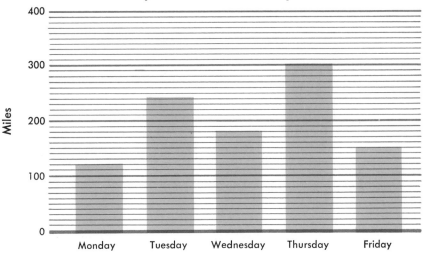

e. What is the total distance that Joe traveled on the five days?

<u>990 miles</u>

f. What is the mean distance per day that Joe traveled on the five-day trip? <u>198 miles</u>

g. If Joe drove for 5 hours on Friday, what was his average speed per hour? <u>30 mph</u>

2. The following graph shows the number of motorcycles registered in a foreign country during a recent year. Use the graph to answer the questions that follow it.

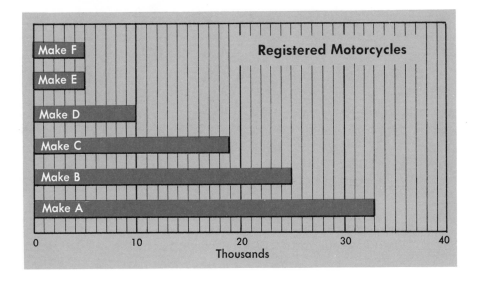

   a. How many Make B motorcycles were registered?   <u>25,000</u>

   b. How many more Make A motorcycles were registered than Make
      B motorcycles?   <u>8,000</u>

   c. The number of Make C motorcycles is what percent less than the
      number of Make B motorcycles?   <u>24%</u>

   d. What was the total number of motorcycles registered? <u>97,000</u>

   e. The price of a Make E motorcycle was $495. What was the total
      cost of all the registered Make E motorcycles?   <u>$2,475,000</u>

   f. What percent of the total number of motorcycles registered was
      the number of Make E motorcycles?   <u>5.2%</u>

   g. If, during the following year, the number of registered Make D
      motorcycles increased by 50%, how many motorcycles of this make
      would there be?   <u>15,000</u>

3. Five boys were graduated from high school and obtained jobs where
   they earned the annual salaries shown in the following graph. Use
   the graph to answer each of the questions that follow it.

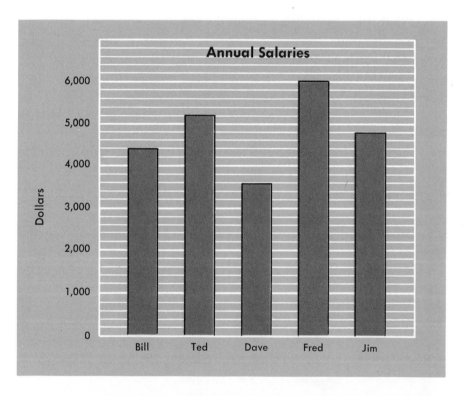

   a. Which boy started working at the highest salary?   <u>Fred</u>

   b. What was the lowest salary at which one of the boys started to
      work?   <u>$3,600.00</u>

c. How much more did Ted earn the first year than Jim? <u>$400.00</u>
d. What were the total earnings of all the boys during the year?
<u>$24,000.00</u>
e. What were the mean earnings of the boys that year?   <u>$4,800.00</u>
f. By what amount did Fred's earnings exceed the mean salary?
<u>$1,200.00</u>
g. By what amount were Dave's earnings less than the mean salary?
<u>$1,200.00</u>
h. Dave's earnings were what percent of Jim's earnings? <u>75%</u>
i. If Bill's earnings increased by 25% the following year, how much
did he earn the second year?   <u>$5,500.00</u>

Section 2:   The Line Graph

The line graph is constructed in much the same way as the bar
graph. For instance, the bottom number on the vertical axis should be
0, while the difference between any two consecutive numbers on this
axis should be the same as the difference between any other two consecutive numbers. If some of the numbers are left off this axis, then a
tear, or cut, should be shown on the graph paper in just the same way
as was shown on the bar graph. Should this not be done, then the same
sort of distortion would result, as was pointed out with reference to the
bar graph.

There is a basic difference, though, between the use of the bar graph
and the use of the line graph. The bar graph should be used when
presenting what is called a *discrete* set of data, while the line graph is
better for a *continuous* set of data. A continuous set of data can be
thought of as a flow of numbers that keeps varying all the time. Such
things as the temperature between 8 A.M. and 10:00 P.M. can be
thought of as a continuous set of numbers, for no matter how frequently you observed the temperature during the day, it would always
have been possible to have observed the temperature at some in-be-
tween times also. For instance, if you checked the thermometer every
hour to get temperature readings, you could have checked it every
half hour for more readings. In fact, if you were fast enough, you
could also get readings on the half second, or quarter second.

Another illustration of a continuous set of data is the measurements
of your height between certain ages. If you measured yourself at age
12 and were 5'2" high, and then measured yourself again at age 14 and
found your height to be 5'6", this wouldn't mean that suddenly you had
grown 4" in height. Rather, it would mean that over the two-year pe-

The line graph is often used to plot a discrete set of data, although, perhaps, it would have been
better to use the bar graph. The creator of the graph used the line in order to direct the reader's
eye from discrete point to discrete point of the graph in moving from left to right.

riod there was a continuous change in your height, starting at the figure
5′2″ and passing through all numbers between 5′2″ and 5′6″.

Discrete sets of data are those in which there are no numbers between any two in the set. As an illustration, consider the numbers in
Exercise 1 on page 516. There are no numbers between the distance
traveled by Joe Clark on Monday and the distance traveled by him
on Tuesday. Also, it is never possible to squeeze any numbers in between these, as you could in the case of the temperature changes, or
your height changes. Similarly, in Exercise 2 on page 517, there are no
numbers between the number of motorcycles in Make A and the number in Make B. The numbers in this exercise are completely distinct
from one another and no other number than those shown exists in the
set. Hence, these numbers represent a discrete set.

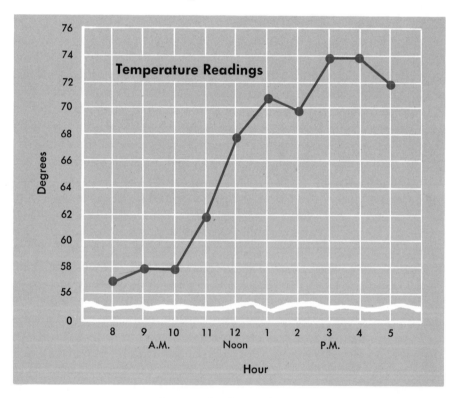

■ ILLUSTRATION 1: The graph above shows the temperature readings for each hour on the hour from 8:00 A.M. to 5 P.M. on a certain
day. What was the mean hourly temperature reading?

▼ EXPLANATION: This problem simply involves adding the temperatures at each of the hours shown and dividing by 10, which is the number of hours during which readings were taken.

Call attention to the jagged line in the graph above. It is there to show that part of the graph
paper has been cut out. However, even if the entire paper were there, comparisons could not
be made between the various temperatures, for it is meaningless to say that one temperature
is twice as warm as another.

● SOLUTION:

Mean hourly temperature
$$= (57 + 58 + 58 + 62 + 68 + 71 + 70 + 74 + 74 + 72) \div 10$$
$$= 664 \div 10$$
$$= 66.4$$

■ ILLUSTRATION 2: Use the graph on page 520 to determine the temperature at 10:30 A.M.

▼ EXPLANATION: Your first reaction in answering this would be to place the edge of a piece of paper parallel to the vertical axis and half-way between 10 A.M. and 11 A.M. You would then notice that the edge of the paper intersected the graph at the 60-degree temperature mark. Based on this, you could say that the temperature at 10:30 A.M. was 60 degrees. Actually, this answer is a pure guess, for you really do not know what the temperature was at 10:30 A.M. You do know that at 10 A.M. it was 58 degrees, and at 11 A.M. it was 62 degrees. But at 10:30 A.M., no one took the temperature and recorded it. Hence, at that time, it may even have been lower than 58 degrees, or, perhaps, higher than 62 degrees, and dropped back to 62 by 11 A.M. Neither of these possibilities seems likely but, since you are not sure that 60 degrees is correct either, though it seems likely to be, it would be best to say that the temperature was *probably* 60 degrees at 10:30 A.M.

Similarly, in answer to the question, "What was the temperature at 5:30 P.M.?" you should say that it was *probably* less than 72 degrees, for it looks as if the temperature is beginning to fall off for the day. However, since you cannot be sure that it did, it is best to introduce some slight doubt into your answer by using the word "probably." Whenever the readings are not shown on the graph, you should never make statements about them with certainty.

Although the line graph is better adapted for a continuous set of data than for a discrete set, it is frequently used to picture the latter. The reason for this is that the eye tends to follow the line of the graph and so makes it possible to see at a glance whether the picture shows an increasing trend, or a decreasing one. Also, when you want to compare two sets of discrete data, it is far easier to do this by drawing the two line graphs on the same set of axes rather than by trying to draw two bar graphs in this way.

■ ILLUSTRATION 3: The graph on page 522 shows the weekly test marks in mathematics that both Joe and Dave received over a five-week period.

a. How much higher was Joe's lowest mark than Dave's lowest mark?

The purpose of the explanation above is to have the students realize that they must temper their statements whenever interpolating between the data, or extrapolating from the data.

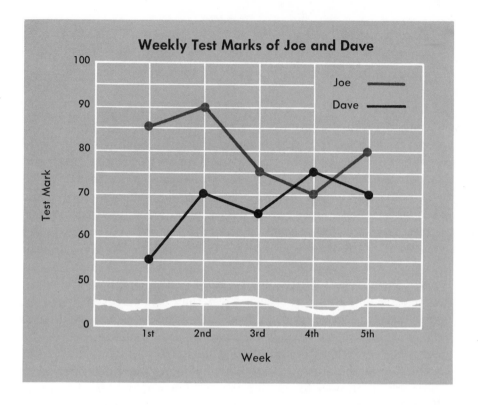

b. During which week did Joe have a test mark that was as high as Dave's highest mark?

▼ EXPLANATION: (a) Joe's lowest mark of 70 occurred during the 4th week. Dave's, which was 55, occurred during the 1st week. Hence, Joe's lowest mark was 15 points higher than Dave's.

● SOLUTION:

$$\text{(a) Number of points higher} = 70 - 55$$
$$= 15$$

▼ EXPLANATION: (b) Dave's highest mark was 75, and it occurred during the 4th week. Joe's test of 75 occurred during the 3rd week.

EXERCISES

1. Mrs. Belmont decided to lose weight. The graph on page 523 shows her weight over the 11-week period during which she was on a diet. Answer the following questions in terms of this graph
   a. What was the total amount of weight that Mrs. Belmont lost over the 11-week period?   24 pounds
   b. How much weight did she lose the first week?   6 pounds

Comparisons between two sets of data—even though they may be discrete sets—lend themselves better to the line graph than to any other graph. Unless the sets are continuous, however, points of intersections of the two graphs are meaningless.

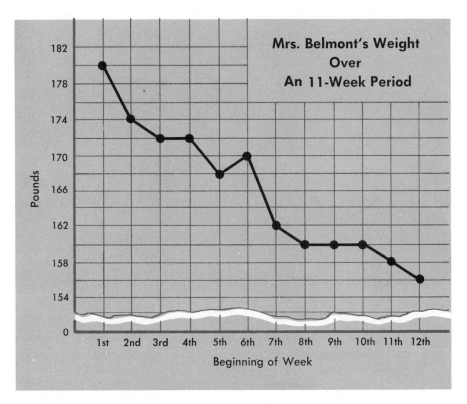

c. During which week did she lose the greatest amount of weight?
   <u>6th</u>

d. During which week did she gain weight?   <u>5th</u>

e. How much did Mrs. Belmont weigh one week before she went on the diet?   Probably <u>180 pounds</u>

f. How much did Mrs. Belmont weigh at the beginning of the 12th week after she began her diet?   Probably <u>156 pounds</u>

g. What was her mean weight over the 11-week period? <u>166 pounds</u>

h. What was her weekly weight loss for each of the 11 weeks?

   6, 2, 0, 4, +2, 8, 2, 0, 0, 2, 2   _____

i. What was her mean weekly weight loss over the 11-week period?
   <u>2.2 pounds</u>

2. The graph on page 524 shows Tom Haley's school bank savings on the first of each month over the past year. Answer the following questions in terms of this graph.

   a. As shown by this graph, when did Tom have the smallest amount of savings?   <u>February 1</u>

   b. What was the largest amount of money that Tom had in the bank as shown by this graph?   <u>$48.00</u>

Use the graph of Exercise 1 to ask the students such questions as, "How much did Mrs. Belmont weigh during the middle of the 8th week?" and "How much did Mrs. Belmont weigh at the beginning of the 13th week?" Through these questions you will be teaching the student to interpolate and extrapolate.

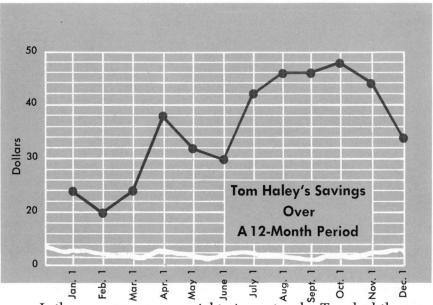

c. Is there any reason you might give as to why Tom had the same
   amount of money in the school savings account on both August 1
   and September 1?   Summer vacation
d. How much less did Tom have in this account on December 1
   than on September 1? $12.00
e. How much money did Tom have in this account on May 15?
                                    Probably either $32.00 or $30.00

f. After April 1, what was the smallest amount of money that Tom
   had in this account, as shown by this graph? $30.00
g. What is the mean amount of savings that Tom had in this account over the first four months as shown by this graph?
                                                          $26.50

h. What is the mean amount of savings that Tom had in this account over the period shown by this graph? $35.67
i. Is it possible for Tom to have had less than $20 in this account
   at any time during the year? Justify your answer. Yes, this may have occurred
3. The graph on page 525 shows the number of pairs of pants sold each at some
   year over the past 10 years by the Southern Wear Processing Com- other ti
   pany. Answer each of the following questions in terms of this graph. the 1st
   a. During which year did the company have its largest sales?   the mor
                                                          8th

b. How many more pairs of pants were sold during the 2nd year
   than during the 4th year?   2,000
c. By what amount did the number of pair of pants sold drop the
   9th year compared to the 8th year?   12,000

Through question 2 i, we are trying to make the student realize that the graph does not include
all the data. A similar question to ask the students is whether it is possible that Tom may have
had more than $48 in the bank at any time during the year.

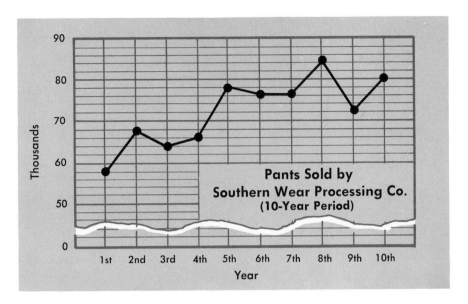

d. By what percent did the sales drop the 9th year compared to the 8th year?   14.3%

e. If the number of pants sold the 11th year was 50% more than the number sold the 10th year, how many pairs of pants were sold during the 11th year?   120,000

f. The company sold each pair of pants during the 2nd year at $6 per pair. What was the total amount of money it received for the pants sold that year? $408,000

g. During the 3rd year, the company sold each pair of pants at $8 per pair. How much more (or less) did it receive for the pants sold the 3rd year than it did the 2nd year? $104,000.00 more

h. What was the mean number of pants sold per year over the 10-year period?   72,200

4. The graph on page 526 shows a comparison of two budgets. One of the budgets is for a family of two where the take-home pay is $500 per month, while the other is for a family of two having a take-home pay of $1,000 per month. Answer each of the following questions in terms of this graph.

a. For what item is the largest amount of money spent on the $500 take-home budget?   Food

b. How much money is saved per month on the $500 take-home pay? $65.00

c. How much money is saved per month on the $1,000 take-home pay? $200.00

Question 3 c prepares the student for Question 3 d. Emphasize that in finding the percent of decrease, it is not only necessary to know the actual decrease, but also the number to which this decrease is being compared. In this case it is the 8th year's sales.

Monthly Budgets for a Family of Two

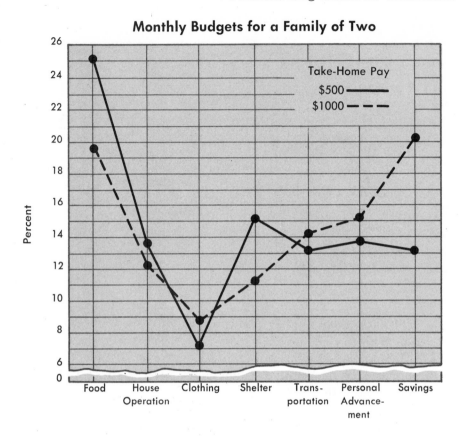

d. Why would a family with a take-home pay of $500 spend a larger percent of its income for food than the family with a take-home pay of $1,000? <u>Am't budgeted for food is approx. same; therefore, n/500 is greater than n/1,000.</u>

e. The family with a take-home pay of $500 spends a larger percent of its income on shelter than the family with a take-home pay of $1,000. Does this mean that it spends more money on this item? Explain your answer. <u>No; the percent is taken on a smaller number.</u>

f. Will a family of 4, having a take-home pay of $500 per month, save the same percent of its income each month as the family of 2? Explain your answer. <u>No; a family of 2 will spend less and, therefore, save</u> more.

g. How much should a family of four spend each month on clothing if the take-home pay is $1,000 per month? <u>Cannot tell from graph.</u>

h. What percent of the take-home pay of $1,500 per month for a family of two will be spent on food? <u>Cannot tell from graph.</u>

i. How much more does the family of two with a monthly take-home pay of $1,000 spend each month for shelter than the family of two with the monthly take-home pay of $500? <u>$35.00</u>

This is the first of several graphs in which budgets are pictured. Try to glean from them certain comparisons involving "why" rather than "what." To wit, "Why should the percent of income for food be greater for a family with a take-home pay of $500 than for one with a take-home pay of $1,000?"

Section 3:   The Circle and Rectangle Graphs

Both the circular and the rectangular graphs are designed to serve the same purpose. Whenever one can be used to picture the information, the other can be used equally well. The choice of one over the other depends entirely on the person who is drawing the picture. If he happens to like circles, his graphs will take the shape of circles; if not, they will take the shape of rectangles.

The purpose of either of these graphs is to show a comparison among the items that make up an entire quantity. For instance, suppose that you wanted a picture of the total number of boys in your high school and, further, you wanted them separated according to freshmen, sophomores, juniors, and seniors. In this case, the individual items would be the number of boys in each of the grades, while the entire quantity would be the number of boys in the school. Were a circle graph used to show this, the entire region bounded by the circle would represent the total number of boys in the student body, while each of the four slices of the region would represent the boys in each of the grades. Of course, this last statement would go equally well were the graph a rectangle rather than a circle. Incidentally, since the circle is divided into slices so that it resembles a pie, it is often called a pie graph.

■ILLUSTRATION: The circle graph below shows the distribution of boys at Clear Valley Regional High School. Answer each of the questions that follow in terms of this graph.

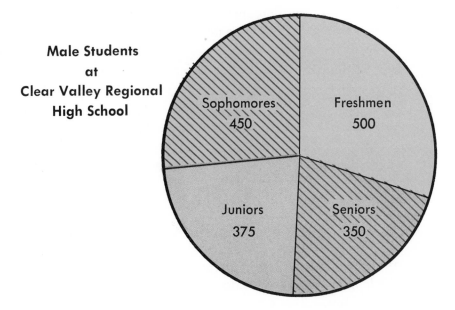

**Male Students
at
Clear Valley Regional
High School**

a. How many boys are there in the entire school?
b. How many more freshmen boys are there than senior boys?

c. Does the number of freshmen girls exceed the number of senior girls?
d. The number of sophomore boys is what percent of the total number of boys in the school?

●SOLUTION:

(a) Number of boys $= 500 + 450 + 375 + 350$
$$= 1{,}675$$

(b) Number of freshmen boys more than senior boys $= 500 - 350$
$$= 150$$

(c) This question really cannot be answered because the graph shows only a picture of the boys at the school and tells us nothing about the distribution of girls.

(d) The question in (d) can be rewritten as: "The number of sophomore boys compares to the total number of boys as what number compares to 100?"

or, $450/1{,}675 = n/100$

$1{,}675 \times n = 450 \times 100$ (Equal Fractions Principle)
$1{,}675 \times n = 45{,}000$
$\qquad n = 45{,}000 \div 1{,}675$ (Product of Two Numbers Principle)
$\qquad n = 26.9$ (approximately)

Hence, the percent of sophomores is approximately 26.9%.

The graph in the illustration above could have been pictured as a rectangle rather than a circle. This is done here.

Male Students at Clear Valley Regional High School

Freshmen	Sophomores	Juniors	Seniors
500	450	375	350

It is relatively simple to compare two items at sight in either the circular or rectangular graph. In the case of the former, you simply compare the arcs of the two slices of the pie, while in the latter, you compare the lengths of the two sections of the rectangle.

See the comment at the bottom of page 515.

Compare this with this.

Compare this with this.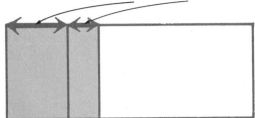

There are times when a circle graph is deliberately used to distort the information presented. This can be done by dividing the circle as shown here, rather than by cutting it up into slices. The person constructing a graph such as this would want to give the impression that the region within the smaller circle is much larger than the region between the circles. Actually, they are just about the same size.

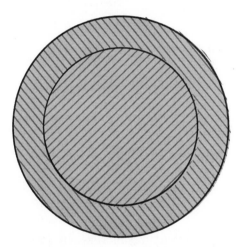

Similarly, to distort the information presented in a rectangular graph, you could cut up the rectangle as shown. By doing this, it would appear that the narrow rectangle at the top is much smaller than the lower one at the right, and yet they are exactly the same in size.

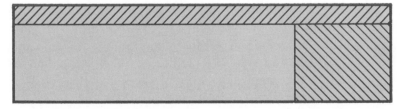

Although graphic representation of data is used less and less frequently for distortion of information, it still occurs. If the graph is a circle, then it is simple to spot attempts at misrepresentation, for any division of the circle other than through sectors is an obvious attempt at trickery.

EXERCISES

1. Julian Edwards receives an allowance of $8 per week. He budgets this money in accordance with the circle graph. Use the information in this graph to answer each of the following questions.

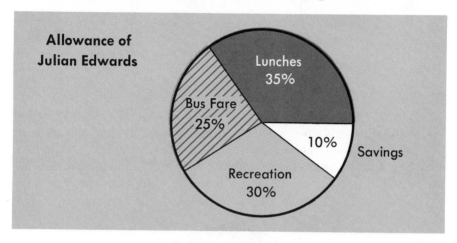

Allowance of Julian Edwards

Lunches 35%

Bus Fare 25%

10% Savings

Recreation 30%

a. How much did Julian spend on each of the items in his budget?
Lunches: $2.80 Recreation: $2.40 Bus fare: $2.00 Savings: $.80

b. How much more did he spend for lunches than he did for bus fare?
$ .80

c. How much less did he save than he spent for recreation?
$1.60

d. How much will Julian save over the 40-week school year?
$32.00

e. If he reduces the amount he spends on recreation by one third and saves this money, how much more will he save each week?
$ .80

f. If school transportation fares increase by 10¢ each day, how much more will he spend on bus fares each week than he now spends?
50¢

g. If his lunches are increased by 4¢ each day, what percent of his allowance will be needed for lunches?
37.5%

2. As part of a study made of last year's graduating class at Southwest High School, the pie graph on page 531 was drawn to show the number of students who had left the school each year. From an original class of 540, the students pictured in the graph had either dropped out of school, or moved out of the school district. Use this graph to answer each of the following questions.

It is important that answers to 1 a be correct, for the answers to each of the other questions in Problem 1 are dependent on these. Perhaps it would be best that if this problem is to be assigned for homework, that part "a" be done in class under a supervised-study arrangement to make certain of correct answers.

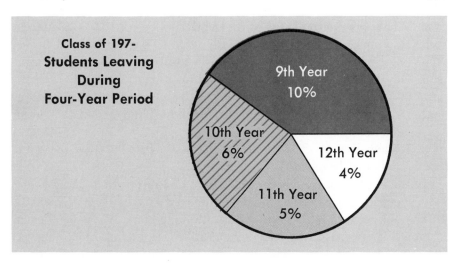

Class of 197-
Students Leaving
During
Four-Year Period

9th Year
10%

10th Year
6%

12th Year
4%

11th Year
5%

a. How many students of the original class of 540 left the school each year? (Round off each answer to the nearest whole number.) **9th: 54; 10th: 32; 11th: 27; 12th: 22**

b. How many students left school over the four-year period? **135**

c. What percent of the original class was graduated from Southwest High School? **75%**

d. How many fewer students left during the 10th year than during the 9th year? **22**

e. What percent fewer left during the 10th year than during the 9th year? **40.7%**

f. How many more students left during the 11th year than during the 12th year? **5**

g. What percent more left during the 11th year than during the 12th year? **22.7%**

h. What is the mean number of students who left annually over the four-year period? **33.75 or 34**

3. The senior class at Franklin High School sold $2,000 worth of candy to finance the class yearbook. A graph of the outcome of this sale is shown here. Use this graph to answer the questions that follow it.

Yearbook Candy Sale
$2,000

Cost of Candy 55%	5%	Loss 8%	Profit 32%

Cost of Prizes

See the comment at the bottom of page 530.

a. What was the total cost of the candy?   _$1,100.00_
b. How much of the $2,000 actually went to pay for the yearbook?
                                                              _$640.00_
c. How much of the $2,000 was spent on prizes to promote the sale of the candy?   _$100.00_
d. If no money were spent on prizes, how large would the profit have been?   _$740.00_
e. If each box of candy were sold for $1.25, what was the total number of boxes sold?   _1,600_
f. If each box of candy were sold for $1.50 rather than $1.25, what would the total selling price of the candy have been? _$2,400.00_

4. The budget of a family of 3 where the take-home pay is $800 each month is shown in the following graph. Use this graph to answer each of the questions that follow it.

Budget for a Family of Three
Take-Home Pay—$800 per Month

Food	House Operation	Cloth-ing	Shelter	Trans-portation	Personal Advance-ment	Savings
$180	$104	$71	$98	$113	$108	$126

a. On what item is the greatest amount of money spent? _Food_
b. How much is spent monthly on the item that requires the least amount of money?   _$71.00_
c. What percent of the take-home pay is used for food? _22.5%_
d. What percent of the take-home pay is used for shelter?
                                                              _12.3%_
e. What percent of the take-home pay is saved?   _15.8%_
f. If the amount spent for shelter is increased by 25%, how much money will be used for this item each month?   _$122.50_
g. How much does the family spend for food over the period of one year?   _$2,160.00_
h. If the amount saved is increased by ⅓, how much of the take-home pay will be saved each month?   _$168.00_
i. If the personal advancement item is increased by 33⅓%, how much money will be devoted monthly to this item?   _$144.00_

Questions such as 4 f, 4 h, and 4 i may be a little difficult for the students to analyze without some help from you. They must not only find the amount of increase, but also add this to the original quantity to determine the new amount devoted to this item.

Section 4: The Pictograph

The pictogaph is simply a contraction for the words *picture graph.* This type of graph is used quite often in newspapers and magazines to catch the eye of the reader. Its appeal to people is the same as the appeal of comic strips, for these graphs consist of drawings of people, or animals, or houses, or whatever it is that the information happens to be about. For instance, if the data were about automobile accidents, then the graph would probably consist of drawings of wrecked cars. However, if the data concerned itself with the number of fish caught in a certain lake each year over the past few years, then the drawings would be of fish.

The pictograph is used primarily to compare information about the same item as it occurs at a number of different times. In all cases it would be much easier to draw a bar graph to show this same comparison, but most people would simply ignore the bar graph, while they might at least tend to glance at the drawings in the pictograph.

■ILLUSTRATION: The graph below shows the number of points scored by Otis Clark during the first four basketball games last season. Use this graph to answer the questions that follow it.

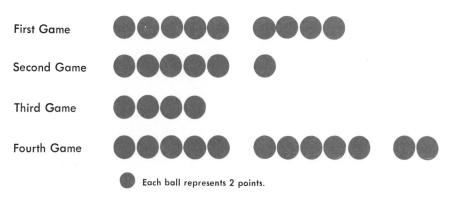

Points Scorded by Otis Clark

Each ball represents 2 points.

a. How many points did Otis score during the first game?

b. How many points did Otis score during the four games?

c. If Otis scored one third fewer points the fifth game than he did the fourth game, how many points did he score during the fifth game?

When presenting information to the layman, the pictograph is used more than any other graph, for it has very definite eye appeal. On the other hand, it is almost never used when presenting technical data, for it is far too inaccurate.

● SOLUTION :

(a) Each ball represents 2 points. Therefore, it is simply a matter of counting the number of balls after the words "First Game," and then multiplying that number by 2.

$$\text{Number of points scored in first game} = 9 \times 2$$
$$= 18$$

(b) Total number of points in four games $= 31 \times 2$
$$= 62$$

(c) Number of points in fourth game $= 12 \times 2$
$$= 24$$

$$\text{Number of points fewer in 5th game} = \tfrac{1}{3} \times 24$$
$$= 8$$

$$\text{Number of points in 5th game} = 24 - 8$$
$$= 16$$

As in the case of each of the other graphs, it is also possible to distort the information through the drawings in a pictograph. If the pictograph is drawn correctly, then all the figures have to be exactly the same size. When this is done, the eye merely compares the number of figures under one condition with the number of figures under a second condition. However, if you wanted to confuse the reader, you would simply draw the figures by giving them the same shape but a different size. As an illustration, the following graph is supposed to picture the number of points that Mike scored during two different basketball games.

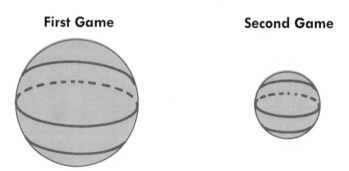

First Game   **Second Game**

A person examining this graph would not know whether to compare the radii of the two balls, or the volumes of the two. If he looked at the radii, he would come to the conclusion that Mike had scored twice the number of points in the first game as he had in the second. But if he examined the volumes, he would come up with the idea that Mike had scored 8 times as many points in the first game as he had in the second!

The person who wants to distort data will usually do so by using the pictograph. Using pictures of different sizes seems reasonable to the layman, and, therefore, the graph would not seem as if it were intended to create a false impression. However, does the reader compare heights, widths, or volumes?

EXERCISES

1. The student government at Grover Lakes High School decided to raise money by selling pennants. The following graph shows the number of pennants sold each week during the five-week sale.

Pennant Sale
Grover Lakes High School

First Week	⚑⚑⚑⚑⚑ ⚑⚑⚑⚑⚑ ⚑⚑⚑⚑⚑ ⚑⚑⚑⚑⚑ ⚑⚑⚑⚑⚑ ⚑⚑
Second Week	⚑⚑⚑⚑⚑ ⚑⚑⚑⚑⚑ ⚑⚑⚑⚑⚑ ⚑
Third Week	⚑⚑⚑⚑⚑ ⚑⚑⚑⚑⚑ ⚑⚑⚑⚑⚑ ⚑⚑⚑⚑⚑ ⚑
Fourth Week	⚑⚑⚑⚑⚑ ⚑⚑⚑⚑⚑ ⚑⚑⚑⚑⚑
Fifth Week	⚑⚑⚑⚑⚑ ⚑⚑⚑⚑

⚑ Each figure represents 3 pennants.

   a. How many pennants were sold during the first week? __81__
   b. How many more pennants were sold during the second week than during the fifth week? __21__
   c. What was the total number of pennants sold? __264__
   d. If each pennant were sold for 75¢, what was the total amount of money collected during the third week? __$47.25__
   e. If a 40% profit were made on the sale of these pennants, what was the total profit on the five-week sale? __$79.20__
   f. What was the mean number of pennants sold weekly? __52.8 or 53__
   g. What was the percent of decrease in the number of pennants sold the fifth week over the number sold during the first week? __66.7%__

2. The following graph shows the enrollment at Burlington Regional High School during the first, fifth, and tenth year after it opened. Use this graph to answer the questions that follow it.

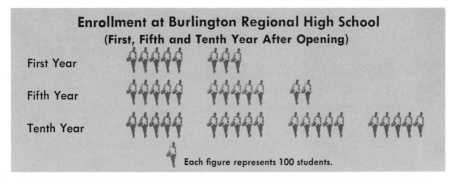

Enrollment at Burlington Regional High School
(First, Fifth and Tenth Year After Opening)

First Year

Fifth Year

Tenth Year

Each figure represents 100 students.

If the school happens to be conducting a fund-raising drive at this time, it would be interesting and timely to have the students in the class present the information either daily, or weekly, in a graphic form similar to that used in Exercise 1.

a. How many students were enrolled in the school during the first year? <u>800</u>

b. How many more students were enrolled in the school the fifth year than the first year? <u>400</u>

c. By what percent had the enrollment increased the fifth year over the first? <u>50%</u>

d. In the fifteenth year after the school is opened, the enrollment is expected to be 25% more than the enrollment in the tenth year. How many students will be registered in the school in the fifteenth year? <u>2,500</u>

e. If 53% of the students during the tenth year were girls, how many girls were there in the school at that time? <u>1,060</u>

f. The average attendance each day during the fifth year was approximately 92% of the student body. How many students could be expected to be absent each day? <u>160</u>

g. What can be said concerning the number of students enrolled at Burlington Regional High School during the sixth year after it was opened? It will probably be a little more <u>than 1,200.</u>

3. The following graph shows the amount of money that should be saved monthly by a family having a take-home pay of $500 per month.

Monthly Savings for a Take-Home Pay of $500 Monthly

Size of Family

2 Persons	🐷🐷🐷🐷🐷 🐷🐷🐷🐷🐷 🐷🐷🐷🐷 🐷
3 Persons	🐷🐷🐷🐷🐷 🐷🐷🐷🐷🐷 🐷🐷🐷🐷
4 Persons	🐷🐷🐷🐷🐷 🐷🐷🐷🐷🐷 🐷
5 Persons	🐷🐷🐷🐷🐷 🐷🐷🐷

🐷 Each figure represents $4.

a. How much should a family of 2 with this income save? <u>$64.00</u>

b. How much less will a family of 4 save each month than a family of 3 with this income? <u>$12.00</u>

c. What will be the annual savings of a family of 5 with this income? <u>$384.00</u>

d. What percent less does a family of 5 save than a family of 2? <u>50%</u>

In the graph of Exercise 2, call attention to the fact that it is impossible to picture a number such as 57 students. This could be done only by drawing a partial figure and placing the numeral somewhere in its immediate vicinity.

e. What percent more does a family of 3 save than a family of 4?

27.3%

f. Mr. Kent, whose monthly take-home pay is $500, has a wife and one child. If he saves 10% more than the graph above indicates for a family of his size, what are his annual savings? $739.20

4. The following graph shows the mean earnings in one of our states of an elementary school graduate, a high school graduate, and a college graduate of 25. Use this graph to answer the questions that follow it.

Mean Annual Earnings at Age 25

Elementary School Graduate		
High School Graduate		
College Graduate		

Each bill represents $500.

E.S.—$4,500.00
H.S.—$5,500.00
C. —$6,500.00

a. What are the mean earnings of each group at 25?

b. By how much do the mean earnings of the high school graduate exceed the mean earnings of the elementary school graduate at 25? $1,000.00

c. By how much do the mean earnings of the college graduate exceed the mean earnings of the high school graduate at 25? $1,000.00

d. By what percent do the mean earnings of the college graduate exceed the mean earnings of the high school graduate at 25? 18.2%

e. If the mean annual earnings of the college graduate in this state are 8% more at 26 than they are at 25, then how much will the average college graduate be earning in this state at 26? $7,020.00

f. Jack Burnett, who is 25, is a high school graduate in this state. If he is earning $127 each week, by how much does his income exceed the mean annual earnings of high school graduates in this state? $1,104.00

Unit 3: The Family Budget

From the number of graphs in Unit 2 that pertain to budgeting, it should be apparent that the budget lends itself quite readily to graphing. And since you have already dealt with the idea of budgeting your earnings, it might be well if you examined this topic a bit more thoroughly at this time.

Use graph of Exercise 4 to illustrate that potential annual earnings increase with the increase in education the person attains. Information such as this can be found in *Information Please Almanac* or *World Almanac*. As a special project, have students report on latest figures for mean annual income.

Everyone who has ever made any study of income planning agrees that family budgets are strictly a family affair. The budget that meets the needs of one family may be completely out of line with one that fills the needs of another family with the same income and the same number of mouths to feed. While one of these families may prefer a flashy new car each year and not care much where it lives, the other family may want its home in a nice residential area and be more than satisfied to drive around in a second-hand sedan. The budgets presented earlier in this chapter, and also the ones about to be presented, are only guidelines based on the thinking of certain economists.

The budgets these men develop are usually an outgrowth of studies of the spending habits of many, many families in various income brackets. Although they offer these budget guides, they are very careful to point out that they are only guides, and that the budget of each individual family should be tailored to its own particular needs. Usually, the economists will suggest, however, that if the family finds that it is spending far more money on some item than the guide budget advises, it might be well to take a good long look to see why. For instance, if an average of $150 per month is spent on clothes while the guide calls for only $70 for this item, then something may be amiss. It may very well be that one of the members of the family is in show business and needs an expensive wardrobe. Then there is no question but that these clothes must be purchased.

The important thing to remember is that any prepared budget is just a starting point to give you some idea of how the average family, with the income you have, is spending its money. When you make up your own budget, you might very well start with one of these guides. Then, over a period of several months, you will probably want to keep a fairly accurate account of how you are spending your money. By comparing your actual spending with your plan for spending—that is, your budget—you will come up with a program that is better suited for yourself than any plan someone else could devise for you.

The budget you set up for yourself, though, should not be a hard-and-fast pattern that never changes. As you grow older, your interests change, your needs change, your income changes, and so, too, your budget should change. Where, at one point in your life you may be saving money for your son's education, sooner or later he is graduated from college. Then the need for saving for this purpose disappears. At this point, you simply readjust your budget to use that money for some other purpose.

Some of the items that should be included in a family budget are shown on page 539.

Read material carefully with students, stressing fact that any budget predetermined by a so-called expert is merely an "average" of what families in a particular income bracket may be spending on certain items. Families differ in their values, and, in different parts of the country, their needs differ.

Food: The usual things such as meat, eggs, vegetables. What other items should be named here?

Home Utilities: Fuel bills, electric bills, gas bills, water bills, household supplies, furniture, draperies. What other items?

Clothes: Suits, dresses, cleaning bills, laundry bills. What other items?

Rent: If you own your own home, this item would include the interest on the mortgage, taxes, homeowner's insurance. What other items?

Transportation: Automobile insurance, gas, oil, payments on car; bus fare. What other items?

Savings, Insurance Contributions: Name some of the insurance items that will be included here.

Miscellaneous: State income tax, membership dues, vacation expenses, books and magazines. What other items?

■ ILLUSTRATION: Mr. Tucker has a take-home pay of $600 per month. His monthly budget includes the following items:

Food: $141	Rent: $80
Home Utilities: $85	Transportation: $77
Clothes: $43	Savings, Insurance: $84
	Miscellaneous: $90

a. What percent of the monthly budget is needed for food?

b. What percent of the monthly budget is needed for the payment of both rent and home utilities?

● SOLUTION:

(a) "The cost of food ($141) compares to the total budget ($600) as what number compares to 100?"

$141/\$600 = n/100$

$600 \times n = 141 \times 100$ (Equal Fractions Principle)

$600 \times n = 14{,}100$

$n = 23.5$ (Product of Two Numbers Principle)

Therefore, the percent spent on food is 23.5%.

(b) Total of both rent and home utilities $= \$80 + \$85$

$= \$165$

"The payment of both rent and home utilities ($165) compares to the total budget ($600) as what number compares to 100?"

$165/\$600 = n/100$

$600 \times n = 165 \times 100$

$600 \times n = 16{,}500$

$n = 27.5$

Therefore, the percent needed for the payment of both rent and home utilities is 27.5%.

See the comment at the bottom of page 515.

EXERCISES   **A**

1. As the monthly take-home pay increases, the part of the budget needed for food decreases. Determine the amount spent for food each month by a family of two in each of the following budget allotments.

	Monthly Take-Home Pay	Percent Used For Food	Amount Used For Food
a.	$1,200	18%	$ 216.00
b.	1,000	19.5%	195.00
c.	800	21.5%	172.00
d.	600	23.5%	141.00
e.	400	26.5%	106.00
f.	200	28.5%	57.00

2. As the size of the family increases, the percent of the budget requirement for clothes also increases. Each of the following families has a monthly take-home pay of $350. How much has each allotted in its budget for clothes?

		Percent Allotted For Clothes	Amount Allotted For Clothes
a.	Family of 2	7.7%	$ 26.95
b.	Family of 3	8.7%	30.45
c.	Family of 4	9.6%	33.60
d.	Family of 5	10.6%	37.10

3. Not only the amount, but the percent, that a family can save increases as the take-home pay increases. Determine the amount put aside for savings each month by a family of three on each of the following budget allotments.

	Monthly Take-Home Pay	Percent Allotted For Savings	Amount Allotted For Savings
a.	$ 250	4.7%	$ 11.75
b.	450	10.8%	48.60
c.	600	11.9%	71.40
d.	800	15.5%	124.00
e.	1,100	18.6%	204.60

4 What is the percent of the monthly take-home pay that is spent for rent in each of the budget allotments for a family of four?

	Monthly Take-Home Pay	Amount Budgeted For Rent	Percent Budgeted For Rent
a.	$1,000	$230	23 %
b.	800	208	26 %
c.	600	174	29 %

B

1. The following is a budget for a family of 4 having a take-home pay of $600 per month.

Food: $153　　　　　　Rent: $85

Home Utilities: $85　　　Transportation: $77

Clothes: $55　　　　　　Savings: $59

Miscellaneous: $86

   a. How much money is budgeted for food for the year? ___$1,836.00___
   b. How much money is budgeted for clothing for the year?

   $660.00

   c. If the monthly rent is increased by 10%, how much money will have to be allotted to this item each month? ___$93.50___
   d. If the increase in rent in (c), above, has to be taken from the savings shown in the budget, by how much will this decrease the monthly savings? ___$8.50___
   e. What percent of the monthly budget is allotted for transportation? ___12.8%___
   f. What percent of the monthly budget is allotted for just food and rent as shown in the budget above? ___39.7%___

2. The following are suggested budgets for families having a take-home pay of $700 per month.

SIZE OF FAMILY

	2	3	4	5
Food	$150	$158	$165	$172
Rent	84	86	90	91
Home Utilities	92	92	92	92
Clothes	55	62	70	76
Transportation	98	98	98	98
Savings	124	110	95	82
Miscellaneous	97	94	90	89

   a. How much more is budgeted monthly for food by a family of 5 than by a family of 2? ___$22.00___
   b. How much more is budgeted monthly for clothes by a family of 4 than by a family of 2? ___$15.00___
   c. How much is budgeted for savings annually by a family of 3?

   $1,320.00

   d. How much is budgeted for savings annually by a family of 5?

   $984.00

   e. How much more is budgeted for savings annually by a family of 3 than by a family of 5? ___$336.00___

If possible, try to determine mean rent paid by families of students in your class. In some parts of the country, the budgetary allotment shown here for rent may be completely out of line. Do not forget, though, that part of money designated for "home utilities" such as heat, may appear as rent cost.

f. What is the mean amount budgeted for food monthly for the four different-sized families above? $161.25

g. What is the mean amount budgeted for clothes for the four different-size families above? $65.75

h. A family of 2 with a take-home monthly pay of $700 rented an apartment at $122 per month. What percent more than the amount shown in the budget above were they paying for rent?

45.2%

i. What percent of the budget of the family of 5 is needed for food?

24.6%

j. What percent of the budget of the family of 2 is needed for food?

21.4%

Unit 4: Chapter Review and Test

1. Determine the mode score in the following set of test scores.

5, 2, 1, 7, 3, 8, 2, 6, 5, 4, 7, 9, 5, 8, 2, 5

5

2. Determine the median score in the following set of test scores.

2, 6, 1, 3, 4, 8, 5, 9, 2, 7, 6, 3, 9, 8, 10

6

3. The 800 students at Robert Clinton High School contributed $104 to the Red Cross Fund Drive. What was the mean contribution of each student? $.13

4. During the three years that John was a member of the varsity football team in high school, he managed to run up a total score of 364 points. He played in 8 games during his sophomore year, 9 in his junior year, and 9 in his senior year. What is the mean number of points he scored per game over the three-year period?   14

5. George Dennis had a part-time job, after school and Saturday, as a shoe salesman. The graph on page 543 shows the total of his weekly sales over a six-week period. Use this graph to answer the questions that follow.

a. During which week did Dennis have his greatest sales?

4th

b. What week's sales were smallest during this six-week period?

$240.00

c. By how much did the first week's sales exceed the sixth week's sales? $100.00

d. What were his total sales over the six-week period? $1,980.00

As in previous chapters, part of this unit can be used as a review, while the remainder is used as a chapter test.

Six-Weeks School Period

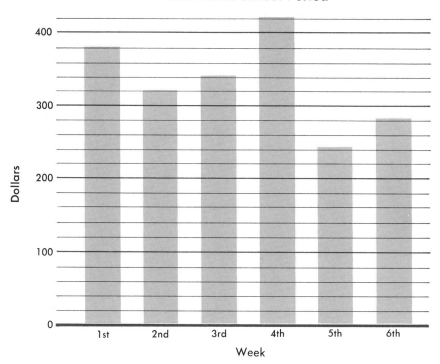

e. What were his mean weekly sales over this six-week period?
<u>**$330.00**</u>

f. If, during the seventh week, he increased his sales by 25% of what it had been the sixth week, how large were his sales during the seventh week?   <u>**$350.00**</u>

g. By what percent did his sales decrease from the fourth to the fifth week?   <u>**42.9%**</u>

6. Frank and Ed are members of the school's golf team. The graph on page 544 gives a comparison of their scores over the past eight matches with other schools. Use this graph to answer the questions that follow it.

a. Which boy had the highest golf score for any one game?
<u>**Frank**</u>

b. What was the lowest score that either boy had?   <u>**93**</u>

c. Which of the boys had the lowest score during the 8 matches?
<u>**Frank**</u>

d. During which match did both boys score the same number of points?   <u>**Second**</u>

e. By how many points did Frank's highest score exceed his least score?   <u>**23**</u>

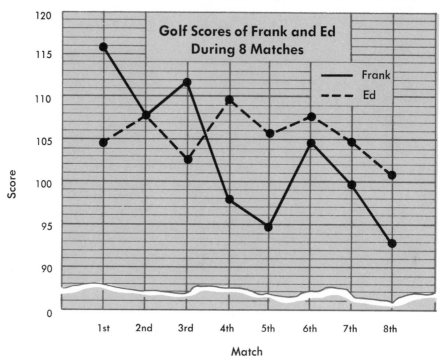

f. By how many points did Ed's highest score exceed his least
score?   **9**
g. What was Frank's mean score over the 8 games?   **103.4**
h. What was Ed's mean score over the 8 games?   **105.8**
i. Which boy improved his game the most over the 8 matches?
                                                                         Frank

7. The record of the Smithville High School soccer team over the past
10 years is shown in the following graph. Use this graph to answer
the questions that follow it.

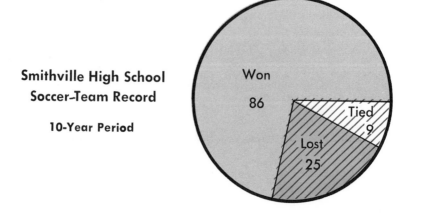

Smithville High School
Soccer-Team Record

10-Year Period

a. What was the total number of games played over the 10-year period? <u>120</u>

b. How many more games were won than lost? <u>61</u>

c. How many more games were won than tied? <u>77</u>

d. How many more games were won than were either lost or tied? <u>52</u>

e. What percent of the games was won? <u>71.7%</u>

f. What percent of the games was lost? <u>20.8%</u>

g. If the team wins all of its 12 games during the eleventh year, what percent of the games will it have won over the eleven-year period? <u>74.2%</u>

8. A suggested budget for a family of 4 with a monthly take-home pay of $900 follows.

> Food: $192   Rent: $102
> Home Utilities: $109   Transportation: $126
> Clothes: $92   Savings: $150
> Miscellaneous: $129

a. What is the amount budgeted for both rent and home utilities for one month? <u>$211.00</u>

b. What is the amount budgeted for transportation for the year? <u>$1,512.00</u>

c. How much money is budgeted for clothes for the year? <u>$1,104.00</u>

d. What percent of the budget is allotted for food? <u>21.3%</u>

e. What percent of the budget is allotted for savings? <u>16.7%</u>

f. By what percent does the food budget exceed the rent budget? <u>88.2%</u>

g. If transportation costs are increased by 12½%, how much will have to be budgeted each month for this item? <u>$141.75</u>

CHAPTER **14**

THE FUNDAMENTAL
OPERATIONS
AND PERCENT

    This chapter is designed as a review of the fundamental operations of arithmetic on whole numbers, decimals, and fractions. You will find that everything included in this chapter has been taught to you at one time or another during your first six or seven years of school. The purpose of including it here is to help refresh your memory in the event that the mechanics of some of the operations may have slipped your mind. In view of this, the explanations that are included are designed primarily to tell you how to perform the necessary steps in arriving at your answer rather than why these steps are necessary.

At this stage of a student's education, the algorithms connected with the four fundamental operations should not be taught as if this were the student's first exposure to them, but rather as a review with emphasis on practice rather than theoretical justification.

Unit 1: Addition

Section 1: Addition of Whole Numbers

EXERCISES   A

Find the sum in each of the following exercises.

1. 4
  1
  5
	2. 0
	  1
	  1
		3. 2
		  3
		  5
			4. 1
			  2
			  3
				5. 3
				  3
				  6

6. 5
  5
 10
	7. 1
	  1
	  2
		8. 0
		  2
		  2
			9. 5
			  1
			  6
				10. 3
				  2
				  5

11. 3
  4
  7
	12. 0
	  4
	  4
		13. 2
		  2
		  4
			14. 2
			  1
			  3
				15. 4
				  4
				  8

16. 4
  2
  6
	17. 2
	  4
	  6
		18. 1
		  3
		  4
			19. 5
			  4
			  9
				20. 0
				  3
				  3

21. 5
  6
 11
	22. 3
	  1
	  4
		23. 6
		  4
		 10
			24. 9
			  0
			  9
				25. 9
				  9
				 18

26. 1
  5
  6
	27. 7
	  2
	  9
		28. 4
		  0
		  4
			29. 5
			  2
			  7
				30. 4
				  3
				  7

31. 2
  5
  7
	32. 4
	  5
	  9
		33. 8
		  0
		  8
			34. 1
			  4
			  5
				35. 3
				  5
				  8

36. 6
  6
 12
	37. 1
	  0
	  1
		38. 5
		  3
		  8
			39. 2
			  6
			  8
				40. 7
				  4
				 11

41. 1
  9
 10
	42. 5
	  7
	 12
		43. 0
		  5
		  5
			44. 7
			  7
			 14
				45. 4
				  6
				 10

46. 2
  7
  9
	47. 1
	  6
	  7
		48. 8
		  4
		 12
			49. 3
			  6
			  9
				50. 6
				  7
				 13

51. 6
  3
  9
	52. 0
	  8
	  8
		53. 7
		  1
		  8
			54. 8
			  7
			 15
				55. 6
				  2
				  8

The exercises in A are the 100 number facts. Stress accuracy, but stress speed even more.
Select exercises at random and select students at random for answers.

56.	57.	58.	59.	60.
2	5	1	6	0
8	8	7	8	6
10	13	8	14	6

61.	62.	63.	64.	65.
6	3	9	8	4
5	7	4	6	7
11	10	13	14	11

66.	67.	68.	69.	70.
0	9	6	9	7
9	3	1	2	6
9	12	7	11	13

71.	72.	73.	74.	75.
7	2	5	7	4
5	0	9	3	8
12	2	14	10	12

76.	77.	78.	79.	80.
8	1	0	8	7
2	8	7	5	1
10	9	7	13	8

81.	82.	83.	84.	85.
8	2	9	3	3
3	9	6	8	0
11	11	15	11	3

86.	87.	88.	89.	90.
9	7	9	7	8
8	8	5	0	1
17	15	14	7	9

91.	92.	93.	94.	95.
6	3	8	4	7
0	9	8	9	9
6	12	16	13	16

96.	97.	98.	99.	100.
9	9	5	6	8
1	7	0	9	9
10	16	5	15	17

B

Find the sum in each of the following exercises.

1.	2.	3.	4.	5.
2	1	4	3	1
3	5	7	9	6
7	8	1	2	4
12	14	12	14	11

6.	7.	8.	9.	10.
2	3	1	4	9
9	5	8	6	1
4	9	6	7	5
15	17	15	17	15

Chapter 14 can be used either as a review of the fundamental operations to be practised at the outset of the course, or special sections of this chapter can be used for review purpose throughout the year as the need arises.

11. 4	12. 2	13. 6	14. 1	15. 4
8	7	5	7	4
5	6	6	8	9
17	15	17	16	17

16. 7	17. 3	18. 5	19. 8	20. 9
4	7	9	1	3
8	7	6	8	6
19	17	20	17	18

21. 6	22. 8	23. 7	24. 6	25. 9
5	7	9	8	5
8	7	4	7	8
19	22	20	21	22

26. 8	27. 6	28. 9	29. 9	30. 9
8	8	7	8	9
7	9	8	8	7
23	23	24	25	25

C

Find the sum in each of the following exercises.

1. 13	2. 17	3. 46	4. 62
34	10	12	27
47	27	58	89

5. 53	6. 21	7. 72	8. 68
46	58	16	21
99	79	88	89

9. 65	10. 34	11. 46	12. 58
27	44	27	63
92	78	73	121

13. 64	14. 45	15. 96	16. 47
57	76	24	65
121	121	120	112

17. 65	18. 78	19. 87	20. 98
66	74	75	56
131	152	162	154

D

Find the sum in each of the following exercises.

1. 23	2. 31	3. 31	4. 41
46	46	18	25
10	21	11	32
79	98	60	98

5. 26	6. 43	7. 16	8. 33
18	27	42	18
30	15	38	44
74	85	96	95

9. 56	10. 62	11. 19	12. 28
23	27	84	63
35	57	36	16
114	146	139	107

13. 85	14. 76	15. 19	16. 36
39	27	86	45
41	32	54	87
165	135	159	168

17. 72	18. 57	19. 76	20. 98
43	65	59	69
88	98	87	87
203	220	222	254

E

Find the sum in each of the following exercises.

1. 123	2. 205	3. 421	4. 533
231	314	307	243
113	260	271	112
467	779	999	888

5. 237	6. 134	7. 515	8. 239
436	625	372	426
521	246	468	874
1,194	1,005	1,355	1,539

9. 624	10. 175	11. 319	12. 581
372	653	584	367
246	365	623	419
1,242	1,193	1,526	1,367

13. 657	14. 585	15. 908	16. 488
743	693	675	874
917	778	247	565
2,317	2,056	1,830	1,927

17. 675	18. 897	19. 986	20. 876
788	689	869	987
696	758	788	969
2,159	2,344	2,643	2,832

Section 2: Addition of Decimals

The mechanics of adding decimal numbers is no different than that of adding whole numbers. Care, however, must be taken to make certain that when the numbers are arranged vertically, the decimal points are placed directly below one another.

■ ILLUSTRATION 1: Find the sum of the following set of numbers.

$$\$4.26, \ \$3, \ \$8.04, \ \$27$$

▼ EXPLANATION: If the numbers to be added include some that are given in terms of dollars only, while others are given in terms of dollars and cents, then it would be best to change all numbers to the dollars and cents form. Thus, in the numbers in the illustration, the $3 and $27 are both written in terms of dollars only. Rewrite·them so that the $3 appears as $3.00, that is, 3 dollars and no cents and the $27 appears as $27.00, that is, 27 dollars and no cents.

● SOLUTION:

$$\begin{array}{r} \$4.26 \\ 3.00 \\ 8.04 \\ 27.00 \\ \hline \$42.30 \end{array}$$

▼ EXPLANATION (continued): Notice that the addition above is done exactly as the addition of whole numbers, with the single exception that it is necessary to place the decimal point in the answer directly in line with the decimal points in the numbers being added.

■ ILLUSTRATION 2: Find the sum of the following set of numbers.

$$\$3.45, \ \$2.58, \ 76\cent, \ 18\cent$$

▼ EXPLANATION: In those cases where some of the numbers are expressed with the dollar symbol ($), while others are expressed with the cent symbol (¢), rewrite the latter in terms of dollars. Thus, the

Insist that students arrange decimal numerals in a vertical fashion before attempting to add. Make certain that they insert a decimal point in each numeral if it does not already appear there.

76¢ and 18¢ should be written as $.76 and $.18 before the numbers are added.

●SOLUTION:

$$\begin{array}{r} \$3.45 \\ 2.58 \\ .76 \\ .18 \\ \hline \$6.97 \end{array}$$

EXERCISES   **A**

Find the sum in each of the following exercises.

1.	$2.15	2.	$4.06	3.	$5.13	4.	$1.65
	3.04		3.12		2.64		4.23
	$5.19		$7.18		$7.77		$5.88
5.	$8.22	6.	$7.90	7.	$6.78	8.	$9.27
	4.69		5.36		8.45		6.99
	$12.91		$13.26		$15.23		$16.26
9.	$14.67	10.	$27.42	11.	$49.75	12.	$16.49
	37.09		53.65		13.86		27.19
	$51.76		$81.07		$63.61		$43.68
13.	$159.95	14.	$105.50	15.	$299.98	16.	$697.19
	42.05		96.49		68.75		489.95
	$202.00		$201.99		$368.73		$1,187.14

B

Find the sum in each of the following exercises.

1.	$2.41	2.	$4.50	3.	$1.22	4.	$5.03
	3.27		2.31		3.43		2.61
	1.30		5.15		2.03		2.15
	$6.98		$11.96		$6.68		$9.79
5.	$6.37	6.	$1.85	7.	$9.42	8.	$7.29
	2.41		4.23		3.27		8.56
	1.16		6.70		5.86		3.35
	$9.94		$12.78		$18.55		$19.20
9.	$24.09	10.	$11.41	11.	$54.23	12.	$41.75
	32.16		13.28		8.64		29.25
	65.42		7.64		10.17		12.19
	$121.67		$32.33		$73.04		$83.19

13. $247.65	14. $352.29	15. $679.95	16. $937.49
109.16	847.63	325.09	895.78
693.27	285.07	437.65	876.88
$1,050.08	$1,484.99	$1,442.69	$2,710.15

C

In each of the following exercises, rearrange the numerals vertically before adding.

1. $2.41 + $3.76 + $4.45 =	$ 10.62
2. $2.56 + $4.07 + $3.98 =	$ 10.61
3. $5.48 + $6.29 + $8.05 =	$ 19.82
4. $3.75 + $7.34 + $9.70 =	$ 20.79
5. $12.03 + $6.74 + $14.39 + $2.49 =	$ 35.65
6. $36.24 + $18.56 + $2.27 + $12.50 =	$ 69.57
7. $4.36 + $43.17 + $29.25 + $3.45 =	$ 80.23
8. $17.95 + $15 + $42.50 + $8 =	$ 83.45
9. $54.80 + $21.55 + $39 + $2.04 =	$117.39
10. $123.60 + $43 + $15 + $2.73 =	$184.33
11. $144.75 + $5.65 + $86 + $7 + $14.36 =	$257.76
12. $46.30 + 54¢ + 85¢ + $3.95 + $8.50 =	$ 60.14
13. 67¢ + $12.85 + 14¢ + $58 + $16.20 =	$ 87.86
14. $125 + 75¢ + $40 + $18.12 + 56¢ =	$184.43
15. $57 + 98¢ + 64¢ + $176.58 + $39 =	$274.20
16. $258.42 + $43 + $125 + 72¢ + 134¢ =	$428.48

Section 3: Addition of Fractions

If the denominators of the fractions are alike, then the addition of fractions becomes the simple matter of merely adding the numerators and writing their sum over the denominator of the fraction. For example:

$$\tfrac{3}{8} + \tfrac{4}{8} = \tfrac{7}{8} \text{ (Just add 3 and 4)}$$

The reasoning for this is shown below.

$\tfrac{3}{8} + \tfrac{4}{8}$

$= 3 \times \tfrac{1}{8} + 4 \times \tfrac{1}{8}$	Meaning of Division
$= \tfrac{1}{8} \times 3 + \tfrac{1}{8} \times 4$	Commutative Law of Multiplication
$= \tfrac{1}{8} \times (3 + 4)$	Distributive Law of Multiplication
$= \tfrac{1}{8} \times 7$	Uniqueness of Addition
$= 7 \times \tfrac{1}{8}$	Commutative Law of Multiplication
$= \tfrac{7}{8}$	Meaning of Division

The reasoning above may well be beyond the level of the students. If this is so, use the explanation that appears at the top of page 554.

Or, if you prefer, you can think of $\frac{3}{8}$ as meaning 3 eighths, while $\frac{4}{8}$ means 4 eighths. And just as you add 3 apples and 4 apples and get 7 apples as their sum, so, too, you can add 3 eighths and 4 eighths and get 7 eighths. Since 7 eighths can be rewritten as $\frac{7}{8}$, the explanation here leads to the same answer as above.

■ILLUSTRATION 1: Add $\frac{5}{8}$ and $\frac{7}{8}$.

▼EXPLANATION: It is usually best to rewrite the problem in vertical form before adding the numbers.

●SOLUTION:

$$\begin{array}{r} \frac{5}{8} \\ +\frac{7}{8} \\ \hline \frac{12}{8} = 1\frac{4}{8} = 1\frac{1}{2} \end{array}$$

▼EXPLANATION (continued): The numeral 12/8 was changed to its equivalent form of $1\frac{4}{8}$ by dividing 8 into 12. The $\frac{4}{8}$ was then reduced to lowest terms by writing it as $\frac{1}{2}$.

■ILLUSTRATION 2: Add $\frac{2}{3}$ and $\frac{3}{4}$.

▼EXPLANATION: Since the two fractions do not have the same denominator, it is necessary to rewrite them as fractions equivalent to those which do have a common denominator. This can be done by multiplying the first fraction by 4/4, which is one form of the identity element of multiplication. The second fraction is multiplied by the identity element 3/3. Hence, both new fractions will have 12 as their denominator. Incidentally, the 12 is selected as the common denominator of the two fractions, for it is the smallest number for which both 3 and 4 are exact divisors. If the denominators had been 6 and 9, then the common denominator for these numbers would have been 18, for 18 is the smallest number for which both 6 and 9 are exact divisors. What would the common denominator have been had the denominators been 6 and 8?

●SOLUTION:

$$\begin{array}{rcccl} \frac{2}{3} & = & \frac{2}{3} \times \frac{4}{4} & = & \frac{8}{12} \\ +\frac{3}{4} & = & \frac{3}{4} \times \frac{3}{3} & = & \frac{9}{12} \\ \hline & & & & \frac{17}{12} = 1\frac{5}{12} \end{array}$$

■ILLUSTRATION 3: Add: $2\frac{3}{4}$ and $15\frac{5}{6}$

●SOLUTION:

$$\begin{array}{rcccl} 2\frac{3}{4} & = & 2\frac{3}{4} \times \frac{3}{3} & = & 2\frac{9}{12} \\ +15\frac{5}{6} & = & 15\frac{5}{6} \times \frac{2}{2} & = & 15\frac{10}{12} \\ \hline & & & & 17\frac{19}{12} = 17 + 1\frac{7}{12} = 18\frac{7}{12} \end{array}$$

▼EXPLANATION: The sum of two mixed numbers is found by adding the whole numbers and then adding the fractions. In this case, it is necessary to add 2 and 15, after which you add $\frac{9}{12}$ and $\frac{10}{12}$. The sum of $17\frac{19}{12}$ can be expressed as $17 + \frac{19}{12}$, and this, in turn, can be re-written as $17 + 1\frac{7}{12}$, which is what is done.

EXERCISES A

Find the sum in each of the following exercises.

1. $\frac{3}{5}$
   $\frac{1}{5}$
   4/5

2. $\frac{2}{7}$
   $\frac{3}{7}$
   5/7

3. $\frac{1}{3}$
   $\frac{1}{3}$
   2/3

4. $\frac{3}{8}$
   $\frac{2}{8}$
   5/8

5. $\frac{4}{9}$
   $\frac{3}{9}$
   7/9

6. $\frac{2}{11}$
   $\frac{3}{11}$
   5/11

7. $\frac{5}{12}$
   $\frac{6}{12}$
   11/12

8. $\frac{5}{14}$
   $\frac{4}{14}$
   9/14

9. $\frac{2}{6}$
   $\frac{3}{6}$
   5/6

10. $\frac{3}{16}$
    $\frac{7}{16}$
    5/8

11. $\frac{3}{4}$
    $\frac{3}{4}$
    1-1/2

12. $\frac{1}{2}$
    $\frac{1}{2}$
    1

13. $\frac{1}{4}$
    $\frac{3}{4}$
    1

14. $\frac{5}{6}$
    $\frac{1}{6}$
    1

15. $\frac{4}{6}$
    $\frac{5}{6}$
    1-1/2

16. $\frac{1}{8}$
    $\frac{7}{8}$
    1

17. $\frac{3}{8}$
    $\frac{5}{8}$
    1

18. $\frac{3}{8}$
    $\frac{7}{8}$
    1-1/4

19. $\frac{5}{8}$
    $\frac{7}{8}$
    1-1/2

20. $\frac{7}{8}$
    $\frac{2}{8}$
    1-1/8

21. $\frac{3}{10}$
    $\frac{5}{10}$
    4/5

22. $\frac{7}{10}$
    $\frac{3}{10}$
    1

23. $\frac{1}{10}$
    $\frac{9}{10}$
    1

24. $\frac{9}{10}$
    $\frac{3}{10}$
    1-1/5

25. $\frac{7}{10}$
    $\frac{8}{10}$
    1-1/2

26. $\frac{5}{12}$
    $\frac{7}{12}$
    1

27. $\frac{7}{12}$
    $\frac{7}{12}$
    1-1/6

28. $\frac{11}{12}$
    $\frac{5}{12}$
    1-1/3

29. $\frac{11}{12}$
    $\frac{10}{12}$
    1-3/4

30. $\frac{8}{12}$
    $\frac{10}{12}$
    1-2/3

31. $\frac{11}{16}$
    $\frac{5}{16}$
    1

32. $\frac{15}{16}$
    $\frac{5}{16}$
    1-1/4

33. $\frac{5}{16}$
    $\frac{13}{16}$
    1-1/8

34. $\frac{7}{16}$
    $\frac{11}{16}$
    1-1/8

35. $\frac{10}{16}$
    $\frac{15}{16}$
    1-9/16

36. $\frac{1}{3}$
    $\frac{1}{3}$
    $\frac{2}{3}$
    1-1/3

37. $\frac{3}{4}$
    $\frac{1}{4}$
    $\frac{1}{4}$
    1-1/4

38. $\frac{1}{6}$
    $\frac{5}{6}$
    $\frac{3}{6}$
    1-1/2

39. $\frac{1}{8}$
    $\frac{3}{8}$
    $\frac{5}{8}$
    1-1/8

40. $\frac{7}{8}$
    $\frac{5}{8}$
    $\frac{4}{8}$
    2

41. $\frac{6}{8}$
    $\frac{7}{8}$
    $\frac{5}{8}$
    2-1/4

42. $\frac{3}{8}$
    $\frac{6}{8}$
    $\frac{5}{8}$
    1-3/4

43. $\frac{7}{10}$
    $\frac{9}{10}$
    $\frac{1}{10}$
    1-7/10

44. $\frac{3}{10}$
    $\frac{7}{10}$
    $\frac{4}{10}$
    1-2/5

45. $\frac{1}{10}$
    $\frac{8}{10}$
    $\frac{6}{10}$
    1-1/2

46. $\frac{5}{12}$
    $\frac{7}{12}$
    $\frac{1}{12}$
    1-1/12

47. $\frac{9}{12}$
    $\frac{7}{12}$
    $\frac{11}{12}$
    2-1/4

48. $\frac{5}{16}$
    $\frac{7}{16}$
    $\frac{10}{16}$
    1-3/8

49. $\frac{3}{16}$
    $\frac{15}{16}$
    $\frac{8}{16}$
    1-5/8

50. $\frac{9}{16}$
    $\frac{11}{16}$
    $\frac{12}{16}$
    2

B

Find the sum in each of the following exercises.

1. $\frac{1}{2}$
$\frac{1}{4}$
3/4

2. $\frac{1}{2}$
$\frac{1}{6}$
2/3

3. $\frac{1}{3}$
$\frac{1}{6}$
1/2

4. $\frac{2}{3}$
$\frac{1}{9}$
7/9

5. $\frac{1}{2}$
$\frac{5}{6}$
1-1/3

6. $\frac{1}{2}$
$\frac{3}{8}$
7/8

7. $\frac{2}{3}$
$\frac{5}{6}$
1-1/2

8. $\frac{1}{4}$
$\frac{1}{8}$
3/8

9. $\frac{3}{4}$
$\frac{3}{8}$
1-1/8

10. $\frac{5}{6}$
$\frac{1}{12}$
11/12

11. $\frac{5}{12}$
$\frac{1}{6}$
7/12

12. $\frac{5}{8}$
$\frac{1}{2}$
1-1/8

13. $\frac{7}{8}$
$\frac{3}{4}$
1-5/8

14. $\frac{5}{16}$
$\frac{1}{4}$
9/16

15. $\frac{1}{6}$
$\frac{2}{3}$
5/6

16. $\frac{7}{12}$
$\frac{2}{3}$
1-1/4

17. $\frac{11}{12}$
$\frac{3}{4}$
1-2/3

18. $\frac{3}{16}$
$\frac{1}{2}$
11/16

19. $\frac{7}{16}$
$\frac{1}{4}$
11/16

20. $\frac{3}{4}$
$\frac{9}{16}$
1-5/16

21. $\frac{1}{2}$
$\frac{1}{3}$
5/6

22. $\frac{2}{3}$
$\frac{1}{2}$
1-1/6

23. $\frac{3}{4}$
$\frac{1}{3}$
1-1/12

24. $\frac{1}{4}$
$\frac{2}{3}$
11/12

25. $\frac{1}{6}$
$\frac{1}{4}$
5/12

26. $\frac{5}{6}$
$\frac{1}{4}$
1-1/12

27. $\frac{3}{4}$
$\frac{5}{6}$
1-7/12

28. $\frac{2}{5}$
$\frac{1}{2}$
9/10

29. $\frac{1}{2}$
$\frac{4}{5}$
1-3/10

30. $\frac{1}{3}$
$\frac{4}{5}$
1-2/15

31. $\frac{3}{5}$
$\frac{2}{3}$
1-4/15

32. $\frac{1}{2}$
$\frac{3}{5}$
1-1/10

33. $\frac{5}{8}$
$\frac{3}{16}$
13/16

34. $\frac{7}{16}$
$\frac{7}{8}$
1-5/16

35. $\frac{3}{8}$
$\frac{9}{16}$
15/16

36. $\frac{3}{4}$
$\frac{7}{16}$
1-3/16

37. $\frac{1}{4}$
$\frac{15}{16}$
1-3/16

38. $\frac{5}{6}$
$\frac{4}{9}$
1-5/18

39. $\frac{5}{9}$
$\frac{5}{6}$
1-7/18

40. $\frac{7}{9}$
$\frac{1}{6}$
17/18

41. $\frac{1}{2}$
$\frac{1}{3}$
$\frac{2}{3}$
1-1/2

42. $\frac{2}{3}$
$\frac{2}{3}$
$\frac{1}{2}$
1-5/6

43. $\frac{3}{4}$
$\frac{1}{2}$
$\frac{1}{2}$
1-3/4

44. $\frac{3}{4}$
$\frac{2}{3}$
$\frac{1}{3}$
1-3/4

45. $\frac{1}{2}$
$\frac{1}{3}$
$\frac{1}{4}$
1-1/12

46. $\frac{1}{2}$
$\frac{2}{3}$
$\frac{3}{4}$
1-11/12

47. $\frac{3}{4}$
$\frac{5}{12}$
$\frac{1}{6}$
1-1/3

48. $\frac{1}{4}$
$\frac{2}{3}$
$\frac{7}{12}$
1-1/2

49. $\frac{11}{12}$
$\frac{5}{6}$
$\frac{2}{3}$
2-5/12

50. $\frac{7}{12}$
$\frac{5}{6}$
$\frac{3}{4}$
2-1/6

C

Find the sum in each of the following exercises.

1. $6\frac{1}{5}$
   $7\frac{2}{5}$
   13-3/5

2. $8\frac{1}{3}$
   $9\frac{1}{3}$
   17-2/3

3. $5\frac{1}{8}$
   $6\frac{3}{8}$
   11-1/2

4. $9\frac{5}{8}$
   $7\frac{1}{8}$
   16-3/4

5. $2\frac{3}{10}$
   $7\frac{7}{10}$
   10

6. $2\frac{1}{2}$
   $3\frac{1}{4}$
   5-3/4

7. $5\frac{1}{6}$
   $4\frac{1}{6}$
   9-1/3

8. $6\frac{5}{8}$
   $2\frac{1}{4}$
   8-7/8

9. $9\frac{1}{3}$
   $7\frac{1}{6}$
   16-1/2

10. $8\frac{3}{4}$
    $3\frac{1}{8}$
    11-7/8

11. $7\frac{5}{12}$
    $9\frac{1}{4}$
    16-2/3

12. $8\frac{7}{12}$
    $4\frac{1}{3}$
    12-11/12

13. $6\frac{2}{3}$
    $3\frac{1}{12}$
    9-3/4

14. $1\frac{3}{10}$
    $2\frac{3}{5}$
    3-9/10

15. $4\frac{1}{10}$
    $6\frac{1}{5}$
    10-3/10

16. $3\frac{1}{2}$
    $4\frac{2}{3}$
    8-1/6

17. $7\frac{1}{2}$
    $6\frac{3}{4}$
    14-1/4

18. $6\frac{5}{6}$
    $9\frac{1}{2}$
    16-1/3

19. $8\frac{5}{8}$
    $7\frac{3}{4}$
    16-3/8

20. $12\frac{3}{8}$
    $9\frac{3}{4}$
    22-1/8

21. $8\frac{9}{10}$
    $7\frac{3}{5}$
    16-1/2

22. $10\frac{5}{12}$
    $9\frac{3}{4}$
    20-1/6

23. $12\frac{1}{2}$
    $7\frac{11}{12}$
    20-5/12

24. $14\frac{2}{3}$
    $11\frac{7}{12}$
    26-1/4

25. $16\frac{5}{12}$
    $9\frac{2}{3}$
    26-1/12

26. $11\frac{5}{6}$
    $12\frac{11}{12}$
    24-3/4

27. $16\frac{3}{4}$
    $14\frac{5}{6}$
    31-7/12

28. $14\frac{15}{16}$
    $16\frac{3}{4}$
    31-11/16

29. $14\frac{3}{8}$
    $9\frac{11}{16}$
    24-1/16

30. $21\frac{5}{8}$
    $20\frac{2}{3}$
    42-7/24

31. $6\frac{1}{2}$
    $5\frac{1}{3}$
    $2\frac{1}{2}$
    14-1/3

32. $5\frac{1}{2}$
    $6\frac{1}{4}$
    $3\frac{1}{4}$
    15

33. $7\frac{1}{2}$
    $9\frac{3}{4}$
    $10\frac{1}{4}$
    27-1/2

34. $1\frac{3}{4}$
    $4\frac{1}{2}$
    $7\frac{3}{4}$
    14

35. $10\frac{2}{3}$
    $5\frac{1}{2}$
    $6\frac{1}{2}$
    22-2/3

36. $2\frac{3}{4}$
    $5\frac{1}{2}$
    $4\frac{1}{2}$
    12-3/4

37. $10\frac{1}{3}$
    $7\frac{2}{3}$
    $9\frac{1}{6}$
    27-1/6

38. $5\frac{3}{8}$
    $7\frac{1}{2}$
    $2\frac{1}{4}$
    15-1/8

39. $6\frac{7}{8}$
    $4\frac{3}{4}$
    $9\frac{1}{4}$
    20-7/8

40. $1\frac{5}{6}$
    $7\frac{1}{2}$
    $8\frac{2}{3}$
    18

41. $16\frac{3}{4}$
    $10\frac{1}{2}$
    $15\frac{1}{3}$
    42-7/12

42. $7\frac{3}{8}$
    $9\frac{3}{4}$
    $6\frac{1}{2}$
    23-5/8

43. $14\frac{1}{4}$
    $2\frac{3}{4}$
    $8\frac{1}{8}$
    25-1/8

44. $11\frac{5}{6}$
    $12\frac{2}{3}$
    $7\frac{1}{2}$
    32

45. $1\frac{1}{6}$
    $2\frac{3}{4}$
    $6\frac{1}{2}$
    10-5/12

46. $11\frac{1}{4}$
    $5\frac{5}{6}$
    $12\frac{3}{4}$
    29-5/6

47. $12\frac{1}{2}$
    $6\frac{1}{6}$
    $14\frac{3}{4}$
    33-5/12

48. $17\frac{1}{2}$
    $14\frac{3}{16}$
    $12\frac{5}{8}$
    44-5/16

49. $24\frac{2}{3}$
    $27\frac{3}{4}$
    $16\frac{5}{12}$
    68-5/6

50. $26\frac{7}{8}$
    $31\frac{7}{16}$
    $28\frac{1}{2}$
    86-13/16

Unit 2: Subtraction

Section 1: Subtraction of Whole Numbers and Decimals

The only time you might run into a bit of difficulty in subtraction of whole numbers is under the following condition:

$$\begin{array}{r} 74 \\ -\ 28 \\ \hline \end{array}$$

Since 8 is larger than 4, you have to employ a special device in determining the answer. The problem is rewritten as:

$$\begin{array}{rcccccl} 74 & = 70 + 4 & = 60 + 10 + 4 & = 60 + 14 \\ -\ 28 & = 20 + 8 & = 20 + 8 & = 20 +\ \ 8 \\ \hline & & & \overline{40 +\ \ 6} = 46 \end{array}$$

That is, the 74 can be thought of as $70 + 4$, and this, in turn, as $60 + 10 + 4$, and, finally, as $60 + 14$. The purpose of this is to rewrite 74 in such a way that the number from which the 8 is subtracted is larger than the 8. Rather than think of the 74 as $70 + 4$, where it is not possible to subtract 8 from 4, you now think of it as $60 + 14$, where 8 can be subtracted from 14.

■ ILLUSTRATION 1: Subtract 35 from 83.
● SOLUTION:

$$\begin{array}{r} 83 \\ -\ 35 \\ \hline 48 \end{array}$$

▼ EXPLANATION: Rather than rewrite the 83 as above, you think of this number first as $80 + 3$; then as $70 + 10 + 3$; and, finally, as $70 + 13$. From a mechanical standpoint, you can imagine the 8 as having been decreased by 1, and the 3 as increased by 10. Now you can complete the computation in the usual manner.

■ ILLUSTRATION 2: Subtract $5.98 from $10.
● SOLUTION:

$$\begin{array}{r} \$10.00 \\ 5.98 \\ \hline \$\ \ 4.02 \end{array}$$

▼ EXPLANATION: As in addition, when subtracting decimals, be careful to place the decimal points directly below one another when writing the numbers vertically. In this case, it is necessary not only to rewrite $10 by inserting a decimal point after the 10, but also to add two zeros. This is done so that there are numerals above the 9 and the 8 in

$5.98. It is advisable to check your answer by adding the difference of $4.02 to the subtrahend of $5.98 to see if the sum is the minuend of $10.00.

$$\begin{array}{r} \$10.00 \\ \underline{5.98} \\ \$\ 4.02 \end{array}$$

EXERCISES **A**

Find the difference in each of the following exercises.

1. 4	2. 6	3. 3	4. 5	5. 4
1	0	2	3	4
3	6	1	2	0
6. 6	7. 5	8. 7	9. 6	10. 2
5	2	6	1	0
1	3	1	5	2
11. 5	12. 6	13. 8	14. 5	15. 6
4	2	0	1	3
1	4	8	4	3
16. 7	17. 3	18. 4	19. 8	20. 2
7	1	3	4	1
0	2	1	4	1
21. 4	22. 7	23. 6	24. 7	25. 6
0	2	4	5	6
4	5	2	2	0
26. 8	27. 6	28. 9	29. 8	30. 9
1	0	3	6	5
7	6	6	2	4
31. 7	32. 3	33. 7	34. 9	35. 8
4	0	1	4	8
3	3	6	5	0
36. 9	37. 1	38. 5	39. 9	40. 8
7	1	0	1	7
2	0	5	8	1
41. 8	42. 9	43. 3	44. 9	45. 5
5	0	3	8	5
3	9	0	1	0

The comment at the bottom of page 547 applies equally as well here for these 55 subtraction facts as it did for the 100 addition facts.

46. 9	47. 8	48. 2	49. 7	50. 9
9	2	2	0	6
0	6	0	7	3

51. 1	52. 4	53. 8	54. 9	55. 7
0	2	3	2	3
1	2	5	7	4

B

Find the difference in each of the following exercises.

1. 10	2. 11	3. 10	4. 12	5. 14
1	3	8	9	7
9	8	2	3	7

6. 11	7. 14	8. 11	9. 10	10. 16
2	6	7	5	8
9	8	4	5	8

11. 12	12. 11	13. 10	14. 13	15. 10
6	6	3	4	9
6	5	7	9	1

16. 12	17. 14	18. 11	19. 10	20. 11
8	5	4	2	9
4	9	7	8	2

21. 18	22. 14	23. 13	24. 11	25. 12
9	8	4	8	7
9	6	9	3	5

26. 13	27. 11	28. 10	29. 12	30. 15
6	5	4	3	7
7	6	6	9	8

31. 16	32. 10	33. 12	34. 13	35. 14
9	6	5	7	9
7	4	7	6	5

36. 15	37. 13	38. 10	39. 12	40. 15
8	5	7	4	6
7	8	3	8	9

41. 13	42. 17	43. 16	44. 15	45. 17
8	9	7	9	8
5	8	9	6	9

C

Find the difference in each of the following exercises.

1.	27	2.	35	3.	48	4.	37	5.	49
	12		14		25		23		42
	15		21		23		14		7

6.	58	7.	46	8.	69	9.	84	10.	97
	43		14		27		52		64
	15		32		42		32		33

11.	76	12.	68	13.	89	14.	76	15.	47
	26		51		74		25		32
	50		17		15		51		15

16.	32	17.	41	18.	53	19.	22	20.	64
	24		15		44		16		26
	8		26		9		6		38

21.	50	22.	54	23.	61	24.	73	25.	62
	23		35		19		48		56
	27		19		42		25		6

26.	87	27.	92	28.	83	29.	67	30.	58
	78		37		29		48		39
	9		55		54		19		19

31.	76	32.	42	33.	64	34.	52	35.	91
	57		25		37		39		78
	19		17		27		13		13

36.	148	37.	354	38.	758	39.	691	40.	574
	27		143		203		130		312
	121		211		555		561		262

41.	315	42.	428	43.	507	44.	346	45.	219
	194		256		321		182		96
	121		172		186		164		123

46.	538	47.	604	48.	657	49.	774	50.	856
	168		293		482		492		364
	370		311		175		282		492

51.	293	52.	572	53.	381	54.	474	55.	563
	124		314		139		255		319
	169		258		242		219		244

56.	624	57.	737	58.	856	59.	583	60.	954
	407		418		429		247		318
	217		319		427		336		636

61. 524	62. 401	63. 500	64. 652	65. 741
367	269	127	467	582
157	132	373	185	159
66. 306	67. 534	68. 763	69. 873	70. 695
209	148	468	585	587
97	386	295	288	108
71. 478	72. 657	73. 504	74. 710	75. 683
299	378	278	395	486
179	279	226	315	197

D

Find the difference in each of the following exercises.

1. $2.46	2. $4.39	3. $5.88	4. $3.69
.35	1.26	2.65	1.27
$2.11	$3.13	$3.23	$2.42
5. $8.27	6. $5.75	7. $6.58	8. $7.31
3.04	2.35	4.17	2.10
$5.23	$3.40	$2.41	$5.21
9. $5.14	10. $2.26	11. $9.57	12. $8.39
3.91	1.84	4.62	1.43
$1.23	$ .42	$4.95	$6.96
13. $6.44	14. $7.06	15. $9.23	16. $7.54
3.72	2.46	5.71	6.83
$2.72	$4.60	$3.52	$ .71
17. $5.45	18. $6.83	19. $2.31	20. $5.64
1.27	2.27	1.19	1.28
$4.18	$4.56	$1.12	$4.36
21. $9.72	22. $8.45	23. $7.17	24. $6.36
5.25	6.39	4.08	4.18
$4.47	$2.06	$3.09	$2.18
25. $4.00	26. $6.00	27. $5.00	28. $8.00
2.98	2.27	3.91	5.49
$1.02	$3.73	$1.09	$2.51
29. $7.00	30. $2.00	31. $3.00	32. $9.00
3.58	.69	2.63	6.34
$3.42	$1.31	$ .37	$2.66

33. $8.43	34. $7.12	35. $4.67	36. $5.24
3.66	2.58	3.88	2.98
$4.77	$4.54	$ .79	$2.26
37. $6.04	38. $5.07	39. $7.18	40. $9.65
3.95	2.89	5.99	7.96
$2.09	$2.18	$1.19	$1.69

Section 2: Subtraction of Fractions

The method used for subtracting one fraction from another is much the same as the method for adding one fraction to another. As before, the denominators must be the same before it is possible to subtract the numerator of the subtrahend from the numerator of the minuend. If the denominators are not the same, then the process for changing them into the same number is identical to the approach used in addition of fractions.

■ILLUSTRATION 1: Subtract ⅓ from ¾.

●SOLUTION:

$$\begin{array}{rcccl} & ① & & ② & & ③ \\ & \frac{3}{4} & = & \frac{3}{4}\times\frac{3}{3} & = & \frac{9}{12} \\ - & \frac{1}{3} & = & \frac{1}{3}\times\frac{4}{4} & = & \frac{4}{12} \\ \hline & & & & & \frac{5}{12} \end{array}$$

▼EXPLANATION: Quite frequently, students will perform Step ② mentally and go directly from Step ① to Step ③. There is no reason why you should not do this if you care to.

The only difficulty that might arise in subtracting one fraction from another is if, after converting the fractions to equivalent fractions having a common denominator, you find that the numerator of the minuend is smaller than the numerator of the subtrahend. The method for overcoming this difficulty will be explained in the following illustration.

■ILLUSTRATION 2: Subtract 5¾ from 7⅜.

●SOLUTION:

$$\begin{array}{rcccccccccc} 7\frac{3}{8} & = & 7\frac{3}{8} & = & 7+\frac{3}{8} & = & 6+1+\frac{3}{8} & = & 6+\frac{8}{8}+\frac{3}{8} & = & 6\frac{11}{8} \\ -\ 5\frac{3}{4} & = & 5\frac{6}{8} & = & 5+\frac{6}{8} & = & 5+\frac{6}{8} & = & 5+\frac{6}{8} & = & 5\frac{6}{8} \\ \hline & & & & & & & & & & 1\frac{5}{8} \end{array}$$

▼EXPLANATION: After changing the mixed numeral $5\frac{3}{4}$ to its equivalent form of $5\frac{6}{8}$, you find that it is not possible to subtract $\frac{6}{8}$ from the $\frac{3}{8}$ in $7\frac{3}{8}$. Hence, it is necessary to rewrite the 7 as 6 + 1, and then to change the form of 1 to the form $\frac{8}{8}$ so that it can be added to the $\frac{3}{8}$

to make the fraction $\frac{11}{8}$. Had it been necessary to add the 1 to a fraction, such as $\frac{4}{5}$, you would have changed the form of the 1 to $\frac{5}{5}$ to give you a total of $\frac{9}{5}$. What form will you change the 1 to if it has to be added to a fraction such as $\frac{2}{3}$? If it has to be added to $\frac{7}{12}$?

■ILLUSTRATION 3: Subtract $5\frac{1}{2}$ from $8\frac{1}{3}$.

●SOLUTION:

$$
\begin{array}{ccc}
① & ② & ③ \\
8\frac{1}{3} = & 8\frac{2}{6} = & 7\frac{8}{6} \\
- 5\frac{1}{2} = & 5\frac{3}{6} = & 5\frac{3}{6} \\
\hline
& & 2\frac{5}{6}
\end{array}
$$

▼EXPLANATION: In going from Step ② to Step ③, you do a number of steps mentally. Thus, you change the 8 into the form $7 + 1$; change the 1 to the numeral $\frac{6}{6}$, and then add the $\frac{6}{6}$ to the $\frac{2}{6}$ for a total of $\frac{8}{6}$. Hence, changing the numeral from the form $8\frac{2}{6}$ to the form $7\frac{8}{6}$ can all be done mentally.

EXERCISES   A

Find the difference in each of the following exercises.

1. $\frac{3}{5}$	2. $\frac{5}{7}$	3. $\frac{3}{4}$	4. $\frac{9}{10}$	5. $\frac{11}{12}$
$\frac{1}{5}$	$\frac{2}{7}$	$\frac{2}{4}$	$\frac{6}{10}$	$\frac{10}{12}$
2/5	3/7	1/4	3/10	1/12
6. $\frac{3}{4}$	7. $\frac{7}{8}$	8. $\frac{1}{2}$	9. $\frac{5}{8}$	10. $\frac{7}{10}$
$\frac{1}{4}$	$\frac{3}{8}$	$\frac{1}{2}$	$\frac{1}{8}$	$\frac{3}{10}$
1/2	1/2	0	1/2	2/5
11. $\frac{7}{16}$	12. $\frac{13}{16}$	13. $\frac{11}{12}$	14. $\frac{11}{12}$	15. $\frac{15}{16}$
$\frac{5}{16}$	$\frac{1}{16}$	$\frac{5}{12}$	$\frac{7}{12}$	$\frac{7}{16}$
1/8	3/4	1/2	1/3	1/2
16. $\frac{9}{10}$	17. $\frac{9}{10}$	18. $\frac{11}{16}$	19. $\frac{17}{20}$	20. $\frac{19}{20}$
$\frac{7}{10}$	$\frac{4}{10}$	$\frac{9}{16}$	$\frac{7}{20}$	$\frac{4}{20}$
1/5	1/2	1/8	1/2	3/4

B

Find the difference in each of the following exercises.

1. $\frac{1}{2}$	2. $\frac{1}{2}$	3. $\frac{1}{3}$	4. $\frac{1}{2}$	5. $\frac{1}{4}$
$\frac{1}{4}$	$\frac{1}{6}$	$\frac{1}{6}$	$\frac{1}{8}$	$\frac{1}{8}$
1/4	1/3	1/6	3/8	1/8
6. $\frac{1}{3}$	7. $\frac{2}{3}$	8. $\frac{3}{4}$	9. $\frac{7}{8}$	10. $\frac{3}{4}$
$\frac{1}{9}$	$\frac{1}{9}$	$\frac{5}{8}$	$\frac{3}{4}$	$\frac{1}{2}$
2/9	5/9	1/8	1/8	1/4

In the solution of Illustration 3, the objective is to teach the student to do mentally as much of the conversion from one mixed numeral to an equivalent one of another form.

11. $\frac{5}{6}$ 12. $\frac{5}{8}$ 13. $\frac{11}{12}$ 14. $\frac{7}{8}$ 15. $\frac{5}{8}$
    $\frac{1}{3}$ $\frac{1}{2}$ $\frac{1}{6}$ $\frac{1}{2}$ $\frac{3}{16}$
    1/2   1/8   3/4   3/8   7/16

16. $\frac{1}{4}$ 17. $\frac{9}{16}$ 18. $\frac{5}{6}$ 19 $\frac{3}{5}$ 20. $\frac{9}{10}$
    $\frac{3}{16}$ $\frac{1}{2}$ $\frac{2}{3}$ $\frac{1}{10}$ $\frac{4}{5}$
    1/16   1/16   1/6   1/2   1/10

21. $\frac{3}{4}$ 22. $\frac{2}{3}$ 23. $\frac{3}{4}$ 24. $\frac{5}{6}$ 25. $\frac{1}{2}$
    $\frac{2}{3}$ $\frac{1}{2}$ $\frac{1}{6}$ $\frac{3}{4}$ $\frac{1}{5}$
    1/12   1/6   7/12   1/12   3/10

26. $\frac{3}{5}$ 27. $\frac{3}{4}$ 28. $\frac{4}{5}$ 29. $\frac{3}{4}$ 30. $\frac{9}{10}$
    $\frac{1}{2}$ $\frac{2}{5}$ $\frac{3}{4}$ $\frac{7}{10}$ $\frac{1}{4}$
    1/10   7/20   1/20   1/20   13/20

C

Find the difference in each of the following exercises.

1. $6\frac{1}{2}$ 2. $8\frac{1}{4}$ 3. $9\frac{4}{5}$ 4. $7\frac{5}{8}$ 5. $5\frac{7}{8}$
   $4\frac{1}{2}$ $5\frac{1}{4}$ $6\frac{1}{5}$ $4\frac{1}{6}$ $3\frac{3}{8}$
   2   3   3-3/5   3-2/3   2-1/2

6. $7\frac{1}{2}$ 7. $9\frac{3}{4}$ 8. $6\frac{1}{3}$ 9. $8\frac{5}{6}$ 10. $7\frac{11}{12}$
   $2\frac{1}{4}$ $4\frac{1}{2}$ $5\frac{1}{6}$ $2\frac{2}{3}$ $3\frac{5}{6}$
   5-1/4   5-1/4   1-1/6   6-1/6   4-1/12

11. $5\frac{2}{3}$ 12. $8\frac{3}{5}$ 13. $7\frac{4}{5}$ 14. $6\frac{5}{12}$ 15. $9\frac{2}{3}$
    $1\frac{1}{2}$ $3\frac{1}{2}$ $2\frac{3}{4}$ $3\frac{1}{4}$ $5\frac{1}{4}$
    4-1/6   5-1/10   5-1/20   3-1/6   4-5/12

16. $18\frac{1}{2}$ 17. $16\frac{5}{16}$ 18. $17\frac{1}{4}$ 19. $15\frac{7}{8}$ 20. $12\frac{5}{6}$
    $3\frac{1}{5}$ $4\frac{1}{4}$ $6\frac{3}{16}$ $2\frac{3}{4}$ $9\frac{2}{3}$
    15-3/10   12-1/16   11-1/16   13-1/8   3-1/6

21. $13\frac{15}{16}$ 22. $11\frac{7}{8}$ 23. $15\frac{3}{4}$ 24. $12\frac{5}{8}$ 25. $14\frac{9}{16}$
    $7\frac{5}{8}$ $2\frac{1}{4}$ $6\frac{3}{5}$ $8\frac{5}{16}$ $6\frac{1}{2}$
    6-5/16   9-5/8   9-3/20   4-5/16   8-1/16

D

Find the difference in each of the following exercises.

1. 7   2. 9   3. 6   4. 8   5. 7
   $5\frac{1}{2}$ $4\frac{1}{4}$ $5\frac{3}{8}$ $6\frac{2}{5}$ $6\frac{1}{3}$
   1-1/2   4-3/4   5/8   1-3/5   2/3

6. 9   7. 12   8. 14   9. 23   10. 17
    $2\frac{3}{4}$ $5\frac{7}{8}$ $2\frac{5}{8}$ $1\frac{4}{5}$ $2\frac{1}{6}$
    ───   ───   ────   ────   ────
    6-1/4   6-1/8   11-3/8   21-1/5   14-5/6

11. 18   12. 16   13. 14   14. 11   15. 10
    $5\frac{2}{3}$ $2\frac{5}{12}$ $8\frac{7}{16}$ $7\frac{9}{16}$ $2\frac{11}{12}$
    ────   ─────   ─────   ─────   ─────
    12-1/3   13-7/12   5-9/16   3-7/16   7-1/12

E

Find the difference in each of the following exercises.

1. $8\frac{1}{4}$ 2. $6\frac{1}{3}$ 3. $7\frac{1}{6}$ 4. $9\frac{5}{8}$ 5. $8\frac{3}{8}$
    $3\frac{3}{4}$ $2\frac{2}{3}$ $2\frac{5}{6}$ $2\frac{7}{8}$ $7\frac{5}{8}$
    ───   ───   ───   ───   ───
    4-1/2   3-2/3   4-1/3   6-3/4   3/4

6. $7\frac{1}{5}$ 7. $9\frac{2}{5}$ 8. $5\frac{1}{5}$ 9. $9\frac{1}{8}$ 10. $6\frac{1}{16}$
    $4\frac{2}{5}$ $6\frac{4}{5}$ $1\frac{2}{5}$ $6\frac{7}{8}$ $1\frac{15}{16}$
    ───   ───   ───   ───   ────
    2-4/5   2-3/5   3-4/5   2-1/4   4-1/8

11. $9\frac{3}{10}$ 12. $9\frac{1}{10}$ 13. $6\frac{5}{12}$ 14. $7\frac{1}{12}$ 15. $8\frac{5}{16}$
    $2\frac{7}{10}$ $8\frac{9}{10}$ $2\frac{7}{12}$ $3\frac{11}{12}$ $5\frac{7}{16}$
    ────   ────   ─────   ─────   ────
    6-3/5   1/5   3-5/6   3-1/6   2-7/8

16. $8\frac{1}{4}$ 17. $9\frac{1}{2}$ 18. $12\frac{3}{8}$ 19. $16\frac{2}{3}$ 20. $12\frac{1}{2}$
    $5\frac{1}{2}$ $4\frac{3}{4}$ $1\frac{3}{4}$ $2\frac{5}{6}$ $1\frac{2}{3}$
    ───   ───   ────   ────   ────
    2-3/4   4-3/4   10-5/8   13-5/6   10-5/6

21. $17\frac{2}{3}$ 22. $18\frac{1}{5}$ 23. $16\frac{2}{3}$ 24. $19\frac{1}{4}$ 25. $15\frac{1}{6}$
    $5\frac{3}{4}$ $4\frac{7}{10}$ $3\frac{1}{2}$ $6\frac{2}{3}$ $4\frac{1}{3}$
    ─────   ────   ────   ────   ────
    11-11/12   13-1/2   12-9/10   12-7/12   10-5/6

26. $11\frac{5}{12}$ 27. $12\frac{5}{8}$ 28. $14\frac{7}{8}$ 29. $13\frac{5}{12}$ 30. $10\frac{3}{4}$
    $7\frac{1}{2}$ $5\frac{3}{4}$ $6\frac{15}{16}$ $7\frac{5}{6}$ $7\frac{5}{6}$
    ─────   ────   ─────   ────   ─────
    3-11/12   6-7/8   7-15/16   5-7/12   2-11/12

31. $21\frac{2}{3}$ 32. $20\frac{1}{3}$ 33. $24\frac{3}{10}$ 34. $25\frac{1}{4}$ 35. $28\frac{1}{8}$
    $12\frac{5}{6}$ $16\frac{3}{4}$ $9\frac{4}{5}$ $17\frac{5}{16}$ $19\frac{3}{16}$
    ────   ─────   ────   ─────   ─────
    8-5/6   3-7/12   14-1/2   7-15/16   8-15/16

Unit 3: Multiplication

Section 1:   Multiplication of Whole Numbers and Decimals

If you have any trouble in multiplication, it is usually in the placement of the decimal point in the answer when finding the product of two decimals. Take a moment to recall just what a decimal is. The numeral .7 is but an equivalent form of the numeral 7/10. Similarly, .07 can be written as 7/100, and .007 as 7/1,000. Should you write this information in vertical form, you begin to get a picture of the relation between the fraction numeral and the decimal numeral.

$$7/10 = .7$$
$$7/100 = .07$$
$$7/1,000 = .007$$

Thus, you can see that the number of zeros in the denominator of the fraction will tell us exactly how many digits there will be to the right of the decimal point in the decimal numeral.

In the case of 7/10, there is 1 zero in the denominator; therefore, there will be 1 digit to the right of the decimal point, and this is the digit 7. For the fraction numeral 7/100, there are 2 zeros in the denominator, and hence there will be 2 digits to the right of the decimal point. Since 7 is the only digit in the numerator, it is necessary to supply a 0 to act as the first digit. Lastly, in the case of 7/1,000, you would know that there have to be 3 digits to the right of the decimal point. With 7 being only 1 of these digits, 2 zeros will have to be supplied for a total of 3 digits (.007). How would you write 7/100,000 in decimal notation?

If the fraction were 253/100, then to write this as a decimal numeral you would have to have 2 digits to the right of the decimal point. In view of this, the decimal numeral would be 2.53, where the 2 digits to the right of the decimal point are the 5 and the 3. How would you write 253/10,000 as a decimal numeral?

Now you are in a position where you can determine the product of two decimals. For example, consider the following exercise:

$$30.6 \times .231$$

This exercise can be rewritten in the fractional form as:

$$306/10 \times 231/1,000$$

Why should there be 1 zero in the denominator of the first fraction and 3 zeros in the denominator of the second fraction? The product of these two fractions will be:

$$70,686/10,000$$

From the fact that there are 4 zeros in the denominator, you know that there will have to be 4 digits to the right of the decimal point when the number is rewritten in decimal notation. Hence, the answer will have to be 7.0686.

Experience has shown that students in consumer mathematics classes do understand the explanation presented above. In the event that time does not permit, you may prefer to delete this background material.

When you write the above problem with its answer immediately next to it,

$$30.6 \times .231 = 7.0686$$

you discover that the total number of digits to the right of the decimal points in the numerals in the problem is the same as the total number of digits to the right of the decimal point in the product. The 6, the 2, the 3, and the 1 make up four digits to the right of the decimal points in the numerals in the exercise (30.6 and .231). In the product, the four digits to the right of the decimal point are 0, 6, 8, and 6. Hence, in general you can say:

> The number of digits to the right of the decimal point in the product of two decimals is exactly the same as the total number of digits to the right of the decimal points in the two decimals.

■ILLUSTRATION: Find the product of 2.35 and .6.
●SOLUTION:

$$
\begin{array}{r}
2.35 \\
\times\ \ .6 \\
\hline
1.410
\end{array}
$$

▼EXPLANATION: There are three digits to the right of the decimal point in the two decimals in the exercise (the 3, the 5, and the 6). Therefore, there will have to be three digits to the right of the decimal point in the product (the 4, the 1, and the 0).

EXERCISES   **A**

Find the product in each of the following exercises.

1. 3	2. 0	3. 4	4. 1	5. 6
$\frac{4}{12}$	$\frac{2}{0}$	$\frac{2}{8}$	$\frac{5}{5}$	$\frac{2}{12}$
6. 1	7. 2	8. 3	9. 6.	10. 3
$\frac{3}{3}$	$\frac{5}{10}$	$\frac{1}{3}$	$\frac{0}{0}$	$\frac{3}{9}$
11. 2	12. 3	13. 1	14. 5	15. 0
$\frac{6}{12}$	$\frac{2}{6}$	$\frac{7}{7}$	$\frac{2}{10}$	$\frac{6}{0}$
16. 4	17. 0	18. 3	19. 4	20. 7
$\frac{1}{4}$	$\frac{8}{0}$	$\frac{5}{15}$	$\frac{4}{16}$	$\frac{1}{7}$

The comment at the bottom of page 547 applies equally as well here for the 100 multiplication facts as it did for the 100 addition facts.

21.   0
     7
 ———
     0
	22. 2
	     4
	 ———
	     8
		23. 3
		     7
		 ———
		   21
			24. 6
			     5
			 ———
			   30
				25. 8
				     2
				 ———
				   16

26.   2
     2
 ———
     4
	27. 1
	     8
	 ———
	     8
		28. 5
		     5
		 ———
		   25
			29. 6
			     3
			 ———
			   18
				30. 9
				     0
				 ———
				     0

31.   4
     0
 ———
     0
	32. 3
	     6
	 ———
	   18
		33. 5
		     1
		 ———
		     5
			34. 8
			     4
			 ———
			   32
				35. 4
				     5
				 ———
				   20

36.   1
     6
 ———
     6
	37. 5
	     4
	 ———
	   20
		38. 3
		     8
		 ———
		   24
			39. 6
			     6
			 ———
			   36
				40. 7
				     2
				 ———
				   14

41.   5
     3
 ———
   15
	42. 0
	     4
	 ———
	     0
		43. 6
		     1
		 ———
		     6
			44. 7
			     5
			 ———
			   35
				45. 4
				     6
				 ———
				   24

46.   0
     0
 ———
     0
	47. 2
	     8
	 ———
	   16
		48. 9
		     3
		 ———
		   27
			49. 6
			     7
			 ———
			   42
				50. 5
				     9
				 ———
				   45

51.   1
     4
 ———
     4
	52. 4
	     7
	 ———
	   28
		53. 0
		     1
		 ———
		     0
			54. 3
			     9
			 ———
			   27
				55. 7
				     3
				 ———
				   21

56.   2
     9
 ———
   18
	57. 5
	     6
	 ———
	   30
		58. 7
		     4
		 ———
		   28
			59. 8
			     3
			 ———
			   24
				60. 9
				     1
				 ———
				     9

61.   4
     8
 ———
   32
	62. 2
	     7
	 ———
	   14
		63. 1
		     1
		 ———
		     1
			64. 4
			     3
			 ———
			   12
				65. 6
				     4
				 ———
				   24

66.   1
     2
 ———
     2
	67. 0
	     9
	 ———
	     0
		68. 7
		     6
		 ———
		   42
			69. 8
			     5
			 ———
			   40
				70. 9
				     3
				 ———
				   27

71.   2
     3
 ———
     6
	72. 7
	     8
	 ———
	   56
		73. 0
		     5
		 ———
		     0
			74. 9
			     5
			 ———
			   45
				75. 3
				     0
				 ———
				     0

76.   6
     8
 ———
   48
	77. 0
	     3
	 ———
	     0
		78. 4
		     9
		 ———
		   36
			79. 8
			     7
			 ———
			   56
				80. 9
				     9
				 ———
				   81

81.   8
     9
 ———
   72
	82. 8
	     0
	 ———
	     0
		83. 7
		     7
		 ———
		   49
			84. 9
			     4
			 ———
			   36
				85. 2
				     1
				 ———
				     2

86. 9	87. 5	88. 8	89. 5	90. 9
7	0	6	8	6
63	0	48	40	54

91. 6	92. 9	93. 2	94. 8	95. 7
9	8	0	1	9
54	72	0	8	63

96. 7	97. 1	98. 9	99. 1	100. 5
0	9	6	0	7
0	9	54	0	35

B

Find the product in each of the following exercises.

1. 23	2. 41	3. 15	4. 24	5. 16
2	3	4	5	3
46	123	60	120	48

6. 18	7. 39	8. 47	9. 53	10. 42
4	2	3	6	4
72	78	141	318	168

11. 45	12. 36	13. 25	14. 28	15. 39
2	4	6	3	5
90	144	150	84	195

16. 43	17. 50	18. 40	19. 60	20. 51
6	7	9	8	7
258	350	360	480	357

21. 52	22. 43	23. 54	24. 43	25. 48
8	5	6	8	9
416	215	324	344	432

26. 64	27. 65	28. 72	29. 68	30. 74
7	4	8	7	6
448	260	576	476	444

31. 76	32. 78	33. 77	34. 79	35. 80
3	5	8	9	8
228	390	616	711	640

36. 82	37. 81	38. 85	39. 87	40. 89
7	8	6	9	5
574	648	510	783	445

41. 93	42. 95	43. 96	44. 94	45. 98
4	6	7	8	9
372	570	672	752	882

C

Find the product in each of the following exercises.

1. 14	2. 16	3. 18	4. 17	5. 18
12	10	12	14	20
168	160	216	238	360
6. 23	7. 25	8. 27	9. 29	10. 32
16	15	20	23	25
368	375	540	667	800
11. 36	12. 39	13. 40	14. 40	15. 44
27	26	29	32	35
972	1,014	1,160	1,280	1,540
16. 47	17. 53	18. 58	19. 61	20. 64
38	39	46	48	51
1,786	2,067	2,668	2,928	3,264
21. 69	22. 70	23. 72	24. 75	25. 78
56	58	64	65	67
3,864	4,060	4,608	4,875	5,226
26. 79	27. 76	28. 83	29. 88	30. 89
69	72	73	76	78
5,451	5,472	6,059	6,688	6,942
31. 92	32. 94	33. 96	34. 97	35. 99
80	83	85	87	98
7,360	7,802	8,160	8,439	9,702

D

Find the product in each of the following exercises.

1. 203	2. 104	3. 406	4. 507	5. 201
4	5	3	6	8
812	520	1,218	3,042	1,608
6. 905	7. 703	8. 802	9. 809	10. 907
2	4	8	7	6
1,810	2,812	6,416	5,663	5,442
11. 430	12. 560	13. 920	14. 740	15. 670
5	4	6	8	9
2,150	2,240	5,520	5,920	6,030
16. 231	17. 542	18. 968	19. 673	20. 845
40	50	20	60	70
9,240	27,100	19,360	40,380	59,150

21. 291	22. 403	23. 509	24. 870	25. 706
60	80	70	60	20
17,460	32,240	35,630	52,200	14,120
26. 902	27. 804	28. 840	29. 760	30. 908
30	50	80	60	90
27,060	40,200	67,200	45,600	81,720

E

Find the product in each of the following exercises.

1. 24	2. 32	3. 47	4. 85	5. 68
.06	.04	.05	.03	.07
1.44	1.28	2.35	2.55	4.76
6. 57	7. 95	8. 76	9. 83	10. 96
.02	.01	.08	.09	.06
1.14	.95	6.08	7.47	5.76
11. 1.05	12. 1.06	13. 1.08	14. 1.09	15. 1.02
23	41	34	17	25
24.15	43.46	36.72	18.53	25.50
16. 1.03	17. 1.04	18. 1.01	19. 1.06	20. 1.08
62	48	93	85	97
63.86	49.92	93.93	90.10	104.76
21. 250	22. 470	23. 640	24. 800	25. 750
.035	.045	.055	.065	.025
8.75	21.15	35.2	52.0	18.75
26. 125	27. 275	28. 576	29. 845	30. 955
.048	.056	.063	.082	.078
6.0	15.4	36.288	69.29	74.49
31. 24.50	32. 56.20	33. 48.40	34. 75.30	35. 86.70
.02	.03	.04	.01	.05
.49	1.686	1.936	.753	4.335
36. 63.50	37. 74.60	38. 85.40	39. 96.80	40. 53.70
.06	.07	.08	.09	.10
3.81	5.222	6.832	8.712	5.37
41. 123.50	42. 145.70	43. 171.20	44. 250.70	45. 275.60
.03	.04	.05	.06	.07
3.705	5.828	8.56	15.042	19.292

46. 340.50	47. 458.30	48. 627.10	49. 734.60	50. 857.90
.08	.06	.05	.08	.09
27.24	27.498	31.355	58.768	77.211
51. 2.04	52. 32.5	53. .064	54. 51.7	55. 7.23
3.1	4.3	.21	.035	.046
6.324	139.75	.01344	1.8095	.33258
56. 29.8	57. 841	58. 706	59. 5.98	60. 7.69
37	5.8	.083	24	79
1,102.6	4,877.8	58.598	143.52	607.51

Section 2: Multiplication of Fractions and Mixed Numbers

The method for determining the product of two fractions consists in finding the product of the numerators and then dividing this product by the product of the denominators.

■ ILLUSTRATION 1 : Find the product of ⅔ and ⅝.
● SOLUTION :

$$\frac{2}{3} \times \frac{5}{7} = \frac{2 \times 5}{3 \times 7} = \frac{10}{21}$$

▼ EXPLANATION : The product of the numerators can be written as 2×5, while that of the denominators can be written as 3×7. These can be replaced by 10 and 21 respectively. Frequently, it is preferable to eliminate the middle step and go directly from the first step ($\frac{2}{3} \times \frac{5}{7}$) to the product ($10/21$).

■ ILLUSTRATION 2 : Find the product of ⅔ and ¾.
● SOLUTION :

$$\frac{2}{3} \times \frac{3}{4} = \frac{6}{12} = \frac{1 \times 6}{2 \times 6} = \frac{1}{2} \times \frac{6}{6} = \frac{1}{2}$$

▼ EXPLANATION : After finding the product of the two fractions, you will notice that 6 is an exact divisor of both the numerator and the denominator. When this occurs, rewrite the numerator as 1×6 and the denominator as 2×6. The fraction $\frac{1 \times 6}{2 \times 6}$ can be expressed in the form of the product of the two fractions ½ and %. Since % is simply another form of the number 1, then the product of ½ and 1 is ½.

■ ILLUSTRATION 3 : Find the product of 6 and 2¼.
● SOLUTION :

$$6 \times 2\frac{1}{4} = \frac{6}{1} \times \frac{9}{4} = \frac{54}{4} = \frac{27 \times 2}{2 \times 2} = \frac{27}{2} = 13\frac{1}{2}$$

▼EXPLANATION: When multiplying a whole number by a mixed number, or when multiplying two mixed numbers together, it is usually best to express each of them as fractions. In this illustration, the 6 is written as 6/1, while the $2\frac{1}{4}$ is written as 9/4. The product is then found and reduced to lowest terms as in Illustration 2. The 9/4 is obtained from $2\frac{1}{4}$ by realizing that $2\frac{1}{4}$ means $2 + \frac{1}{4}$. The sum of these two numbers is then obtained by using the method for finding the sum of two fractions by obtaining a common denominator. An easier method, however, is to multiply the 2 by the 4 and add the numerator of 1 to that product for a sum of 9. The 9 is then written over the denominator of 4. How would you change $5\frac{2}{3}$ to a fraction?

EXERCISES A

Find the product in each of the following exercises.

1. $\frac{1}{2} \times \frac{3}{5}$ = 3/10
2. $\frac{1}{2} \times \frac{5}{7}$ = 5/14
3. $\frac{1}{3} \times \frac{4}{5}$ = 4/15
4. $\frac{2}{3} \times \frac{4}{5}$ = 8/15
5. $\frac{2}{3} \times \frac{5}{7}$ = 10/21
6. $\frac{3}{4} \times \frac{1}{2}$ = 3/8
7. $\frac{1}{4} \times \frac{3}{5}$ = 3/20
8. $\frac{1}{4} \times \frac{1}{5}$ = 1/20
9. $\frac{3}{4} \times \frac{3}{5}$ = 9/20
10. $\frac{4}{5} \times \frac{2}{5}$ = 8/25
11. $\frac{1}{6} \times \frac{1}{3}$ = 1/18
12. $\frac{5}{7} \times \frac{2}{3}$ = 10/21
13. $\frac{1}{8} \times \frac{5}{6}$ = 5/48
14. $\frac{3}{8} \times \frac{3}{5}$ = 9/40
15. $\frac{5}{8} \times \frac{1}{6}$ = 5/48
16. $\frac{5}{6} \times \frac{5}{8}$ = 25/48
17. $\frac{1}{6} \times \frac{7}{8}$ = 7/48
18. $\frac{1}{8} \times \frac{1}{10}$ = 1/80
19. $\frac{3}{8} \times \frac{7}{10}$ = 21/80
20. $\frac{7}{8} \times \frac{9}{10}$ = 63/80
21. $\frac{1}{5} \times \frac{1}{12}$ = 1/60
22. $\frac{1}{7} \times \frac{5}{12}$ = 5/84
23. $\frac{5}{7} \times \frac{11}{12}$ = 55/84
24. $\frac{3}{8} \times \frac{9}{16}$ = 27/128

B

Find the product in each of the following exercises and reduce each answer to its lowest terms.

1. $\frac{1}{2} \times \frac{2}{5}$ = 1/5
2. $\frac{1}{3} \times \frac{3}{5}$ = 1/5
3. $\frac{2}{3} \times \frac{6}{7}$ = 4/7
4. $\frac{2}{3} \times \frac{5}{8}$ = 5/12
5. $\frac{3}{4} \times \frac{1}{6}$ = 1/8
6. $\frac{3}{4} \times \frac{2}{9}$ = 1/6
7. $\frac{1}{4} \times \frac{2}{5}$ = 1/10
8. $\frac{4}{5} \times \frac{1}{2}$ = 2/5
9. $\frac{1}{5} \times \frac{5}{6}$ = 1/6
10. $\frac{4}{5} \times \frac{7}{10}$ = 14/25
11. $\frac{2}{5} \times \frac{5}{8}$ = 1/4
12. $\frac{2}{3} \times \frac{9}{10}$ = 3/5
13. $\frac{5}{6} \times \frac{2}{5}$ = 1/3
14. $\frac{5}{8} \times \frac{4}{5}$ = 1/2
15. $\frac{3}{10} \times \frac{5}{9}$ = 1/6
16. $\frac{5}{12} \times \frac{2}{5}$ = 1/6
17. $\frac{5}{12} \times \frac{3}{10}$ = 1/8
18. $\frac{7}{8} \times \frac{2}{5}$ = 7/20

19. $\frac{3}{8} \times \frac{5}{12} =$ _5/32_   20. $\frac{3}{16} \times \frac{2}{3} =$ _1/8_

21. $\frac{5}{16} \times \frac{4}{5} =$ _1/4_   22. $\frac{2}{3} \times \frac{15}{16} =$ _5/8_

23. $\frac{4}{5} \times \frac{5}{12} =$ _1/3_   24. $\frac{9}{16} \times \frac{8}{9} =$ _1/2_

C

Find the product in each of the following exercises and reduce each answer to its lowest terms.

1. $4 \times 1\frac{1}{2} =$ _6_   2. $6 \times 2\frac{1}{2} =$ _15_

3. $10 \times 5\frac{1}{2} =$ _55_   4. $3\frac{1}{2} \times 6 =$ _21_

5. $4\frac{1}{2} \times 8 =$ _36_   6. $7\frac{1}{2} \times 12 =$ _90_

7. $6 \times 1\frac{1}{3} =$ _8_   8. $12 \times 2\frac{2}{3} =$ _32_

9. $9 \times 3\frac{1}{3} =$ _30_   10. $3 \times 6\frac{2}{3} =$ _20_

11. $15 \times 1\frac{2}{3} =$ _25_   12. $21 \times 1\frac{1}{7} =$ _24_

13. $2\frac{2}{5} \times 10 =$ _24_   14. $3\frac{4}{5} \times 5 =$ _19_

15. $5\frac{1}{4} \times 8 =$ _42_   16. $3\frac{1}{4} \times 12 =$ _39_

17. $2\frac{1}{4} \times 16 =$ _36_   18. $3\frac{1}{6} \times 12 =$ _38_

19. $2\frac{5}{6} \times 3 =$ _8-1/2_   20. $2\frac{3}{8} \times 4 =$ _9-1/2_

21. $4\frac{5}{8} \times 6 =$ _27-3/4_   22. $10 \times 3\frac{3}{10} =$ _33_

23. $5 \times 4\frac{7}{10} =$ _23-1/2_   24. $15 \times 6\frac{9}{10} =$ _103-1/2_

D

Find the product in each of the following exercises and reduce each answer to its lowest terms.

1. $1\frac{1}{2} \times 2\frac{1}{2} =$ _3-3/4_   2. $1\frac{1}{4} \times 2\frac{1}{2} =$ _3-1/8_

3. $1\frac{1}{3} \times 2\frac{1}{4} =$ _3_   4. $2\frac{1}{2} \times 2\frac{1}{4} =$ _5-5/8_

5. $2\frac{1}{3} \times 2\frac{1}{2} =$ _5-5/6_   6. $2\frac{2}{3} \times 1\frac{1}{4} =$ _3-1/3_

7. $3\frac{1}{2} \times 1\frac{1}{3} =$ _4-2/3_   8. $3\frac{1}{3} \times 1\frac{1}{5} =$ _4_

9. $2\frac{3}{4} \times 1\frac{1}{3} =$ _3-2/3_   10. $2\frac{3}{4} \times 3\frac{1}{2} =$ _9-5/8_

11. $2\frac{3}{4} \times 3\frac{3}{4} =$ _10-5/16_   12. $4\frac{1}{2} \times 2\frac{1}{2} =$ _11-1/4_

13. $3\frac{1}{4} \times 4\frac{1}{2} =$ _14-5/8_   14. $3\frac{3}{4} \times 4\frac{1}{2} =$ _16-7/8_

15. $5\frac{1}{4} \times 5\frac{1}{3} =$ _28_   16. $6\frac{1}{4} \times 3\frac{1}{3} =$ _20-5/6_

Section 3: Multiplication of a Whole Number and a Mixed Number

When finding the product of a whole number and a mixed number, if either number is relatively large, it is frequently easier to change the mixed number to a decimal instead of to a fraction.

■ILLUSTRATION: Find the product of 148 and 12½.
●SOLUTION:

$$
\begin{array}{r}
148 \\
\times\ 12.5 \\
\hline
740 \\
296 \\
148 \\
\hline
1850.0
\end{array}
$$

▼EXPLANATION: The ½ in the mixed number 12½ is changed to the decimal .5, and the 12½ is rewritten as 12.5. The computation is then completed in the same manner as when finding the product of two decimals.

EXERCISES

Find the product in each of the following problems.

1. 48 × 5½	=	264	2. 76 × 9½	=	722
3. 120 × 6½	=	780	4. 85 × 4½	=	382.5
5. 59 × 7½	=	442.5	6. 157 × 3½	=	549.5
7. 24½ × 12	=	294	8. 68½ × 10	=	685
9. 35½ × 16	=	568	10. 125½ × 46	=	5,773
11. 137½ × 23	=	3,162.5	12. 168½ × 31	=	5,223.5
13. 24 × 6¼	=	150	14. 36 × 5¼	=	189
15. 64 × 10¼	=	656	16. 76 × 18¼	=	1,387
17. 129 × 20¼	=	2,612.25	18. 158 × 25¼	=	3,989.50
19. 58¼ × 12	=	699	20. 71¼ × 40	=	2,850
21. 85¼ × 28	=	2,387	22. 116¼ × 20	=	2,325
23. 243¼ × 22	=	5,351.50	24. 250¼ × 37	=	9,259.25
25. 56 × 7¾	=	434	26. 92 × 6¾	=	621
27. 104 × 8¾	=	910	28. 84¾ × 16	=	1,356
29. 114¾ × 32	=	3,672	30. 156¾ × 45	=	7,053.75

Unit 4:   Division

Section 1:   Division of Whole Numbers and Decimals

If you have difficulty at any time in division, you will usually find it at the time you are dividing one decimal by another. The trouble involves the placement of the decimal point in the answer. Since you are usually able to divide when the divisor is a whole number, it seems apparent that if the divisor is a decimal, it would be best to change it

Throughout the book the emphasis was placed on the fact that wherever possible, a mixed numeral should be replaced by its decimal equivalent numeral before applying the operation of multiplication.

into a whole number. For instance, consider the division of 6.853 by 42.71:

$$6.853 \div 42.71$$

This exercise can be written in the fractional form,

$$6.853/42.71$$

Changing the denominator (or divisor) 42.71 into a whole number would require multiplying that number by 100. If you do this, though, you would change the problem from:

$$6.853/42.71 \text{ to } 6.853/4271.$$

However, these two fraction numerals are not equivalent. Were you also to multiply the numerator by 100, then the new numeral would be equivalent to the old one.

$$\frac{6.853}{42.71} = \frac{6.853}{42.71} \times \frac{100}{100} = \frac{685.3}{4271}$$

The first fraction is equivalent to the last one, for to obtain the last one you multiplied the first by 100/100, which is but another form of the number 1. The number 1, as you recall, is the identity element of multiplication. The product of any number with this one will leave the number unchanged. Hence, in this case, the numeral is changed from the form 6.853/42.71 to the form 685.3/4271, but both fraction numerals represent the same number.

Notice that in the illustration above, the decimal point is moved two places to the right in the denominator to make that number a whole number. The decimal point is also moved two places to the right in the numerator. Hence, in general, you can say:

> If it is necessary to change the divisor to a whole number by moving the decimal point, then move the decimal point in the dividend exactly the same number of places and in the same direction.

How many places will the decimal point have to be moved in the following divisor?

$$1.025)\overline{6.35}$$

How many places will it have to be moved in the number 6.35? What will the new divisor be? What will the new dividend be?

See the explanation at the bottom of page 567.

■ILLUSTRATION: Divide 2.028 by 2.6.

●SOLUTION:

$$
\begin{array}{r}
.78 \\
2.6_\wedge\overline{)2.0_\wedge28} \\
1\ 8\ 2 \\
\hline
2\ 08 \\
2\ 08 \\
\hline
0
\end{array}
$$

▼EXPLANATION: To change the divisor 2.6 to a whole number, it is necessary to move the decimal point one place to the right. Hence, the same thing has to be done with the decimal point in the dividend 2.028. The carets indicate where the new decimal points should be placed. Before beginning to divide, place the decimal point in the answer directly above its new position in the dividend.

EXERCISES   **A**

Find the quotient mentally in each of the following exercises.

1. $5 \div 1 =$ __5__	2. $12 \div 2 =$ __6__
3. $20 \div 4 =$ __5__	4. $15 \div 5 =$ __3__
5. $6 \div 3 =$ __2__	6. $10 \div 2 =$ __5__
7. $21 \div 3 =$ __7__	8. $4 \div 2 =$ __2__
9. $8 \div 4 =$ __2__	10. $18 \div 3 =$ __6__
11. $16 \div 2 =$ __8__	12. $8 \div 1 =$ __8__
13. $20 \div 5 =$ __4__	14. $18 \div 6 =$ __3__
15. $14 \div 7 =$ __2__	16. $15 \div 3 =$ __5__
17. $32 \div 4 =$ __8__	18. $24 \div 3 =$ __8__
19. $9 \div 1 =$ __9__	20. $45 \div 5 =$ __9__
21. $24 \div 4 =$ __6__	22. $14 \div 2 =$ __7__
23. $3 \div 1 =$ __3__	24. $25 \div 5 =$ __5__
25. $12 \div 6 =$ __2__	26. $21 \div 7 =$ __3__
27. $12 \div 3 =$ __4__	28. $16 \div 4 =$ __4__
29. $7 \div 1 =$ __7__	30. $18 \div 2 =$ __9__
31. $9 \div 3 =$ __3__	32. $4 \div 1 =$ __4__
33. $42 \div 6 =$ __7__	34. $30 \div 5 =$ __6__
35. $4 \div 4 =$ __1__	36. $30 \div 6 =$ __5__
37. $24 \div 8 =$ __3__	38. $6 \div 6 =$ __1__
39. $6 \div 1 =$ __6__	40. $35 \div 5 =$ __7__
41. $28 \div 4 =$ __7__	42. $42 \div 7 =$ __6__
43. $40 \div 8 =$ __5__	44. $24 \div 6 =$ __4__
45. $3 \div 3 =$ __1__	46. $10 \div 5 =$ __2__

The comment at the bottom of page 547 applies equally as well here for these 80 division facts as it did for the 100 addition facts.

47. $36 \div 6 =$ ___6___   48. $56 \div 7 =$ ___8___
49. $40 \div 5 =$ ___8___   50. $28 \div 7 =$ ___4___
51. $2 \div 1 =$ ___2___   52. $12 \div 4 =$ ___3___
53. $48 \div 6 =$ ___8___   54. $32 \div 8 =$ ___4___
55. $27 \div 9 =$ ___3___   56. $5 \div 5 =$ ___1___
57. $35 \div 7 =$ ___5___   58. $16 \div 8 =$ ___2___
59. $1 \div 1 =$ ___1___   60. $63 \div 9 =$ ___7___
61. $48 \div 8 =$ ___6___   62. $7 \div 1 =$ ___7___
63. $56 \div 8 =$ ___7___   64. $36 \div 9 =$ ___4___
65. $7 \div 7 =$ ___1___   66. $64 \div 8 =$ ___8___
67. $63 \div 7 =$ ___9___   68. $72 \div 8 =$ ___9___
69. $49 \div 7 =$ ___7___   70. $45 \div 9 =$ ___5___
71. $54 \div 9 =$ ___6___   72. $8 \div 8 =$ ___1___
73. $27 \div 3 =$ ___9___   74. $18 \div 9 =$ ___2___
75. $2 \div 2 =$ ___1___   76. $72 \div 9 =$ ___8___
77. $36 \div 4 =$ ___9___   78. $54 \div 6 =$ ___9___
79. $8 \div 2 =$ ___4___   80. $81 \div 9 =$ ___9___

B

Find the quotient in each of the following exercises.

1. $48 \div 3 =$ ___16___   2. $52 \div 2 =$ ___26___
3. $81 \div 3 =$ ___27___   4. $86 \div 2 =$ ___43___
5. $75 \div 5 =$ ___15___   6. $85 \div 5 =$ ___17___
7. $64 \div 4 =$ ___16___   8. $76 \div 4 =$ ___19___
9. $92 \div 4 =$ ___23___   10. $84 \div 6 =$ ___14___
11. $96 \div 6 =$ ___16___   12. $98 \div 7 =$ ___14___
13. $135 \div 3 =$ ___45___   14. $192 \div 3 =$ ___64___
15. $207 \div 3 =$ ___69___   16. $184 \div 4 =$ ___46___
17. $256 \div 4 =$ ___64___   18. $384 \div 4 =$ ___96___
19. $512 \div 4 =$ ___128___   20. $628 \div 4 =$ ___157___
21. $235 \div 5 =$ ___47___   22. $430 \div 5 =$ ___86___
23. $675 \div 5 =$ ___135___   24. $590 \div 5 =$ ___118___
25. $324 \div 6 =$ ___54___   26. $504 \div 6 =$ ___84___
27. $744 \div 6 =$ ___124___   28. $828 \div 6 =$ ___138___
29. $161 \div 7 =$ ___23___   30. $245 \div 7 =$ ___35___
31. $336 \div 7 =$ ___48___   32. $469 \div 7 =$ ___67___
33. $256 \div 8 =$ ___32___   34. $360 \div 8 =$ ___45___
35. $504 \div 8 =$ ___63___   36. $768 \div 8 =$ ___96___
37. $198 \div 9 =$ ___22___   38. $387 \div 9 =$ ___43___
39. $666 \div 9 =$ ___74___   40. $954 \div 9 =$ ___106___

C

Find the quotient in each of the following exercises.

1. $384 \div 24$ = 16		2. $480 \div 32$ = 15
3. $525 \div 25$ = 21		4. $414 \div 23$ = 18
5. $351 \div 27$ = 13		6. $805 \div 35$ = 23
7. $608 \div 38$ = 16		8. $943 \div 41$ = 23
9. $1,058 \div 46$ = 23		10. $1,813 \div 49$ = 37
11. $1,508 \div 52$ = 29		12. $1,512 \div 54$ = 28
13. $322 \div 14$ = 23		14. $592 \div 16$ = 37
15. $846 \div 18$ = 47		16. $663 \div 17$ = 39
17. $3,712 \div 64$ = 58		18. $2,275 \div 65$ = 35
19. $5,628 \div 67$ = 84		20. $3,456 \div 72$ = 48
21. $4,056 \div 78$ = 52		22. $5,644 \div 83$ = 68
23. $6,192 \div 86$ = 72		24. $7,644 \div 91$ = 84

D

Find the quotient in each of the following exercises.

1. $4,500 \div 125$ = 36	2. $3,289 \div 137$ = 24
3. $7,290 \div 162$ = 45	4. $10,672 \div 184$ = 58
5. $4,738 \div 103$ = 46	6. $7,004 \div 206$ = 34
7. $34,036 \div 508$ = 67	8. $58,546 \div 802$ = 73
9. $9,933 \div 231$ = 43	10. $9,288 \div 258$ = 36
11. $8,424 \div 324$ = 26	12. $32,376 \div 568$ = 57
13. $48,766 \div 659$ = 74	14. $62,264 \div 724$ = 86
15. $61,539 \div 843$ = 73	16. $54,834 \div 962$ = 57
17. $25,235 \div 245$ = 103	18. $75,235 \div 367$ = 205
19. $267,208 \div 526$ = 508	20. $447,811 \div 637$ = 703

E

Find the quotient in each of the following exercises.

1. $.54 \div .6$ = .9	2. $4.2 \div .7$ = 6.
3. $56 \div .8$ = 70.	4. $.24 \div .3$ = .8
5. $.02 \div .2$ = .1	6. $.2 \div .02$ = 10.
7. $8.4 \div .06$ = 140.	8. $.85 \div .5$ = 1.7
9. $81 \div .09$ = 900.	10. $.72 \div .08$ = 9.
11. $3.5 \div .1$ = 35.	12. $.64 \div .04$ = 16.
13. $156 \div 1.2$ = 130.	14. $18.2 \div .13$ = 140.
15. $.675 \div .25$ = 2.7	16. $1.116 \div 3.6$ = .31
17. $1.458 \div .54$ = 2.7	18. $.2294 \div .062$ = 3.7
19. $45.75 \div 7.5$ = 6.1	20. $1.29 \div .86$ = 1.5
21. $6.448 \div 1.04$ = 6.2	22. $826.8 \div 1.06$ = 780.
23. $89.64 \div 1.08$ = 83.	24. $1.0355 \div 1.09$ = .95

Section 2: Division of Fractions and Mixed Numbers

Division of fractions is performed by changing the operation to multiplication. To do this, you simply invert the divisor. The inverse of a fraction—sometimes called the *multiplicative inverse*—is a second fraction in which the numerator of the first fraction is the denominator of the second fraction and the denominator of the first fraction is the numerator of the second fraction. Thus:

$$\text{the inverse of } \frac{2}{5} \text{ is } \frac{5}{2}$$

Similarly, the inverse of $3/4$ is $4/3$. What is the inverse of $2/7$? Of $5/8$? Of $1/6$? Of $7/1$? Of 8?

■ILLUSTRATION 1: Divide $2/3$ by $5/6$.

●SOLUTION:

$$\frac{2}{3} \div \frac{5}{6} = \frac{2}{3} \times \frac{6}{5} = \frac{12}{15} = \frac{4 \times 3}{5 \times 3} = \frac{4}{5}$$

▼EXPLANATION: The operation is changed from division to multiplication by inverting the divisor. Thus, the exercise is changed from the form:

$$2/3 \div 5/6$$

to the form:

$$2/3 \times 6/5$$

and the computation is completed as in the case of the product of two fractions.

■ILLUSTRATION 2: Divide $4/5$ by 8.

●SOLUTION:

$$\frac{4}{5} \div 8 = \frac{4}{5} \div \frac{8}{1} = \frac{4}{5} \times \frac{1}{8} = \frac{4}{40} = \frac{1 \times 4}{10 \times 4} = \frac{1}{10}$$

▼EXPLANATION: Once you realize that the numeral 8 can be written in the form 8/1, the computation becomes identical with that of the previous illustration.

■ILLUSTRATION 3: Divide $3\frac{1}{2}$ by $2\frac{1}{4}$.

●SOLUTION:

$$3\tfrac{1}{2} \div 2\tfrac{1}{4} = \frac{7}{2} \div \frac{9}{4} = \frac{7}{2} \times \frac{4}{9} = \frac{28}{18} = \frac{14 \times 2}{9 \times 2}$$

$$= \frac{14}{9} = 1\tfrac{5}{9}$$

The statement given at the top of this page is actually the definition of division, i.e., the quotient of *a* and *b* is the product of *a* with the multiplicative inverse of *b*.

▼EXPLANATION: Each of the mixed numbers is changed to an improper fraction, and the problem is completed in the same manner as the two previous illustrations. If the mixed numbers are relatively large, change them to decimals and divide as was done in the illustration on page 578.

EXERCISES   **A**

Find the quotient in each of the following exercises.

1. $\frac{3}{5} \div \frac{1}{2} =$ ___6/5___	2. $\frac{1}{2} \div \frac{3}{7} =$ ___7/6___
3. $\frac{5}{4} \div \frac{1}{3} =$ ___15/4___	4. $\frac{1}{4} \div \frac{3}{5} =$ ___5/12___
5. $\frac{2}{3} \div \frac{5}{7} =$ ___14/15___	6. $\frac{3}{4} \div \frac{1}{5} =$ ___15/4___
7. $\frac{4}{5} \div \frac{2}{5} =$ ___2___	8. $\frac{1}{6} \div \frac{2}{3} =$ ___1/4___
9. $\frac{5}{6} \div \frac{1}{3} =$ ___5/2___	10. $\frac{3}{8} \div \frac{5}{6} =$ ___9/20___
11. $\frac{5}{8} \div \frac{5}{6} =$ ___3/4___	12. $\frac{1}{6} \div \frac{7}{10} =$ ___5/21___
13. $\frac{7}{8} \div \frac{3}{10} =$ ___35/12___	14. $\frac{3}{8} \div \frac{9}{16} =$ ___2/3___
15. $\frac{2}{3} \div \frac{5}{6} =$ ___4/5___	16. $\frac{3}{5} \div \frac{9}{10} =$ ___2/3___
17. $\frac{3}{8} \div \frac{15}{16} =$ ___2/5___	18. $\frac{5}{8} \div \frac{7}{16} =$ ___10/7___
19. $\frac{3}{10} \div \frac{4}{15} =$ ___9/8___	20. $\frac{5}{9} \div \frac{5}{15} =$ ___5/3___
21. $\frac{7}{10} \div \frac{21}{25} =$ ___5/6___	22. $\frac{5}{9} \div \frac{20}{21} =$ ___7/12___

B

Find the quotient in each of the following exercises.

1. $8 \div \frac{1}{2} =$ ___16___	2. $10 \div \frac{1}{3} =$ ___30___
3. $6 \div \frac{1}{4} =$ ___24___	4. $12 \div \frac{3}{4} =$ ___16___
5. $16 \div \frac{4}{5} =$ ___20___	6. $10 \div \frac{2}{5} =$ ___25___
7. $\frac{4}{5} \div 2 =$ ___2/5___	8. $\frac{3}{5} \div 6 =$ ___1/10___
9. $\frac{1}{2} \div 2 =$ ___1/4___	10. $\frac{5}{9} \div 10 =$ ___1/18___
11. $\frac{5}{8} \div 15 =$ ___1/24___	12. $\frac{3}{8} \div 24 =$ ___1/64___

C

Find the quotient in each of the following exercises.

1. $1\frac{1}{2} \div 2 =$ ___3/4___	2. $3\frac{3}{4} \div 3 =$ ___5/4___
3. $4\frac{1}{2} \div 3 =$ ___3/2___	4. $3\frac{1}{5} \div 8 =$ ___2/5___
5. $4\frac{2}{3} \div 7 =$ ___2/3___	6. $5\frac{1}{4} \div 7 =$ ___3/4___
7. $6 \div 1\frac{1}{2} =$ ___4___	8. $10 \div 2\frac{1}{2} =$ ___4___
9. $3 \div 3\frac{1}{5} =$ ___15/16___	10. $24 \div 5\frac{1}{3} =$ ___9/2___
11. $18 \div 4\frac{1}{2} =$ ___4___	12. $14 \div 2\frac{5}{8} =$ ___16/3___

D

Find the quotient in each of the following exercises.

1. $2\frac{1}{2} \div 1\frac{1}{2} =$ ___5/3___   2. $2\frac{3}{4} \div 1\frac{1}{4} =$ ___11/5___
3. $3\frac{1}{2} \div 2\frac{1}{2} =$ ___7/5___   4. $1\frac{3}{4} \div 1\frac{1}{4} =$ ___7/5___
5. $2\frac{1}{3} \div 3\frac{1}{2} =$ ___2/3___   6. $3\frac{1}{4} \div 1\frac{1}{4} =$ ___13/5___
7. $4\frac{3}{4} \div 2\frac{3}{8} =$ ___2___   8. $1\frac{3}{4} \div 3\frac{1}{2} =$ ___1/2___
9. $5\frac{1}{4} \div 2\frac{1}{2} =$ ___21/10___   10. $6\frac{1}{2} \div 2\frac{1}{4} =$ ___26/9___
11. $5\frac{1}{4} \div 3\frac{1}{2} =$ ___3/2___   12. $7\frac{1}{2} \div 1\frac{7}{8} =$ ___4___

Unit 5:   Percents

Section 1:   Expressing Percent Numerals as Decimal Numerals and Decimal Numerals as Percent Numerals

A percent numeral is simply another way of expressing a fraction numeral where the denominator of that fraction is 100. For instance, the percent numeral 23% is but an equivalent form of the fraction 23/100. Similarly, 56% and 56/100 are equivalent; so are 3.5% and 3.5/100; and 125% and 125/100. Hence, each time you see the percent symbol, you should immediately think in terms of a fraction where the denominator of that fraction is 100.

■ILLUSTRATION 1: Write the percent numeral 15% in its equivalent fractional form.

●SOLUTION:

$$15\% = \frac{15}{100} = \frac{3 \times 5}{20 \times 5} = \frac{3}{20}$$

▼EXPLANATION: As noted above, the numerals 15% and 15/100 are equivalent. After writing 15% as 15/100, the fraction is reduced to lowest terms.

■ILLUSTRATION 2: Write the percent numeral 6% in its equivalent decimal form.

●SOLUTION:

$$6\% = \frac{6}{100} = .06$$

▼EXPLANATION: The numeral 6%, as you learned above, can be written in the fractional form of 6/100. But on page 567, you learned that the fraction numeral 6/100 can be expressed as the decimal .06. Hence, the percent numeral 6% and the decimal numeral .06 are equivalent.

You now know that each percent numeral can be expressed as a fraction numeral with 100 as its denominator. You also know that each fraction numeral having a denominator of 100 can be expressed as a decimal with two digits to the right of the decimal point. Therefore, you can say that a percent numeral can be expressed as a decimal numeral with two digits to the right of the decimal point. Thus:

$$23\% = .23$$
$$58\% = .58$$
$$115\% = 1.15$$

How would you express 46% as a decimal numeral? 65%? 96%? 127%? 8%?

Another way of examining the above is to realize that each of the numerals 23, 58, and 115 has a decimal point which, although it does not now appear in the numerals, can be written to the right of the last digit without in any way affecting the numerals. Thus, 23% is the same as 23.%, while 58% is the equivalent of 58.%. How can you write 115% with a decimal point and yet retain the percent symbol? Hence, if you rewrite each of the three equalities above and insert the missing decimal points, they become:

$$23.\% = .23\,{}_{\uparrow}$$
$$58.\% = .58\,{}_{\uparrow}$$
$$115.\% = 1.15\,{}_{\uparrow}$$

We deliberately placed the arrows in the numerals at the right to show where the decimal points had been when the numbers were written in percent form. In each case, when the number was changed from its percent form to its decimal form, the decimal point was moved two places to the left of where it had been. This condition will always be true whenever a percent numeral is changed to a decimal numeral.

■ILLUSTRATION 3: Write the percent numeral 4½% in its equivalent decimal form.

●SOLUTION:

$$4\tfrac{1}{2}\% = 4.5\% = .04\,5_{\uparrow}$$

▼EXPLANATION: Before trying to change the mixed numeral percent value 4½% to a decimal, it is best first to write it as 4.5%. Now the problem reduces to the simple situation of merely moving the decimal point two places to the left of where it appears in its percent form. The arrow points to where it had been. It also shows that the decimal point is now two places to the left of where the arrow is.

To change a number from its decimal form to its equivalent percent form involves nothing more than reversing the process just learned. Since you move the decimal point two places to the left in changing from a percent to a decimal, you will now move the decimal point two places to the right to change from a decimal to a percent form.

■ILLUSTRATION 4: Write the decimal numeral .085 in its equivalent percent form.

●SOLUTION:

$$.085 = {}_{\uparrow}08.5\%, \text{ or } 8.5\%$$

▼EXPLANATION: The arrow shows where the decimal point had been when the number was written as a decimal. In the percent form, it is two places farther to the right.

EXERCISES A

Write each of the following percent numerals as equivalent decimal numerals.

1. 15% .15	2. 26% .26	3. 53% .53
4. 72% .72	5. 93% .93	6. 31% .31
7. 49% .49	8. 67% .67	9. 85% .85
10. 14% .14	11. 60% .60	12. 70% .70
13. 80% .80	14. 90% .90	15. 10% .10
16. 2% .02	17. 8% .08	18. 3% .03
19. 5% .05	20. 7% .07	21. 124% 1.24
22. 136% 1.36	23. 158% 1.58	24. 235% 2.35
25. 375% 3.75	26. 150% 1.50	27. 250% 2.50
28. 140% 1.40	29. 320% 3.20	30. 460% 4.60
31. 100% 1	32. 200% 2	33. 300% 3
34. 400% 4	35. 500% 5	36. 26.5% .265
37. 47.8% .478	38. 52.3% .523	39. 34.6% .346
40. 367% 3.67	41. 3.5% .035	42. 6.5% .065
43. 4.2% .042	44. 5.7% .057	45. 9.3% .093
46. 105.4% 1.054	47. 207.8% 2.078	48. 184.7% 1.847
49. 169.1% 1.691	50. 300.2% 3.002	51. 14.65% .1465
52. 29.37% .2937	53. 51.04% .5104	54. 62.71% .6271
55. 84.39% .8439	56. 2.54% .0254	57. 4.65% .0465
58. 3.75% .0375	59. 5.25% .0525	60. 6.35% .0635
61. 3.50% .035	62. 4.50% .045	63. 7.50% .075
64. 9.50% .095	65. 10.50% .105	66. 10.05% .1005

B

Write each of the following percent numerals as equivalent decimal numerals.

1. 14½% .145	2. 16½% .165	3. 21½% .215
4. 53½% .535	5. 67½% .675	6. 8½% .085

7. 4½%	.045	8. 3½%	.035	9. 6½%	.065
10. 1½%	.015	11. 128½%	1.285	12. 157½%	1.575
13. 220½%	2.205	14. 325½%	3.255	15. 450½%	4.505
16. 27¼%	.2725	17. 86¼%	.8625	18. 37¼%	.3725
19. 72¼%	.7225	20. 93¼%	.9325	21. 5¼%	.0525
22. 7¼%	.0725	23. 8¼%	.0825	24. 1¼%	.0125
25. 3¼%	.0325	26. 158¼%	1.5825	27. 194¼%	1.9425
28. 237¼%	2.3725	29. 205¼%	2.0525	30. 370¼%	3.7025
31. 32¾%	.3275	32. 47¾%	.4775	33. 61¾%	.6175
34. 80¾%	.8075	35. 76¾%	.7675	36. 6¾%	.0675
37. 9¾%	.0975	38. 3¾%	.0375	39. 7¾%	.0775
40. 2¾%	.0275	41. 116¾%	1.1675	42. 100¾%	1.0075
43. 200¾%	2.0075	44. 150¾%	1.5075	45. 250¾%	2.5075

C

Write each of the following decimal numerals as equivalent percent numerals.

1. .54	54%	2. .76	76%	3. .42	42%
4. .85	85%	5. .93	93%	6. .27	27%
7. .19	19%	8. .30	30%	9. .40	40%
10. .67	67%	11. .04	4%	12. .05	5%
13. .06	6%	14. .09	9%	15. .01	1%
16. .07	7%	17. .02	2%	18. .08	8%
19. .03	3%	20. .10	10%	21. 1.25	125%
22. 2.50	250%	23. 1.75	175%	24. 1.50	150%
25. 1.46	146%	26. 3.47	347%	27. 3.10	310%
28. 2.05	205%	29. 1.07	107%	30. 1.01	101%
31. .145	14.5%	32. .267	26.7%	33. .394	39.4%
34. .876	87.6%	35. .105	10.5%	36. .283	28.3%
37. .504	50.4%	38. .309	30.9%	39. .324	32.4%
40. .207	20.7%	41. .065	6.5%	42. .073	7.3%
43. .058	5.8%	44. .061	6.1%	45. .027	2.7%

D

Write each of the following percent numerals as fraction numerals.

1. 27%	27/100	2. 53%	53/100	3. 89%	89/100
4. 19%	19/100	5. 47%	47/100	6. 13%	13/100
7. 49%	49/100	8. 23%	23/100	9. 97%	97/100
10. 31%	31/100	11. 7%	7/100	12. 3%	3/100
13. 9%	9/100	14. 1%	1/100	15. 17%	17/100

16. 119% __119/100__   17. 137% __137/100__   18. 143% __143/100__
19. 151% __151/100__   20. 169% __169/100__   21. 203% __203/100__
22. 207% __207/100__   23. 229% __229/100__   24. 247% __247/100__
25. 281% __281/100__   26. 10% __1/10__   27. 20% __1/5__
28. 30% __3/10__   29. 40% __2/5__   30. 50% __1/2__
31. 60% __3/5__   32. 70% __7/10__   33. 80% __4/5__
34. 90% __9/10__   35. 25% __1/4__   36. 75% __3/4__
37. 5% __1/20__   38. 15% __3/20__   39. 35% __7/20__
40. 45% __9/20__   41. 100% __1__   42. 200% __2__
43. 300% __3__   44. 400% __4__   45. 500% __5__
46. 150% __3/2__   47. 250% __5/2__   48. 350% __7/2__
49. 125% __5/4__   50. 175% __7/4__   51. 225% __9/4__
52. 120% __6/5__   53. 140% __7/5__   54. 260% __13/5__

Section 2: Practical Applications of Percent

The practical applications of percent depend on an understanding of the following two principles.

The Product of Two Numbers Principle: If the product of two numbers is divided by one of these numbers, the quotient will be the other of the numbers.

The Equal Fractions Principle: If two fractions are equal, then the products of their opposites are also equal.

Both of these principles were examined at some length earlier in the book. The first of these appeared in Chapter 1, page 36, while the second was discussed in Chapter 3, page 101. It might be well to refer to these pages for review. The two following illustrations are included to help recall these principles.

■ILLUSTRATION 1: Find the replacement for **n** in the sentence

$$5 \times n = 85$$

that will make this sentence true.

▼EXPLANATION: The sentence above states that 85 is the product of two numbers, where one of these numbers is 5. Hence, by the Product of Two Numbers Principle, you know that if the product, 85, is divided by 5, the quotient will have to be the replacement for **n**.

●SOLUTION:

$$5 \times n = 85$$

Therefore, $n = 85 \div 5$

or, $n = 17$

In the event the students in your class have been taught the "Percentage Formula," you may prefer to develop this section by using that formula.

■ILLUSTRATION 2: Find the replacement for **n** in the sentence

$$45/125 = n/100$$

that will make this sentence true.

●SOLUTION:

$45/125 = n/100$	①
$125 \times n = 100 \times 45$	②
$125 \times n = 4{,}500$	③
$n = 4{,}500 \div 125$	④
$n = 36$	⑤

▼EXPLANATION: In Sentence ①, 45 and 100 are one pair of opposites, while **n** and 125 are the other pair. Hence, by the Equal Fractions Principle, the product of 45 and 100 must be equal to the product of **n** and 125. It is these products that are shown equal in Sentence ②. Sentences ② and ③ are the same, except that 100×45 is replaced with its product of 4,500. Sentence ④ is obtained from Sentence ③ by using the Product of Two Numbers Principle. And, finally, Sentence ④ and Sentence ⑤ are the same, except that the numeral 36 replaces $4{,}500 \div 125$.

To apply these two principles to applications involving percent, you must first realize that any fraction, and, in particular, a percent numeral, can be thought of as representing a comparison between the numerator and the denominator of the fraction. Thus, the fraction ½ represents a comparison of 1 to 2; that is, the denominator is twice the size of the numerator. Or, if you prefer, you can think of it as the numerator being half the size of the denominator.

Similarly, the number 15% is a comparison of the number 15 to the number 100, for the percent value of 15% is but another form of the fraction 15/100. Hence, when you are asked, "What number is 15% of 140?", you must realize that you are really being asked to determine the number that compares with 140 in the same way that 15 compares with 100.

■ILLUSTRATION 3: What number is 15% of 140?

●SOLUTION:

Rewrite the question as:

"What number compares with 140 as 15 compares with 100?"

This can be written with symbols as:

$n/140 = 15/100$	
$100 \times n = 15 \times 140$	Equal Fractions Principle
$100 \times n = 2{,}100$	$(15 \times 140 = 2{,}100)$
$n = 2{,}100 \div 100$	Product of Two Numbers Principle
$n = 21$	$(2{,}100 \div 100 = 21)$

There is something interesting about the above problem that you should examine now for, by doing so, you will be able to shorten the computation in future problems. If, instead of writing the 15% as a fraction, you had written it as a decimal, the right side of the first equation would have been .15 rather than 15/100. And since .15 can be written as .15/1, the first equation above can appear as:

$$n/140 = .15/1$$

Then, applying the Equal Fractions Principle, you get:

$$1 \times n = .15 \times 140$$
$$\text{or,} \qquad n = .15 \times 140 \qquad \textcircled{1}$$
$$n = 21$$

Thus, by examining Equation ①, you see that the answer to the question, "What number is 15% of 140?" can be obtained by changing 15% to a decimal and multiplying that decimal by 140.

In fact, each and every situation that concerns itself with determining a certain percent of a number can be attacked by changing the percent numeral to its equivalent decimal numeral and multiplying that decimal by the number that follows the word "of." Apparently, then, from a computational standpoint, the word "of" implies the operation of multiplication. What number is 20% of 50? 30% of 80? 50% of 125?

■ ILLUSTRATION 4: What amount of money is 4½% of $600?
● SOLUTION:

$$n = 4\tfrac{1}{2}\% \text{ of } \$600$$
$$n = 4.5\% \times \$600$$
$$n = .045 \times \$600$$
$$n = \$27$$

▼ EXPLANATION: The 4½% is first changed to the form 4.5% and, finally, to the decimal numeral .045 before it is multiplied by $600.

In the illustrations above, you were asked to determine a certain percent of a number. Now consider what you would do if asked to find what percent one number is of another. For instance, if asked to determine what percent 60 is of 75, you are, in other words, being asked to find the number that compares with 100 in the same way that 60 compares with 75. Hence, the method of attack here is no different than that used in Illustration 3 on page 588, for just as before, you must now set up two equal fractions. What are these two fractions?

■ ILLUSTRATION 5: What percent of $125 is $150?

Since the need for finding a certain percent "of" a number arises so frequently in applications, it is best that the method used in Illustration 4 be taught the student rather than resorting to the proportion.

●SOLUTION:

Rewrite the question as:

"$150 compares with $125 as what number compares with 100?" And this can be written with symbols as,

$$150/125 = n/100$$
$$\text{Hence: } 125 \times n = 100 \times 150$$
$$125 \times n = 15,000$$
$$n = 15,000 \div 125$$
$$n = 120$$

The number you found compares with 100 as $150 compares with $125. Hence, in answer to the question, "What percent of $125 is $150?" the answer will be 120%.

▼EXPLANATION: The question that often arises when writing the original equation is, "Which number should be compared with which number?" In other words, which number will be the numerator and which one will be the denominator? Should you compare 150 to 125, or 125 to 150? Since most people want to place the larger number in the denominator, this problem was deliberately stated so that the smaller number was the one that must appear in the denominator. Mechanically speaking, the simplest way to recall which number will be the base of comparison—that is, the denominator of the first fraction—is to find the number that immediately follows the word "of." In this illustration, that number is $125.

It is important to realize that, before you can find what percent one number is of another, it is necessary to know both of the numbers. For instance, consider the situation where Joe earns $2.60 per hour and Fred earns $2.20 per hour. If you wanted to know what percent more per hour Joe earns than Fred, you would have to know how much more Joe earns each hour than Fred. The problem does not ask you to compare Joe's hourly earnings to Fred's, but, rather, to compare how much *more* Joe is earning than Fred. Hence, in this case the two numbers that are to be compared are $.40—the amount more earned—and $2.20, which is Fred's hourly salary.

■ILLUSTRATION 6: Last year Artco Products employed 80 people. This year it employs only 65 people. By what percent did its employment drop over the past year?

●SOLUTION:

The question can be written as:

"The decrease compares with last year's employment as what number compares with 100?"

$$\text{Decrease} = 80 - 65$$

And the question can be written with symbols as:
$$15/80 = n/100$$
$$80 \times n = 100 \times 15$$
$$80 \times n = 1,500$$
$$n = 1,500 \div 80$$
$$n = 18\tfrac{3}{4}$$

Therefore, the percent of decrease is 18¾%.

▼ EXPLANATION: To find the percent of decrease, you must first find the decrease of 15 people. Notice that in problems calling for the percent of decrease or percent of increase, the base of comparison is always the original amount. In this illustration, the original amount was the number of people employed last year.

EXERCISES   A

Find the number requested in each of the following problems.

1. 25% of 40	= 10	2. 50% of 70	= 35
3. 10% of 150	= 15	4. 30% of 200	= 60
5. 80% of 400	= 320	6. 75% of 12	= 9
7. 2% of 600	= 12	8. 5% of 300	= 15
9. 9% of 800	= 72	10. 16% of 700	= 112
11. 125% of 80	= 100	12. 150% of 38	= 57
13. 100% of 92	= 92	14. 200% of 85	= 170
15. 400% of 67	= 268	16. 900% of 146	= 1,314
17. 250% of 64	= 160	18. 325% of 24	= 78
19. 16.5% of 38	= 6.27	20. 14.4% of 170	= 24.48
21. 23.7% of 310	= 73.47	22. 46.1% of 430	= 198.23
23. 2.3% of 75	= 1.725	24. 5.8% of 560	= 32.48
25. 4.9% of 148	= 7.252	26. 6.4% of 212	= 13.568
27. 7.61% of 500	= 38.05	28. 3.47% of 2,000	= 69.4
29. 3½% of 50	= 1.75	30. 4½% of 160	= 7.2
31. 7½% of 240	= 18	32. 14½% of 96	= 13.92
33. 5¼% of 500	= 26.25	34. 6¼% of 1,200	= 75
35. 1¼% of 180	= 2.25	36. 10¼% of 230	= 23.575
37. 6¾% of 2,100	= 141.75	38. 3¾% of 3,600	= 135
39. 15¾% of 4,500	= 708.75	40. 20¾% of 5,800	= 1,203.5

B

Find the number requested in each of the following problems.

1. 10 is what percent of 40?	25%
2. 30 is what percent of 150?	20%
3. 50 is what percent of 40?	125%
4. 60 is what percent of 80?	75%

5. 50 is what percent of 25? _____200%_____
6. 75 is what percent of 50? _____150%_____
7. 72 is what percent of 60? _____120%_____
8. 126 is what percent of 90? _____140%_____
9. 18 is what percent of 30? _____60%_____
10. 96 is what percent of 128? _____75%_____
11. $3 is what percent of $30? _____10%_____
12. $15 is what percent of $300? _____5%_____
13. $36 is what percent of $450? _____8%_____
14. $123 is what percent of $2,050? _____6%_____
15. $252 is what percent of $3,150? _____8%_____
16. $51 is what percent of $340? _____15%_____
17. $117 is what percent of $180? _____65%_____
18. $26 is what percent of $208? _____12.5%_____
19. $123 is what percent of $328? _____37.5%_____
20. $371 is what percent of $424? _____87.5%_____
21. $3.12 is what percent of $39? _____8%_____
22. $10.92 is what percent of $84? _____13%_____
23. $66.42 is what percent of $54? _____123%_____
24. $4.56 is what percent of $28.50? _____16%_____
25. $2.50 is what percent of $12.50? _____20%_____
26. $13.16 is what percent of $23.50? _____56%_____
27. $30.24 is what percent of $47.25? _____64%_____
28. $23.52 is what percent of $24.50? _____96%_____
29. $94.83 is what percent of $65.40? _____145%_____
30. $276.42 is what percent of $135.50? _____204%_____

C

Find the number requested in each of the following problems.
1. 15 is what percent more than 10? _____50%_____
2. 20 is what percent more than 16? _____25%_____
3. 35 is what percent more than 20? _____75%_____
4. 33 is what percent more than 30? _____10%_____
5. 70 is what percent more than 50? _____40%_____
6. 18 is what percent less than 24? _____25%_____
7. 63 is what percent less than 140? _____55%_____
8. 108 is what percent less than 150? _____28%_____
9. 231 is what percent less than 275? _____16%_____
10. 61 is what percent less than 244? _____75%_____

D

Solve each of the following problems.

1. In a basket of 80 peaches, 5% of them were spotted. How many of the peaches were spotted? __4__

2. Tires that normally sell for $32 were reduced 25% during a sale. By how much was each tire reduced in price? __$8__

3. During one year, the price of gasoline rose 4¢ per gallon. If it had sold for 32¢ a gallon, what was the percent of increase? __12.5%__

4. The state tax is 2½% of the selling price of an article. How much tax will have to be paid on a suit that sells for $28.80? __$ .72__

5. Two years ago, a certain brand shirt could be purchased for $4.50. This same shirt now costs $5.22. What was the percent of increase over the two-year period? __16%__

6. Mr. Burke has a take-home pay of $150 per week. If $42 of this amount is budgeted for food, what percent of his take-home pay is needed for this item? __28%__

7. Jim's car was giving him 14 miles to the gallon of gasoline. By replacing the spark plugs and the points, he found that his gasoline mileage is now 125% of what it had been. How many miles to the gallon is Jim now getting from his car? __17.5 miles__

8. Ed has a part-time after-school job. When he first started working, he earned $1.60 an hour. At present, his hourly salary is $2. What percent of increase in hourly pay has he received? __25%__

9. Mrs. Riley has a charge account on which she has to pay a charge of 1½% per month on the unpaid monthly balance. How much will the charge be during a month in which she had a balance of $46? __$ .69__

10. Mr. Jacobs purchased stock in a company at $75 a share. When he recently sold the stock, he received only $61.50 for each share. By what percent did the value of the stock decrease? __18%__

Unit 6: Rounding Off Numbers

Although rounding off numbers is relatively simple, the difficulty arises over the many different ways various individuals prefer to do it. Thus, some businessmen will round off the cost of a sale to the nearest penny, while others will always round off the cost to the next higher penny. Social security computation is rounded off to the next higher dime, while the internal revenue department wants you to complete your income tax form by rounding off each amount to the nearest

An effort is made in Unit 6 to cover each and every situation a person might encounter as a consumer, wherein he would be called upon to round off a number.

dollar. In some computation, it is best to round off an answer to the nearest whole number, while in others, the nearest tenth, or nearest hundredth, or even the nearest thousandth is best.

Here are a few of the ways numbers can be rounded off. Consider the following number:

$$7\ 6.\ 2\ 8\ 3\ 5$$

tenth · hundredth · thousandth · ten thousandth

If you want to round off this number to the nearest tenth, you will examine the digit immediately to the right of the tenth's digit. If that number is a 5 or greater, you will add 1 to the tenth's digit and drop all other digits to its right. On the other hand, if that digit is less than 5, that is, a 4, 3, 2, 1, or 0, you will add nothing to the tenth's digit, but merely drop all digits to its right. Thus, in the number above, the digit to the right of the tenth's digit is an 8. Since this is greater than 5, you add 1 to the tenth's digit, thus making it a 3, and drop the digits to its right. Hence, 76.2835, when rounded off to the nearest tenth, becomes 76.3.

To round off the number above to the nearest hundredth, again examine the digit immediately to its right. In this case, the digit to the right is a 3. Since 3 is less than 5, simply drop all digits to the right of the hundredth's digit and leave the answer as 76.28. What will the above number be when rounded off to the nearest thousandth?

When a number is to be rounded off to the nearest whole number, it implies that no digits are to appear to the right of the decimal point. In such cases, you examine the first digit to the right of the decimal point and, as before, if it is 5 or greater, you increase the digit to the left of the decimal point by 1; if it is less than 5, the digit to the left of the decimal point remains the same. In either event, all digits to the right of the decimal point are dropped. In rounding off the number 76.2835 to the nearest whole number, you examine the digit 2, which is the first digit to the right of the decimal point. Since this digit is less than 5, you do not increase the 6, which is the first digit to the left of the decimal point. After dropping all digits to the right of the decimal point, you find that the number 76.2835, when rounded off to the nearest whole number, becomes 76.

■ILLUSTRATION 1: Round off 376.8054 to the nearest hundredth.

▼EXPLANATION: To round off this number to the nearest hundredth, examine the first digit to the right of the hundredth's digit. Since this is a 5, you must add 1 to the hundredth's digit and drop all digits to its right.

$$376.80\underset{\uparrow}{5}4$$

●SOLUTION:

The number 376.8054, when rounded off to the nearest hundredth, will be 376.81

■ILLUSTRATION 2: Round off the number $45.632 to the nearest cent.

▼EXPLANATION: Since the 2, which is the first digit to the right of 3 cents, is less than 5, it is dropped. The procedure here is the same as in the previous illustration.

●SOLUTION:

The number $45.632, when rounded off to the nearest cent, will be $45.63.

■ILLUSTRATION 3: Round off the number $45.632 to the next higher cent.

▼EXPLANATION: When reading a number in dollars and cents, you need but two digits to the right of the decimal point for the cents amount. For the moment, ignore the third digit to the right of the decimal point. By doing this, the amount becomes 45 dollars and 63 cents. Since the third digit of 2 does represent some small amount of money (2 tenths of a cent), and since you are asked to round off the number to the next higher cent, the amount will be 45 dollars and 64 cents.

●SOLUTION:

The number $45.632, when rounded off to the next higher cent, will be $45.64.

■ILLUSTRATION 4: Round off the number $45.63 to the nearest dime.

▼EXPLANATION: The dime amount less than $45.63 is $45.60, while the dime amount greater than $45.63 is $45.70. Since 63¢ is closer to 60¢ than to 70¢, the answer is $45.60.

●SOLUTION:

The number $45.63, when rounded off to the nearest dime, is $45.60.

Had you been asked in Illustration 4 to round off the number to the next 10¢ or dime amount, the answer would have been $45.70. A difficulty arises when you round off a number, such as $54.92, to the next dime amount. When this is done, the next dime amount will be 100 cents. Hence, you change 54 dollars to 55 dollars, and your answer becomes $55.00. How would you round off $29.94 to the next higher dime?

■ILLUSTRATION 5: Round off the number $39.63 to the nearest dollar.

▼EXPLANATION: This problem is the same as one in which you are asked to round off a number to the nearest whole number. In this case, you look at the first digit to the right of the decimal point. Since it is a 6 and, therefore, greater than 5, the number to the left of the decimal point is increased by 1. Increasing 9 by 1 makes it a 10, which, in turn, makes the number 39 a 40.

●SOLUTION:

> The number $39.63, when rounded off to the nearest dollar, is $40.

EXERCISES   **A**

Round off each of the following numbers to the nearest tenth.

1. 23.41 ___23.4___   2. 35.82 ___35.8___   3. 47.68 ___47.7___
4. 64.17 ___64.2___   5. 58.05 ___58.1___   6. 42.96 ___43.0___
7. 87.98 ___88.0___   8. 79.97 ___80.0___   9. 69.05 ___69.1___

B

Round off each of the following numbers to the nearest hundredth.

1. 41.672 ___41.67___   2. 58.593 ___58.59___   3. 34.876 ___34.88___
4. 42.935 ___42.94___   5. 60.197 ___60.20___   6. 21.399 ___21.40___
7. 72.998 ___73.00___   8. 89.996 ___90.00___   9. 49.095 ___49.10___

C

Round off each of the following numbers to the nearest whole number.

1. 67.21 ___67___   2. 84.73 ___85___   3. 95.04 ___95___
4. 68.54 ___69___   5. 123.75 ___124___   6. 146.49 ___146___
7. 181.39 ___181___   8. 117.92 ___118___   9. 329.82 ___330___
10. 439.59 ___440___   11. 619.49 ___619___   12. 499.61 ___500___

D

Round off each of the following numbers to the nearest cent.

1. $4.672 ___$4.67___   2. $5.837 ___$5.84___   3. $2.835 ___$2.84___
4. $6.027 ___$6.03___   5. $12.291 ___$12.29___   6. $16.396 ___$16.40___

7. $27.898 __$27.90__   8. $35.993 __$35.99__   9. $46.996 __$ 47.00__

10. $59.991 __$59.99__   11. $59.998 __$60.00__   12. $99.999 __$100.00__

E

Round off each of the following numbers to the next higher cent.

1. $6.341 __$ 6.35__   2. $1.542 __$ 1.55__   3. $.623 __$ .63__

4. $.836 __$ .84__   5. $27.752 __$27.76__   6. $35.849 __$35.85__

7. $62.291 __$62.30__   8. $49.992 __$50.00__   9. $29.905 __$29.91__

F

Round off each of the following numbers to the nearest dime.

1. $2.34 __$ 2.30__   2. $4.61 __$ 4.60__   3. $5.86 __$ 5.90__

4. $9.12 __$ 9.10__   5. $16.43 __$16.40__   6. $27.02 __$27.00__

7. $84.07 __$84.10__   8. $53.55 __$53.60__   9. $67.93 __$67.90__

10. $85.96 __$86.00__   11. $39.91 __$39.90__   12. $89.97 __$90.00__

G

Round off each of the following numbers to the next higher dime.

1. $3.21 __$ 3.30__   2. $4.57 __$ 4.60__   3. $6.03 __$ 6.10__

4. $8.15 __$ 8.20__   5. $35.89 __$35.90__   6. $43.01 __$43.10__

7. $51.45 __$51.50__   8. $69.91 __$70.00__   9. $39.96 __$40.00__

H

Round off each of the following numbers to the nearest dollar.

1. $7.23 __$ 7__   2. $5.48 __$ 5__   3. $6.87 __$ 7__

4. $2.16 __$ 2__   5. $32.59 __$ 33__   6. $44.80 __$ 45__

7. $53.49 __$ 53__   8. $68.50 __$ 69__   9. $157.08 __$157__

10. $126.46 __$126__   11. $109.63 __$110__   12. $129.40 __$129__

13. $349.75 __$350__   14. $299.20 __$299__   15. $399.50 __$400__

I

Round off each of the following numbers as indicated.

1. 12.347   to the nearest tenth   __12.3__

2. 16.482   to the nearest hundredth   __16.48__

3. 11.271   to the nearest tenth   __11.3__

4. 24.693   to the nearest whole number   __25__

5. 58.529   to the nearest hundredth   __58.53__

 6. 69.891   to the nearest tenth   _____69.9_____
 7. 40.497   to the nearest whole number ___40_____
 8. 39.952   to the nearest tenth   _____40.0_____
 9. 49.967   to the nearest hundredth   _____49.97_____
10. 69.991   to the nearest hundredth   _____69.99_____
11. 79.992   to the nearest tenth   _____80.0_____
12. 99.593   to the nearest whole number ___100_____

J

Round off each of the following numbers as indicated.
 1. $14.673   to the nearest cent   ___$ 14.67___
 2. $18.226   to the nearest cent   ___$ 18.23___
 3. $24.61   to the nearest dime   ___$ 24.60___
 4. $34.52   to the next higher dime   ___$ 34.60___
 5. $41.273   to the next higher penny ___$ 41.28___
 6. $67.41   to the nearest dollar   ___$ 67___
 7. $59.236   to the nearest cent   ___$ 59.24___
 8. $29.92   to the nearest dime   ___$ 29.90___
 9. $29.92   to the next higher dime   ___$ 30.00___
10. $59.50   to the nearest dollar   ___$ 60___
11. $31.295   to the nearest penny   ___$ 31.30___
12. $31.295   to the next higher penny ___$ 31.30___
13. $49.63   to the nearest dollar   ___$ 50___
14. $99.91   to the next higher dime   ___$100.00___
15. $99.91   to the nearest dollar   ___$100___

INDEX